Animal Reproduction

McGraw-Hill Publications in the Agricultural Sciences

John R. Campbell, *College of Agriculture, University of Illinois, Consulting Editor in Animal and Plant Sciences*

Carl Hall, *College of Engineering, Washington State University, Consulting Editor in Agricultural Engineering*

Brown: Farm Electrification
Campbell and Lasley: The Science of Animals That Serve Mankind
Campbell and Marshall: The Science of Providing Milk for Man
Christopher: Introductory Horticulture
Crafts and Robbins: Weed Control
Cruess: Commercial Fruit and Vegetable Products
Dickson: Diseases of Field Crops
Eckles, Combs, and Macy: Milk and Milk Products
Edmonds, Senn, Andrews, and Halfacre: Fundamentals of Horticulture
Jones: Farm Gas Engines and Tractors
Kipps: The Production of Field Crops
Kohnke: Soil Physics
Kohnke and Bertrand: Soil Conservation
Krider and Carroll: Swine Production
Lassey: Planning in Rural Environment
Laurie and Ries: Floriculture: Fundamentals and Practices
Laurie, Kiplinger, and Nelson: Commercial Flower Forcing
Maynard, Hintz, Loosli, and Warner: Animal Nutrition
Metcalf, Flint, and Metcalf: Destructive and Useful Insects
Muzik: Weed Biology and Control
Smith and Wilkes: Farm Machinery and Equipment
Sorensen: Animal Reproduction: Principles and Practices
Thompson and Troeh: Soils and Soil Fertility
Thompson and Kelly: Vegetable Crops
Thorne: Principles of Nematology
Treshow: Environment and Plant Response
Walker: Plant Pathology
Warwick and Legates: Breeding and Improvement of Farm Animals

Animal Reproduction
Principles and Practices

A. M. Sorensen, Jr.
Professor of Animal Science
Texas A&M University

McGraw-Hill Book Company

New York   St. Louis   San Francisco   Auckland   Bogotá   Düsseldorf
Johannesburg   London   Madrid   Mexico   Montreal   New Delhi
Panama   Paris   Sao Paulo   Singapore   Sydney   Tokyo   Toronto

ANIMAL REPRODUCTION
Principles and Practices

1 2 3 4 5 6 7 8 9 0   FGRFGR   7 8 3 2 1 0 9

Library of Congress Cataloging in Publication Data

Sorensen, Anton Marinus, date
    Animal reproduction, principles and practices.

    (McGraw-Hill publications in the agricultural sciences)
    Includes index.
    1. Livestock—Reproduction. 2. Livestock—Breeding.
3. Reproduction. 4. Veterinary physiology.
2. Veterinary anatomy. I. Title.
SF105.S73   636.089'26   78-17167
ISBN 0-07-059670-0

This book was set in Times Roman by Cobb/Dunlop Publisher
Services Incorporated. The editor was C. Robert Zappa;
the production supervisor was Dominick Petrellese. The
drawings were done by J & R Technical Services, Inc.
The cover was designed by Tana Klugherz.
Fairfield Graphics was printer and binder.

To my
Tommie

Contents

Preface

Purpose: To bring the student, whether in the classroom, in an easy chair, behind a desk, or flying across the sky, a readable, interesting account of the miracle of life as it unfolds before us.

> "And God said, let the earth bring forth the living creature after his kind, cattle—and beast of the earth after his kind: and it was so. So God created man in his own image —male and female created he them." Genesis 1:24–27

Uniqueness: A practical approach based on scientific underlying principles of reproduction. Components down to the cellular level, compounds interacting with body functions, scientific investigations, technology, and management are combined to assist the livestock man in understanding and planning his approach to livestock production.

Approach: Organization is designed for a flow of knowledge. The sequence of events in the reproductive pattern of the male and female is presented, followed by bringing the two together, resulting in a new offspring.

New terms are explained in the text as they are first mentioned. The plural and literal definition follow each new term. Words are best remembered by function rather than sound or sight.

Terminology is patterned after *Nomina Anatomica Veterinaria*[1] and *Dorland's Illustrated Medical Dictionary.*[2]

References to figures in the text appear mostly as (Fig. 2–4/3). The first number indicates the chapter; the second denotes the figure within the designated chapter and the third number indicates the part labeled in that particular figure. Thus (2–4/3) denotes Chapter 2, Figure 4, and part 3.

Throughout this book standard terms are used for orientation.

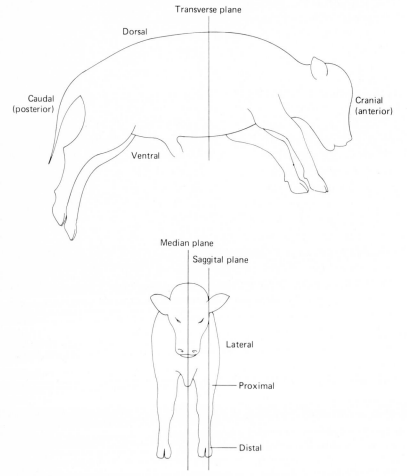

Figure 0-1 Orientation.

Cranial (anterior) refers to the front or head end of the body.

Caudal (posterior) is just the opposite of cranial; meaning toward the tail end or rear of the body.

[1]World Association of Veterinary Anatomists, *Nomina Anatomica Veterinaria,* 2nd Ed. Published by the International Committee on Veterinary Anatomical Nomenclature, Vienna, 1973.

[2]*Dorland's Illustrated Medical Dictionary,* 25th Ed. W. B. Saunders Co., Philadelphia, 1975.

Dorsal (back) toward or near the top of the head or back.

Ventral (belly) underside of the body of the standing four-legged animal.

Median plane (middle) denotes a plane longitudinally through the body that divides it into two equal parts.

Saggital plane (straight) is a plane parallel to the median plane but to one side.

Lateral (side) denotes an area away from or relatively farther from the median plane.

Transverse (crosswise) refers to a section across the longitudinal plane of the body perpendicular to the median plane or across the long axis of any organ or limb.

Proximal (close) relatively nearer the body; the attached end of a limb.

Distal (far) relatively farther from the body; the free or unattached end of a limb.

At the beginning of each chapter is a statement of concepts for the chapter material. At the conclusion of the chapter are sample questions testing the reader's understanding of that material.

The bovine (cattle) is the basic animal throughout the text with comparative anatomy and physiology of the ovine (sheep), porcine (swine), and equine (horse). The human is also compared, though not in equal detail.

References: Alphabetical lists of references follow each chapter so the reader may pursue specific subjects further. It is not the purpose of the book to reference extensively any particular item. The approach is one of practicality. It is hoped that the reader will delve deeper into areas that arouse his curiosity. (Note: superior numbers are used in the text to refer to the numbered references.)

Acknowledgments: Sincere thanks are due a multitude of people who offered words of encouragement and advice during the writing. Thank you John Campbell and McGraw-Hill for asking me to write the book and for your help. Thank you R. O. Berry for initiating my interest in reproduction many years ago. Thank you J. M. Armstrong, J. E. Smallwood, W. E. Haensly, W. L. Sippel, W. L. Schwartz, J. C. Reagor, and D. L. Morris for comments on specific sections of the text. Thank you to those who consented to the use of materials, particularly for illustrations, and due credit is cited with the specific figures.

Thank you Mrs. Becky Morris for deciphering my hieroglyphics and typing the manuscript in a professional and understanding fashion. Thank you many undergraduate students and graduate students whose ever-searching-for-knowledge attitude has kept the author continually searching also.

Thank you Tommie, for being my wife and mother of our children Susan and Walt, for standing by me, praising me when I didn't deserve it, prodding me when I needed it, and understanding and encouraging me through this endeavor.

A. M. Sorensen, Jr.

Common Conversion Factors

To convert from		To		Multiply by
Centimeters	cm	inches	in	0.3937
Feet	ft	meters	m	0.3048
Grams	gm	ounces	oz	0.0353
Inches	in	centimeters	cm	2.5400
Kilograms	kg	pounds	lb	2.2046
Liters	l	quarts	qt	1.0567
Meters	m	feet	ft	3.2808
Meters	m	inches	in	39.3700
Micrometers	μm	inches	in	3.937×10^{-5}
Milliliters	ml	ounces	oz	0.0338
Millimeters	mm	inches	in	0.0394
Ounces	oz	grams	gm	28.3495
Ounces	oz	liters	l	0.0297
Ounces	oz	milliliters	ml	29.5729
Pints	pt	liters	l	0.4732
Pounds	lb	kilograms	kg	0.4536
Quarts	qt	liters	l	0.9463
Centigrade (Celsius)	C	Fahrenheit	F	$°C \times 1.8 + 32$
Fahrenheit	F	Centigrade	C	$°F - 32 \div 1.8$

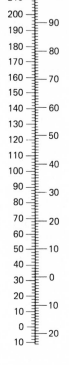

Centimeters

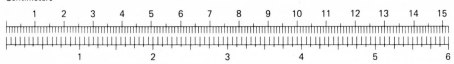

Inches

Macroscopic Male Functional Anatomy

When you have completed this chapter you should be able to:

- Identify and relate the gross anatomical structures of the male reproductive system,
- Describe the function of each gross structure,
- Differentiate reproductive structures of the bull, ram, boar, stallion, and man, and
- Trace a spermatozoon from its origin to the exterior.

The study of the male anatomy and function will begin at the point of origin of the sperm and systematically follow it through the various segments of the system, adding the accessory glands at their appropriate times.

It must be understood in the beginning that dimensions given for any particular organ are estimates for average mature animals. The actual structures may vary considerably based upon breed, age, nutritive state, and, particularly, sexual maturity.

Sperm are produced in the testes (Fig. 1–1/21), which are carried in a pendulous manner between the rear legs in a pouch of skin, the scrotum. The testes are raised and lowered by muscles in the wall of the scrotum and the spermatic cord to maintain a rather constant testicular temperature.

1 — Rectum
2 — Left bulbourethral gland
3 — Prostate gland
4 — Vesicular glands
5 — Urinary bladder
6 — Right deferent duct
7 — Deep inguinal ring
8 — Superficial inguinal ring
9 — Free part of penis
10 — Preputial cavity
11 — Prepuce (sheath)
12 — Left crus of penis
13 — Bulbospongiosus muscle
14 — Floor of pelvis
15 — Retractor penis muscles
16 — Sigmoid flexture of penis
17 — Penis body
18 — Pampiniform plexus
19 — Epididymis
20 — Cremaster muscle
21 — Left testis
22 — Tunica dartos
23 — Scrotum

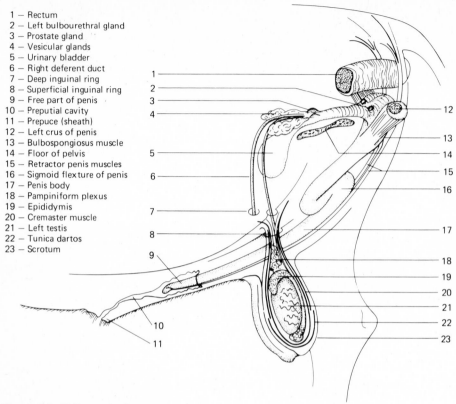

Figure 1-1 Bull reproductive tract.

Sperm leave the testes via efferent ductules into the head of the epididymis (Fig. 1-1/19). They pass through its body into the tail of the epididymis where they are stored until passing into the deferent duct (Fig. 1–1/6), which passes into the body cavity and subsequently into the cranial part of the urethra. Accessory fluids are added by the vesicular glands, prostate gland, and bulbourethral glands, in that order, (Fig. 1–1/4, 3, 2) to act as a carrier for the concentrated sperm. This semen then passes through the urethra surrounded by the penis, which originates just below the anus. It passes through an S curve of the penis and through the glans penis to the exterior (Fig. 1–1/16, 9). Retractor penis muscles (Fig. 1–1/15) help draw the penis back into the protective prepuce when in the quiescent state.

Now let us look at this passageway in more detail. Figures 1–2 and 1–3 should be referred to constantly as you read the anatomy and function section.

TESTIS (Testes: Witness)

There are two testes, ovoid in shape and each measuring 7 cm (3 in) in diameter and 13 cm (5 in) in length (Table 1–1). They lie in a vertical plane, side by side, in the scrotum. They have two primary purposes: to produce sperm, the male germ cells;

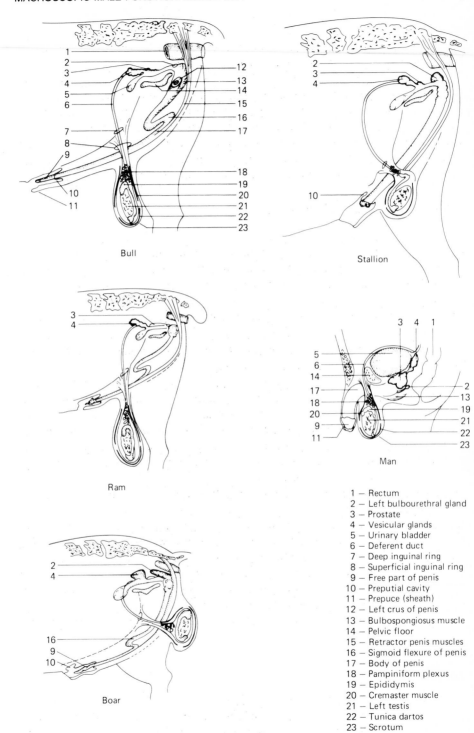

Bull

Stallion

Ram

Man

Boar

1 — Rectum
2 — Left bulbourethral gland
3 — Prostate
4 — Vesicular glands
5 — Urinary bladder
6 — Deferent duct
7 — Deep inguinal ring
8 — Superficial inguinal ring
9 — Free part of penis
10 — Preputial cavity
11 — Prepuce (sheath)
12 — Left crus of penis
13 — Bulbospongiosus muscle
14 — Pelvic floor
15 — Retractor penis muscles
16 — Sigmoid flexure of penis
17 — Body of penis
18 — Pampiniform plexus
19 — Epididymis
20 — Cremaster muscle
21 — Left testis
22 — Tunica dartos
23 — Scrotum

Figure 1-2 Comparative male anatomy.

Table 1-1 Male Anatomical Structures

Organ	Bull cm (in)	Ram cm (in)	Boar cm (in)	Stallion cm (in)	Man cm (in)
Testes	13×7×7 (5×3×3)	10×6×5 (4×2×2)	13×6×6 (5×2×2)	11×6×5 (4×2×2)	5×3×2 (2×1.5×1)
Position	Pendulous vertical	Pendulous vertical	Inverted below anus	Pendulous horizontal	Pendulous vertical
Epididymis, length	17 (7)	14 (6)	17 (7)	14 (6)	7 (3)
Deferent ducts	100 (40)	75 (30)	70 (8)	75 (30)	30 (12)
Ampulla	12×1 (5×.5)	7×.5 (3×.2)	—	20×2 (8×1)	5×1 (2×.5)
Vesicular glands	12×3 (5×1)	6×2 (2×1)	14×6 (6×2)	17×4 (7×2)	5×2 (2×1)
Shape	Lobulated	Lobulated	Pyramidal	Pear	Lobed
Prostate gland				2 lateral lobes	3 lobes
Bulb	3×1 (1×.5)	Absent	2×1 (1×.5)	5×2 (2×1)	4×3×2 (2×1.5×1)
Disseminate part	1×11 (.5×5)	Diffused	Some	Absent	Absent
Bulbourethral glands	3 (1)	1 (.5)	12×3 (5×1)	4 (2)	1 (.5)
Shape	Round	Round	Finger	Round	Round
Penis					
Type	Fibroelastic	Fibroelastic	Fibroelastic	Musculocavernous	Musculocavernous
Sigmoid flexure	Postscrotal	Postscrotal	Prescrotal	Absent	Absent
Glans penis					
Shape	Taper	Lobe with filiform appendage	Corkscrew	Rounded with a concave face	Rounded
Prepuce	Prominent to tight	Small–opens perpendicular	Secretory glands and a diverticulum	Double fold	Close fitting

and to produce testosterone, the male sex hormone. Circumference of the two testes in the scrotum approximates 42 cm (16 in).[23]

Each testis (Fig. 1–3) is covered with a shiny tough connective tissue called the visceral vaginal tunic (tunica vaginalis propria). This was derived from the peritoneum as the testis descended. It functions to support the testis. Directly beneath this is the tunica albuginea testis (Fig. 1–3/17), which also supports the testis and is a connective tissue capsule surrounding the tortuous blood vessels near the surface of the testis. Septula testis (Fig. 1–3/15) are strands of connective tissue that branch from this layer and connect to the mediastinum testis (Fig. 1–3/12), which is the connective tissue core of the testis. This network of connective tissue holds the seminiferous tubules and interstitial cells in place and gives form and support to the testis.

The bulk of the testis consists of the seminiferous tubules and interstitial cells. The seminiferous tubules produce the sperm and will be discussed in more detail later. The interstitial cells are interspersed between the tubules and produce testosterone.

Mediastinum Testis (Middle Partition)

The mediastinum testis of the bull, ram, and boar is rather distinct and centrally located. Less connective tissue in the stallions's testis gives it a softer texture, and, if sectioned, the seminiferous tubules and interstitial cells seem to fall rather freely from the outer covering.

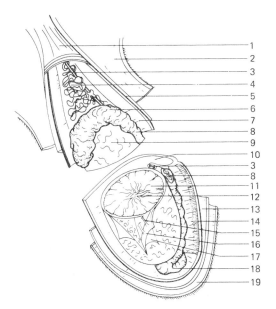

1 — Spermatic cord
2 — Scrotum
3 — Deferent duct
4 — Pampiniform plexus
5 — Cremaster muscle
6 — Head of epididymis
7 — Parietal vaginal tunic
8 — Body of epididymis
9 — Testis
10 — Vaginal cavity
11 — Seminiferous tubules
12 — Mediastinum testis
13 — Tunica dartos
14 — Mesorchium
15 — Septula testis
16 — Tunica albuginea testis
17 — Visceral vaginal tunic
18 — Tail of epididymis
19 — Scrotum

Figure 1-3 The testis and its coverings. *(Adapted from Smallwood, 1973, An Introductory Study to Bovine Anatomy, J. W. Caine, San Antonio.)*

Rete Testis (Rete Testes: Straight)

Spermatozoa pass from the seminiferous tubules into a network of collecting tubules called the rete testis (called straight because they have a rather straight configuration). These structures are located in the mediastinum testis and collect the sperm as they pass from the seminiferous tubules (Fig. 1–4/4).

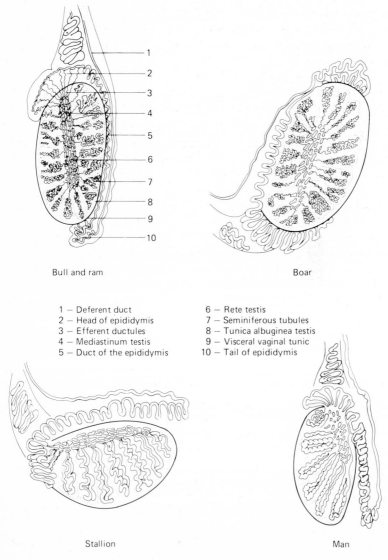

Bull and ram

Boar

1 — Deferent duct	6 — Rete testis
2 — Head of epididymis	7 — Seminiferous tubules
3 — Efferent ductules	8 — Tunica albuginea testis
4 — Mediastinum testis	9 — Visceral vaginal tunic
5 — Duct of the epididymis	10 — Tail of epididymis

Stallion

Man

Figure 1-4   Internal testis structure.

Efferent Ductule (Efferent Ductules: Tube-Carry To)

The sperm next pass into a group of approximately 15 tubules, the efferent ductules, which carry the sperm from the testis proper to a further collecting tubule, the duct of the epididymis (Fig. 1–4/2).

The size and firmness of the testes are important in selecting breeding stock. These are the producing structures, and sperm production is related to size. Relative sizes are given in Table 1–1. Scrotal circumference may be measured with a flexible tape (Fig. 1–5) and is more closely related to testicular size than is testicular length.[23] Correlation between scrotal circumference and sperm output per week for young bulls was .81; for 3-year-old bulls, .72; and for 4-year-old bulls, .64. Heritability estimates are given as .67, so evidently bulls can be selected for sperm productivity on the basis of scrotal circumference. Scrota of Holstein bulls reached greatest circumference at 48 months of age (41.6 cm, 16.5 in) as compared to those of Angus bulls at 24 months (40.0 cm, 16 in).[11] Tone is a measure of productivity, as it indicates the packed sperm being accumulated within the seminiferous tubules and the tubular structures. This can be measured by palpation of the testes or, more accurately, by a tonometer, which is a spring-loaded device that measures resistance to a force, or firmness.[12] Consistency or tone is highest in young bulls and decreases gradually until maturity when it increases slightly and remains constant until old age.

Of course there are extremes in both size and tone that should be considered. Testes that are too large may be easily damaged not only because of their size but because of their pendulous nature. Those that are too small should be criticized because of a smaller mass of productive units. Hard testes may indicate compaction or infection, whereas a soft spongy condition may indicate poor productivity or perhaps overuse of the male.

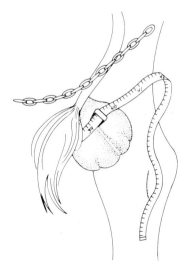

Figure 1-5 Measuring testes circumference.

Testes of the ram, boar, and stallion are similar in size to those of the bull. Average sizes are given in Table 1–1.

The location of the testes varies among the different species of livestock (Fig. 1–2). Those of the bull and ram are supported in a vertical, pendulous position. This places the body of the epididymis on the posterior border and the tail of the epididymis ventral to the testes. The boar testes are located between the hams ventral to the anus and are inverted. The body of the epididymis is now craniodorsal and the tail of the epididymis becomes caudodorsal. The action of the cremaster and dartos muscles are limited and the position of the testes changes little in relation to the body upon contraction. The stallion carries his testes in a horizontal manner, and the body of the epididymis is loosely attached and dorsal. The tail of the epididymis is caudal. The action of the cremaster and dartos muscles is limited in the stallion, like the boar, because of position. The testes of man are pendulous, like those of the bull, except that since man walks upright the testes are positioned similar to the boar regarding the anus. They are approximately one-tenth the size of bull testes and weigh 14 to 25 g each.[13,19]

EPIDIDYMIS (Epididymides: on Testis)

The epididymis consists of three parts that have no clear demarcation but rather change gradually from one part to the next. The head or caput of the epididymis wraps over the dorsal third of the testis and collects sperm from the numerous efferent ductules into a single coiled tubule. This tube, the duct of the epididymis, forms the bulging head of the epididymis and then continues into the body of the epididymis and moves ventrally over the testis. As it reaches the ventral area of the testis it becomes very coiled again and forms the bulging tail of the epididymis (Fig. 1–6/13).

The epididymis has four main functions. First, it serves as a maturation area for the sperm. As sperm reach the head of the epididymis, they are immature to a large extent as indicated by the presence of a cytoplasmic droplet on the neck, midpiece, or tail. As they pass through the epididymis, this droplet passes off the tail and the sperm is then mature. Second, it acts as a passageway for sperm from the efferent ductules to the deferent duct. Third, it concentrates the sperm by absorbing some of the fluid as the sperm pass through. Fourth, it serves as a storage area. The primary storage is in the tail of the epididymis on the ventral surface. These stored sperm should be mature and ready for nature's intended use. Orgebin-Crist [31] adds a fifth function of dissolution of aging sperm. This function is questioned by a number of researchers, however.

The bulging tail of the epididymis is an indicator to the livestock producer of the sperm-producing ability and the reserve supply of his sire. It should be visible to the eye and firm to the touch. Palpation of each testis and tail of the epididymis should always accompany semen evaluation. The epididymides of the ram and boar resemble those of the bull in shape and attachment.

The head of the epididymis of the stallion is attached, but the body is only

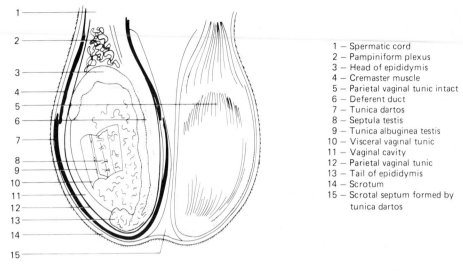

1 — Spermatic cord
2 — Pampiniform plexus
3 — Head of epididymis
4 — Cremaster muscle
5 — Parietal vaginal tunic intact
6 — Deferent duct
7 — Tunica dartos
8 — Septula testis
9 — Tunica albuginea testis
10 — Visceral vaginal tunic
11 — Vaginal cavity
12 — Parietal vaginal tunic
13 — Tail of epididymis
14 — Scrotum
15 — Scrotal septum formed by
     tunica dartos

Figure 1-6 Caudal view of the relation of epididymis and deferent duct to the testis in the bull. *(Adapted from Smallwood, 1973, An Introductory Study of Bovine Anatomy, J. W. Cain, San Antonio.)*

loosely attached and the tail is almost separated. This makes complete castration more difficult, and in animals where segments of the epididymis are left, male sexual activity may continue and in some instances be accentuated. The condition is called "proud cut." This response is difficult to explain since testosterone, the male hormone, is produced as far as is known only by the testes and not by the epididymis. We do not currently have an explanation for this phenomenon. Further research is needed to more completely explain this phenomenon. It is, however, imperative when castrating stallions to make sure the epididymis is exposed and completely removed.

Removal or transection of the epididymis[29,38] may be used to develop teaser bulls and rams, but it is not as satisfactory as numerous other methods since apparent recanalization occurs and sperm then pass through the tract as normal.

DEFERENT DUCT (Deferent Ducts: Tube-Carry Away)

This long tubular structure is attached to the tail of the epididymis and passes dorsally along the medial side of the testis, and cranially to the body of the epididymis, then continues into the spermatic cord, through the inguinal rings. It then enters the body cavity and loops up over the urinary bladder and enters the urethra (Fig. 1–1, 1–2). The deferent duct acts as a passageway for the sperm in ejaculation and to a small extent affords limited storage area for sperm. The muscular walls are capable of peristaltic contractions beginning at the tail of the epididymis and passing rapidly to the urethra, causing a spurt of sperm into the urethra and subsequently to the exterior. The terminal deferent ducts have thickened walls with some glands present. These areas are the *ampullae* of the deferent ducts and are sometimes called the ejaculatory ducts.

The deferent ducts of the ram enlarge like those of the bull to form ampullae. The entire tubular structure is smaller. Ampullae are absent in the boar. The ducts remain the same size as they approach the urethra. The stallion's ampullae are very large and may reach 2 to 3 cm (1 in) in diameter and 15 to 20 cm (7 in) in length. Glands are numerous within the walls, and musculature is organized to form ejaculatory ducts opening on the colliculus seminalis.

A common means of sterilizing the male without interfering with his sexual behavior is to sever the deferent ducts. This is termed vasectomy and entails exposure of each deferent duct in its spermatic cord and removing a segment so that the passageway is interrupted. Igboeli and Rahka[24] showed that spermatogenesis was not abolished and the testis size was not affected. Vasectomy is a simple surgical procedure and is a common practice for producing a "teaser" male to determine estrus in the female. Greater detail will be given in the section on preparing teaser animals. Vasectomy of man is a common method of birth control.

SCROTUM (Scroti: Bag)

Surrounding the testes is the scrotum, which is the protective covering of thick skin covered with hair (Fig. 1–3). The scrotum is divided into two compartments by a median septum so that there are actually two cavities, one for each testis. The scrotum is also a part of the thermoregulatory mechanism to maintain the testes at the optimum temperature for spermatogenesis—approximately 5°C (9°F) below body temperature.

The scrotum may be shortened artificially to hold the testes next to the body, resulting in sterilization. This procedure is called "short scrotum."[32] It is brought about by grasping the lower scrotum and manually forcing the testes into the upper sacs. An elastrator ring or tight rubber band is then placed around the lower scrotum to retain the testes next to the body. The lower scrotum sloughs after a period of about three to four weeks. The animal is sterile but maintains normal testosterone production.

The purpose of short-scrotum bulls is to increase feedlot efficiency through improved feed conversion, rate of growth, and more desirable carcasses.[2,33] The carcasses are usually heavier, leaner, and have larger rib-eye muscles than steers. Testicular weights at slaughter were approximately one-half those of intact bulls on a comparable program.

Fat in the scrotum is another detrimental factor related to spermatogenesis. Fat acts as an insulator and depresses spermatogenesis. Show stock are usually fed to a high degree of finish or fatness and can be temporarily infertile as a result. Breeding stock should never be fattened, so as to elimate this danger. There is less emphasis placed on fat or finish in the show rings today because we are finally realizing that breeding stock are raised for reproduction and not for slaughter.

Tunica Dartos (Flayed Cover)

A sheetlike structure called the tunica dartos is in the wall of the ventral one-third to one-half of each sac of the scrotum. It consists of smooth muscle and elastic connective tissue. The tunica dartos contracts in cold weather to wrinkle the skin thereby raising the testis for warmth, and relaxes in warm weather to allow the testis to be suspended distant to the body. The dartos muscles also contract in periods of stress such as running, fright, or combat to protect the testes from harm. The muscles are under the influence of androgen since they do not develop in castrates and are controlled by the perineal nerves.[39]

Each sac of the scrotum is lined with a shiny connective tissue membrane derived from the peritoneum in the embryonic development, which is called the parietal vaginal tunic (tunica vaginalis communis). The cremaster muscle is attached to the outer surface of the parietal vaginal tunic in the scrotum.

Inside the parietal vaginal tunic is the vaginal cavity, separating it from the visceral vaginal tunic. The visceral vaginal tunic is the outside or peritoneal covering of the testes proper.

DESCENT OF TESTES

Each testis begins as an undifferentiated gonad in the abdominal area of the embryo. As differentiation takes place, the gonad forms the testis and the tubular structures adjacent to it form the passageway for sperm to the exterior (Fig. 1–7). The peritoneum, which lines the abdominal cavity and covers the structures protruding into it, forms an evagination in the area of the gubernaculum.[35,44,45,46,47] The gubernaculum is a gelatinous mass that swells under the peritoneum directionally toward the scrotum. Intraperitoneal pressure combined with this growth forms the vaginal process into which the testis passes, carrying with it a peritoneal covering. Gier and Marion[20,21] contend that there is only a single layer of peritoneum in the vaginal sac and the testes descend into the evagination without being covered with peritoneum. I think it logical to assume that the bulging germinal ridge and the accompanying reproductive structures are covered with peritoneum as are other structures in the abdominal cavity.

The testis passes through the deep inguinal ring, the inguinal canal, and the superficial inguinal ring en route to the scrotum. The inguinal rings and canal normally constrict, and in our domestic species this prevents the return of the testes to the body cavity and/or the passage of intestine into the vaginal cavity.

In rare incidences, the inguinal canal does not close and the testis may return. Internal temperature depresses spermatogenesis in such instances. Also, loops of intestine may pass into the scrotal sac as a hernia. This is relatively common in the human and pig (Fig. 1–8). Hernias may be surgically corrected by closing the inguinal canal. The major difficulty with inguinal hernias in pigs is in relation to

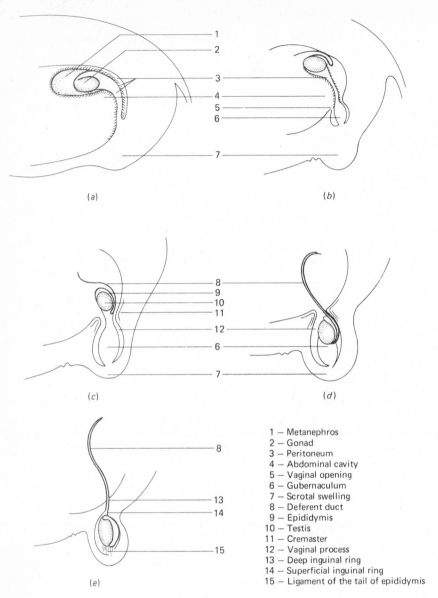

Figure 1-7   Lateral view of the descent of the testes.

castration. Care must be taken to refrain from puncturing the loop of intestine when opening the scrotal sac for removal of the testes.[37]

    Other abnormalities that occur in the descent of the testes are the formation of hydroceles (water sacs) or varicoceles (vein swellings) along the path of descent or in the vaginal cavity (Fig. 1–9). Varicoceles are common in man, and since blood

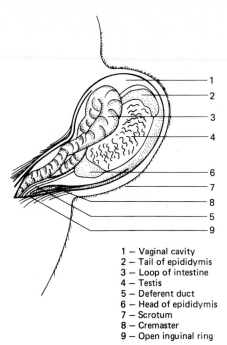

1 — Vaginal cavity
2 — Tail of epididymis
3 — Loop of intestine
4 — Testis
5 — Deferent duct
6 — Head of epididymis
7 — Scrotum
8 — Cremaster
9 — Open inguinal ring

Figure 1-8 Scrotal hernia in a boar with a loop of intestine in the vaginal cavity.

flow is slowed even further than normal, cooling of the testes would supposedly be enhanced. This apparently is not so.[39]

The testis inside the scrotum is finally covered by the visceral vaginal tunic and is separated from the parietal vaginal tunic by an extension of the peritoneal cavity,

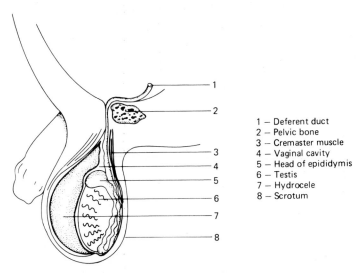

1 — Deferent duct
2 — Pelvic bone
3 — Cremaster muscle
4 — Vaginal cavity
5 — Head of epididymis
6 — Testis
7 — Hydrocele
8 — Scrotum

Figure 1-9 Hydrocele of the scrotum in the human.

the vaginal cavity. The attachment to the lining of the scrotum is on the medial side along the body of the epididymis and deferent duct called the mesorchium (Fig. 1-3/14) and ventrally in the area of the gubernaculum, which is now the ligament of the tail of the epididymis (Fig. 1-7/15).

CASTRATION

Castration is the removal of the gonads, or testes, to render the male sterile. This may be accomplished in several ways. In developing steers for show purposes, it is desirable to maintain a full appearance between the legs. The scrotum is slit on the sides into the vaginal cavity and the testes and spermatic cords are pulled from the scrotum to expose the epididymides and the deferent ducts. The exposed spermatic cord is then scraped until severed, or cut with an emasculator, which crushes and severs, to reduce hemorrhage following removal. The scrotum then heals and retains a near full appearance.

Most range calves are castrated by cutting off the bottom third of the scrotum and removing the testes as above.

A burdizzo may also be used to clamp and crush the deferent ducts and the testicular artery, rendering the animal sterile. Enough blood vessels are left to maintain the scrotal sac, since the blood supply to the scrotum is not contained in the spermatic cord. This is used in cattle and sheep.

An elastrator may be used in castrating sheep. This consists of placing a very strong, small rubber ring around the neck of the scrotum. The testes and scrotum then die from lack of nourishment and slough.

Special care must be taken in castrating stallions that the entire epididymis and part of the spermatic cord are removed. Incomplete removal may result in a "proud cut" condition as described earlier. A slit is usually made on the ventral surface for removal.

Pigs are inverted, pressure is placed against the scrotal area drawing the skin taut over the testes, and an incision is made into the ventral part of the vaginal cavity of each side of the scrotum. Removal is then the same as in cattle, sheep, and horses.

CRYPTORCHID (Hidden Testis)

Failure of one or both of the testes to descend properly leads to a condition called cryptorchidism. If both testes are retained in the abdomen the animal is sterile, because spermatogenesis will not occur at body temperature. However, the interstitial cells of the testes can produce the male sex hormone testosterone at this temperature. The animal then takes on all the characteristics of a male, with libido and outward sexual characteristics but without the ability to produce sperm. Surgery is necessary to remove retained testes but is not recommended. The animal may be used as a teaser animal for detecting estrus in females.[34]

A variation of this condition is the monorchid or unilateral cryptorchid where one testis descends and the other is retained. The animal is fertile in this instance, but would be undesirable for a herd sire because of the possibility of propagating such an undesirable trait. Removal of the single descended testis would yield a condition similar to a bilateral cryptorchid.

Wensing and Colenbrander[48] blame the faulty development of the gubernaculum for the cryptorchid condition. If there is poor extra-abdominal development of the gubernaculum the testes will not move out of the cavity. Excessive gubernacular development in the vaginal canal would also block descent of the testes. The testes in either instance may become lodged in the abdomen, inguinal canal, groin, femoral or perineal regions along the path of descent.

The cryptorchid stallion may be identified by palpating the superficial inguinal ring and determining passage of the deferent duct through it.[1] A testis that has not passed through the superficial inguinal ring will not have pulled the deferent duct with it; therefore it will be absent.

Castration of the cryptorchid horse can be a complex surgical procedure and should be performed only by a competent veterinarian.

Libido of cryptorchids is commonly increased over the normal male. Liptrap and Raeside[26] freed testes and inserted them into the abdominal cavity to develop experimental cryptorchid boars. The hormone production was higher than boars of similar ages even though the testes were only one-fourth the size of the normal boar testes.

Heritability of cryptorchidism has been documented in goats[18,42] and bulls.[49] It is therefore very important when selecting breeding stock to look for testicular development and, if in doubt about descent, palpate the scrotum to determine the presence of both testes.

The approximate time during the gestation period when descent of the testes occurs in the following selected species is: bull, 100–105 days; boar, 100–110 days; stallion, 300 days; and man, 210 days.[20] Cryptorchidism is most common in those species (boar, stallion) where descent occurs in late gestation.

SPERMATIC CORD

This cordlike structure is located above the testis and contains numerous structures: smooth muscle fibers, pampiniform plexus, testicular artery and vein, nerves, lymphatics, and deferent duct. The cords pass through the superficial inguinal rings in the external abdominal oblique muscles and penetrate the abdominal cavity at the deep inguinal ring, which is formed by several muscles.

Cremaster (Suspend)

The cremaster muscle is a continuation of the abdominal musculature and attaches to the parietal vaginal tunic. It has the ability to raise the testis, and, in conjunction with the dartos muscle, to help maintain a rather constant testicular temperature.

It pulls the testis close to the body in cold weather. It covers the spermatic cord. Failure of the cremaster to support the testis allows it to rest on the floor of the scrotum.

Pampiniform Plexus (Tendril Braid)

This network of blood vessels is located in the spermatic cord between the testis and the superficial inguinal ring. The testicular vein in this area is very coiled and forms a meshlike structure around the testicular artery. The cooler blood in the surrounding venous network cools the incoming blood of the testicular artery and supports the thermoregulatory mechanism along with the dartos and cremaster muscle.

Temperature Regulation

Imagine then, if you will, what happens when a sudden change in temperature drops the thermometer reading several degrees. The cremaster muscles contract and pull the testes up, and the dartos muscles contract pushing the testes next to the body for warmth. Temperature is maintained and spermatogenesis continues. In extremely cold areas the scrotum has been known to freeze. If this happens, the testes may still be warmed somewhat; but if the lower scrotum sloughs and then heals, the testes may be held adjacent to the body permanently, causing sterility through increased temperature.

When the environmental temperature is above that of the testes, the cremaster and the dartos relax, resulting in a pendulous scrotum. In addition, the tortuous vessels of the pampiniform plexus slow the blood passage and expose it to the cooling environment of the scrotum. This cooler venous blood then cools the incoming arterial blood and a regulation of the testes' temperature is maintained.

Bulls[28] and rams[14,30] have been subjected to increased environmental temperatures to study the effects on sperm production. Percentage normal sperm and semen volume were not affected in the bulls, but sperm motility was lower, 56 percent, in hot bulls as compared to 72 percent in controls during the third through eighth week of exposure. Aged acrosomes in hot bulls increased by the third week and remained at a high level.

Rams that are shorn and subjected to increased temperature respond similarly to controls, while unshorn rams respond with poor motility, decreased percent normal cells, and lowered concentration. Spermatogenic activity declines with subjection to elevated temperatures but recovers after some time.

Waites and Moule[40] found the temperature deep in the testes remained close to that inside the scrotal skin when rams were exposed to temperatures ranging from 28 to 40°C (82 to 104°F).

Scrotal insulation was applied by means of a glass-wool lined bag in a group of Hereford bulls, and live sperm decreased to about 65 percent of the controls by 2 to 3 weeks.[8] Normal sperm dropped to 60 percent of controls. Recovery was noted by the sixth week of insulation.

These experiments tell us that animals can acclimatize after a period of several weeks in a higher temperature environment. Therefore, if we are going to move breeding males from one climate to another, we must realize the consequences of such a move and plan ahead to alleviate a period of low or decreased fertility.

Summer sterility in rams is a common phenomenon and is predominant in coarse-wool breeds, although temperature and humidity may even affect fine-wool breeds. Continuous heat is more detrimental than intermittent high and low temperatures.[22]

VESICULAR GLANDS (Glandulae Vesiculares: Sac Acorn)

These are paired secretory glands located dorsal to the urinary bladder and lying adjacent to the ampullae of the deferent ducts. They are lobulated in the bull, measuring 12 X 3 cm (5 X 1 in), and are similar in appearance to a cluster of grapes covered by a membrane (Fig. 1–10/4). The undulating surface is caused by foldings of tubular, glandular segments of the organ. They are highly secretory, supplying approximately 90 percent of the volume of the bull's ejaculate. They enter the cranial part of the urethra as two openings on the surface of the colliculus seminalis.

Vesicular glands of the ram resemble the shape of those of the bull, but are considerably smaller, 6 X 2 cm (2 X 1 in). The boar has large vesicular glands that are pyramidal in shape, 14 X 6 cm (6 X 2 in). They contribute considerably to the large volume of the boar's ejaculate. The stallion has pear-shaped vesicular glands similar in size to those of the bull and boar, 17 X 4 cm (7 X 2 in). The vesicular glands of the bull, ram, and boar are similar to a tube folded on itself, while those of the stallion are hollow structures (actual seminal vesicles) filled with secretion. Vesicular glands of man are also lobulated amd measure 5 X 2 cm (2 X 1 in).

Vesicular glands are commonly called seminal vesicles after an early term used when it was thought that they stored sperm. They do not store sperm in the bull, ram, and boar, but there is a mixing in the stallion with some storage.

Fertility doesn't seem to be affected by removal of the vesicular glands.[17]

COLLICULUS SEMINALIS (Mound Seed)

This is a bulging area of the dorsal pelvic urethra just caudal to the urethral orifice. On the caudoventral surface are two slitlike openings, and into each slit is an opening from one deferent duct and one vesicular gland. This is the mixing area for sperm and the first accessory fluid, and the mixture is then called "semen." The colliculus seminalis swells during sexual excitement and ejaculation to assist in closing the urethral orifice, preventing urine from mixing with the semen. The semen passes into the urethra and follows this continuous tube past the other accessory glands and through the penis to the exterior.

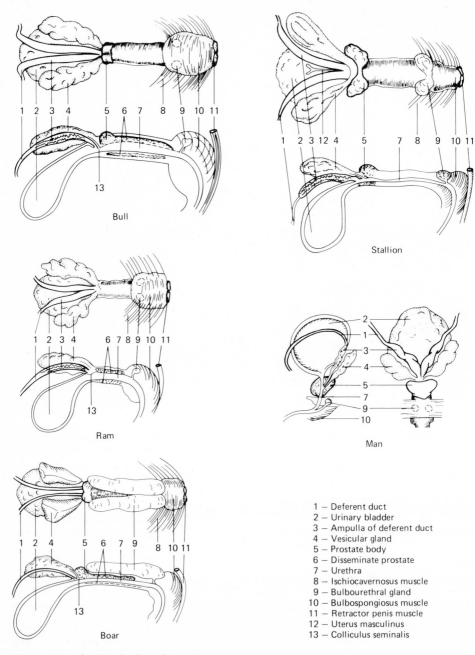

Figure 1-10 Genital glands and structures.

1 — Deferent duct
2 — Urinary bladder
3 — Ampulla of deferent duct
4 — Vesicular gland
5 — Prostate body
6 — Disseminate prostate
7 — Urethra
8 — Ischiocavernosus muscle
9 — Bulbourethral gland
10 — Bulbospongiosus muscle
11 — Retractor penis muscle
12 — Uterus masculinus
13 — Colliculus seminalis

Bull

Stallion

Ram

Man

Boar

PROSTATE (Before)

Just caudal to the vesicular glands and wrapped across the urethra is the bilobed portion of the prostate gland (Fig. 1–10/5) in the bull. This gland secretes a slick fluid that cleanses and lubricates the urethra and adds a small volume to the semen. Numerous openings from the prostate may be seen in the urethra just beneath the gland and along the urethra caudally to the area of the bulbourethral gland as they enter from the disseminate part of the gland. The prostate secretes before and during ejaculation and the secretion may be seen as a clear fluid dripping from the glans penis preparatory to coitus.

The prostate gland of the ram is disseminate. There is a slight enlargement caudal to the vesicular glands with diffusion over the wall of the dorsal urethra. The prostate of the boar is similar to that of the bull. The prostate of the stallion is distinctly lobed and wrapped across the urethra caudal to the vesicular glands. It is softer in texture than that of the bull. The prostate of human males encircles the urethra and may enlarge in later life to restrict or obliterate the urethra. Difficulty in urine flow occurs, and the urethra must then be enlarged surgically by removing a portion of the enlarged prostate gland.

PELVIC URETHRA

This portion of the urethra is surrounded by skeletal muscle capable of continuing the wave of contraction during ejaculation. It houses the colliculus seminalis in the craniodorsal urethra and receives fluid from the vesicular glands and sperm from the ampullae. In addition, the openings of the ducts from the prostate gland empty its contents into the urethra prior to and during ejaculation.

BULBOURETHRAL GLANDS (Bulge Water)

Under the terminal or caudal part of the rectum is a bulging muscle, the bulbospongiosus muscle (bulbocavernosus). It encases the urethra as it changes from a horizontal plane to moving ventrally under the anus. Just under the cranial border of this muscle are two rounded accessory glands, the bulbourethral glands, measuring approximately 3 cm (1 in) in diameter (Fig. 1–10/9). Usually it is necessary to dissect the muscle to expose them. Their functions are very similar to those of the prostate: cleansing and lubricating the urethra and adding a small volume of fluid to the semen.

The bulbourethral glands of the ram and stallion are similar in shape to those of the bull but are in proportion to their body size. The boar's glands are much larger and are cigar-shaped bodies lying side by side on the dorsal surface of the urethra, measuring 12 X 3 cm (5 X 1 in). They add considerable fluid to the boar ejaculate, whose volume is approximately 20 times that of the bull. These glands, also called Cowper's glands, are small, rounded glands in man, 1 cm (.2 in).

PENIS (Penises: Tail)

The root of the penis is in the area of the bulbospongiosus muscle (Fig. 1–11). Connective tissue forms three spongy areas, one surrounding the urethra (the bulb of the penis) and the other two lateral ones (the crura of the penis). The crura come together just below the bulbospongiosus muscle to form the corpus cavernosum penis. The corpus cavernosum penis is covered by a tough white connective tissue wrapper, the tunica albuginea (Fig. 1–12/4). Engorgement of the corpus cavernosum penis during sexual excitement causes rigidity of the penis to assist in intromission during copulation. This engorgement results from a stoppage of venous return from the penis by the ischiocavernosus muscles, which enclose the two crura and create a pumplike action at the base of the penis, resulting in pressures within the goat's penis of 7000 mm Hg during copulation compared to an average quiescent blood pressure in the corpus cavernosum of 19 mm Hg.[9] Comparable figures for the bull were 1727 and 33 mm Hg.[25] The semen is propelled rapidly along the urethra of the penis by contraction of the bulbospongiosus muscle followed by a wavelike contraction of the urethra by blood in the corpus cavernosum.[43]

As excitement decreases, venous flow is restored and the pressure returns to normal. Figure 1–13 shows the changes occurring in the penis and muscles during ejaculation.

The bull has a fibroelastic type of penis, which means that it is very fibrous with some elasticity. Because of its structure it actually changes little in size, either in diameter or length, during erection.

As the penis is followed ventrally, it forms an S curve or sigmoid flexure. The purpose of this section of some 25 cm (10 in) is to fold during the relaxed state of the penis to allow retraction and protection of the penis. Upon erection, the flexure is straightened and the penis is extended for copulation purposes.

The connective tissue structure of the fibroelastic penis is composed of lon-

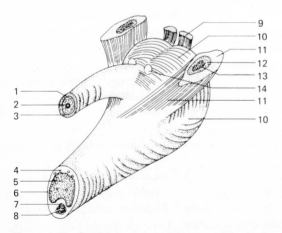

1 – Disseminate prostate
2 – Pelvic urethra
3 – Urethral muscle
4 – Blood vessels of the penis
5 – Corpus cavernosum penis
6 – Tunica albuginea penis
7 – Corpus spongiosum penis
8 – Penile urethra
9 – Retractor penis muscle
10 – Bulbospongiosus muscle
11 – Ischiocavernosus muscle
12 – Left crus of penis
13 – Erectile tissue of left crus
14 – Left bulbourethral gland

Figure 1-11 Craniolateral view of the root of the bovine penis.

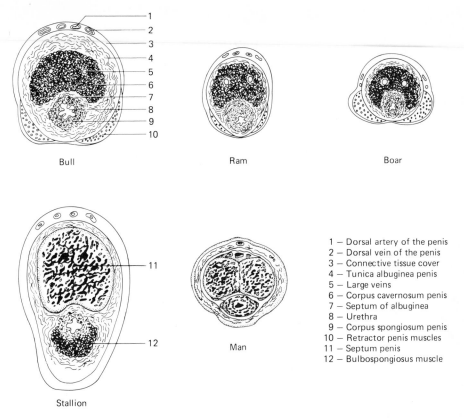

1 — Dorsal artery of the penis
2 — Dorsal vein of the penis
3 — Connective tissue cover
4 — Tunica albuginea penis
5 — Large veins
6 — Corpus cavernosum penis
7 — Septum of albuginea
8 — Urethra
9 — Corpus spongiosum penis
10 — Retractor penis muscles
11 — Septum penis
12 — Bulbospongiosus muscle

Figure 1-12 Cross-section of the penis cranial to the sigmoid flexure in the bull, ram, and boar and midway of the penis body in the stallion and man.

gitudinal fibers running the length of the penis and wrapping over in a coiled fashion toward the terminal end in the bull.[7] A coiling of the glans penis then may occur as the penis is turgid and extended. These deviations may be as much as a 300° spiral. The condition is congenital and not acquired in later life.[5,6] Seidel and Foote[36] used movie film to capture coiling during ejaculation and showed a spiraling effect at the peak of extension and ejaculation. Spiraling is commonly seen in electroejaculation when higher voltage is used and the penis is at the maximum extension.

Some penises are deviated to one side or ventrally so the bull cannot properly insert it for copulation. Numerous surgical procedures have been developed to correct this,[41] but it is best to eliminate these bulls from your breeding stock to eliminate possible offspring with the defect.

A bull may fracture his penis. This is usually done during coitus when a small cow collapses or moves quickly sideways. Ranchers commonly refer to this as a "broken" penis, but it is only a tearing and rupturing of the dense connective tissue and cavernosum, since no bone is present. The immediate symptoms are a shortening of the stride, a slightly arched back, stiffness in walking, and overall indications of

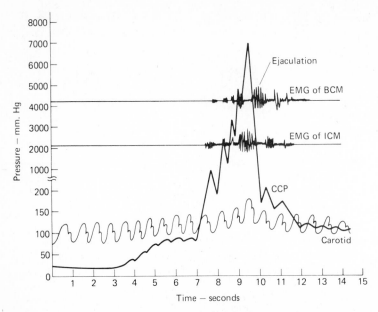

Figure 1-13　Pressures and electromyograms (EMG) associated with erection and ejaculation in the goat. CCP = corpus cavernosus penis, ICM = ischiocavernosus muscles, BCM = bulbocavernosus muscles. *(Beckett et al.[9])*

pain. There may be a prolapse of the prepuce and usually there is extensive swelling just in front of the scrotum. Urination is usually not interfered with, since the corpus spongiosum withstands the bending very well. Surgery is suggested in instances where a very good sire is involved. Recovery depends on keeping the bull sexually stimulated to reduce adhesions internally.[16]

The ram and boar both have fibroelastic penises with sigmoid flexures. The only difference from the bull occurs in the boar, where the flexure is cranial to the scrotum rather than caudal. This is caused, of course, by a change in location of the scrotum rather than the flexure.

The stallion has a vascular (musculocavernosous) type penis rather than fibroelastic. This type penis has softer, more sparse connective tissue that depends upon engorgement of the cavernosum for length and diameter as well as turgidity. There are two retractor penis muscles in the horse, as in other classes of livestock. They are attached cranially, almost at the glans, and cause a shortening by constricting and wrinkling the relaxed body of the penis.

Man also has a vascular-type penis and depends upon engorgement for increased size and length for copulation. There are no retractor penis muscles so that the penis remains extended in the relaxed state.

RETRACTOR PENIS MUSCLES

To aid in retraction and extension, paired retractor penis muscles contract during the resting stage and relax during periods of sexual excitement. These muscles are attached in the area of the last sacral vertebra at the upper extremity and on the ventral side of the body of the penis cranial to the sigmoid flexure (Fig. 1–1). Relaxation of these muscles without erection results in the penis protruding from the protective sheath in a pendulous manner and possible damage. Imagine a bull in thick brush country or prickly pear-infested range and the pain and damage associated with this condition. All thoughts of mating would probably be lost, and infection and loss of reproductive ability could result.

When selecting bulls, take a careful look at the underline of the animal to make sure the penis is not extended when relaxed. Careful selection can eliminate the necessity of replacing a herd sire in a short time.

GLANS (Acorn)

The body of the penis continues between the legs, between the spermatic cords, and forms the free part of the penis with the softer terminal portion called the glans (Fig. 1–14/4). At the base of the free part of the penis is the attachment of the prepuce, which is folded over the penis during relaxation and partially covers the penis upon extension. The glans is normally contained inside the prepuce for protection. A pocket formed at the base surrounding the penis where it attaches to the prepuce is called the fornix of the prepuce. The softer texture of the glans results from less connective tissue and engorgement than the body and protects the vagina and cervix of the female from damage upon the male's thrusting during copulation.

The glans and free part of the penis of the bull is 10 cm (4 in) long and tapers gradually to a rounded tip. There is a slight twisting so that the urethra, which was on the ventral surface, exits on the right side. There is a clear distinction between the body and free part of the penis.

The bull's penis can be manually protruded from the sheath at about one month of age. However, he is 4 to 6 months old before it naturally approaches the orifice of the sheath. Actual protrusion occurs at puberty of 8 to 9 months. The frenulum along the base of the penis is last to separate between the penis and prepuce.[3]

The frenulum fails to detach in some animals and usually causes a folding of the tip of the glans penis back to its junction with the body of the penis at the preputial attachment (Fig. 1–15).[4] The condition may be corrected by snipping the persistent frenulum; if the vascular system is well developed, surgery is necessary. The condition appears to be heritable, but no positive proof has been given.[10]

The ram's glans penis is more difficult to describe. It is slightly larger than the body of the penis and is clearly defined. The glans caps the free part and is a rather irregularly shaped, rounded body from which a small tubular extension called the urethral process (filiform appendage) (Fig. 1–14/6) protrudes 10 to 15 mm (.5 in). This is a continuation of the urethra and, although soft, does become erect during sexual excitement. Apparently, it is not necessary for reproduction, since removal does not interfere. It is believed to oscillate upon ejaculation, spraying semen on the face of the cervix.[27] Penile development in rams has been correlated with weight of the lambs, with most having a free penis in the sheath at 118 days of age.[50]

The free part of the penis of the boar is very distinctive in shape. It forms a soft

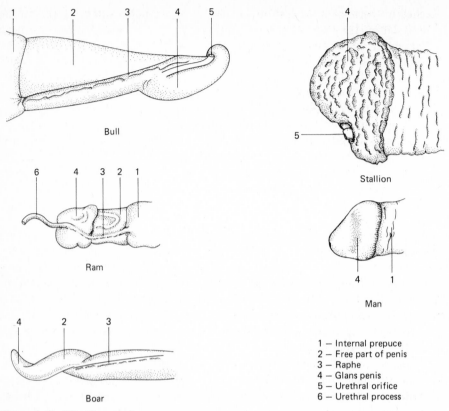

Bull

Stallion

Ram

Man

Boar

1 — Internal prepuce
2 — Free part of penis
3 — Raphe
4 — Glans penis
5 — Urethral orifice
6 — Urethral process

Figure 1-14 The glans penis.

twisting structure in the relaxed state and is difficult to distinguish from the body of the penis. Upon erection, it resembles a corkscrew as it becomes turgid. The glans, which is the most distal part, enters the cervix of the sow and there is a rotating motion of the glans during copulation. As far as is known, this is the only domestic animal in which penetration of the cervix takes place during copulation.

The stallion's glans penis is only slightly larger than the body of the penis in

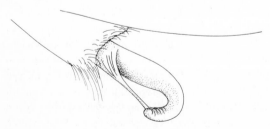

Figure 1-15 Intact frenulum in a mature bull.

the relaxed state. There is a definite difference between it and the body where the prepuce joins. It is rounded with a concave face from which the urethra protrudes 5 to 10 mm (.3 in). There are also several grooves and crevices on the face that accumulate debris that should be cleaned periodically for hygienic purposes. Upon erection, the glans becomes turgid but changes little in size until intromission. When the glans is in the cranial vagina it enlarges to approximately twice its size and the swollen glans seats itself against the open cervix of the estrual mare. The semen is then pumped into the cervix and uterus by the pistonlike glans. Upon completion of copulation the glans relaxes and, although still swollen, is withdrawn from the vagina and soon returns to its normal shape and size.

The glans of man is rounded and tapers only slightly. It is clearly defined from the body of the penis and increases to two or three times its original size upon erection.

PREPUCE (Foreskin)

The prepuce consists of an external layer of skin covered by hair, and an internal layer that surrounds the free part of the penis. This internal layer is soft, folded tissue and should remain inside until extension of the penis. Preputial glands secrete onto the surface to keep the area lubricated. Cranial and caudal preputial muscles provide for a limited amount of movement. The prepuce and free part are usually adhered in the newborn. With continued growth of the penis and multiplication of cells in the area, the penis gradually separates from the surrounding prepuce. The prepuce becomes a covering for part of the body of the penis upon erection and extension, thereby protecting it during coitus.

The boar has very active preputial glands and a diverticulum within the area, which accumulates urine, cellular debris, and preputial fluid that give rise to the characteristic boar odor (Fig. 1–16). This apparently is an attractant for the estrual sow, but is very pungent and penetrates the tissue of the boar so that his meat is inedible. If a boar is to be slaughtered, he is castrated and allowed a period of several months for the odor to dissipate. Otherwise it may be present and the carcass condemned. Experimentally, the preputial glands and diverticulum have been removed without interfering with breeding while eliminating the odor.[15]

The preputial area of the bull and ram is relatively free of depressions and cavities. The stallion accumulates cellular debri in folds of the prepuce, and this causes a drying and caking during the nonbreeding season (Fig. 1–17). The area should be cleaned thoroughly with warm soapy water and rinsed thoroughly before the breeding season, and washing of the penis and preputial area should be conducted at each mating.

Circumcision of the male child is removal of the prepuce or foreskin. This is usually done within a few days of birth. The human preputial glands secrete and, if the area is not cleaned frequently, may trap bacteria and become odoriferous. Circumcision began in biblical times to distinguish Jews from gentiles, but has since been adopted for reasons of personal hygiene.

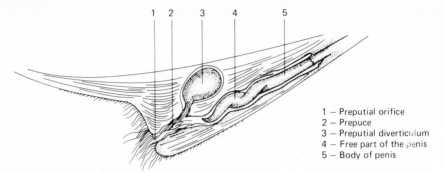

1 — Preputial orifice
2 — Prepuce
3 — Preputial diverticulum
4 — Free part of the penis
5 — Body of penis

Figure 1-16   The preputial area of the boar.

SHEATH

The outer covering of the opening for the penis is commonly called the sheath. The sheath is covered with hair the same as the body but usually has long coarse hairs coming from the preputial orifice. It has been speculated that the coarser, longer hairs are related to masculinity, but there is no proof of this or of any association between breeding efficiency and length of hairs.

The sheath of the bull may be classified as tight, normal, or pendulous. Tight sheaths are not particularly discriminated against, but may pose problems when trying to collect semen with an artificial vagina where the hand is placed on the sheath to guide the penis into the artificial vagina. Pendulous sheaths are found mostly in bulls with some Zebu breeding (Fig. 1–18). Brahman and Santa Gertrudis bulls particularly must be selected for sheaths that are not excessively pendulous. A pendulous sheath may be damaged, and usefulness of an otherwise good herd sire be lost. Be sure to select herd sires with a desirable sheath.

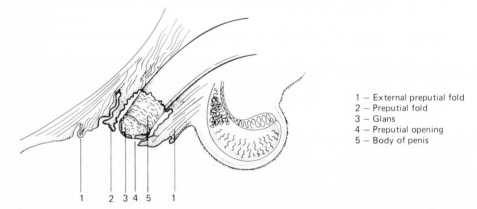

1 — External preputial fold
2 — Preputial fold
3 — Glans
4 — Preputial opening
5 — Body of penis

Figure 1-17   Preputial anatomy of the stallion.

(a)

(b)

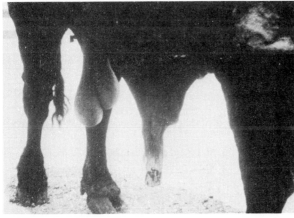

(c)

Figure 1-18 Sheaths of bulls. Desirable sheath of European breeds (a), and Zebu breeds (b), and undesirable sheath on Zebu breeds.

The bull's sheath usually opens in line with the ventral surface of the animal. The ram, however, has an opening that is almost perpendicular to the belly wall. This, however, apparently does not interfere with either extension or intromission.

The sheaths of the boar and stallion are relatively close to the body and do not usually present any problems.

PROLAPSE

Occasionally the prepuce will evert or prolapse and expose the more delicate preputial tissue lining the sheath. The reason for this is unknown and correction must be of a surgical nature. Circumcision of the prolapsed area entails removal of a portion of the prepuce. Success is limited and circumcision should be used only after consideration of the consequences. The male must be sexually active to move the penis in and out of the opening to prevent restriction during healing. The condition is apparently heritable. Healing of the moist tissue is slow, and the probabilities of it reoccurring are high.

WHAT DID YOU LEARN?

1 Trace a spermatozoon from its origin to the exterior, naming the structures through which it passes and the accessory glands as they contribute.
2 Name four functions of the epididymis.
3 Why is temperature so critical to the testes and what three structures regulate it?
4 What does monorchid mean? How can you determine the condition?
5 What causes a scrotal hernia?
6 Where is sperm mixed with the accessory fluids first to become "sperm"?
7 Give the functions of the prostate gland.
8 How does the penis of the stallion differ from that of the bull in cross section?
9 Describe the free part of the boar's penis.
10 How is the bull's penis retained in the sheath in the relaxed state?

REFERENCES

1 Adams, O. R. 1964. An improved method of diagnosis and castration of cryptorchid horses. *J.A.V.M.A.* 145:439–446.
2 Albaugh, Allen, F. D. Carroll, K. W. Ellis, and Reuben Albaugh. 1975. Comparison of carcasses and meat from steers, short scrotum bulls and intact bulls. *J. Anim. Sci.* 41:1627–1631.
3 Ashdown, R. R. 1960. Development of penis and sheath in the bull calf. *J. Agric. Sci.* 54:348–352.
4 ——. 1962. Persistence of the penile frenulum in young bulls. *Vet. Rec.* 74:1464–1468.
5 Ashdown, R. R. and M. A. Combs. 1967. Spiral deviation of the bovine penis. *Vet. Rec.* 80:737–738.

6   Ashdown, R. R., S. W. Rickets, and R. C. Wardley. 1968. The fibrous architecture of the integumentary coverings of the bovine penis. *J. Anat.* 103:567–573.

7   Ashdown, R. R. and J. A. Smith. 1969. The anatomy of the corpus cavernosum penis of the bull and its relationship to spiral deviation of the penis. *J. Anat.* 104:153–159.

8   Austin, J. W., E. W. Hupp, and R. L. Murphree. 1961. Effect of scrotal insulation on semen of Hereford bulls. *J. Anim. Sci.* 20:307–310.

9   Beckett, S. D., R. S. Hudson, D. F. Walker, R. I. Vachon, and T. M. Reynolds. 1972. Corpus cavernosum penis pressure and external penile muscle activity during erection in the goat. *Biol. Reprod.* 7:359–364.

10 Carroll, E. J., W. A. Aanes, and L. Ball. 1964. Persistent penile frenulum in bulls. *J.A.V.M.A.* 144:747–749.

11 Coulter, G. H., L. L. Larson, and R. H. Foote. 1975. Effect of age on testicular growth and consistency of Holstein and Angus bulls. *J. Anim. Sci.* 41:1383–1389.

12 Coulter, G. H., T. R. Rounsaville, and R. H. Foote. 1976. Heritability of testicular size and consistency in Holstein bulls. *J. Anim. Sci.* 43:9–12.

13 Crouch, J. E. 1974. *Functional Human Anatomy,* 2nd ed. Lea & Febiger, Philadelphia. Pp. 430–448.

14 Dutt, R. H. and P. T. Hamm. 1957. Effect of exposure to high environmental temperature and shearing on semen production of rams in winter. *J. Anim. Sci.* 16:328–334.

15 Dutt, R. H., E. C. Simpson, J. C. Christian, and C. E. Barnhart. 1959. Identification of the preputial glands as the site of production of sexual odor in the boar. *J. Anim. Sci.* 18:1557. (Abstr.)

16 Farquharson, J. 1952. Fracture of the penis in the bull. *Vet. Med.* 47:175–176.

17 Faulkner, L. C., M. L. Hopwood, and J. N. Wiltbank. 1968. Seminal vesiculectomy in bulls. *J. Reprod. Fert.* 16:179–182.

18 Fechheimer, N. S. 1970. Genetic aspects of testicular development and function. In Johnson, Gomes, and VanDemark, eds. *The Testis.* Vol. 3. Academic Press, New York. Pp. 1–40.

19 Gardner, E., D. J. Gray, and R. O'Rahilly. 1975. *Anatomy: A Regional Study of Human Structure,* 4th ed. W. B. Saunders Co., Philadelphia. Pp. 467–474.

20 Gier, H. T. and G. B. Marion. 1969. Development of mammalian testes and genital ducts. *Biol. Reprod.* 1:1–23

21 ———. 1970. Development of the mammalian testis. In Johnson, Gomes, and Van-Demark, eds. *The Testis.* Vol. 1. Academic Press, New York. Pp. 1–45.

22 Hafez, E. S. E. 1959. Reproductive capacity of farm animals in relation to climate and nutrition. *J.A.V.M.A.* 135:606–614.

23 Hahn, J., R. H. Foote, and G. E. Seidel, Jr. 1969. Testicular growth and related sperm output in dairy bulls. *J. Anim. Sci.* 29:41–47.

24 Igboeli, G. and A. M. Rahka. 1970. Bull testicular and epididymal functions after long-term vasectomy. *J. Anim. Sci.* 31:72–75.

25 Lewis, J. E., D. F. Walker, S. D. Beckett, and R. I. Vachon. 1968. Blood pressure within the corpus cavernosum penis of the bull. *J. Reprod. Fert.* 17:155–156.

26 Liptrap, R. M. and J. I. Raeside. 1970. Urinary steroid excretion in cryptorchidism in the pig. *J. Reprod. Fert.* 21:293–301.

27 Masson, Jorge. 1971. In S. J. Roberts, ed. *Veterinary Obstetrics and Genital Diseases (Theriogenology).* Ithaca, New York. P. 621.

28 Meyerhoeffer, D. C., R. P. Wettemann, M. E. Wells, and E. J. Turman. 1976. Effect of elevated ambient temperature on bulls. *J. Anim. Sci.* 43:297. (Abstr.)

29   Moller, K. 1971. Sterilization of bulls. *New Zealand Vet. J.* 19:185–187.

30   Moule, G. R. and G. M. H. Waites. 1963. Seminal degeneration in the ram and its relation to the temperature of the scrotum. *J. Reprod. Fert.* 5:433–446.

31   Orgebin-Crist, M. C. 1969. Studies on the function of the epididymis. *Biol. Reprod. Suppl.* 1:155–175.

32   Ray, E. E. and T. H. Belling, Jr. 1967. The effects of shortening the scrotum on growth rate in lambs. *Growth* 31:39–42.

33   Ray, E. E., W. M. Cox, and W. N. Capener. 1973. Effects of shortening the scrotum on growth, carcass characteristics, and consumer acceptance of fed beef. *New Mex. St. Univ. Agr. Exp. Sta. Res. Rept. 248.*

34   Schanbacher, B. D. and J. J. Ford. 1976. Endocrinology and behavior of cryptorchid rams. *J. Anim. Sci.* 43:302 (Abstr.)

35   Scorer, C. G. 1965. The natural history of testicular descent. *Proc. Roy. Soc. Med.* 58:933–934.

36   Seidel, G. E., Jr. and R. H. Foote. 1969. Motion picture analysis of ejaculation in the bull. *J. Reprod. Fert.* 20:313–317.

37   Shrock, Peter. 1971. The processus vaginalis and gubernaculum. *Surgical Clinics of North America* 51:1263–1268.

38   Smith, A. P. 1967. Epididymal transection for sterilizing bull. *J.A.V.M.A.* 150:633.

39   Waites, G. M. H. 1970. Temperature regulation and the testis. In Johnson, Gomes, and VanDemark, eds. *The Testis.* Vol. 1 Academic Press, New York. Pp. 241–279.

40   Waites, G. M. H. and G. R. Moule. 1961. Relation of vascular heat exchange to temperature regulation in the testis of the ram. *J. Reprod. Fert.* 2:213–224.

41   Walker, D. F. 1964. Deviations of the bovine penis. *J.A.V.M.A.* 145:677–682.

42   Warwick, B. L. 1961. Selection against cryptorchidism in Angora goats. *J. Anim. Sci.* 20:10–14.

43   Watson, J. W. 1964. Mechanism of erection and ejaculation in the bull and ram. *Nature* 204:95–96.

44   Wensing, C. J. G. 1968. Testicular descent in some domestic mammals. I. Anatomical aspect of testicular descent. *Koninkl. Nederl. Akademie Van Wetenschappen: Amsterdam Proc., Series C* 71:423–434.

45   ———. 1973. Testicular descent in some domestic mammals. II. The nature of the gubernacular change during the process of testicular descent in the pig. *Koninkl. Nederl. Akademie Van Wetenschappen: Amsterdam Proc., Series C* 76:190–195.

46   ———. 1973. Testicular descent in some domestic mammals. III. Search for the factors that regulate the gubernacular reaction. *Koninkl. Nederl. Akademie Van Wetenschappen: Amsterdam Proc., Series C* 76:196–202.

47   ———. 1973. Abnormalities of testicular descent. *Koninkl. Nederl. Akademie Van Wetenschappen: Amsterdam Proc., Series C* 76:373–381.

48   ——— and B. Colenbrander. 1973. Cryptorchidism and inguinal hernia. *Koninkl. Nederl. Akademie Van Wetenschappen: Amsterdam Proc., Series C* 76, no. 5. pp. 489–494.

49   Wheat, J. D. 1961. Cryptorchidism in Hereford cattle. *J. Hered.* 52:244–246.

50   Wiggins, E. L. and C. E. Terrill. 1953. Variation in penis development in ram lambs. *J. Anim. Sci.* 12:524–535.

CHAPTER 2

Microscopic Anatomy and Spermatogenesis

When you have completed this chapter you should be able to:

- Distinguish reproductive organs by cell types,
- Relate function of an organ to the cell types present, and
- Follow spermatogenesis from its beginning to the mature spermatozoon.

The animal body is made up of organs working together for a common purpose. Organs in turn are composed of tissues, which are composed of cells. In order for us to understand body functions we need to study each component. We have studied the male reproductive organs. Now let us delve deeper into the constituents of those organs.

CELL TYPES

The cells that cover the surfaces of the body are called epithelial cells. These cover both internal and external surfaces as well as lining glands, vessels, and cavities. They are classified according to the number of layers of cells and shape. A brief explanation of these general epithelial cell types and their functions is given and a description of connective tissue and muscle cells will follow.

Stratified Squamous Epithelium (Layered Scaly On)

These cells are found in layers with the basal cells being rounded or cuboidal in appearance and the cells gradually changing to flattened cells as they approach the surface. From the top, they are rounded with a central nucleus (Fig. 2–1). They are protective cells and are found on abrasive surfaces such as the skin. As the cells multiply and the layers increase, the cells move beyond a source of nourishment from the basement membrane and die. This death, or cornification, forms a hard layer of protective cells, which is best seen in a calloused area due to much abrasion and overgrowth. We find these cells on the penis, and lining the vagina. They serve to protect. A single layer, or simple squamous epithelium, is also found on some surfaces.

Cuboidal Epithelium

Cuboidal describes the shape of these cells. The cells are found on the lining of tubular structures or surfaces and are only slightly resistant to abrasion. They line the rete testes and are on the surface of the ovaries. They are usually only a single cell thick but may be stratified.

Columnar Epithelium

The term columnar is descriptive for this type epithelium. The cells, in vertical section, appear as a series of columns side by side with basal nuclei. This type may be divided into several variations. *Simple columnar* epithelial cells are rather uniform in size and shape and stand side by side. They line tubular structures or passageways for fluids such as the deferent ducts. *Pseudostratified columnar* epithelial cells appear to be layered with one columnar cell on top of another. However, this is false, as the columns are all seated on the basement membrane; but due to crowding, which usually results from rapid growth, some nuclei are pushed outward toward the surface while others are trapped near the base. These also line tubular structures such as the uterus. *Ciliated columnar* epithelium is distinguished by a brush or hairlike border that is capable of moving. The cilia beat in a wavelike manner to move objects over their surface and are found in the efferent ductules and the oviducts. *Stereociliated columnar* epithelium is similar in appearance to ciliated cells except the cilia are not beating. These cilia are strictly brushes without motility. Objects moving across them are brushed. The epididymis is lined with these. *Secretory columnar* epithelium has the capacity to develop fluid in the cell, store it, and expel it onto the surface or into a lumen. These cells usually have a clear area when stained, indicating secretion, and they assume a goblet shape as the extremity swells with secretion. Many are found in the cervix.

Glandular Cells

These cells are secretory and fall into several configurations (Fig. 2–1). Some line *tubular*-type glands and are triangular or pie-shaped with basal nuclei. They secrete

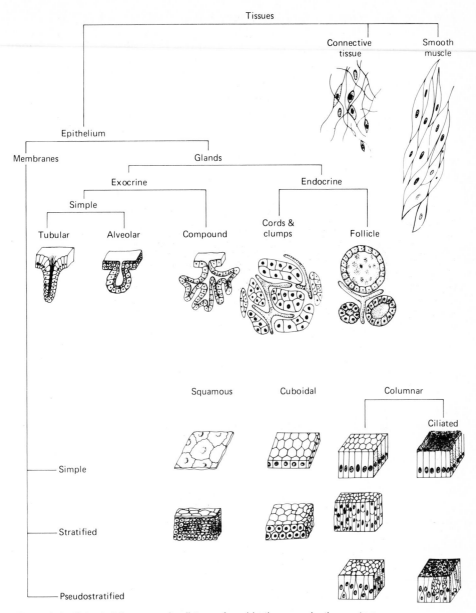

Figure 2-1   Selected tissues and cell types found in the reproductive system.

into the lumen and the secretion passes quickly through ducts to the surface. Other secretory cells are in well-organized *alveolar* glands with large storage areas. These cells appear very similar to those described earlier and change height with secretory activity. Variations of these may appear *compound* in shape. The secretion is stored in the lumen of the gland until passed out. A third type of secretory cell is found in endocrine glands where they are shaped like *cords and clumps,* which have neither ducts nor lumens. They are rounded or polyhedral in shape and the secretion fuses through and between surrounding cells into the bloodstream. Follicle-type glands usually have large cavities for fluid storage and thin secretory walls of cells.

Connective Tissue

These strandlike cells have a nucleus centrally located with slender filaments so that a mass of the cells may form a network for support. Thick layers of these cells may be covered with collagen fibers to form a shiny outer membrane on organs called the serosa. Their support therefore may be either internal or external or both.

Muscle

The main muscle cell type that is involved in reproductive organs is the smooth or involuntary muscle fiber. These cells are elongated with a central nucleus and the ends tapered. They lie side by side and in cross section appear as round cells with nuclei. In longitudinal section, they are long and tapering. Their contraction and relaxation cause movement of fluids and bodies carried by the fluid.

SCROTUM

The outer skin is protective and therefore made of stratified squamous epithelium. This epithelium is continually growing, and as the healthy cells are pushed farther from their source of nourishment at the basement membrane, they die. The hardened dead cells protect the underlying soft tissues. The scrotum also has hair or wool covering it, which assists in temperature regulation (Fig. 2–2). Inside the tough outer skin is a layer of connective tissue fascia and the tunica dartos composed of non-striated muscle fibers. Another layer of fascia separates this from the parietal vaginal tunic.

Parietal Vaginal Tunic (Wall Sheath Covering)

This layer of fascia lining the scrotum is composed of dense connective tissue covered by a serous membrane of simple squamous epithelium forming a very slick surface against which the testis moves freely without abrasion. This is a continuation of the peritoneum. The vaginal cavity separates the parietal layer from the visceral layer of the vaginal tunics.

TESTIS

The testis is composed of two covering tissues, the visceral vaginal tunic and the tunica albuginea. Internally, the seminiferous tubules, interstitial cells, nerves, blood vessels, rete testes, and efferent ductules are found.

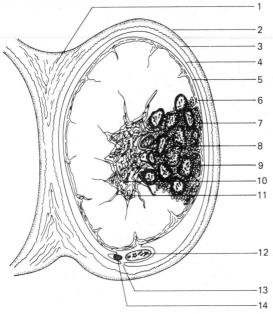

1 — Scrotal septum
2 — Scrotum
3 — Tunica dartos
4 — Parietal vaginal tunic
5 — Vaginal cavity
6 — Visceral vaginal tunic
7 — Tunica albuginea testis
8 — Seminiferous tubules
9 — Interstitial cells
10 — Rete testis
11 — Mediastinum testis
12 — Body of epididymis
13 — Mesorchium
14 — Deferent duct

Figure 2-2   Cross-section of the testis and its surrounding membranes midway of the longitudinal axis.

Visceral Vaginal Tunic (Internal Organ Sheath Covering)

The visceral vaginal tunic is the outer covering of the testis proper. It is dense connective tissue covered with simple squamous epithelium. Its purpose is to give shape and support to the testis. It is continuous with the peritoneum during testicular descent.

Tunica Albuginea (Covering White)

Under the visceral vaginal tunic is a dense thick white layer of connective tissue, the tunica albuginea. These two layers give structure to the testis, and the tunica albuginea contains the larger blood vessels near the surface of the testis. Branching from the tunica albuginea are septula, or bands of loose connective tissue, that connect to the loose connective tissue mediastinum at the core of each testis. These septula are distinct and complete in the boar, but thin and inconspicuous in ruminants.[13] The mediastinum is also made of connective tissue. It is located mainly in the cranial pole of the stallion testis but throughout the length of other domestic animals. This network gives structure and shape to the testis, holding the seminiferous tubules, interstitial cells, and rete testis in place.

Seminiferous Tubules (Seed-Bearing Tube)

The sperm-producing units of the testis are the seminiferous tubules. They make up the mass of the testis and are supplied nutrients by the many blood vessels that traverse the septula of the internal testis. These tubules are very long and coiled and microscopic in size (Fig. 2–3). The length of these tubules in one group of stallions measured 2419 m (7934 ft).[38]

Younger bulls have a greater semen-producing capacity per unit volume of the testis than do older bulls. There is also a decrease in the proportion of testicular tissue with age until maturity, and then the decrease becomes smaller.[21] The dorsal region of the testis has a significantly higher volume of producing tissue, and aging is related to fibrosis, particularly in the ventral area. Even after these statements, it must be remembered that testicular weight, volume, and daily sperm production in bulls have all been shown to increase up to about seven years of age.[16]

A basement membrane lines the tubule, and resting on this are the initial spermatogenic cells, the spermatogonia. Supporting the basement membrane are collagen fibers.[10] There is a developmental progression of cells from the periphery of the tubule to the internal lumen called spermatogenesis. As a study of the cell types is made, the next layer will be primary spermatocytes followed by secondary spermatocytes, spermatids, and the spermatozoa in the lumen.

Sustentacular cells are ramified, pillar-shaped cells extending from the basement membrane through all layers of the developing spermatogenic cells to the lumen of the tubule[30] (Fig. 2–3). Their purpose is to sustain the spermatogenic cells during their progression and maturation and number about 25 to 30 in a cross section of a tubule from the bull. They are also called cells of Sertoli. The nucleus is pale staining and ovoid, and the outline of the cell is indistinct. Cytoplasmic branches separate the germinal cells, and only a plasma membrane separates the sustentacular cell contents and the germinal cells.[39] Mature sustentacular cells do not divide. They may produce estrogen. Sustentacular cells are apparently very susceptible to aging, since relative volume of the sustentacular nuclei is reduced as much as 52 percent between young and old bulls.[21]

Spermatogenesis (Seed Production)

The development of the spermatozoon is a process of cell division beginning with a rounded immobile cell and terminating in an elongated motile cell. During this process the chromosome number is halved. Two rather distinct parts exist: spermatocytogenesis and spermiogenesis.

Spermatocytogenesis (Seed Cell Production) This is the division of cells from the beginning of sperm formation until a change in shape occurs.

Spermatogonia The original cells in the process of spermatogenesis are the Type A spermatogonia, which may require testosterone for development from embryonic gonocytes.[36] The A type spermatogonia are the stem cells containing two or more nucleoli and lie dormant on the basement membrane until some unknown factor causes them to divide mitotically, forming other A type cells which subsequently form dormant A cells and active B cells. The B cells are similar to Type A cells except that they contain only one nucleolus. They are sometimes on the basement membrane but will be pushed inward as multiplication occurs (Fig. 2-4).

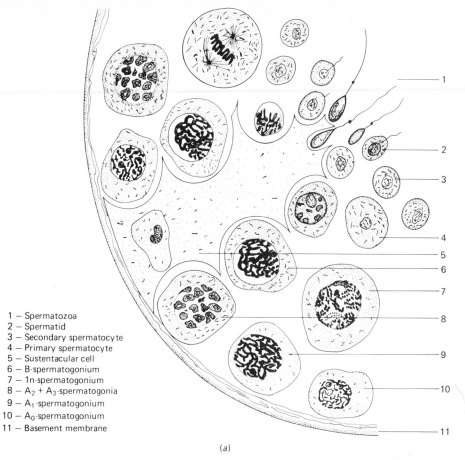

1 — Spermatozoa
2 — Spermatid
3 — Secondary spermatocyte
4 — Primary spermatocyte
5 — Sustentacular cell
6 — B-spermatogonium
7 — 1n-spermatogonium
8 — $A_2 + A_3$-spermatogonia
9 — A_1-spermatogonium
10 — A_0-spermatogonium
11 — Basement membrane

(a)

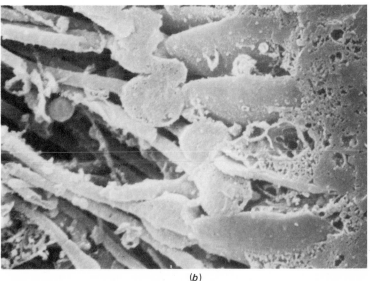

(b)

Figure 2-3 Spermatogenic and supporting cells of the seminiferous tubule (a). Scanning electron photomicrograph (4500) $\times$ (b). *(From Nowell and Faulkin.[26])*

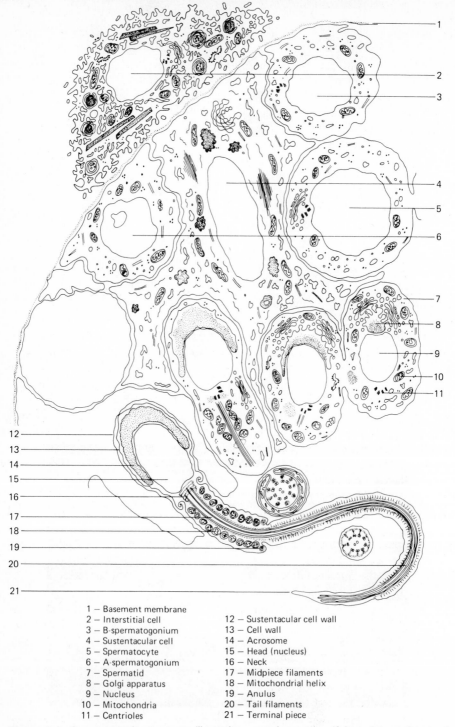

1 — Basement membrane
2 — Interstitial cell
3 — B-spermatogonium
4 — Sustentacular cell
5 — Spermatocyte
6 — A-spermatogonium
7 — Spermatid
8 — Golgi apparatus
9 — Nucleus
10 — Mitochondria
11 — Centrioles
12 — Sustentacular cell wall
13 — Cell wall
14 — Acrosome
15 — Head (nucleus)
16 — Neck
17 — Midpiece filaments
18 — Mitochondrial helix
19 — Anulus
20 — Tail filaments
21 — Terminal piece

Figure 2-4 Spermatogenic structures illustrating spermiogenesis. *(Adapted from Constantinides.[10])*

Spermatocytes The B type spermatogonia progress through a series of divisions to form 16 primary spermatocytes from each spermatogonium. This process takes 15 to 16 days in the ram. The 2N chromosome number has not changed. This number is 60 for the stallion and bull, 38 in the boar, 54 in the ram, and 48 in man. Each primary spermatocyte divides to form two secondary spermatocytes. These cells are pushed toward the lumen of the seminiferous tubule as division occurs. This step takes 15 to 16 days also. Primary spermatocytes have been found as early as 9 weeks of age in the ram and secondary spermatocytes at 18 weeks.[8]

Spermatids Following division of the secondary spermatocytes, two spermatids are formed from each. This takes only 1 to 2 days; therefore, we can see only a few secondary spermatocytes because of their short life. They are also pushed toward the lumen and surrounded by the sustentacular cells. During the two cell divisions from the primary spermatocyte to the spermatid, under the influence of testosterone,[35] the chromosome number has been halved so that the spermatid now has a 1N complement of chromosomes.

Spermiogenesis (Seed Production) This stage of development is marked by the transformation of spermatids into spermatozoa.

Spermatozoa These motile, tadpolelike cells result from metamorphosis of the spermatid. The spermatid is a round cell with the usual organelles (Fig. 2–4). Each of these is destined to change into a functional unit of the mature spermatozoon.

The cell wall is retained as the outer covering of the spermatozoon. The cytoplasm gradually is moved alongside the nucleus to the newly developed tail and slides off the end to leave only a very small segment of the original cytoplasm. The nucleus elongates and flattens but remains relatively constant in size and forms the greater part of the head of the sperm cell.

The major differences occur in the organelles. The Golgi apparatus assembles at one pole of the nucleus while the centrioles move to the opposite end. The mitochondria align themselves laterally. The cytoplasm elongates as this occurs.

The Golgi then accumulates secretions from the surrounding area to form the acrosomal vesicle. This begins to flatten over the surface of the nucleus. A large dense ring and a smaller ring form around the distal centriole as it begins to form filaments, and the mitochondria migrate to form a helical structure around these filaments. The cytoplasm continues to elongate.

Finally the cranial sperm head is covered by the acrosome. The acrosome is of different configuration in different species and helps determine the shape of the head. The axial filaments of the tail continue to elongate and the smaller ring from the distal centriole area forms an anulus around the filaments at the distal end of the midpiece. Mitochondria form a spiral sheath around the axial filaments to form the midpiece. The cytoplasm has now moved onto the neck or body region of the spermatozoon and the tail is extended free past the midpiece.

The final nuclear shape determines the shape of the head, and this varies with species.

The immature spermatozoon is passed through the tubular structures of the testes to the epididymis where the droplet passes off the trail and the sperm is considered mature.

The mature ram spermatozoon head is approximately 8 micrometers (μm) long, 4 μm wide, and 1 μm thick. The midpiece is approximately 14 μm long and the mainpiece of the tail is 40 to 45 μm long. The entire sperm then measures approximately 65 μm (.0026 in).[29]

Table 2–1 gives dimensions of sperm for the various domestic animals and man.

Ultrastructure of Spermatozoa As electronmicroscopy has advanced, the ultrastructure of the spermatozoon has revealed some very interesting details of this miraculous little cell (Fig. 2–5). The entire spermatozoon is covered by a cell membrane. This is most closely attached at the base of the head and the end of the midpiece at the anulus.[19,31]

The head of the sperm is a homogeneous nucleus covered anteriorly by a three-layered cap and posteriorly by a loose, thin, dense, postnuclear cap (Fig. 2–5). The nucleus in the bull measures approximately 0.2 to 0.3 μm thick.[31] The acrosomal cap forms apically between the nuclear membrane and the cell membrane. The foreport, which is largest, contains substances with enzymatic activity, and the postacrosomal dense lamina forms the equatorial segment of the head covering[5,14] and what has been termed the postnuclear cap. The sperm head of the stallion is covered by the acrosome on the anterior two-thirds and a distinct marginal thickening or apical ridge is seen on the curbed anterior edge.[34] Beneath the acrosome is the perforatorium. The base of the head is recessed at the point of attachment of the midpiece and tail.

The boar sperm head with its acrosomal cap closely resembles that of the bull.[41]

The normal bovine sperm tail consists of the structure found in most flagella. There are nine large outer fibers and nine smaller inner fibers encircling two central fibers (Fig. 2–5). These originate in the recessed implantation socket in the base of the head and are immediately covered by the mitochondrial helix of the midpiece.[4,32] The alternate contraction and expansion of the coarse fibers in the neck are the probable mechanism for initiating the whipping motion of the tail to move the sperm forward. The wrapping, or helical formation, of the midpiece is due to

Table 2-1 Spermatozoon Dimensions (μm)

	Bull	Ram	Boar	Stallion	Man
Head					
Length	9	8	8	7	5
Width	4	4	4	4	4
Thickness	1	1	1	2	3
Midpiece	13	14	11	10	5
Tail	44	43	38	42	45
Total length	65	65	57	58	55

Partially from White.[40]

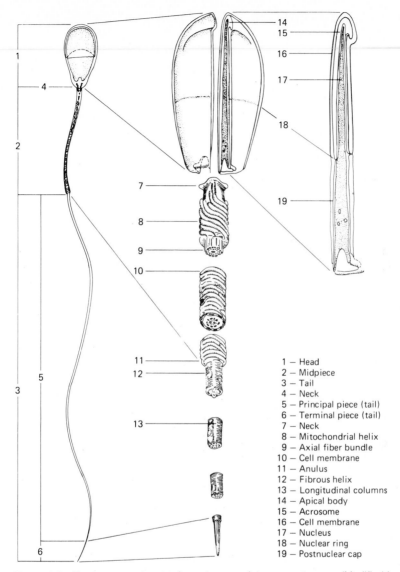

1 — Head
2 — Midpiece
3 — Tail
4 — Neck
5 — Principal piece (tail)
6 — Terminal piece (tail)
7 — Neck
8 — Mitochondrial helix
9 — Axial fiber bundle
10 — Cell membrane
11 — Anulus
12 — Fibrous helix
13 — Longitudinal columns
14 — Apical body
15 — Acrosome
16 — Cell membrane
17 — Nucleus
18 — Nuclear ring
19 — Postnuclear cap

Figure 2-5 The component parts of a mature ungulate spermatozoon. *(Modified from Saacke and Almquist.[31,32])*

mitochondria being arranged end to end without any regularity as to beginning or ending of each segment. There may be 65 to 75 turns among these cells. The anulus, sometimes called Jensen's ring, is found as an intact circle at the terminal end of the midpiece.

The cytoplasmic droplet may be found adjacent to the neck or anywhere along the midpiece and tail depending upon stage of sperm maturation. It is bounded by the cell membrane and is composed of fine, curved tubules with many small and some large vesicles and some cytoplasm.[6] It probably represents remnants of disintegrating Golgi apparatus and vesicles of the endoplasmic reticulum of the original spermatid.

The tail or flagellum is divided into the principal piece and the terminal piece (Fig. 2–5). The principal piece is a continuation of the midpiece structure without the mitochondrial helix but surrounded by a fibrous sheath. Lying on the dorsal and ventral aspects of the principal piece are longitudinal columns of filamentous subunits running the length of the sheath.[14] These apparently are associated with the whipping motion of the tail for locomotion. These are inconspicuous in the boar.

The terminal piece is covered only by the membrane. The fibers of the principal piece diminish in diameter and some will terminate as they reach the terminal piece. The two sets of fibers converge distally before terminating.[14]

Cyclic Activity Spermatogenesis occurs in a wavelike pattern in the seminiferous tubules so that adjacent areas may be in different stages of the spermatogenic cycle. Amann (personal communication) has divided the cycle into eight stages as shown in Fig. 2–6. Stages I, II, and III represent the replenishing, through division, of the spermatogonia. Spermatogenesis actually begins at stage III and completes the development in approximately 4.5 cycles with the release of approximately 192 spermatozoa.

Degeneration of testicular components or potential germ cells during the first three-fourths of spermatogenesis is only 4 percent in young bulls compared to 19 percent in mature bulls.[2] Losses in mature bulls may be divided into 7 percent during spermatogonial multiplication, 7 percent during the primary spermatocyte formation, and 5 percent during the meiotic divisions. There apparently is very little loss during metamorphosis of the spermatids.

Length of time for completion of a cycle and for spermatogenesis to occur is 13.5 and 54 days for the bull, 10.4 and 49 days for the ram,[9] 8.6 and 34.4 days for the boar,[37] and 16 and 74 days for man.[9]

A detailed review of spermatogenesis is given by Courot et al.[11] and Ortavant et al.[28] and of functional anatomy of the sperm by Afzelius[1] and Fawcett.[15]

Consider the significance of the above times for spermatogenesis to be completed. If a sire were injured in the area of the scrotum and infection developed resulting in a fever, spermatogenesis would be arrested. Certain stress conditions such as an extended period of travel associated with stress of climate, excitement, and new surroundings may cause a cessation of sperm production in a male. Although the sperm that had been produced prior to infection or stress are still viable, these may soon be exhausted and none are there to replace them. Then it would take approximately 49 days for the ram to replenish his supply and the boar approximately 35 days. Between the time of exhaustion of the viable sperm stored and the production of new sperm the animal is for all practical purposes sterile.

Many cattlemen, as well as other livestock breeders, will sometimes purchase a sire that has been semen evaluated as "satisfactory" and load him into a trailer for a long trip home. The trip may be several days long over rough terrain and even perhaps with high temperatures. When the bull is turned into a group of cows to

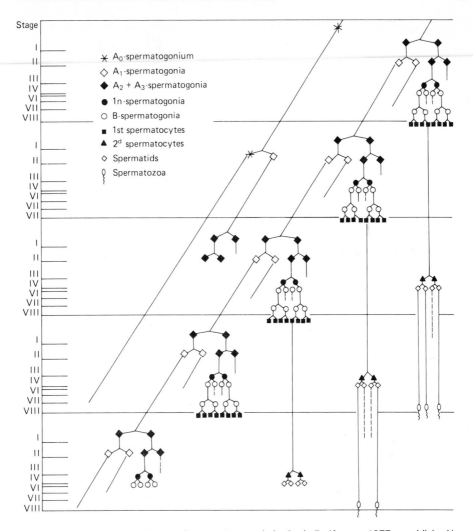

Figure 2-6 The tentative pattern of spermatogenesis in the bull. *(Amann 1977 unpublished.)*

breed, he does a fine job for a few weeks and then cows start returning to be bred for a second time. The new owner of the bull is upset and has the bull's semen evaluated. It is of poor quality with some immature cells. The new owner immediately blames the rancher from whom he purchased the bull and demands satisfaction in the form of a new bull or return of the sale price.

If the new owner had known the effects of stress on spermatogenesis and the time required for new sperm to be developed, he would have planned ahead for a lag in production and rested the sire before using him. Then the reserve would be sufficient and new production available for a continuing breeding program.

An individual actually purchased a bull and wanted to protect the testes from damage en route to his new home. A support made of sheepskin with the wool on it was placed over the testes and used to suspend them. It was a hot day and when the bull was subsequently checked for semen evaluation, all the sperm were dead and the bull never recovered to produce satisfactory sperm.

Tubuli Recti (Tubule Straight)

These straight portions of the seminiferous tubules carry the sperm from the many seminiferous tubules to the rete testis. They are found primarily in the boar and stallion because of the distance from the coiled tubules to the rete. They resemble the rete testis and are lined by simple cuboidal or simple squamous epithelium (Fig. 2–7). The tubules decrease in diameter as they approach the rete testis in many instances.

Interstitial Cells (Set Between)

Between the coiled seminiferous tubules are the interstitial cells (Fig. 2–8). These cells are irregularly polyhedral-shaped cells. Pressure of the surrounding tubules determines the shape to a large extent. The cells are also called cells of Leydig. Their purpose is to produce the male sex hormone, testosterone. They constitute approximately 7 percent of the total testicular volume in the bull and represent 20 percent in the adult boar.

Rete Testis

The straight tubules of the testis are located in the mediastinum and are composed of many connecting canals. They collect the sperm from the seminiferous tubules. The pressure of sperm production pushes the spermatozoa into the tubules. They are lined with simple cuboidal or simple squamous epithelium (Fig. 2–9) and act as a passageway to the efferent ductules. In the boar, many cells have blebs of secretion on the surface. This fluid acts to carry sperm.[33] Sometimes the bull rete testis may be lined with stratified cuboidal epithelium.[12] The rete testis is surrounded by the connective tissue of the mediastinum. A good review of the intertubular tissue is given by Hooker.[20]

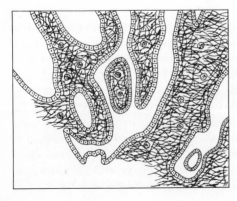

Figure 2-7   Tubuli recti.

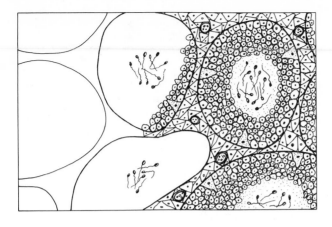

Figure 2-8 Interstitial cells.

EFFERENT DUCTULES

The efferent ductules of the testes collect immature spermatozoa from the rete and move them through the surface of the testes into the epididymis. There are 12 to 25 of the tubules that collect the sperm, depending on species. They are lined with cuboidal or ciliated pseudostratified columnar epithelium (Fig. 2–10). The cilia are motile and therefore actively move the spermatozoa through the ductules. Microvilli on the surface of some of the cells indicate resorptive capacity for the cells.

In addition to the ciliated cells there are secretory cells with large granules. These add fluid for transportation into the head of the epididymis. Some researchers place the efferent ductules as a part of the head of the epididymis. The many ductules form into a single duct as they enter the head of the epididymis.[22] Spermatozoa in these structures show weak vibrating movement but no forward progress.[17]

EPIDIDYMIS

The epididymis is a single convoluted tube in the head portion, then straightens somewhat into the body, and then becomes very coiled in the tail. The epididymis is covered with a shiny membrane of connective tissue called the serosa. This gives shape and support to it. Muscle fibers are beneath the serosa.

Stroma or structural connective tissue supports the tubule proper composed of a basement membrane and steriociliated pseudostratified columnar epithelium[18] (Fig. 2–11). These brushlike borders are long and straight in the head region, are nonmotile, and act as a brush to the sperm cells as they move past. It seems logical that the mechanical action is one reason for the passage of the cytoplasmic droplet from the tail of the sperm as it passes through the epididymis. Immature sperm enter the head of the epididymis with the droplet located anywhere from the base of the sperm head to the tip of the tail. These sperm are capable of moving vigorously in a circular pattern.[17] This droplet moves off the tail during passage through the

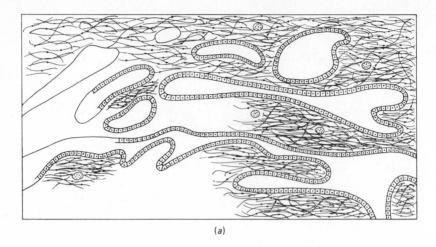

(a)

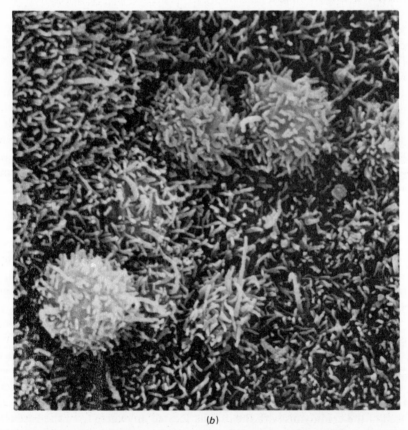

(b)

Figure 2-9   Rete testis (a). SEM showing microvilli on the surface of cuboidal epithelium (b) 5500 X. *(From Nowell and Faulkin.[26])*

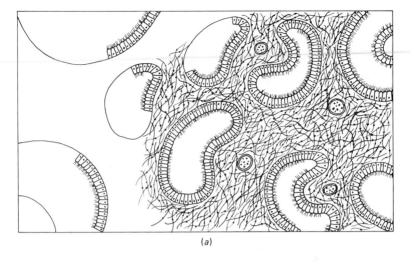

(a)

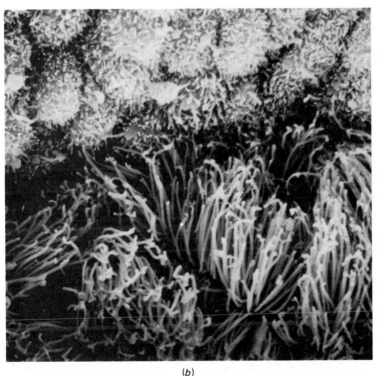

(b)

Figure 2-10 Efferent ductules (a). SEM of motile cilia and other cells with microvilli, 3750 X (b). *(From Nowell and Faulkin.[26])*

epididymis and should not be present on mature sperm stored in the tail. This passage through the epididymis takes approximately 10 days in the bull. Increasing numbers of sperm show progressive forward movement with longitudinal rotation.

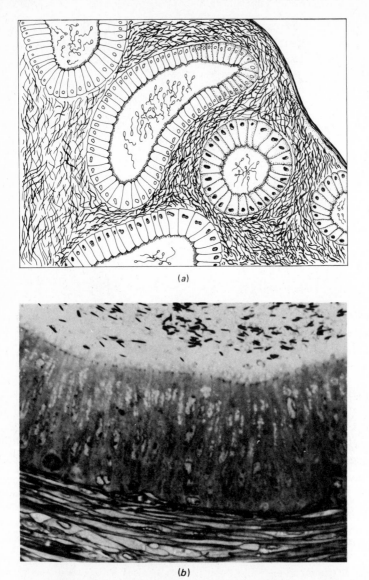

(a)

(b)

Figure 2-11 Head of the epididymis (a). SEM of epithelium with sterecilia, 390 X (b). *(From Nowell and Faulkin.[26])*

The columnar cells become lower and the steriocilia become sparse and shorter as the deferent duct is approached[18] (Fig.2–12). Height of the cells may vary according to concentration in that particular segment. Absorption of fluids and the products of sperm breakdown are apparent in the epididymis.[27]

Sections through the tail of the epididymis would reveal a very dense mass of mature sperm with little or no motility until diluted. The bull stores approximately 45 percent of the epidididymal sperm in this region. The turnover of sperm in this area is very rapid, with sperm being resorbed or passed out in ejaculation or during

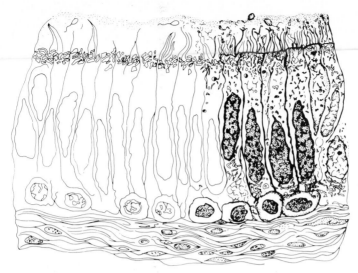

Figure 2-12 Tail of the epididymis.

urination.[23] The size of the sperm decreases by approximately 10 percent from the head to the tail of the epididymis as fluids are absorbed.[7]

DEFERENT DUCT

These long deferent ducts receive the concentrated sperm from the tail of the epididymis and transport them to the colliculus seminalis. They form a part of the spermatic cord and then enter the abdominal cavity where they are covered with a peritoneal fold. They are firm tubular structures covered by a serosa. Under the serosa are three thin layers of muscle. The outer layer next to the serosa has fibers oriented in a longitudinal direction, the middle layer passes in a circular direction around the duct, and the inner layer is oriented longitudinally.[3] The peristaltic, or milking, wavelike contraction of these muscles starts at the tail of the epididymis and moves rapidly over its length to propel the sperm through it.

The mucosa inside the muscles contains the lamina propria, which is the loose connective tissue matrix forming prominent longitudinal folds on the lining of the duct and the epithelium (Fig. 2–13). The epithelium is similar to the epididymis in the lower duct with numerous stereociliated pseudostratified columnar epithelial cells but changes rather quickly into pseudostratified columnar epithelium and then into simple columnar, which lines the remainder of the duct.

Ampulla

The ampulla is present in the stallion, bull, and ram, but not in the boar. The epithelium is low columnar. It has numerous tubuloalveolar glands lined with secretory columnar epithelial cells, which secrete a carrier for the sperm (Fig. 2–14).

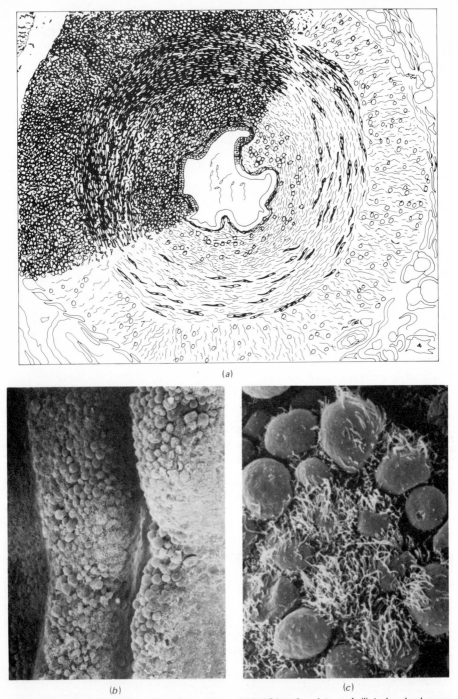

(a)

(b)   (c)

Figure 2-13   Deferent duct (a). SEM of the mucosa 532 X (b) and a mixture of ciliated and columnar cells in the distal duct 3000 X (c). *(From Nowell and Faulkin.[26])*

For this reason it is best to classify the ampulla as an accessory gland. The stallion has very organized ampullae which are commonly called ejaculatory ducts. The large ampullae store considerable sperm; approximately a number equivalent to one ejaculation in the bull.

VESICULAR GLANDS

Like the previous structures, these glands are covered with a serosa for support. There are two layers of muscle surrounding the gland—an outer longitudinal and an inner circular. These contract upon sexual excitement and ejaculation to add fluid from the reservoirs of the glands.

The mucosa consists of the lamina propria, which forms many deep folds that are capable of expanding greatly. The glandular structure is tubuloalveolar, in the bull and boar, with a central lumen collecting secretion from glandular tubes. The stallion has a true vesicle or pocket structure with branching pockets. Epithelium may be simple or pseudostratified columnar of a secretory nature (Fig. 2–15). Epithelial height is governed by secretory activity. The vesicular secretion is white or yellowish in color and gelatinous and amounts to approximately 25 to 30 percent of the ejaculate in the bull, 10 to 30 percent in the boar, and 7 to 8 in the ram. It composes 40 to 80 percent of the ejaculate in man.[24]

PROSTATE GLAND

The tissue of the prostate is primarily secretory. There is an outer serosa with an underlying thin layer of muscle. The mucosa consists of the stroma, which maintains the integrity of the organ. The glandular structure is tubuloalveolar and the ducts open into the urethra. Location varies considerably with species.

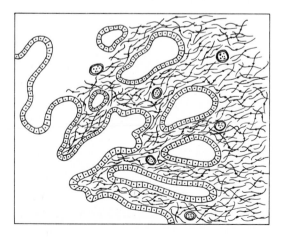

Figure 2-14 The glandular ampulla.

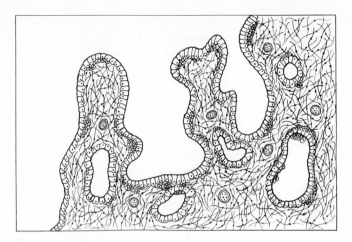

Figure 2-15 Vesicular glands.

The epithelium is simple cuboidal or columnar cells that line the glands and irregularly distributed small basal cells either rounded or flattened (Fig. 2–16). The ducts near the urethra are lined by transitional epithelium. Concretions are sometimes found in older animals, particularly men.[25] The gland may be divided into the external and internal or disseminate portions. External designates that portion lying on the pelvic urethral surface, and the disseminate is in the submucosal area. There is only an external portion in the stallion. The prostate of the bull is on the surface but mainly developed encircling the urethra. The disseminate gland of the ram is over the dorsal and lateral areas of the urethra. The boar's prostate has an external plate and an encircling internal portion. The prostate supplies 4 to 6 percent of the ejaculate in ruminants, 25 to 30 percent in the stallion, and 35 to 60 percent in the boar. It supplies 15 to 30 percent in man.[24]

PELVIC URETHRA

Serosa is the outer connective tissue covering, and under it lie the pelvic urethral muscles. Longitudinal folds are present in the mucosa. The epithelium lining the urethra is transitional (Fig. 2–17).

BULBOURETHRAL GLANDS

These glands are compound tubuloalveolar and similar to the prostate gland in structure and function. The lining epithelium is tall, simple columnar cells with round or flat basal nuclei (Fig. 2–18). Cuboidal, columnar, or transitional epithelium is found in the ducts, varying with size and location. The gland is surrounded by the bulbocavernosus muscles in the stallion and ruminants. The ischioglandular muscle surrounds the gland of the boar. Its secretion composes 15 to 30 percent of the ejaculate of the boar and aids in coagulation of the boar ejaculate.

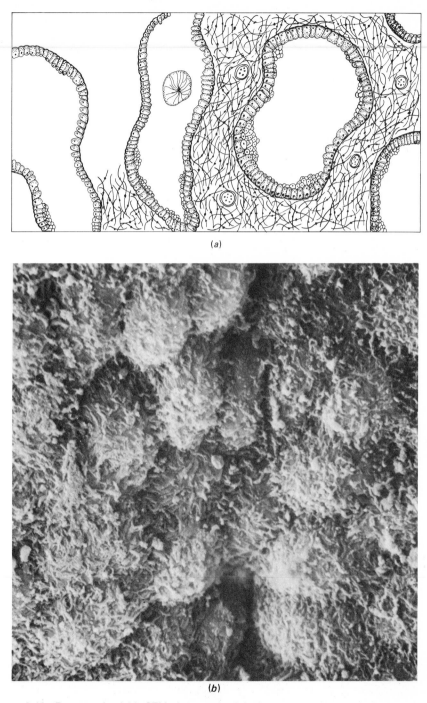

(a)

(b)

Figure 2-16 Prostate gland (a). SEM photograph of the secretory cells with microvilli covering them, 3800 X (b). *(From Nowell and Faulkin.[26])*

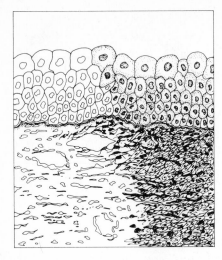

Figure 2-17   Pelvic urethra.

PENIS

The crura of the penis are spongy areas of loose connective tissue, the corpus cavernosum. This tissue has a tremendous capacity for filling with blood to facilitate rigidity of the penis. As the crura meet and form the penis proper, a thick white connective tissue covering, the tunica albuginea, is formed around the penis for support and structure. The corpus cavernosum forms an upper and lower segment designated as corpus cavernosum penis and corpus cavernosum urethra (corpus spongiosum). A septum of connective tissue separates the two. The cavernous portion is lined with endothelium and surrounded by many smooth muscle cells and connective tissue. A cross section at the distal portion of the sigmoid flexure would also reveal the two retractor penis muscles on the ventral lateral surfaces. The lining epithelium gradually changes to stratified cuboidal or columnar epithelium with patches of transitional epithelium (Fig. 2–19). The corpus cavernosum of the ani-

Figure 2-18   Bulbourethral glands.

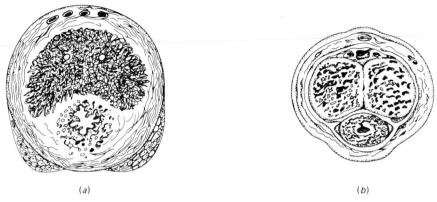

(a)   (b)

Figure 2-19 Cross-section of the fibroelastic penis (a) and the vascular penis (b).

mals having the fibroelastic penis, (bull, boar, and ram) is much more dense than those having a vascular-type penis, (stallion and man).

GLANS

The tunica albuginea continues over the glans covered by stratified squamous epithelium for protection (Fig. 2–20). Internally the corpus cavernosum urethra makes up the entire spongy portion around the urethra; the urethra is lined with transitional or stratified squamous epithelium.

PREPUCE

This tissue is actually a continuation of the outer skin and consists of stratified squamous epithelium. It contains secretory glands opening onto the internal surface

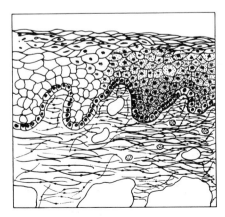

Figure 2-20 Cross-section of the glans penis.

for lubrication and is covered with hair and sebaceous glands in domestic animals. Upon erection and extension of the penis, the prepuce covers the penis and the stratified squamous epithelium protects it against abrasion.

SHEATH

The outer skin is covered with stratified squamous epithelium; intermixed are hair or wool follicles.

WHAT DID YOU LEARN?

1 What is the major purpose of ciliated columnar epithelial cells? Where are they found in the male reproductive system?
2 What do the following words mean?

    a   tunica   e   parietal
    b   corpus   f   spermatocytogenesis
    c   recti   g   efferent
    d   albuginea   h   sustentacular

3 What is the function of the sustentacular cells?
4 From what does the helical portion of the midpiece of the sperm form?
5 At what point of sperm progression through the tract does forward motion occur?
6 What is the purpose of interstitial cells?
7 What are the very beginning cells of spermatogenesis in the seminiferous tubules called?
8 How many spermatozoa form from a single primary spermatocyte in the ram?
9 How long does spermatogenesis take in the bull?
10 Explain the effect of infection of a cut on the scrotum of a bull and resulting reproductive response.

REFERENCES

1 Afzelius, B. A., ed. 1975. *The Functional Anatomy of the Spermatozoon.* Pergamon, Oxford.
2 Amann, R. P. 1962. Reproductive capacity of dairy bulls. IV. Spermatogenesis and testicular germ cell degeneration. *Amer. J. Anat.* 110:69–78.
3 Berns, D. M., R. A. Rodzen, E. E. Brueschke, and L. J. D. Zaneveld. 1974. Vasa deferentia of the human and dog: A study with the SEM. In *Scanning Electron Microscopy.* Part III. *Proceedings of the Workshop on Advances in Biomedical Applications of the SEM,* IIT Research Institute, Chicago.
4 Blom, E. and A. Birch-Andersen. 1960. The ultrastructure of bull sperm. I. The middle piece. *Nord. Vet. Med.* 12:261–276.
5 ———. 1965. The ultrastructure of bull sperm. II. The sperm head. *Nord. Vet. Med.* 17:193–212.
6 Bloom, G. and L. Nicander. 1962. Electron microscopical study of the protoplasmic droplet of mammalian spermatozoa. *Int. J. Fert.* 7:355.

7 Brotherton, J. 1976. Difference in size between spermatozoa from the cauda epididymidis and the caput epididymidis of the rat. *J. Reprod. Fert.* 48:365–366.

8 Carmon, J. L. and W. W. Green. 1952. Histological study of the development of the testis of the ram. *J. Anim. Sci.* 11:674–687.

9 Clermont, Y. 1972. Kinetics of spermatogenesis in mammals: Seminiferous epithelium cycle and spermatogonial renewal. *Physiol. Rev.* 52:198–236.

10 Constantinides, P. 1974. *Functional Electronic Histology.* Elsevier, New York.

11 Courot, M., M. T. Hochereau-de Reviers, and R. Ortavant. 1970. Spermatogenesis. In Johnson, Gomes, and VanDemark, eds. *The Testis.* Vol. 1. Academic Press, New York. Pp. 339–442.

12 Dellman, H. 1971. *Veterinary Histology: An Outline Text–Atlas.* Lea & Febiger, Philadelphia.

13 Dellman, H. and K. Wrobel. 1976. Male reproductive system. In Dellman and Brown, eds. *Textbook of Veterinary Histology.* Lea & Febiger, Philadelphia. Pp. 293–318.

14 Fawcett, D. W. 1970. A comparative view of sperm ultrastructure. *Biol. Reprod. Suppl.* 2:90–127.

15 ———. 1975. The mammalian spermatozoon. *Developmental Biology* 44:394–436.

16 Foote, R. H., G. E. Seidel, Jr., J. Hahn, W. E. Berndtson, and G. H. Coulter. 1977. Seminal quality, spermatozoal output, and testicular changes in growing Holstein bulls. *J. Dairy Sci.* 60:85–88.

17 Gaddum, P. 1968. Sperm maturation in the male reproductive tract: Development of motility. *Anat. Rec.* 161:471–482.

18 Glover, T. D. and L. Nicander. 1971. Some aspects of structure and function in the mammalian epididymis. *J. Reprod. Fert. Suppl.* 13:39–50.

19 Hancock, J. L. 1966. The ultra-structure of mammalian spermatozoa. In McLaren, ed. *Advances in Reproductive Physiology.* Vol. 1. Logos Press, London. Pp. 125–154.

20 Hooker, C. W. 1970. The intertubular tissue of the testis. In Johnson, Gomes, and VanDemark, eds. *The Testis.* Vol. 1. Academic Press, New York. Pp. 483–550.

21 Humphrey, J. D. and P. W. Ladds. 1975. A quantitative histological study of changes in the bovine testis and epididymis associated with age. *Res. Vet. Sci.* 19:135–141.

22 Ladman, A. A. 1973. The male reproductive system. In Greep and Weiss, eds. *Histology.* 3rd ed. McGraw-Hill, New York. Pp. 847–890.

23 Martan, J. 1969. Epididymal histochemistry and physiology. *Biol. Reprod.* 1:134–154.

24 Nalbandov, A. V. 1976. *Reproductive Physiology of Mammals and Birds.* 3rd ed. W. H. Freeman, San Francisco.

25 Narbaitz, R. 1974. Embryology, anatomy, and histology of the male accessory glands. In Brandes, ed. *Male Accessory Sex Organs: Structure and Function in Mammals.* Academic Press, New York. Pp. 10–15.

26 Nowell, J. A. and L. J. Faulkin. 1974. Internal topography of the male reproductive system. *Scanning Electron Microscopy.* Part III. IIT Research Institute. Pp. 640–646.

27 Orgebin-Crist, M. C. 1969. Studies on the function of the epididymis. *Biol. Reprod.* 1:155–175.

28 Ortavant, R., M. Courot, and M. T. Hochereau de Reviers. 1977. Spermatogenesis in domestic mammals. In Cole and Cupps, eds. *Reproduction in Domestic Animals.* 3rd ed. Academic Press, New York. Pp. 203–227.

29 Randall, J. T. and M. H. G. Friedlaender. 1950. The microstructure of ram spermatozoa. *Exptl. Cell Res.* 1:1–32.

30 Roosen-Runge, E. C. 1969. Comparative aspects of spermatogenesis. *Biol. Reprod.* 1:24–39.

31 Saacke, R. G. and J. O. Almquist. 1964. Ultrastructure of bovine spermatozoa. I. The head of normal, ejaculated sperm. *Amer. J. Anat.* 115:143–162.

32 ———. 1964. Ultrastructure of bovine spermatozoa. II. The neck and tail of normal, ejaculated sperm. *Amer. J. Anat.* 115:163–184.

33 Setchell, B. P., T. W. Scott, J. K. Voglmayr, and G. M. H. Waites. 1969. Characteristics of testicular spermatozoa and the fluid which transports them into the epididymis. *Biol. Reprod.* 1:40–66.

34 Sharma, O. P. 1976. Scanning electron microscopy of equine spermatozoa. *J. Reprod. Fert.* 48:413–414.

35 Steinberger, E. 1971. Hormonal control of mammalian spermatogenesis. *Physiol. Rev.* 51:1–22.

36 Steinberger, E. and G. E. Duckett. 1967. Hormonal control of spermatogenesis. *J. Reprod. Fert. Suppl.* 2:75–87.

37 Swierstra, E. E. 1968. Cytology and duration of the cycle of the seminiferous epithelium of the boar; duration of spermatozoan transit through the epididymis. *Anat. Rec.* 161:171–186.

38 Swierstra, E. E., M. R. Gebauer, and B. W. Pickett. 1974. Reproductive physiology of the stallion. I. Spermatogenesis and testis composition. *J. Reprod. Fert.* 40:113–123.

39 Vilar, O., M. I. Perez del Cerro, and R. E. Mancini. 1962. The Sertoli cell as a "bridge cell" between the basal membrane and the germinal cells: Histochemical and electron microscope observations. *Exptl. Cell Res.* 27:158–161.

40 White, I. G. 1958. Biochemical aspects of mammalian semen. *Anim. Breed. Abstr.* 26:109–123.

41 Yasuda, Y. And I. Tanimura. 1974. Scanning electron microscopy of boar spermatozoa before and after frozen-thawed treatment. *Int. J. Fert.* 19:149–158.

Hormones and Puberty in the Male

When you have completed this chapter you should be able to:

- Identify the major hormones of reproduction and their general actions,
- Distinguish between releasing hormones, hypophyseal, and gonadal hormones,
- Relate action to specific male hormones and their sources,
- Understand the factors affecting puberty and their interactions,
- Relate age, size, and weight to puberty, and
- Determine factors to be considered in selecting breeding stock.

The coordinated functions of the reproductive system are controlled to a large extent by a group of substances called hormones. Whenever a link in the chain of activity is broken, reproduction may decrease significantly or cease completely. These hormones are of several varieties; those related to reproduction will be discussed here, with brief reference to secondary hormones.

HORMONE (To Set In Motion)

A hormone is a substance produced by a cell or group of cells that passes through and between the cells into the bloodstream, which then transports it to a target organ or tissue in the body to bring about a reaction that helps to coordinate the functioning of the entire body.

The best way to understand the definition is to follow one of the hormonal pathways. Follicle Stimulating Hormone (FSH) is a hormone produced by the adenohypophysis. It passes from the cells of this gland into the body circulation. As it passes to the seminiferous tubules of the testes it stimulates spermatogenesis (Fig. 3–1).

A hormone assists in the reaction but does not become an integral part of it. In the chain of events, a gland may produce a hormone, which then stimulates another gland to produce a second hormone in turn, and even a third gland to produce a hormone before the final target organ is stimulated. There are also interactions between hormones whereby the end product may depress further stimulation of the producing gland.

Hormones may be categorized in several ways. One of the best is according to their origin. The hormones that are primarily associated with reproduction are produced by the hypothalamus, hypophysis, and gonads.

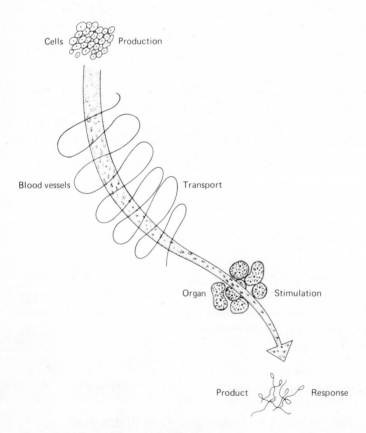

Figure 3-1 General hormonal pathway.

Hypothalamic (Under Innerchamber)

These hormones are produced by a portion of the brain called the hypothalamus, which is located centrally in the base of the brain immediately under the middle and larger portion of the diencephalon called the thalamus. It is composed of several hypothalamic nuclei—masses of cells with specific designations (Fig. 3–2).

The hypothalamus secretes releasing hormones, inhibitory hormones, oxytocin, and vasopressin. They are all protein in nature.

Releasing Hormones

Gonadotropic releasing hormone (GNRH) is secreted by the hypothalamus and passes via the portal blood vessels into the adenohypophysis, which lies suspended beneath the hypothalamus (Fig. 3–3).

Proposed methods of the neurosecretory mechanism include (Fig. 3–4):

1   Extrahypothalamic neurostimulation of the hypothalamic neurons to secrete releasing hormones, which pass down the axons;

2   Secretion of releasing hormones by extrahypothalamic neurons, which pass into the hypothalamus and hence through the portal vessels; and

3   Secretion by neurons within the hypothalamus.[14]

The releasing hormones—Gonadotropic Releasing Hormone (GNRH), Follicle Stimulating Hormone Releasing Hormone (FSHRH), and Luteinizing Hormone Releasing Hormone (LHRH)—in turn cause the release of Follicle Stimulating Hormone (FSH) and Luteinizing Hormone (LH), secreted by the adenohypophysis. There has been considerable discussion as to whether there is a single gonadotropin releasing hormone (GNRH) or two, FSHRH and LHRH.[6,8,39,40]

Other releasing hormones, less related to reproduction, are Thyrotropic Releasing Hormone (TRH), Corticotropic Releasing Hormone (CRH), Growth Hormone Releasing Hormone (GH-RH), and Melanocyte Stimulating Hormone Releasing Hormone (MRH).

Inhibitory Hormones

Prolactin inhibiting hormone (PIH) is synthesized in the hypothalamus and passes via the portal vessels to depress release of Prolactin (PRL) by the adenohypophysis.

Another inhibiting hormone, Melanocyte Inhibiting Hormone (MIH), though not related to reproduction, has been identified.

Oxytocin (Quick Birth)   This hormone is secreted by the neurons of the hypothalamus and passes down the axons into the neurohypophysis where it is stored until release (Fig. 3–4). It is active at the time of birth, and causes milk release through contraction of fine muscle fibers.

Vasopressin is another hormone secreted and stored in like manner but not specifically related to reproduction.

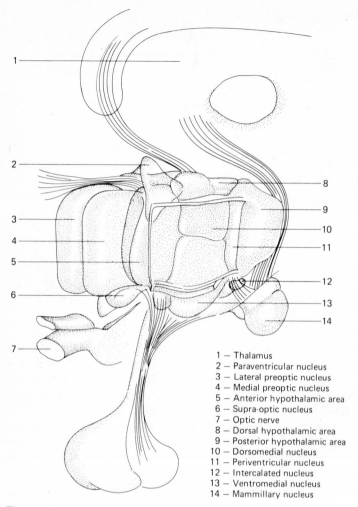

1 — Thalamus
2 — Paraventricular nucleus
3 — Lateral preoptic nucleus
4 — Medial preoptic nucleus
5 — Anterior hypothalamic area
6 — Supra-optic nucleus
7 — Optic nerve
8 — Dorsal hypothalamic area
9 — Posterior hypothalamic area
10 — Dorsomedial nucleus
11 — Periventricular nucleus
12 — Intercalated nucleus
13 — Ventromedial nucleus
14 — Mammillary nucleus

Figure 3-2 The hypothalamus and its nuclei.

The actions of the hypothalamic releasing hormones are summarized in Table 3–1.

Hypophyseal (Under Outgrowth)

The hypophysis (pituitary) is a gland of dual origin located ventral to the hypothalamus. It is very well protected in its saddle-shaped depression of the sphenoid bone called the sella turcica (saddle Turkish) and is composed of two rather distinct parts (Fig. 3–5) according to function: the adenohypophysis (glandular) and the neurohypophysis (nerve).

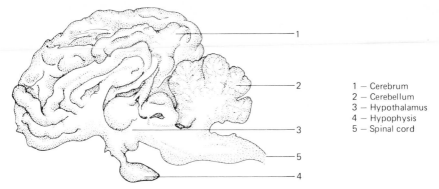

1 — Cerebrum
2 — Cerebellum
3 — Hypothalamus
4 — Hypophysis
5 — Spinal cord

Figure 3-3 Relative position of the hypophysis to the brain and hypothalamus.

Anatomical divisions are more clearly designated as:

1 pars distalis (anterior pituitary)
2 pars tuberalis (stalk)
3 pars intermedia (intermediate lobe)
4 pars nervosa (posterior pituitary)

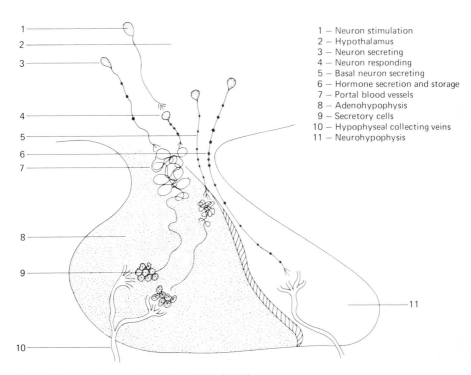

1 — Neuron stimulation
2 — Hypothalamus
3 — Neuron secreting
4 — Neuron responding
5 — Basal neuron secreting
6 — Hormone secretion and storage
7 — Portal blood vessels
8 — Adenohypophysis
9 — Secretory cells
10 — Hypophyseal collecting veins
11 — Neurohypophysis

Figure 3-4 Hypothalamic-hypophyseal relationships.

Table 3-1   Hypothalamic Hormones and Their Actions on Reproduction

Source	Hormone	Target organ	Action
Hypothalamus	Gonadotropic Releasing Hormone (GNRH)	Pars distalis of adenohypophysis	Stimulate release of FSH and LH (ICSH)
	Follicle Stimulating Hormone Releasing Hormone (FSHRH)	Pars distalis of adenohypophysis	Stimulate release of FSH
	Luteinizing Hormone Releasing Hormone (LHRH) or Interstitial Cell Stimulating Hormone Releasing Hormone (ICSHRH)	Pars distalis of adenohypophysis	Stimulate release of LH or ICSH
	Prolactin Inhibitory Hormone (PIH)	Pars distalis of adenohypophysis	Inhibit release of PRL
	Oxytocin	Mammary myo-epithelium	Milk letdown
		Uterine myome-trium	Sperm transport and uterine muscle contraction

The first three are actually parts of the adenohypophysis but are distinguished by their anatomical location. All three are secretory glandular structures.[21]

The adenohypophysis originates from the oral cavity as an outgrowth of the ectodermal tissue called Rathke's Pouch. In apposition, a segment of brain tissue in the hypothalamic area evaginates and retains its connection to the ventral brain (Fig. 3–6). The cells from the roof of the mouth continue to proliferate until they encounter the neural tissue and then they surround it while severing relationship with the oral cavity.

The adenohypophysis then develops into a gland with secretory potential, while the neurohypophysis is made of nerve elements continuous with those of the hypothalamus and serves as a storage area for some hormones produced by the hypothalamus.

Adenohypophysis (Gland Under Outgrowth) This glandular portion of the hypo-

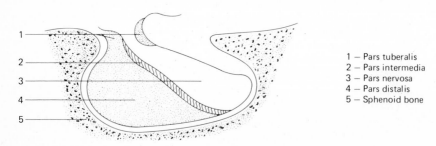

1 — Pars tuberalis
2 — Pars intermedia
3 — Pars nervosa
4 — Pars distalis
5 — Sphenoid bone

Figure 3-5 The hypophysis of the cow, medial section.

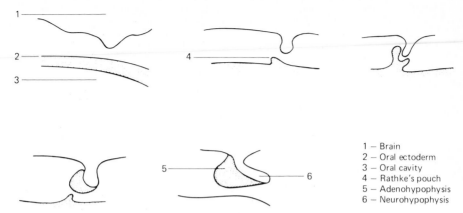

1 — Brain
2 — Oral ectoderm
3 — Oral cavity
4 — Rathke's pouch
5 — Adenohypophysis
6 — Neurohypophysis

Figure 3-6 Development of the embryonic hypophysis.

physis secretes gonadotropins (FSH and LH) and prolactin (PRL), which are specifically related to reproduction. In addition, it secretes Thyroid Stimulating Hormone (TSH), Adrenocorticotropic Hormone (ACTH), and Growth Hormone (GH), which maintain normal body functions. These hormones are protein in composition.

Gonadotropins (seed nourish) These hormones stimulate the gonads to produce the germ cells for reproduction, and hormones to prepare and maintain the reproductive system and activity for developing a new life.

Follicle stimulating hormone This hormone is commonly referred to as FSH. It is secreted by the basophilic cells of the adenohypophysis[20] and stimulates spermatogenesis in the male and follicular growth in the female.

Luteinizing hormone or interstitial cell stimulating hormone This hormone, designated as LH or ICSH, is identified by two names because of research that was conducted at the same time on the male and female and discovery of this hormone almost simultaneously. It is produced by the basophils of the adenohypophysis and stimulates ovulation and growth of luteal (yellow) cells in the corpus luteum (yellow body) of the ovary following ovulation. Hence the name LH. The same hormone in the male, designated ICSH, initiates spermatogenesis and stimulates interstitial cells of the testes to produce testosterone.

Prolactin PRL is produced by the acidophilic cells of the adenohypophysis. It stimulates the corpus luteum in its development and maintenance in the rat and possibly the sheep and assists in glandular growth of the mammary tissue.

Pars Tuberalis (Part Tube) This portion wrapped around the neck of the hypophysis is a continuation of the pars distalis and functions as an integral part of it.

Pars Intermedia (Part In Between) This glandular portion has no particular relationship to reproduction. Secretions from this portion are mainly recognized for the effects on color change or pigmentation.

Neurohypophysis (Nerve Under Outgrowth) This portion of the hypophysis maintains its integrity as a neural structure. Neurons in the hypothalamus secrete oxytocin, which follows the axons into the neurohypophysis for storage and later passage into the blood vessels of that structure. There are no known hormones produced in the neurohypophysis.

Hypophyseal hormones and their action relating to reproduction are summarized in Table 3–2.

Gonadal (Seed)

This group of hormones entails those produced by the testes and ovaries. They are steroids and therefore very different in chemical nature from the previous protein hormones. They are not digested in the gastrointestinal tract as are the proteins.

Testicular

Androgens (male produce) The more common hormones included in this group are androstenedione, testosterone, and androsterone. They are all designated androgens because of the interrelationship that exists and similarity of response. Androstenedione is a precursor of the more active testosterone, and androsterone is the excretory product.

They are produced by the interstitial cells of the testes and govern masculine traits of an individual.

Ovarian

Estrogens (excite produce) The more common estrogenic hormones are estradiol, estrone, and estriol. Estrone and estradiol are the naturally occurring hormones of

Table 3-2 Hypophyseal Hormones and Their Actions on Reproduction

Source	Hormone	Target organ	Action
Adenohypophysis	Gonadotropin		
	Follicle Stimulating	Ovary	Follicular growth
	Hormone (FSH)	Testis	Spermatogenesis
	Luteinizing Hormone	Ovary	Ovulation and CL formation
	(LH) or Interstitial	Testis	Testosterone production
	Cell Stimulating		and sperm production
	Hormone (ICSH)		
	Prolactin	Ovary	Progesterone secretion
		Mammary	Lactation
Neurohypophysis	No hormones produced	Myometrium	Sperm transport, parturition
	here. Oxytocin is	Mammary	Milk letdown
	stored and released.		

the ovarian follicle produced by the granulosa cells and theca interna. Estriol is the excretory product. Estrogens are excitatory in action.

Progestogens (before carry) These hormones include progesterone and pregnanediol. Progesterone is the product of the luteal cells of the ovary and pregnanediol is the excretory product. They maintain pregnancy and therefore depress activity of the musculature and certain secretory areas of the female reproductive system while stimulating support of the developing new life.

　　Gonadal hormones and their functions in the reproductive process are summarized in Table 3–3.

Other Hormonal Sources

The sources previously discussed are of a continuing nature because of the presence of the organs or glands at all times. There are hormones of like action to some of those discussed previously that are produced by developed structures whose life span and productive period are limited. These include the placenta of pregnant animals and the endometrial cups of the pregnant mare.

Placenta (Flatcake) The extraembryonic membranes and their attachment to the uterine wall produce hormones with similar action to the gonadotropic hormones. The pregnant woman excretes large quantities of LH (ICSH) substance. This is designated Human Chorionic Gonadotropin (HCG) because it comes primarily from the outer extraembryonic membrane, the chorion. It is usually recovered from the urine of pregnant women.

　　Estrogens and progestogens are also produced by the placenta.

Table 3-3　Gonadal Hormones and Their Actions in Reproduction

Source	Hormone	Target organ	Action
Testis	Androgens	Primary and secondary sex organs	Growth and development
		Seminiferous tubules	Spermatogenesis
		Muscles	Development
		Brain	Libido
		Endocrine glands	Interaction
Ovary	Estrogens	Primary and secondary sex organs	Growth and development
		Mammary	Duct growth
		Endometrium	Vascular growth
		Myometrium	Activity
		Body tissues	Growth
		Brain	Libido
		Endocrine glands	Interaction
	Progestogens	Primary and secondary sex organs	Growth and development
		Mammary	Alveolar development
		Endometrium	Glandular growth
		Endocrine glands	Interaction

Endometrial Cups These structures develop on the uterine lining as cellular products of the placenta and perhaps should be classified as placental sources. A substance rich in FSH is produced here and obtained from the mare's blood serum. It
is therefore called Pregnant Mare Serum Gonadotropin (PMSG).

Hormones of the placenta and endometrial cups are summarized in Table 3–4.

These general comments on hormones will form a base for more detailed
discussion later. A very important fact to remember is that we are concerned with
a chain of events. If any link is broken or nonfunctional, then the entire program
is no good. For instance, if the hypothalamus does not function to produce releasing
hormones, everything is upset. If the hypothalamus produces releasing hormones
but the pituitary cannot or does not respond, everything is upset. If the hypothalamus and pituitary function properly but the gonads are nonfunctional, everything is upset. Therefore each step is necessary not only in stimulating but, in some
instances, in depressing.

MALE HORMONES

The action of hormones in the male begins with releasing hormones from the
hypothalamus. In turn, hormones are produced by the adenohypophysis and gonads.
Interplay between all hormones regulates the male reproductive structures and
functions.

Gonadotropic Releasing Hormone (GNRH)

GNRH is produced in the hypothalamus and passes through the portal blood
systems to the adenohypophysis during the prepuberal period. The mechanism by
which GNRH is initiated and its release are not clearly understood. GNRH is a high
molecular weight protein and therefore must be administered by methods other than
oral or else it will be digested as other proteins.

Follicle Stimulating Hormone (FSH)

FSH is produced by the pars distalis of the adenohypophysis. It is released upon the
signal of FSHRH and passes into the hypophyseal collecting veins to be carried

Table 3-4 Other Hormones and Their Actions in Reproduction

Source	Hormone	Target organ	Action
Placenta (chorion)	Chorionic gonadotropin (HCG)	Gonads	Mainly LH or ICSH in action with some FSH
(endometrial cups)	Pregnant mare serum (PMS)	Gonads	Mainly FSH with some LH (ICSH) action
	Estrogens	Sex organs and mammary	Growth and development
	Progestogens	Sex organs and mammary	Growth and development

throughout the body. The target organs are the testes and specifically the seminifer-ous tubules. FSH stimulates spermatogenesis and acts synergistically with ICSH and testosterone in this function. There is preparation of the sustentacular cells as well as the spermatogenic cells before puberty,[7] and as ICSH and testosterone increase in potency, puberty is attained as is the development of mature spermatozoa[48] (Fig. 3–7).

FSH stimulates spermatogenesis in its early stages through the secondary sper-matocyte, and then testosterone is responsible for further division. Hypophysectomy will arrest spermatogenesis and injections of extracts of the pars distalis will main-tain spermatogenesis. This would show the necessity of gonadotropins but would not separate FSH and ICSH effects. Apparently both in combination with testosterone are necessary.

FSH apparently is not a strong stimulant alone. Only high levels injected into hypophysectomized rats show any stimulation of growth of the accessory organs.[55] Only slight effects are seen on testicular weight and development. FSH is very active in combination with LH and testosterone.

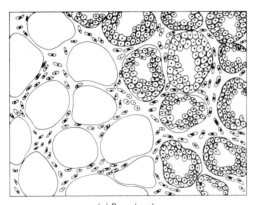

(a) Prepuberal

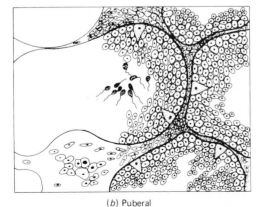

(b) Puberal

Figure 3-7 Seminiferous tubules of prepuberal and puberal testes.

The effect of light or perhaps the length of exposure to light regulates the gonadotropin output. Inadequate discharges of gonadotropins then decreases sexual activity.[31] Long light days cause reproductive quiescence in rams particularly but does not seem to affect other species so drastically. As day length shortens in the fall of the year, FSH levels increase along with LH and, subsequently, testosterone. Sperm production increases as a result, and the rams become sexually active again until daylight time lengthens in the spring.

Purified FSH is commercially available and the source is usually sheep or swine pituitary glands. Another source of FSH is the pregnant mare. During pregnancy between days 40 and 120, FSH levels in the pregnant mare rise drastically, plateau, and then decrease rapidly to normal. Blood serum from the mare during this period is collected and utilized as a source of FSH. It is called pregnant mare serum gonadotropin (PMSG) because of its source.

The particular source of PMSG is from the endometrial cups, which form on the uterine lining of the pregnant mare from platelets of cells detached from the chorion of the extraembryonic membranes. These cells maintain their integrity for only about 80 days and then disintegrate; the source of PMSG is then removed.

Urine from postmenopausal women is also high in FSH and serves as a commercial source.

Interstitial Cell Stimulating Hormone Releasing Hormone (ICSHRH)

ICSHRH is produced by the hypothalamus and enters the adenohypophysis via the portal vascular system. It in turn stimulates the basophilic cells to produce and release ICSH. High levels of ICSHRH have been noted in bulls between 6 and 10 months of age[27] and therefore must be active in initiating puberty.

Interstitial Cell Stimulating Hormone (ICSH)

ICSH is released from the adenohypophysis into the hypophyseal collecting veins for distribution throughout the body. The target organ for ICSH is the testis and specifically the interstitial cells. Testosterone production results. ICSH is high early in the life of the male, and bulls have been studied where the ICSH level rose from approximately 2 months of age until puberty.

ICSH injected into hypophysectomized animals will maintain testicular size and function.[55] The effect is most dramatic on the interstitial cells. The effect is also marked when HCG is injected into intact bulls[38] because of its ICSH activity.

The ICSH level is drastically affected by light. Lengthening of the daylight hours is accompanied by a decrease in ICSH; shortening of daylight hours results in an increase. This is particularly true in rams and to a lesser degree in other classes of livestock. Sexual desire as well as increased sperm production result from shortening the hours of light, which are both associated with testosterone levels and, consequently, ICSH level.[24,30] The decreasing light photoperiod acts in two different ways: (1) by stimulating the hypothalamohypophyseal system and (2) by decreasing the intensity of the negative feedback of testosterone.[32,33] ICSH production is regulated to some extent by a "negative feedback" coming from testosterone.[6,9,10,17] This mechanism is neurohumoral with the neural pathway being primarily to the hypothalamus, functioning through inhibition of ICSHRH, and the humoral or blood-borne pathway functioning primarily via the adenohypophysis and secretion of ICSH directly (Fig. 3–8).

ICSH may be obtained from animal pituitaries, but the most common source is from pregnant women. Urine of pregnant women is purified and serves as a source from day 50 to day 120 of pregnancy. As in the mare, gonadotropin levels rise to a peak, plateau, and fall during this time. The woman produces high levels of ICSH from the chorion of the extraembryonic membranes; hence the name, human chorionic gonadotropin (HCG).

Androgens

Testosterone is the major androgen in the bull and man and is produced by the interstitial cells in response to ICSH circulating in the vascular structure of the testis.[38] It is steroid in nature, which indicates that it is insoluble in water and therefore may be administered orally as well as by injection. Androstenedione is the major androgen in the stallion. Androgens exert their influence during embryonic life and throughout the life of the male (Fig. 3–9).

Sexual Differentiation The embryo goes through a stage of differentiation to develop the sexual organs dictated by the genetic makeup of the individual. Androgens are responsible for the embryonic differentiation to some extent as indicated by development of the female system in their absence. Subsequently, injections of androgens into female embryos will cause development of masculinized genitalia.

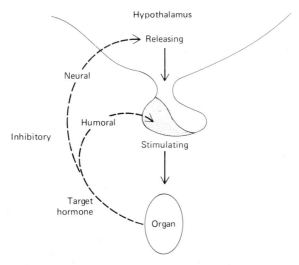

Figure 3-8 "Negative feed-back" mechanism between the target hormone and the parent secretory units.

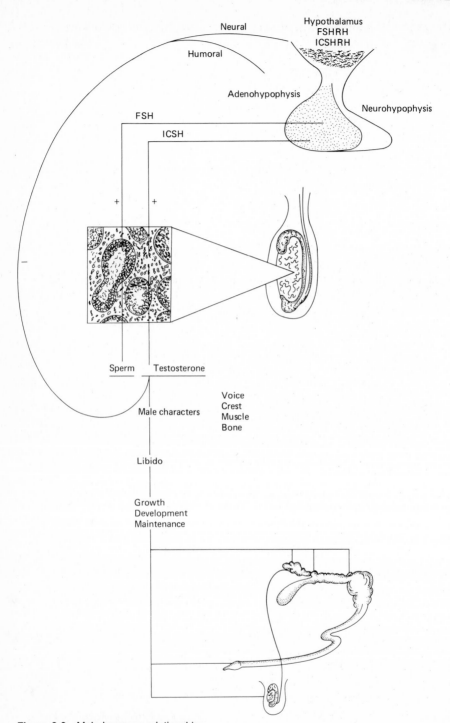

Figure 3-9   Male hormone relationships.

Androgens have been used with limited success in assisting in the descent of testes that are slow in moving into the scrotum.

Primary Sex Organ Development and Maintenance Growth of the primary organs is seen specifically during the prepuberal period. The testes increase in size as the seminiferous tubules increase in number and spermatogenesis is initiated. With increased vascularization to the scrotal area, growth of all the components takes place: cremaster, testis, epididymis, and deferent duct.

The penis grows under the influence of androgens, and the glans and terminal penis separate from the preputial area as cellular tissues differentiate to stratified squamous epithelium. The growth of penile tissues progresses with formation of the sigmoid flexure, in some species, and development of the vascular bed in the penis proper.

Castration, resulting in removal of androgens, causes cessation of growth and regression. Supplying androgens to castrates from an extraneous source will cause some growth but not to a normal size. Injection of testosterone into intact males may depress spermatogenesis by causing degeneration of the spermatogenic cells themselves.[29] Testicular size is thereby reduced, and some time is required for recovery of both spermatogenesis and size following cessation of injection.

Accessory Gland Development and Maintenance The growth of the vesicular, prostate, and bulbourethral glands is under the influence of androgens. These grow prepuberally as androgens increase in potency and continue until maturity. Secretion is a part of growth and development and increases to maturity also. In later life, accessory glands may be overstimulated by high levels of androgens and result in overgrowth and become detrimental to the health of the male.

Castration removes the stimulus for growth. Early castration results in arrest of growth, while later castration causes regression. Androgen therapy will stimulate growth, development, and maintenance, but to a lesser extent than normal.

Libido Sexual desire in the male remains relatively high because of the rather consistent level of androgens. The psychic or mental response is not understood, but a combination of androgens and psychic behavior leads the male to search out females in estrus.

Castration removes sexual desire in young animals and most mature animals. There are some mature males that have served numerous females that retain libido even after castration. These are usually detrimental and a nuisance and should be removed as quickly as possible. A possible use for such animals is as teasers for detecting females in estrus for artificial insemination.

The administration of androgens to animals with low libido will result in sexual activity. Dosage levels will vary with age, size, and disposition of the male. Even castrated females have been androgenized for teaser animals because there is no penis for transmission of possible disease.[22]

Absence of libido in breeding males may be increased by the use of androgens, but it is best to go to a higher level of stimulation and use some source of ICSH to help the interstitial cells produce a greater amount of androgen.

Hormone Interaction Androgens interact with the hypothalamus and adenohypophysis in a negative feedback manner. This is a delicate balance of stimulator, responsive organs, and end product. ICSHRH stimulates release of ICSH, which stimulates production of androgens, which in turn causes its many reactions as well as going back to the beginning of the sequence and giving a neurohumoral signal. If production of androgens is low or satisfactory, no signal goes to the hypothalamus and adenohypophysis, and the glands continue their normal level of production. If androgens are produced above normal, the neurohumoral pathway carries information to inhibit the hypothalamus and adenohypophysis in their production, and the whole system returns to equilibrium.

Secondary Sex Characteristics A male animal is usually referred to as being masculine. The characteristics that lead to this nomenclature are under the influence of androgens, and the absence of androgens will cause feminine characteristics or perhaps a castrate appearance.

Hair The hair is usually coarser and perhaps curlier in the male than in the female. It may be drier in appearance. Hair on some bulls' heads takes on a curly appearance termed "burly." Facial hair in man is controlled by testosterone. Baldness is genetically controlled but also influenced by testosterone.

Horns Horns in bulls are usually larger at the base and longer. Horns in sheep may be sex linked, with only males developing horns.

Antlers are definitely influenced by testosterone increases, but shedding of the velvet and eventual shedding of the antlers is controlled by testosterone. Castration of the male in velvet will cause retention of the velvet and antlers; reduced testosterone under normal conditions causes shedding of the antlers. If testosterone is administered when antlers are present, they will be retained until the testosterone levels drop.[16]

Voice The vocal cords grow and change the timbre of the voice as puberty is attained. The treble voice of a calf, lamb, or boy becomes bass during this period. It is probably more noticeable in man than in domestic animals. Castration will cause retention of the soprano or treble sounds. This knowledge led to castration of boys for papal choirs up to the nineteenth century to ensure soprano voices.

Muscle The anabolic (constructive metabolism) effect of androgens is evidenced mostly by the muscular development in the male. Nitrogen retention and its conversion to amino acids and muscle proteins gives a particular conformation to the male. In general, there is heavier muscling throughout; however, the muscles of the shoulders and thighs are more pronounced, as well as the neck.

The enlarged neck as seen particularly in bulls is called the crest. This thickened area is an accumulation of muscle fibers and grows primarily on top of the neck but forms on the sides as well. The crest should not be confused with the hump on Zebu cattle, which is common to male and female alike. The beneficial effects of testoster one have been shown in feedlot trials where intact rams or rams with scrotal ablation (short scrotum) have made higher daily gains with better feed conversion and higher carcass weight and yield grades than castrates.[41]

Bone The growth of the long bones of the legs and the cervical vertebrae are particularly influenced by androgens. These bones have a growing point called the epiphyseal plate from which the bone lengthens. This plate remains active in the absence of gonadal hormones. Androgens depress this growing point, which results in mature intact males being shorter than mature castrated males. Late sexual maturity or puberty usually results in larger males, as may be seen in comparing Santa Gertrudis cattle to Herefords or Holstein to Jerseys. Human castrates, called eunuchs, grow to greater heights and were used as harem guards in early days. Apparently, the choice of eunuchs was based on more than size.

Testosterone is influenced greatly by season of the year. This is particularly so in rams, and because of this effect rams are spoken of as having a period of summer sterility. Actually, sperm continue to be produced but libido is very poor or completely lacking. Testosterone levels are highest in the winter months when days are shortest and subsequently mating activity is highest.[25,36,42] These differences may not be as great in cool climates,[15] since there appears to be an interaction of temperature and day length.

Spring values of testosterone in bulls has been found to be higher than in the fall.[13] The increasing of daylight length stimulates the gonadotropic hormone secretion, which in turn stimulates testosterone production. As length of daylight and temperature increase, testosterone production decreases; as a result, libido decreases.

No clear-cut statement can be made for all species regarding the effect of light on hormone production.

Male steroids, or androgens, may be produced by the adrenal cortex and particularly by tumors. These hormones may cause all of the effects mentioned in the section on androgens in either the male, female, or castrate. Such conditions may be responsible for masculine traits in women.

PUBERTY

Puberty marks that time in an animal's life when it attains breeding capability. The male attains puberty when androgens are produced, sperm are produced, and the reproductive organs have matured so that the penis is free of its sheath, permitting the male to serve and impregnate the female (Fig. 3–10).

Puberty should not be confused with sexual maturity, as the latter is attained at a later date when all systems are functioning at their maximum. Puberty is the time of *first* breeding potential, while sexual maturity is the time of *maximum* breeding potential.

Many definitions have been given the term puberty, and the reader should look for specific nomenclature, particularly when reading scientific literature. Some researchers consider the presence of sperm in the seminiferous tubules as an indication

> LIBIDO +
>
> SPERM PRODUCTION +
>
> SEX ORGAN DEVELOPMENT =
>
> PUBERTY

Figure 3-10 Measures of puberty.

of puberty. Other criteria used are sperm in the epididymis, ejaculation in response to electric stimulation, erection and extension of the penis, freeing of the penis from the prepuce, and signs of sexual aggressiveness. For our purposes, we will use the definition given in the first paragraph—the age at which an animal reaches breeding capability.

Table 3–5 is a generalization of data based on literature and discussion with livestock producers and researchers. More exacting data are given in some of the references that follow, but this general information should be acceptable for daily usage. There are so many factors influencing puberty that one must spell out specific conditions to be more accurate.

Puberty is influenced by numerous factors: hormonal, genetic, nutritional, and environmental (Fig. 3–11).

Hormonal Factors

The initial hormonal stimulus begins in the hypothalamus where the gonadotropic releasing hormone (GNRH) is produced. This stimulates the anterior pituitary to secrete follicle stimulating hormone (FSH), which then acts to sensitize the testes to interstitial cell stimulating hormone (ICSH). Androgens in turn are produced by the testes. The combination of all this hormone interplay results in puberty.[23] Androgens and gonadotropins initiate spermatogenesis, androgens stimulate growth of the penis and accessory glands, and finally libido occurs. Secondary sex characteristics appear rapidly as puberty approaches and the androgen level rises.

Table 3-5 Age at Puberty and Initial Use for Breeding

Male	Puberty		Breeding
	Months	Range (mo)	Months
Bull	10	6–18	18–24
Ram	7	4–12	10–14
Boar	6	4–8	6–8
Stallion	18	12–24	18–24
Man	13 years	11–15 years	—

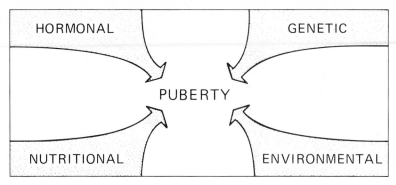

Figure 3-11   Factors affecting attainment of puberty.

The hormonal factors are interwoven with genetic, nutritional, and environmental factors so that different stages of development are attained at different times.

Androstenedione is one of the androgens found in the testes and apparently converts to testosterone. The bull calf has a high ratio of androstenedione to testosterone before puberty (1:1) but as the ratio declines, puberty results and the ratio continues to decline until it reaches 1:10 in the mature bull.[45]

A period of increased plasma ICSH between 6 and 9 months in Holstein bulls is followed by accelerated organ growth and spermatogenesis and puberty at 9 to 10 months of age.[28] Another response to hormonal influences can be observed in the related growth of organs. In the bull, the weights of the testes, vesicular glands, and epididymides are significantly correlated.[1]

Spermatozoa have been found in various parts of the reproductive system at differing times. Data have been taken from slaughter animals of unknown history, while others have been controlled closely. Spermatozoa have been found in the seminiferous tubules at 28 weeks of age in bulls.[1] Spermatogenic activity was noted at 10 weeks and presence of spermatozoa at 32 weeks by other researchers.[34] Ejaculates were obtained as early as 39 weeks of age in Swedish Red and White bulls.[2] The percent spermatozoa with proximal protoplasmic droplets decreased greatly after one year of age, and the ejaculates improved in volume, motility, and concentration throughout an experimental period to 15 months of age.

In the ram, androgen secretion rises sharply from 6 weeks of age and spermatogenesis begins about 9 weeks of age, according to some researchers,[43] while other workers found sperm appearing first at 21 weeks of age,[34] and yet others found sperm in the lumen of the seminiferous tubules when rams weighed near 28 kg (62 lb) but not as early as 18 kg (40 lb).[52]

Sperm have been observed in the boar testes as early as 20 weeks of age.[35]

Young Welsh stallions are found to be sexually active and will serve an artificial vagina several weeks before any spermatozoa will appear in the collection.[44] Sperm appear on the average at 13 months of age and at a weight of 180 kg (397 lb). In Welsh horses, puberty usually occurs after the first winter when daylight hours begin to lengthen.

One group of quarter horse stallions reached puberty at an average age of 16 months and an average weight of 367 kg (809 lb), and the gel-free portion of the ejaculate measured 16.4 ml. There was 22 percent progressive motility measured at that time,[18] which is low but acceptable for that age animal.

Separation of the penis from the prepuce usually occurs over an extended period of time beginning at birth and continuing until puberty at about 10 months in the bull. The sigmoid flexure is ill defined, and the glans penis is completely attached to the prepuce at birth.[19] It is not uncommon for a young bull to extend his penis in the erect state, denoting libido, with the prepuce still partially attached. There may be a slight tearing of the connection at this time, hastening the separation at the raphe area of the penis. The rapid growth of this primary sex organ is under the influence of androgens particularly and results in freeing the terminal penis and glans penis.[3] Complete separation comes at about the same age as puberty. Separation occurred in a group of Angus and Hereford bulls at 37 and 38 weeks,[54] and the first ejaculate containing sperm occurred at 41 weeks.

The urethral process of the ram is freed and the glans penis separated from the prepuce at an age of about 10 weeks.[46] Weight is apparently a major factor in attaining puberty. Observations on a large group of Merino rams showed little development of the reproductive system before reaching a weight of 27 kg (60 lb), but at this time the glans was freed, sperm were present, and the animals had reached puberty.[52]

The human is much more variable in reaching puberty than domestic animals. The hormonal responses include increased height as well as reproductive phenomena. The testes are under the influence of the maternal hormones during pregnancy and are actively growing. At birth, when this source of hormones is removed, the testes become rather quiescent, and this condition does not change until puberty when the hormones again stimulate growth and development of the spermatogenic and interstitial cells.[47] Growth of the testes begins between 10 and 13 ½ years of age.[49] The penis and accessory glands respond at approximately the same time (11 to 14 ½) and pubic hairs begin at 10 to 15 years of age.

Genetic Factors

Genetic influence may be noted in all classes of livestock. Examples in cattle are seen in the ages at puberty in Jerseys and Santa Gertrudis, which represent some of the extremes in size. The Jersey reaches puberty on average planes of nutrition at 6 to 8 months of age compared to 14 to 18 months for the Santa Gertrudis. Larger breeds are commonly slower in reaching puberty than smaller breeds. This is also evident in horses when the Shetland pony is compared to the draft horse. There may be some who would argue whether size and age at puberty are inversely related because of hormones rather than genetics. This assumption is based on the knowledge that the androgens depress growth of the long bones, and if androgens are produced sooner the animal will be smaller. This only points out the interaction between hormones and genetic factors mentioned earlier. The genetic action may well play an important role through hormone production and release.

Crossbred bulls have been shown to reach puberty at younger ages than straightbred stock.[4] The breeding-ability age for crossbreds was 51 weeks as compared to 57 weeks for straightbreds in one experimental group. These ages are based on ability to copulate and produce potentially fertilizing numbers of sperm. The cattle involved were Hereford, Angus, Charolais, and crosses between these breeds. Another report from Texas research[26] showed crossbred bulls reaching puberty at 45 weeks compared to straightbred bulls at 46 weeks.

A good example of genetic influence may be illustrated by the following account of a rancher's actual experience. He maintained a high-quality grade Hereford herd of cattle for years but wished to increase his herd by adding heifer replacements. He knew of a rancher with cattle of the caliber he wanted and purchased several of his heifers as yearlings. These big growthy heifers had the bone and scale he desired. As he approached the middle of the breeding season, he realized the heifers were not cycling. Upon examination of the reproductive organs, they were found to be immature and he had a choice of waiting for maturity or selling them and buying other replacements. He then started probing for answers to his dilemma and found that the rancher from whom he purchased the heifers selected for growthy heifers and therefore late-maturing animals who bred when they were at least two years of age.

This illustrates that genetic selection over years of management for large animals delayed hormonal influences, which then affected age at puberty.

Inbred boars reach puberty at different ages depending upon the line of breeding.[51] Five different research lines reached puberty at 24, 26, 27, 28, and 29 weeks of age. Another group of boars was selected for breeding purposes, and one year the average age at puberty was 28 weeks and the following year 29.[53] Therefore, selection for age at puberty is feasible.

Nutritional Factors

Nutrition is very important and may even be the most important governing factor leading to the onset of puberty. Overfeeding hastens puberty while underfeeding delays it. There is reason to suppose that it influences hormonal initiation and therefore may bring about the various phenomena previously discussed.

Nutrition has been varied according to TDN, energy, protein, and numerous other components. Most researchers have used a high level and a low level of nutrients to compare with the recommended nutrient needs for normal growth and development.

In a long-term study of dairy bulls, Cornell workers found that bulls reared on 130, 100, and 60 percent of Morrison's recommended TDN came into semen production at 37, 43, and 51 weeks of age and weighed 292 kg (644 lb), 262 kg (578 lb), and 235 kg (519 lb), respectively.[5] A similar experiment on nutritional levels at Pennsylvania gave ages and weights at puberty of 44 weeks and 356 kg (784 lb), 45 weeks and 291 kg (643 lb), and 61 weeks and 237 kg (523 lb).[12] It is of considerable interest to note that those bulls on the high plane of nutrition became much slower in sexual response and had weaknesses in their feet and legs around 3 and 4 years of age. Another group of Holstein bulls fed at levels of 100 percent TDN and 60 percent TDN reached puberty at ages and weights of 45 weeks and 267 kg (588 lb) and 52 weeks and 160 kg (352 lb), respectively.[50] All of these studies show the interaction between nutrition and size, as well as reproduction, and emphasize the fact that animals cannot be selected on the basis of only age or only size. Apparently, energy needed to reach puberty is more constant than age or weight,[37] but exacting requirements have not been determined.

Not as many data are available on beef bulls, but apparently the same determining factors are active and the breed of the animal plays an important role in responses related to puberty.

The effect of nutrition on puberty in boars may be illustrated by the following research. Hampshire boars were fed 100, 70, and 50 percent of the National Research Council's recommendations. Average ages and weights at puberty were 29 weeks and 101 kg (223 lb), 30 weeks and 78 kg (171 lb), and 31 weeks and 61 kg (135 lb), respectively. Weight was significantly different, but not age, at puberty.[11] Boars on the higher plane produced a greater volume of semen, but there were no significant differences in libido, motility, or concentration. Fertility of these boars based on matings and resulting pregnancies did not differ.

Environmental Factors

Environment influences age at puberty mostly by adverse effects due to stress. Undesirable conditions in the Gulf Coast area include insects, high temperatures, and high humidity. Animals in the Plains area may not be influenced by these stress conditions, but drought conditions and dust storms may play an important role in the age at which puberty is reached. The Northern and Mountain areas are influenced by cold winters; if young are growing and approaching puberty under these conditions, puberty may be retarded. Environment may affect nutritive factors, which in turn may be favorable or detrimental to the young attaining puberty.

In Table 3–5 the age for breeding has been listed. Animals should be used as quickly as possible in order to reduce the generation interval on the male side and prove out young sires, so that they may be used more heavily if they are desirable or culled from a herd if they are undesirable. It should be noted that there is a varying lag in time between puberty and the age for breeding different species. The bull is ready to go into the breeding herd when he is about 18 months to 2 years of age on a limited scale. Commonly, range cattle are placed in herds with a ratio of one bull to 25 or 30 cows. With young bulls of 18 months to 2 years of age, the ratio should be reduced so that there is one bull to approximately 15 cows.

In the case of the ram, season has a great deal to do with the age of the animal at first breeding. Young rams will be used first in the fall of the year following the summer infertility stage; this means they will be approximately 1 year of age when they are ready to go into a breeding herd. Again, the number of ewes that are put with them should be somewhat limited. Most ranchers will use one mature ram to 50 to 60 ewes, and it would be desirable for one young ram to be put with 25 to 30. Rams held over to the second fall may be treated as mature rams.

Young boars that are grown out quickly under good nutritive conditions and good environment will be ready to breed when they are 6 to 8 months of age. This again would be limited breeding, and if they are pasture mated, one boar to approximately 15 sows would be desirable.

If stallions are used under range conditions, they may be first turned with the mares at 18 to 24 months of age and bred to 10 to 15 mares the first breeding season.

In the case of all of these young breeding animals, there should be a check of semen before they are turned out and again during the breeding season to see if they are capable of breeding and maintaining their sperm production under the circumstances. If immature cells are present in the ejaculate, then certainly it would be desirable to remove the sire for a period of time to give him a rest and replace him with another sire.

WHAT DID YOU LEARN?

1 What does gonadotropic mean?
2 List the gonadal hormones and give a general statement concerning the action of each.
3 Relate the four parts of the hypophysis to function.
4 Follow the hormonal sequence in the male, beginning and ending with ICSHRH.
5 List the effects of testosterone on secondary sex characteristics in the bull.
6 Which will be larger at 4 years of age, a bull or steer of like breeding?
7 What four major factors affect initiation of puberty?
8 If you were selecting breeding stock at or near puberty, would you base your selection on age, size, weight, or a combination? Why?
9 What should the bull-to-cow ratio be when using young bulls for the first time compared to mature bulls?
10 What is the average age at puberty for the boar and stallion?

REFERENCES

1 Abdel-Raouf, M. 1960. The postnatal development of the reproductive organs in bulls with special reference to puberty. *Acta Endocr. Suppl.* 49–109.
2 ———. 1965. Sexual behavior and semen picture of bulls of the Swedish red and white breed between the ages of 9 and 15 months. *Nord. Vet. Med.* 17:318.
3 Ashdown, R. R. 1960. Development of penis and sheath in the bull calf. *J. Agr. Sci.* 54:348–351.
4 Bellows, R. A., T. M. Riley, N. M. Kieffer, J. J. Urick, J. S. Brinks, and R. T. Clark. 1964. Preliminary studies of sperm production and breeding ability in young, straight, and crossbred bulls. *J. Anim. Sci.* 23:593. (Abstr.)
5 Bratton, R. W., S. D. Musgrave, H. O. Dunn, and R. H. Foote. 1959. Causes and prevention of reproductive failures in dairy cattle. II. Influence of underfeeding and overfeeding from birth to 80 weeks of age on growth, sexual development, and semen production of Holstein bulls. *Cornell Univ. Agr. Exp. Sta. Bull. 940.*
6 Convey, E. M. 1973. Neuroendocrine relationships in farm animals: A review. *J. Anim. Sci.* 37:745–757.

7   Courot, M. 1967. Endocrine control of the supporting and germ cells of the impuberal testis. *J. Reprod. Fert. Suppl.* 2:89–101.

8   Crighton, D. B. 1973. Review of releasing hormones in domestic animals. *Vet. Rec.* 93:254.

9   Davidson, J. M. 1967. Neuroendocrine mechanisms in the control of spermatogenesis. *J. Reprod. Fert. Suppl.* 2:103–116.

10 Davidson, J. M. and G. J. Bloch. 1969. Neuroendocrine aspects of male reproduction. *Biol. Reprod.* 1:67–92.

11 Dutt, R. H. and C. E. Barnhart. 1959. Effect of plane of nutrition upon reproduction performance of boars. *J. Anim. Sci.* 18:3–13.

12 Flipse, R. J. and J. O. Almquist. 1961. Effect of total digestible nutrient intake from birth to four years of age on growth and reproductive development and performance of dairy bulls. *J. Dairy Sci.* 44:905–914.

13 Foote, R. H., N. Munkenbeck, and W. A. Greene. 1976. Testosterone and libido in Holstein bulls of various ages. *J. Dairy Sci.* 59:2011–2013.

14 Gay, V. L. 1972. The hypothalamus: Physiology and clinical use of releasing factors. *Fertil. and Steril.* 23:50–63.

15 Gomes, W. R. and M. C. Joyce. 1975. Seasonal changes in serum testosterone in adult rams. *J. Anim. Sci.* 41:1373–1375.

16 Goss, R. J. and J. K. Rosen. 1973. The effect of latitude and photoperiod on the growth of antlers. *J. Reprod. Fert. Suppl.* 19:111–118.

17 Hall, P. F. 1970. Endocrinology of the testis. In A. D. Johnson, W. R. Gomes, and N. L. VanDemark, eds. *The Testis.* Vol. 2. Academic Press, New York. Pp. 1–72.

18 Hauer, E. P., H. C. Kellgren, S. E. McCraine, and C. K. Vincent. 1970. Puberal characteristics of Quarter horse stallions. *J. Anim. Sci.* 30:321. (Abstr.)

19 Igboeli, G. and A. M. Rakha. 1971. Puberty and related phenomena in Angoni (Short Horn Zebu) bulls. *J. Anim. Sci.* 33:647–650.

20 Jubb, K. V. and K. McEntee. 1955. Observations on the bovine pituitary glands. I. Review of literature on the general problem of adenohypophyseal functional cytology. *Cornell Vet.* 45:576–592.

21 ———. 1955. Observations on the bovine pituitary gland. II. Architecture and cytology with special reference to basophil cell function. *Cornell Vet.* 45:593–601.

22 Kiser, T. E., J. H. Britt, and H. D. Ritchie. 1977. Testosterone treatment of cows for use in detection of estrus. *J. Anim. Sci.* 44:1030–1035.

23 Kragt, C. L. and J. F. Masken. 1972. Puberty-physiological mechanisms of control. *J. Anim. Sci. X Biennial Symposium on Animal Reproduction Suppl.* 1., Vol. 34. Pp. 1–18.

24 Lincoln, G. A. and W. Davidson. 1977. The relationship between sexual and aggressive behaviour, and pituitary and testicular activity during the seasonal sexual cycle of rams, and the influence of photoperiod. *J. Reprod. Fert.* 49:267–276.

25 Lodge, J. R. and G. W. Salisbury. 1970. Seasonal variation and male reproductive efficiency. In A. D. Johnson, W. R. Gomes, and N. L. VanDemark, eds. *The Testis.* Vol. 3. Academic Press, New York. P. 139.

26 Long, C. R., T. G. Jenkins, and T. S. Stewart. 1977. Results of cattle research. *Tex. Agr. Exp. Sta. Tech. Rept. 77-1.* Pp. 33–56.

27 Macmillan, K. L. and H. D. Hafs. 1968. Pituitary and hypothalamic endocrine changes associated with reproductive development of Holstein bulls. *J. Anim. Sci.* 27:1614–1620.

28 ———. 1969. Reproductive tract of Holstein bulls from birth through puberty. *J. Anim. Sci.* 28:233–239.

29 Meineke, C. F. and L. E. McDonald. 1961. The effects of exogenous testosterone on spermatogenesis of bulls. *Amer. J. Vet. Res.* 22:209–215.

30 Moule, G. R. 1950. The influence of a rapid decrease in the hours of daylight on the sexual desire of Merino rams. *Australian Vet. J.* 26:84–87.

31 Ortavant, R., P. Mauleon, and C. Thibault. 1964. Photoperiodic control of gonadal and hypophyseal activity in domestic mammals. *Ann. N. Y. Acad. Sci.* 177:157–193.

32 Pelletier, J. and R. Ortavant. 1975. Photoperiodic control of LH release in the ram. I. Influence of increasing and decreasing light photoperiods. *Acta Endocrinol. (Copenhagen)* 78:435–441.

33 ———. 1975. Photoperiodic control of LH release in the ram. *Acta Endocrinol. (Copenhagen)* 78:442–450.

34 Phillips, R. W. and F. N. Andrews. April 1936. The development of the testes and scrotum of the ram, bull and boar. *Mass. Agr. Exp. Sta. Bull. 331.*

35 Phillips, R. W. and J. H. Zeller. 1943. Sexual development in small and large types of swine. *Anat. Rec.* 85:387–400.

36 Purvis, K., A. W. Illius, and N. B. Haynes. 1974. Plasma testosterone concentrations in the ram. *J. Endocrinol.* 61:241.

37 Reid, J. T. 1960. Effect of energy intake upon reproduction in farm animals. *J. Dairy Sci.* 43:103–122.

38 Savard, K., N. R. Mason, J. T. Ingram, and F. X. Gassner. 1961. The androgens of bovine spermatic venous blood. *Endocrinol.* 69:324–330.

39 Schally, A. V., A. Arimura, and A. J. Kastin. 1973. Hypothalamic regulatory hormones. *Science* 179:341–350.

40 Schally, A. V., A. Arimura, A. J. Kastin, H. Matsuo, Y. Baba, T. W. Redding, R. M. G. Nair, L. Debeljuk, and W. F. White. 1971. Gonadotropin-releasing hormone: One polypeptide regulates secretion of luteinizing and follicle-stimulating hormones. *Science* 173:1036–1038.

41 Schanbacher, B. D. and J. J. Ford. 1976. Luteinizing hormone, testosterone, growth and carcass responses to sexual alteration in the ram. *J. Anim. Sci.* 43:638–643.

42 Schanbacher, B. D. and D. D. Lunstra. 1976. Seasonal changes in sexual activity and serum levels of LH and testosterone in Finnish Landrace and Suffolk rams. *J. Anim. Sci.* 43:644–650.

43 Skinner, J. D., W. D. Booth, L. E. A. Rowson, and H. Karg. 1968. The post-natal development of the reproductive tract of the Suffolk ram, and changes in the gonadotrophin content of the pituitary. *J. Reprod. Fert.* 16:463–477.

44 Skinner, J. D. and J. Bowen. 1968. Puberty in the Welsh stallion. *J. Reprod. Fert.* 16:133–135.

45 Skinner, J. D., T. Mann, and L. E. A. Rowson. 1968. Androstenedione in relation to puberty and growth of the male calf. *J. Endocrinol.* 40:261–262.

46 Skinner, J. D. and L. E. A. Rowson. 1968. Puberty in Suffolk and cross-bred rams. *J. Reprod. Fert.* 16:479–488.

47 Sniffen, Ronald C. 1952. Histology of the normal and abnormal testis at puberty. *Ann. N. Y. Acad. Sci.* 55:609–618.

48 Steinberger, E. and Duckett, G. E. 1967. Hormonal control of spermatogenesis. *J. Reprod. Fert. Suppl.* 2:75–87.

49 Tanner, J. M. 1962. *Growth at Adolescence.* 2nd ed. Blackwell, Oxford. Pp. 28–39.

50 VanDemark, N. L. and R. E. Mauger. 1964. Effect of energy intake on reproductive performance of dairy bulls. I. Growth, reproductive organs, and puberty. *J. Dairy Sci.* 47:798–806.

51 Warnick, A. C., E. L. Wiggins, L. E. Casida, R. H. Grummer, and A. B. Chapman. 1949. The age of puberty in a herd of inbred swine. *J. Anim. Sci.* 8:646. (Abstr.)

52 Watson, R. H. C. S. Sapsford, and I. McCance. 1956. The development of the testis,

epididymis and penis in the young Merino ram. *Australian J. Agr. Res.* 7:574–590.

53 Wiggins, E. L., A. C. Warnick, R. H. Grummer, L. E. Casida, and A. B. Chapman. 1951. Variation in puberty phenomena in inbred boars. *J. Anim. Sci.* 10:494–504.

54 Wolf, F. R., J. O. Almquist, and E. B. Hale. 1965. Prepuberal behavior and puberal characteristics of beef bulls on high nutrient allowance. *J. Anim. Sci.* 24:761–765.

55 Woods, M. C. and M. E. Simpson. 1961. Pituitary control of the testis of the hypophysectomized rat. *Endocrinol.* 69:91–125.

Ejaculation and Semen Collection

When you have completed this chapter you should be able to:

- Understand the preparation for copulation and the activities during the process,
- Develop a knowledge of the ejaculate itself regarding time involved in ejaculation, point of deposition in the female, and its composition,
- Recognize the advantages and disadvantages of the various methods of collecting semen, and
- Understand in more detail the use of the artificial vagina and electroejaculator for collecting semen.

EJACULATION

Ejaculation is the result of a series of events normally initiated with libido on the part of the male. Libido, or sexual desire, is caused by testosterone, the male sex hormone, and is present to some extent continually in the male. State of health dictates to some extent the level of libido, since animals in poor health have less desire to mate. The presence of a female in estrus increases sexual activity of the male although he will try to mount females that are not in estrus.

Bull

The bull is constantly in search of a cow that will stand to be mated. Visual appraisal of the cow herd helps in determining this condition because cows are homosexual in nature and when in estrus will stand to be mounted by other cows and young calves as well as attempt to mount other cows. They also arch their backs and elevate their tails.[6] The bull also uses his olfactory senses to smell odors emitted by the female. These odors are difficult to isolate in domestic animals but are evidently there because the male will raise his head and sniff the air and roll his upper lip wrong side out (flehmen) (Fig. 4–1) when trying to isolate an estrous female. Bellowing cows will also attract the bull.

Hale[12] conducted an experiment at Pennsylvania State University that yielded considerable information concerning mating behavior in the bull. Six pairs of twin bulls were used in the research. Shortly after arrival at the age of 5 to 38 days, the eyes of one of each pair were enucleated. The intact bulls therefore retained the ability to see, hear, and smell while the operated bulls could only hear and smell. The testes developed the same in each set of twins.

Bulls without vision moved about the area without any response until they bumped into a cow. They would then mount any part—front, back, or side—without sniffing the vulva. Some bulls passed within inches of cows in estrus without any cognizance of their presence. Visual stimuli are a help to the initial act of ejaculation but apparently are not necessary thereafter.

Even with the previous work, it is well known that in the teasing procedure preceding copulation the intact bull will smell the vulva, sniff the air, move up beside the cow and lay his head on her rump, and make attempts to mount her. Erection

Figure 4-1 Flehmen expressed by the male.

usually begins during this process but is not complete until mounting occurs. Clear fluid drips from the sheath resulting from secretions expelled from the prostate and bulbourethral glands to cleanse and lubricate the urethra.

Erection, extension, and mounting occur simultaneously followed by intromission, thrusting, and ejaculation. The whole process takes only a second and the bull dismounts immediately. He may then repeat the process in a few minutes or seem to be satisfied with the breeding and move to look for other subjects. A bull may mate with as many as 10 cows in a day depending on stimuli of estrous cows.[25]

The penis appears to search for the lips of the vulva upon mounting and, as soon as the opening is found, thrusts into the vagina; ejaculation occurs against the face of the cervix. Spiral deviation of the penis in a counterclockwise direction occurs in about 50 percent of normal bulls. The penis will only penetrate the cervix in rare instances and even then will penetrate only a short distance because of the anatomy of the cow's cervix.

The movement of sperm through the male system starts in the tail of the epididymis where the muscular walls contract. A peristaltic rush of contractions follows from this point through the length of the deferent duct and through the colliculus seminalis. The colliculus seminalis swells during this procedure and occludes the urethral orifice while the muscles of the urethral opening contract so that no urine will pass during ejaculation.

Contraction of the thin muscular covering of the vesicular glands forces fluid from them to mix with the sperm as they pass through the colliculus seminalis. The mixture is then called semen. Just caudal to the colliculus seminalis are the openings of the prostate through which a small amount of fluid is added as the semen is passed on through the urethral canal by continued peristaltic motion. Contraction of the bulbourethral muscle adds the fluid of the bulbourethral gland to the semen also as the contractions move past.

There is little musculature to cause contraction throughout the penis, and the urethra becomes a rather tight, straight tube during erection through which the sperm moves rapidly.

The ejaculate itself is a single spurt of fluid in the amount of 5 to 15 ml (Table 4–1). It is well mixed at this time without any distinct fractions. The concentration of sperm is between 800 to 1200 million cells per milliliter, which means then that 4 to 18 billion sperm are emitted at ejaculation. Approximately 5 percent of the cells will be abnormally formed and 75 percent of the sperm will be motile in a normal ejaculate.

Ram

In natural mating conditions, the ram seeks the ewe in estrus, smells the vulva, and pushes against the rump with his neck and head, like the bull. Clear accessory fluid drips from the sheath prior to mounting. Erection and extension of the penis is then followed by rapid mounting and intromission.

Copulation in the sheep is of very short duration (less than one second). The penis remains in the sheath until mounting and then there is a sudden extension,

Table 4-1   Ejaculation and Semen Characteristics

	Bull	Ram	Boar	Stallion	Man
Time lapse for ejaculation	1 sec	1 sec	5–25 min	30–60 sec	
Point of semen deposition	os cervix	os cervix	cervix	os cervix	os cervix
Ejaculate volume (ml)	5–15	.8–1.2	150–200	40–100	2–6
Composition of ejaculate	single fraction	single fraction	fractionated sperm-free sperm-rich coagulum	fractionated sperm-free sperm-rich mucus	coagulated single fraction
Concentration sperm/ml $\times 10^6$	800–1,200	2,000–3,000	200–300	200–500	50–150
Total sperm/ ejaculate $\times 10^9$	4–18	1.6–3.6	30–60	8–50	.1–.9
% motile	75	95	70	70	65
% normal	95	95	90	90	60

thrust, and ejaculation followed by dismounting. Following copulation, the ram may repeat his performance or search out other prospects for breeding. Rams have been observed to mate 29 ewes in a day's time,[25] and reports vary up to 60.

The movement of sperm through the tract is the same as that for the bull. Sperm is emitted through the filiform appendage and is ejaculated on the face of the cervix in a spraying manner.

The ram's ejaculate is small in volume but very concentrated—.8 to 1.2 ml and 2 to 3 billion sperm per milliliter. Motility is high and abnormalities few—95 percent and less than 5 percent respectively.

Boar

The boar prepares for mating by courting the sow. The preputial fluids giving off the characteristic odor attract the sows to him and in addition he seeks those in estrus. He also sniffs the vulva and lays his head beside the rump. He will push the sow with his head and raise her off her hind feet by rooting motions in the flank and between the hind legs. Chomping and foaming at the mouth are characteristic at this time. The boar is a highly sexually excitable animal.

Fluids from the prepuce as well as from the accessory glands are expelled during the preparatory stage and the corkscrew-shaped glans penis may be observed as it extends briefly in a twisting motion. Rhythmic urination may be observed. Upon mounting, the glans penis searches the face of the swollen vulva of the sow until it finds the opening. The penis is then extended and passes through the tapered opening of the cervix so that it actually penetrates the cervix during coitus and the sperm are deposited into the cervix proper and the uterus because of the large volume. The thrusting and retraction of the corkscrew glans causes a screwing motion into the sow's cervix.

Copulation is a prolonged process in the boar, as long as 5 to 25 minutes. The boar may be very active and then rest for a few minutes before resuming thrusting and ejaculation. He merely rests on the sow at this time and it is wise to use breeding crates to help hold his weight when he is breeding smaller sows. Following breeding, the boar is usually content to rest for a while before searching for another mate.

The ejaculate itself is fractionated so that the initial phase is composed of accessory fluids and gelatinous pellets with very few sperm present. It is clear and will change to a cloudy or milky appearance as the second or sperm-rich phase begins. Following ejaculation of the sperm-rich portion there will be a phase of fluid with coagulum, which resembles tapioca. Sperm will be entrapped in the gelatinous fraction and are very difficult to separate. It is not uncommon for the sperm-rich and coagulated fractions to mix.

Volume is very high, 150 to 200 ml, and the concentration is very low, 200 to 300 million per milliliter. Motility is lowest of all domestic animals, 70 percent, and the rate of abnormal cells is highest, 10 percent. Total number of cells per ejaculate ranges from 30 to 60 billion.

Stallion

The stallion is also very sexually active. The mare usually approaches the stallion and squats and urinates. The stallion has certain courting patterns that he follows. He will usually approach the mare from the side rather than the rear because if she is not in estrus and ready to be bred, she will probably kick at him. He will nip at her withers, cheek, lips, and flank and push against her with his neck (Fig. 4–2). He will also nuzzle the vulva and throw his head in the air followed by flehmen. The specific odor of a mare in estrus originates in the flank. An estrous mare will usually urinate at this time and he will sniff the urine and vulva.

Erection and extension follow and the stallion aligns himself with the mare before mounting. Accessory fluids are seen dripping from the glans during this phase of preparation. The glans penis becomes turgid and enlarged due to the vascular type construction. The penis initially is covered by the internal fold of the prepuce, which smooths over the penis upon extension.[32] The glans is approximately the same size as the body as it searches for the lips of the vulva and enters. The stallion makes several thrusting motions to insert the penis fully and seat it against the cervix. The glans then swells to approximately twice its diameter and acts as a piston during ejaculation. The cervix of the mare opens and the semen is deposited directly into the cervix and even into the body of the uterus in many instances. Ejaculation occurs over a period of several seconds (30 to 60). The initial searching and thrusting are followed by a less excited period in which continued thrusting is made and a rather characteristic pumping of the tail during ejaculation occurs. Upon completion of ejaculation, the stallion rests for a few seconds before dismounting. The penis is relaxed when disengaged so that the shaft is back to normal, but the glans is still somewhat enlarged although soft. Usually some semen will be dragged from the vagina during removal. The stallion is usually quiet for a time before seeking another mate.

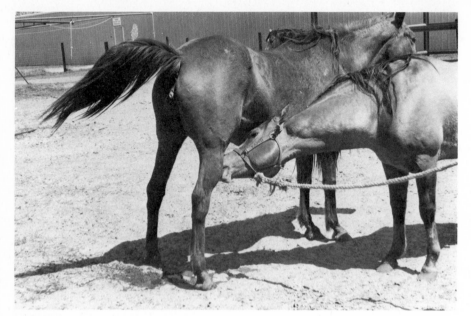

Figure 4-2   Stallion courting the mare.

The ejaculation of the stallion is also fractionated, although not as distinctly as the boar's. The first fraction is primarily accessory fluids and very poor in sperm concentration. It is primarily vesicular fluid. A second milky fraction is rich in sperm, and the third fraction is a stringy mucus. The last fraction usually is much thicker and tenacious at the beginning of the breeding season or in stallions used only sparingly. As the stallion is used heavily, it is common for the gelatinous portion to almost completely disappear. There are great variations in the separation of the last two fractions also. Some stallions do not have distinct fractions, while others yield the sperm-rich before the gelatinous, and yet others yield the gelatinous before the sperm-rich fraction. The stallion somewhat resembles the boar in his ejaculate; volume is high, 40 to 100 ml, concentration is low, 200 to 500 million per ml, motility is a mediocre 70 percent, and abnormalities is a high 10 percent.

Man

Erection of the human penis is similar to the stallion, since both are vascular type. The glans is seated against the cervix at ejaculation and the semen deposited in the anterior vagina on the face of the cervix. Ejaculation occurs in a pulsating flow of sperm as a single fraction. Volume is between 2 and 6 ml, concentration is 50 to 150 million per ml,[31] motility is 65 percent, and abnormalities is 40 percent.

IMPOTENTIA COEUNDI (Not Power Together)

Some bulls develop a condition called intromission phobia or impotency. This is usually characterized by high sexual desire without completion of the act. The bull may mount the cow but never make connection between the penis and vulva. The hind limbs do not flex as in preparation for a leap and thrust, and the penis many times is directed into the escutcheon or area below the vulva. The bull usually dismounts after several feeble attempts and the cow becomes restless and moves away.[11] It is difficult to correct such a condition. One method that yields limited success is to thrust an artificial vagina on the penis as the bull mounts. One researcher[14] had three bulls on which this was tried, and it succeeded in one of them. An estrous cow was utilized, and as the bull mounted, the AV was thrust on the partially extended penis. The bull ejaculated normally and encountered no further difficulties thereafter. Another bull did not respond, and resection of the retractor penis muscles corrected his condition. A third bull did not respond to any treatment. The condition responds to varying treatments with none of them being foolproof.

SEMEN COLLECTION

Semen may be collected in a number of ways, and the method sometimes is governed by the intended purpose for future use. A sample for evaluation may need be only a very small volume and not as clean a sample as one for use in artificial insemination. Let's discuss some of these methods of collection.

Recovery

This follows normal copulation (Fig. 4–3).

A pipette such as an inseminating catheter with an attached suction bulb may be inserted into the vagina following ejaculation, and the semen is then syphoned into it. This semen is contaminated with the fluids of the female tract but is satisfactory for evaluation. It may also be used for artificial insemination when trying to overcome some obstruction in the cervix or satisfy breeding restrictions of some purebred societies. After filling the catheter it may be passed through the cervix to penetrate tortuous lumens, malformed cervical folds protruding into the anterior vagina as is relatively common in the mare, and to add semen to that already passing through the cervix in natural service.

Spooning Spooning is used to recover by using a long-handled sterile spoon to dip and recover semen from the floor of the anterior vagina following copulation.

Sponge A sponge may be placed in the vagina prior to copulation and removed afterward to obtain a sample. This may be a type of tampon.

Cup A cup or suitable container may be used to catch drippings from the penis of the stallion as he dismounts following serving the mare. This is usually a dilute sample as the concentrated fraction comes before this portion, which is composed primarily of accessory fluids.[16] The glans penis is still enlarged at this time and drags semen from the vagina. This semen may be used the same as that collected by syphoning.

Blotting Blotting the vagina following copulation is used in sows and may be used

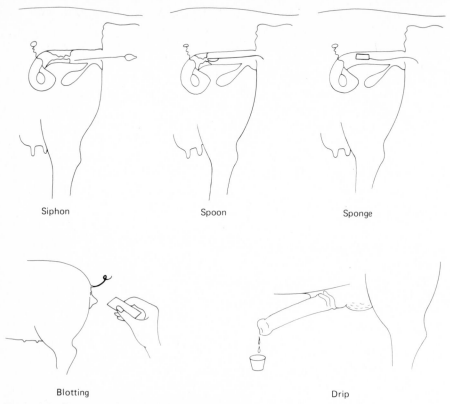

Siphon   Spoon   Sponge

Blotting   Drip

Figure 4-3 Recovery of semen following copulation.

in others. This consists of simply placing the flat side of a microscope slide against the lips of the vulva immediately following dismounting of the boar and sampling the semen pulled from the vagina. The volume is very small but may be used for immediate evaluation.

Massage

Semen may be collected from the bull, in most instances, by massage. The bull is restrained and the gloved arm and hand are lubricated before inserting through the anus into the rectum (Fig. 4-4). The area of the ampullae, vesicular glands, and prostate is located under the rectum. The fingertips then are used to exert a downward pressure milking this area caudally. This stimulates and mechanically causes the sperm to be passed through the urethra by gravity to drip from the prepuce. There is usually no erection or extension. The semen is usually of poor quality and the response less than perfect. This method of collection is restricted to the bull.

In one trial using 21 bulls, massage was utilized and the ejaculate compared with that obtained by the artificial vagina.[7] Sexual preparation was essential and only the sperm-rich fraction was collected. Stripping the vesicular glands and ampullae sometimes caused ejaculation as a single stroke rather than drippings. Massage was

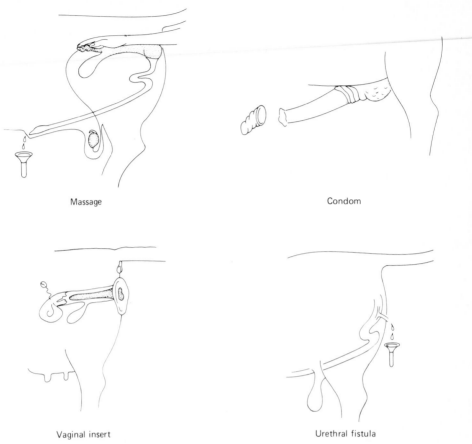

Massage

Condom

Vaginal insert

Urethral fistula

Figure 4-4 Collecting semen by massage, condom, insert, and fistula.

86 percent successful in obtaining suitable samples for insemination compared to 93 percent for those using the artificial vagina. Approximately 50 percent of the bulls ejaculated within 2 minutes of the beginning of massage. Conception rates were comparable based on 90-day nonreturns.

It was found that bulls could be massaged every 4 or 5 days, and irritation of the rectum was not a problem. There was a higher incidence of bacteria, which was best controlled if the semen were cooled and processed quickly. Libido appeared to slacken with the number of massage collections, and preparation time lengthened.

Condom

The stallion ejaculate may be recovered by placing a condom over the glans penis as he is prepared for mounting the mare. This thin rubber sleeve covers the glans during ejaculation and is removed containing the semen as the stallion dismounts. It is a rather exacting technique requiring some experience in covering the glans in the beginning.

The condom is a common method for collecting semen from man.

Vaginal Insert

This sperm collector consists of a tapered insert with a flange on the end that may be placed in the vagina prior to copulation. The male ejaculates in the cranial portion and the collection is relatively free of contamination. The difficulties override the advantages; therefore it is in little demand. It is difficult to insert, some males do not like the feel, the penis may bypass the flange, and the rigidity of the flange may damage the penis.[15]

Urethral Fistula

The male urethra may be cannulated with a tube just under the anus with a T-type cannula allowing passage of urine through the urethra proper or collection of sperm under the anus at the time of copulation.[23] This is only useful experimentally since rather exacting surgery is involved.

Artificial Vagina

The first artificial vagina was reportedly devised by G. Amantea, a professor of physiology at the University of Rome in 1914. This was used to collect semen from the dog. In the years following, numerous Russian researchers developed artificial vaginas for the bull, stallion, and ram.

This method is closest to the natural conditions and is assumed to yield the most normal ejaculate of all methods used. An attempt is made to simulate the normal or best temperature, pressure, lubrication, and position to obtain the optimum response of the male. The artificial vagina (AV) is basically the same for all males. It consists of an outer rigid or semirigid support with an inner jacket containing controlled-temperature water and pressure and a collecting funnel and container (Fig. 4–5).

The *bull AV* (Fig. 4–6) is usually made of an outer casing of hard rubber. Commercial AVs are available and component parts may be purchased. A piece of radiator hose 41 cm (16 in) long and 8 cm (3 in) in diameter makes a good casing. Two 1 cm (1/2 in) holes should be drilled 15 cm (6 in) from one end on opposite sides of the casing. A piece of rubber tubing forms a 15 cm (6 in) sleeve over this with retaining rubber bands placed tightly around each end. This forms a pocket into which water may flow during the thrust of the penis, maintaining pressure and also eliminating splashing the collector with hot water. A rubber inner liner 15 cm (6 in) longer than the casing is slipped inside and folded over one end and secured by a strong rubber band. The other end is left open temporarily. A flexible rubber funnel is then slipped over the folded inner liner and secured by a rubber band. The smaller end of the funnel is attached to a collecting test tube of 15 ml capacity. The open end of the AV is filled with water so that the cavity between the casing and inner liner contains water at 43 to 46°C (110 to 115°F) to within about 2 cm (1 in) of the top. The inner liner is folded over the open end and secured. Valves are unnecessary for filling this type AV. The final step is to lubricate the face of the AV with a sterile

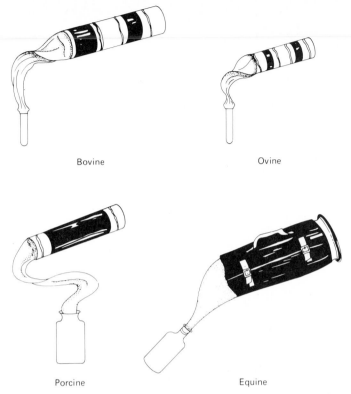

Bovine

Ovine

Porcine

Equine

Figure 4-5 Artificial vaginas for domestic animals.

lubricant such as KY jelly. Use only enough to allow the penis to move in easily. The lubricant will be carried inside as the thrust is made.

Length, temperature, and pressure are important and must be experimentally determined. The penis should extend into the collecting cone during ejaculation. If the AV is too short the collecting tube may be pushed off, and if too long, the ejaculate will be partially lost as well as exposed to temperature above or below optimum for survival. Animals are individuals and will require individual attention. If temperature is too low or pressure too low, the male may mount and push into the AV without making a thrust or ejaculating. If the temperature is too high, the male will quickly withdraw his penis and dismount. Repeated attempts to get him to remount may be necessary before this bad experience is overcome. If the pressure is too great, entry will be difficult, or if entry is obtained then disengagement may be difficult.

In colder climates, an insulator of some sort is needed for protecting the AV and/or the collecting tube. A padded or quilted cover may be placed over the entire unit or just over the tube. In very cold weather, a modified AV may be used for the bull in which the casing and water jacket are approximately 76 cm (30 in) long. The

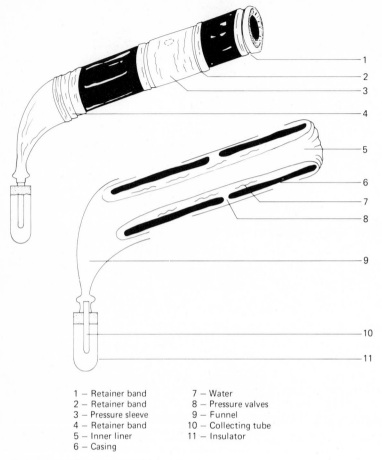

1 – Retainer band   7 – Water
2 – Retainer band   8 – Pressure valves
3 – Pressure sleeve   9 – Funnel
4 – Retainer band   10 – Collecting tube
5 – Inner liner   11 – Insulator
6 – Casing

Figure 4-6   The bovine artificial vagina.

funnel portion is an elongated inner liner that is attached to the collecting tube and both are enclosed inside for warmth.

The *ram AV* (Fig. 4–5) is a miniature of the bull AV and the same precautions apply.

The *boar AV* (Fig. 4–5) is 5 cm (2 in) in diameter and 25 cm (10 in) long. It is constructed the same as for the bull except for the collecting tube and container. The tube should allow the penis to extend past the casing 8 to 10 cm (3 to 4 in).[1] An insulated 200 to 300 ml container is needed for the large volume of the ejaculate, and a cheesecloth strainer should be used. Pressure is much more important than temperature. Water or air may be used in the AV. Temperature should be approximately 40°C (105°F). The boar is very sexually aggressive and may usually be collected without difficulty as long as the pressure is maintained. The bull AV may be used with good success.

The *stallion AV* is larger, with the same requirements as for the other species. The most popular and most workable model is the Missouri Model (Fig. 4–5), which has a leather casing for support with a double-walled liner and molded funnel that fits by friction into a regular plastic baby bottle. Both temperature (46 to 49°C, 115 to 120°F) and pressure are very important, and with this particular model the hands can exert pressure as needed during ejaculation. Other models have only a heavy rubber-walled water jacket without a cover, while others are very rigid, such as the model used by Pickett[21] at Colorado.

Collection Some important factors may be considered when collecting semen by use of the AV. Protection of the animal used as a mount, the animal being collected, and the collector is necessary. Do not take chances with a male getting ready to mount a female for breeding. His mind is on one thing and one thing only and should not be distracted.

The collection of semen from the bull with the AV will be discussed first. The mount may be a female in estrus, a teaser animal, or a dummy. It may be necessary to collect a new bull on an estrous cow because he may be frightened by new surroundings, but if he is confronted with a cow wanting to be bred, his chances of complying are better than with any other mount. After the bull is accustomed to collection, anestrous cows, steers, other bulls, or a dummy may be used. Many of the large bull studs use mounter steers because they are docile and strong.

It may be necessary to restrain the mount animal in some way. With experience, only tying the animal will be necessary. A breeding rack with footrests on either side will support the heavier bulls during collection. The bull's sheath is cleaned and the belly brushed to remove debri and then he is led in by an assistant and kept under control at all times. He is led near the mount and allowed to tease and be teased by the mere presence of the mount animal. The penis usually extends slightly and a clear fluid from the accessory glands drips from it. This cleans and lubricates the urethra in preparation for ejaculation. As the attendant allows the bull to mount the teaser animal, the sheath is grasped and the penis directed into the artificial vagina (Fig. 4–7). The AV should be held near the buttocks on a line parallel to the vagina and the bull allowed to serve the AV rather than thrusting the AV on his penis. The bull makes a single thrust and usually completely leaves the ground in the process. Motion pictures show rhythmic movements of the dew claws during ejaculation and a time from contact with the AV through ejaculation of 1.36 seconds.[24] He will then quickly dismount and should be led a short distance away until the sample may be visually appraised to see if a second ejaculate is required. If a second is needed, most bulls will return in a few minutes and ejaculate successfully. The collector must be careful to avoid touching the penis during collection because the bull usually will dismount and lose interest if it is handled.

Bull semen may be separated into fractions during collection for research purposes[9] but is not commonly considered to be fractionated.

Collection of semen from the *ram* is very similar to the bull. The artificial vagina is prepared and readied for the ram to mount. As he mounts, the sheath is

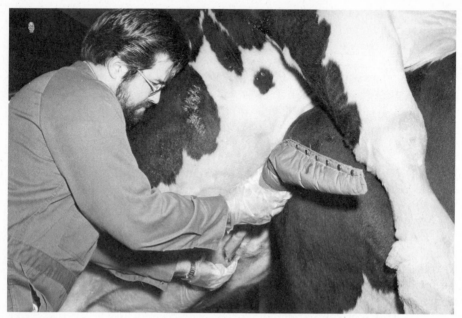

Figure 4-7 Collecting semen from the bull. *(Courtesy of Central Ohio Breeding Association.)*

grasped and the penis directed into the AV. The collector must be alert because the ram moves very quickly and makes a rapid single thrusting motion. An estrous ewe yields the best response by the ram. If the ram becomes disinterested, grasping the wool just in front of the dock of the ewe and shaking the tail will stimulate him.

The AV is not used widely on *boars* but is a satisfactory method. A great deal of pressure is essential. As the boar mounts the sow or dummy, the penis itself may be grasped and directed into the lubricated AV. Many boars will mount, dismount, and remount before they decide to complete the act. Once mounted and settled, the ejaculatory process will take several minutes. Since the ejaculate is fractionated, it is advisable to let the first "sperm-poor" fraction fall on the ground, collect the "sperm-rich" fraction, and let the "gelatinous" fraction fall. The collection is then more dense and free of coagulum than if all were collected.

A modification of the bull-type AV leaves a tubular portion over the glans penis that may be grasped by the hand after insertion. Exerting pressure by squeezing the glans elicits ejaculation.[27] The best stimulus is an estrous sow, but some patience and training yield good results when a dummy is used.

The *stallion* is brought into the presence of a hobbled mare, with her tail wrapped for collection, and teased by bringing him close to the mare without allowing mounting. Two buckets of warm water should be prepared and the stallion's penis washed with a mild soapy water followed by a thorough rinsing with clean water. Blot the penis dry to reduce friction and possible premature ejaculation. He is then allowed to approach the mare from the side and tease her before mounting. Teasing usually increases the quality of the ejaculate. As the stallion mounts,

Figure 4-8 Collecting semen from the stallion.

the collector moves in from the side and behind the stallion's front hoof and directs the erect penis into the lubricated AV. The stallion is allowed to move forward, inserting his penis into the lubricated AV, which is on a level with and just to one side of the vulva. The AV is held at the angle of natural entry for the penis and he is allowed to serve the AV; the AV is not taken to him (Fig. 4–8). Stallions can be taught bad habits of partial entry if the AV is moved to him, and this may later interfere with conception to natural service.

In the flexible model AVs, the hands can feel the penis and exert pressure during copulation. Squeezing the penis rhythmically according to urethral constrictions as he makes a thrust stimulates ejaculation. Upon dismounting, the AV is disengaged and the stallion's penis is washed before returning him to his stall. The complete collection lasts only 30 seconds to one minute.

The ejaculate is usually collected in its entirety and must be strained before use to remove the gelatinous portion. A few layers of sterile cheesecloth are sufficient. It may be strained during the collection process.

The stallion may not ejaculate on each attempt. Studies report from 1.38 to 1.9 mounts per ejaculate.[21] Total sperm in first ejaculates is usually greater than in the second ejaculate.

Use of a rigid-wall AV restricts palpation of the penis during ejaculation through the wall, but the hands may feel the pulsations of the urethra at the opening of the AV.[2]

An open-model AV has been used to study the ejaculatory process. An average of seven intravaginal thrusts were made before ejaculation. Pressure in the AV increased from 66 mm hg at the beginning of copulation to 142 just before ejaculation and 70 during emission of semen. Five to ten jets were emitted, with the early ones under high pressure with a spattering effect and lower-pressure spurts later. The first three jets contained 80 percent of the ejaculate.[26]

A large percent (38) of the total sperm in the ejaculate has been designated as lost in the AV collection[22] due to adherence to the filter (63 percent), to the rubber-ware (22 percent), and to the collection bottle (15 percent). It is difficult to correct these losses, but every attempt should be made to obtain the maximum number of sperm at each collection. Average values during this research were 109 ml per ejaculate composed of 68 ml gel and 41 ml of gel-free portion. Concentration was 398×10^6/ml for a total of 17×10^9 sperm. This included the entire ejaculate, but when available sperm were calculated, the number was reduced to 14×10^9. Only the latter sperm are available for use, which emphasizes the need for extreme caution during collection and separation.

Gloved-Hand Method

An alternate method for obtaining the boar ejaculate is the gloved-hand method. The equipment needed is a plastic glove and a collecting device composed of a wide-mouthed thermos with cheesecloth stretched over the top.[10]

The boar is allowed to tease and mount as with the AV. The gloved hand then massages and strips the odoriferous fluid from the prepuce. After this is expelled, the glove may be removed. The erected and extended glans penis is grasped with the hand and held firmly to the side of the mount for collection (Fig. 4–9). Pressure is of utmost importance, and, if released, the boar will retract his penis and dismount. This can be a very tiring procedure, particularly for the beginning collector.

The first clear fluid is allowed to fall and the thicker sperm-rich fraction then collected into the warm thermos. The cheesecloth eliminates the gelatinous portion entering the container. When the ejaculate becomes almost entirely of a gelatin consistency, collection is stopped but pressure is maintained until the boar has completed copulation to his own satisfaction. He will dismount and relax his penis when he is through.

Electroejaculation

This method of semen collection was derived from observations of persons being electrocuted who ejaculated in response to the electrical stimulus. The first attempts to electroejaculate laboratory animals were crude and consisted of electrodes being placed in the mouth and nape of the neck. Of course, the whole body was stimulated and too frequently overstimulated. The electrodes were then moved to the anus and lumbar area to localize the effect. It was not long before probes were developed with inlaid electrodes which could be inserted into the rectum to further localize stimulation and response. Further refinement led to finger electrodes and stimulation of specific nerve centers for ejaculation without side effects.

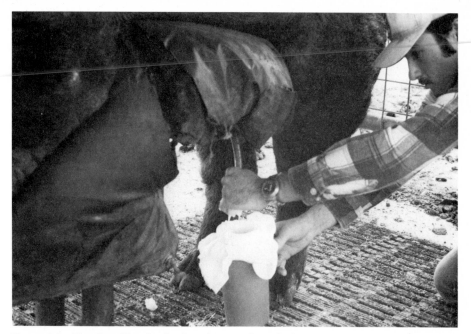

Figure 4-9 The gloved-hand collection of semen from the boar.

The advantage of electroejaculation lies in the ability to collect semen without sexual response from the male. This means that range animals that are unaccustomed to chutes, restraints, and people may be collected the same as those handled daily, without excitement or stress. Males that are unable to copulate for reasons of injury or impotency may be collected. There is no need for a female in estrus for collection.

Males may be collected while in a normal breeding program without upsetting the breeding program. This means semen may be collected for evaluation or for processing to be used at a later date. Bulls have been collected by electroejaculation routinely for artificial insemination while being used in a handmating program without detrimental effects.

The semen collected by electroejaculation is equal in quality to that collected by the artificial vagina,[3] and processing, storage, and later use are comparable.

Disadvantages to electroejaculation lie mainly in the cost of equipment and the possibility of misuse. The better machines on the market plus a microscope and other smaller items will cost approximately $1,000. Over a period of years of usage, this can be rather inexpensive, however. Saving the calf crop from one single-sire herd may be worth the entire cost. Misuse is an inexcusable disadvantage and may be overcome by diligence and experience; electroejaculation is an art as much as a method. The operator must feel the response of the animal and be alert to every reaction. Overstimulation can cause damage to the sire through overexcitement, exhaustion, and, in rare instances, death. The electroejaculator is not a toy to be played with by anyone who can afford it. It should be treated with care and respect.

There are a number of reputable electroejaculators on the market (Fig. 4–10). One of the first to find wide use was the Marden Electroejaculator. This unit is designed on a vacuum-tube chassis and requires a source of electricity for power. A portable generator or converter may be used in the field. Voltage is critical and may need to be checked with a voltmeter if response is not as expected. The ability to replace tubes is an advantage in case the instrument is damaged. The standard probes for the instrument are solid lucite with four embedded electrodes running the length of the probe. One disadvantage is in the way the wire enters the base of the electrode. It may be mashed and severed or shorted if one is not careful.

Transistor models have been developed with and without the need for an outside power source. They are efficient units and the main disadvantage is in repair. They must be returned to the manufacturer. The battery-powered models have rechargeable batteries and are well adapted to use under range conditions. One unit manufactured by Standard Precision Electronics is a small compact model that takes up little space and carries a battery sufficient for 50 to 100 collections. This is usually sufficient for a day's work when collecting from a power source.

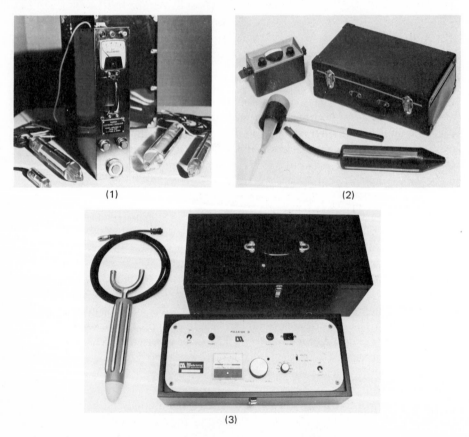

(1)   (2)

(3)

Figure 4-10   Three models of electroejaculators; (1) Marden, (2) Standard Precision Electronics, (3) Lane.

Probes are of different designs. Sizes vary from small probes for rams and billies measuring 2.5 X 15 cm (1 X 6 in) to giant-size probes for bulls that are 10 X 45 cm (4 X 18 in). A normal-size bull probe is approximately 7.5 X 40 cm (3 X 16 in). Early probes had electrodes encircling the probe, but now most probes are designed with the four electrodes laid into or on the surface longitudinally. A newer model has three electrodes on the ventral surface only of an oval-shaped tubular probe. The handle is also molded into the probe in a horseshoe shape to assist in insertion and retention, as the tail falls into the horseshoe and helps hold the probe in the rectum. Small hand-held electrodes[8] or finger electrodes usually give response without major side effects. The electrodes are placed over the ampullae and vesicular glands to induce emission of sperm from the deferent ducts and ampullae. Then the electrode is moved caudally to stimulate the centers of erection and ejaculation.[4] Contraction of the musculature of the male's hindquarters is reduced; however, constriction of the rectum and anus makes the procedure uncomfortable for the operator. A second person must keep the operator informed of the ejaculatory process as well as collect the sample.

Bull The bull should be restrained in a holding facility that resembles natural surroundings as nearly as possible (Fig. 4–11). A wooden chute with a dirt floor and free of loud noises works best. The bull should be comfortably restrained. In most instances a bar can be placed behind the bull to restrict forward to backward movement, and a board removed from the lower side of the existing chute will allow collection of the semen sample underneath. If highly excitable animals are being collected, a squeeze chute may be necessary. Again, only as much restraint as is necessary should be used. He will respond best when standing naturally. The bull usually raises his right hind leg when stimulated; therefore, it is best to prepare for collection from the right side, as he will turn the extended penis in that direction for ejaculation. Of course there are some left-footed bulls, so you can't outguess them all.

Other necessary equipment includes a collecting device. A pliable plastic funnel and a 15 ml test tube are the simplest. A rubber ring similar to a short AV with only the funnel and collecting tube attached may be used and also may be placed on a handle. This allows collection from a distance of 30 to 45 cm (12 to 18 in). Protection of the collecting tube may be a large, pliable plastic tube with a stopper in which a hole has been drilled to fit the collecting tube. Some method of maintaining temperature is also essential. Warm water, 37 to 43°C (100 to 110°F) may be placed in the protection tube, or a plastic bag may be filled with warm water and attached to the funnel while covering the tube. Temperature control must always be maintained to eliminate any shock by sudden changes.

A bucket of warm water is needed to wash and lubricate the probe. A second bucket of warm water is used for washing the sheath and surrounding belly wall to guarantee a clean sample. After all preparations have been completed the bull is brought into the chute for collection. Care should be taken to refrain from exciting the bull any more than is necessary. A bar or chain should be placed behind the animal just above the hocks. Movement should be restricted to only a few inches

Figure 4-11 Setup for collecting bull semen with the electroejaculator.

forward and backward or sideways. It is usually best to refrain from catching the
bull's head in a squeeze. If it is caught, the operator should be constantly aware of
movement so that if the bull lies down or falls down, he will not choke himself.
Chutes with open-stanchion type headgates are much preferable to those with restraints across under the neck.

The probe is next wet with water and inserted through the anus into the rectum
(Fig. 4–12). This is most easily accomplished by grasping the tail with one hand and
pulling on it while inserting the probe with a pushing, slightly turning motion with
the other. Unnecessary raising of the tail will constrict the anal sphincter; therefore,
only raise it horizontally. Once the probe is completely inside, hold the tail down
to reduce the chances of the bull's expelling it. Usually, expulsion will not occur after
stimulations start.

The testes of the bull and sheath should be observed during the probe insertion;
and as soon as stimulation begins, the scrotum and testes should be palpated for
firmness, balance, and size, as well as prominence of the tail of the epididymis.
Scrotal measurements may be made during stimulation to reduce danger from
kicking.

As the probe is inserted, the ejaculator should be turned on. When insertion is
completed, stimulation should begin in a rhythmic manner at low power. There
should be stimulation followed by a one-second pause, then relaxation followed by
a one-second pause, and the rhythm maintained throughout stimulation until ejaculation. The power should be low in the beginning to gain the confidence of the bull
and get him working with you in a rhythmic manner. Increase in power should
accompany refractoriness of the bull to the existing power level. Changes should be

Figure 4-12 Inserting the probe for electroejaculation.

made gradually throughout the procedure. Maximum power will reach approximately 20 volts.

The usual response of the bull is to rock forward upon stimulation, bellow, and return to a normal stance upon relaxation. The testes will be pulled against the body, the hind legs will contract, and the penis may be seen in the sheath as it erects. Following several stimulations, the penis extends itself and clear fluid from the accessory glands drips from the sheath or extended glans penis. There is no need to collect this for there are very few sperm present. Continued stimulation will cause extension of the penis, and spurts of clear fluid will accompany the forward thrust. The fluid will change density to a milky color, indicating that the sperm fraction is beginning (Fig. 4–13). At this time the collection funnel should be placed directly over the glans penis and remain there during the further rhythmic stimulations until the ejaculated fluid begins to change to clear fluid again. Remove the funnel and cease stimulation. After evaluation of the semen, the bull may be released if the sample is satisfactory, or reejaculated immediately for an additional sample if there is question.

When the bull is released, he may limp slightly or drag the rear leg that has been stimulated the most. This usually subsides in a very few steps, and it is not uncommon for range bulls to immediately search out and breed cows following electroejaculation.

There are some peculiarities that may be of interest when using electroejaculation. Hereford bulls usually respond as has been described here. Angus bulls usually extend their penis when the probe is inserted but retract it upon initial stimulation and then follow a normal pattern. They also are very vociferous, bellowing upon each stimulation and even sometimes between. Brahman bulls may lie down when initially stimulated, making collection impossible. It is usually best to release such bulls and recycle them through the chute. Be prepared to form a sling behind the

Figure 4-13 Collecting semen during electroejaculation.

bull's forelegs and under the flank to support him during ejaculation. A sack or some sort of padding should cover the penile area under the belly so that it is not damaged during the support.

Some bulls seem to be stimulated in reverse so that the penis is more tightly folded at the sigmoid flexure and will not extend itself. This usually accompanies a low-power source but may occur at other times as well. The best remedy comes by pushing forward on the sigmoid flexure to cause extension of the penis; once it is extended, it usually remains so. The probe man may do this from the rear, or it may become necessary to manipulate the penis from the side by reaching between the legs and cupping the fingers over the sigmoid flexure to straighten it and then catch the penis at the point of insertion of the retractor penis muscle to hold this area anterior to the scrotum. During all of this procedure, the rhythmic stimulation should be maintained.

In addition to retraction of the penis, there are other factors to be considered and expected to some extent. Muscular contraction ordinarily causes lateral and posterior elevation of one of the hind legs. The hindquarters will be lifted free of the ground at higher levels of stimulation.[5] The fetlock will buckle in some bulls and should be straightened before continued stimulation. Some bulls become hyperexcitable with the lowest-voltage stimulation. By all means, have a firm footing available for the male. If he is slipping and sliding while being stimulated, it is doubtful that ejaculation will result.

Comparison of the bull ejaculates collected by electroejaculation have been made with AV collection, and the responses are mixed. Apparently, they are approximately equal when optimum procedures are utilized for the bull[3] and ram.[18] Other researchers report poorer results for semen evaluation from electroejaculates from the ram.[13]

Ram Collection of semen from the ram is similar to the procedures for the bull, but some differences should be understood. A smaller probe is used, although the power source remains the same. The ram may be restrained by restricting him in a chute, placing your knee in his flank to trap him against a fence, or he may be laid on his side and his feet and legs restrained. Collection is usually made into a small 10 ml beaker and the warmth of the hand used to maintain temperature. If the penis is not extended, it may be necessary to push the sheath and prepuce back onto the shaft of the penis to expose the glans for semen collection. Surprisingly enough, it may take an equivalent number of stimulations and power to obtain an ejaculate as from the bull.

A later-model transistorized probe has been described that utilizes a lower-peak voltage and is much lighter to manipulate. Its use does not result in as much musculature contraction.[19] A one-man collection procedure for electroejaculating rams has been described by O'Brien[20] in which the ram is restrained with a three-point tiedown and the operator can then stimulate and collect by himself.

Boar The boar may be restrained in a calf chute or similar mechanism and ejaculated the same as the bull. A small bull probe 4 X 20 cm (1.5 X 8 in) may be used. The gloved-hand method is so successful that this method is seldom used.

Stallion No accounts of electroejaculation of the stallion were found in the literature. The author has attempted collection from a jack, and the response of the animal was little different from the bull. The ejaculate consisted of a creamy-colored fluid without sperm, and it is not known if he was producing sperm at the time or not. The AV functions so well in horses and jacks that no further attempts were made.

Primates Primates have been collected by electroejaculation by different methods. A strip electrode may be placed at the base of the penis and another contact to the glans. This was successful in 93 of 103 attempts in macaques.[28] Eight of eleven monkeys were successfully collected by another researcher using the same method.[17] A bipolar electrode was placed in the rectum of another group of primates and collection successfully made, with 66 percent of the ejaculates being rich in sperm.[30] The probe method apparently gives better reliability for obtaining the ejaculate, while the penile method yields better concentration.[29]

WHAT DID YOU LEARN?

1   Describe passage of the sperm through the tract during ejaculation.
2   Where is semen deposited by the boar during copulation?

3   What males have fractionated ejaculates?
4   How long does copulation last in the bull, boar, ram, and stallion?
5   How many sperm are ejaculated by the stallion?
6   What is the most acceptable method of collecting semen from the boar?
7   What collection method most closely resembles the natural ejaculatory process?
8   What four criteria are considered in trying to simulate natural conditions when collecting semen with the AV?
9   What advantages are associated with electroejaculation over collection with the AV?
10 What can be done if a bull goes "in reverse" upon electrical stimulation?

REFERENCES

1   Aamdal, J., I. Hogset, O. Sveberg, and N. Koppang. 1958. A new type of artificial vagina and a new collection technique for boar semen. *J.A.V.M.A.* 132:101–104.

2   Asbury, A. C. and J. P. Hughes. 1964. Use of the artificial vagina for equine semen collection. *J.A.V.M.A.* 144:879–882.

3   Austin, J. W., E. W. Hupp, and R. L. Murphree. 1961. Comparison of quality of bull semen collected in the artificial vagina and by electroejaculation. *J. Dairy Sci.* 44:2292–2297.

4   Ball, L. 1974. Electroejaculation of bulls. *Proc. 5th Tech. Conf. on A.I. and Reprod. and A.I.* Pp. 95–100.

5   Barker, C. A. V. 1958. The collection of semen from bulls, rams and bucks by electro-ejaculation. *Can. J. of Comp. Med.* 22:3–8.

6   Blockey, M. A. deB. 1976. Sexual behaviour of bulls at pasture: A review. *Therio.* 6:387–392.

7   Debruyne, R. 1961. The collection of semen in bulls by massage of the ampullae through the rectum. *Proc. 4th Int. Congr. On Anim. Reprod. and A.I.* 2:283–290.

8   Easley, G. T. 1970. A hand electrode for the electroejaculation of bulls. *Bov. Pract.* 5:12–13, 16.

9   Faulkner, L. C., J. F. Masken, and M. L. Hopwood. 1964. Fractionation of the bovine ejaculate. *J. Dairy Sci.* 47:823–825.

10 First, N. L. 1968. Collection, evaluation and insemination of boar semen. *Proc. 2nd Tech. Conf. on A.I. and Reprod.* pp. 52–54.

11 Fraser, A. F. 1957. Intromission phobia in the bull. *Vet. Rec.* 69:621–622.

12 Hale, E. B. 1966. Visual stimuli and reproductive behavior in bulls. *J. Anim. Sci. Suppl.* 25:36–44.

13 Hulet, C. V., W. C. Foote, and R. L. Blackwell. 1964. Effects of natural and electrical ejaculation on predicting fertility in the ram. *J. Anim. Sci.* 23:418–424.

14 Kendrick, J. W. 1954. Psychic impotence in bulls. *Cornell Vet.* 44:289–293.

15 Lambert, W. V. and F. F. McKenzie. 1940. Artificial insemination in livestock breeding. *USDA Circ. No. 567.*

16 Mann, T., R. V. Short, A. Walton, R. K. Archer, and W. C. Miller. 1957. The "tail-end sample" of stallion semen. *J. Agr. Sci.* 49:301–312.

17 Mastroianni, L., Jr. and W. A. Manson, Jr. 1963. Collection of monkey semen by electroejaculation. *Proc. Soc. Exp. Biol. Med.* 112:1025–1027.

18 Mattner, P. E. and J. K. Voglmayr. 1962. A comparison of ram semen collected by the artificial vagina and by electroejaculation. *Aust. J. Exp. Agric. Anim. Husb.* 2:78–81.

19 Nichols, G. De La M. and D. G. Edgar. 1964. A transistorized rectal probe for ejaculat-
    ing rams. *New Zealand Vet. J.* 12:145–146.
20 O'Brien, C. A. 1965. Faster fertility testing by a simplified electro-ejaculator method.
    National Wool Grower 55:15–17.
21 Pickett, B. W. 1968. Collection and evaluation of stallion semen. *Proc. 2nd Tech. Conf.
    on A.I. and Reprod.* Pp. 80–87.
22 Pickett, B. W., M. R. Gebauer, G. E. Seidel, and J. L. Voss. 1974. Reproductive
    physiology of the stallion: Spermatozoal losses in the collection equipment and gel.
    J.A.V.M.A. 165:708–710.
23 Rowson, L. E. A. 1947. Collection of semen by means of the urethral fistula. *Vet. Rec.*
    59:289–291.
24 Seidel, G. E., Jr. and R. H. Foote. 1969. Motion picture analysis of ejaculation in the
    bull. *J. Reprod. and Fert.* 20:313–317.
25 Sumner, S. L., R. Ancalmo, and A. C. Warnick. 1968. Behaviour of bulls and rams
    during the breeding season. *J. Anim. Sci.* 27:1197. (Abstr.)
26 Tischner, M., K. Kosiniak, and W. Bielanski. 1974. Analysis of the pattern of ejaculation
    in stallions. *J. Reprod. Fert.* 41:329–335.
27 Turkheimer, A. R., D. C. Young, and R. H. Foote. 1958. Technics for semen collection;
    semen production in young boars. *Cornell Vet.* 48:291–299.
28 Valerio, D. A., E. B. Ellis, M. L. Clark, and G. E. Thompson. 1969. Collection of semen
    from macaques by electroejaculation. *Lab. Anim. Care* 19:250–252.
29 VanPelt, L. and P. E. Keyser. 1970. Observations on semen collection and quality in
    macaques. *Lab. Anim. Care* 20:726–733.
30 Weisbroth, S. and F. A. Young. 1965. The collection of primate semen by electro-
    ejaculation. *Fertil. and Steril.* 16:229–234.
31 White, I. G. 1958. Biochemical aspects of mammalian semen. *Anim. Breed. Abstr.*
    26:109–123.
32 Wierzbowski, S. and E. S. E. Hafez. 1961. Analysis of copulatory reflexes in the stallion.
    Proc. 4th Int. Congr. on Anim. Reprod. and A.I. Pp. 176–179.

Breeding
Soundness
Evaluation

When you have completed this chapter you should be able to:

- Enumerate and explain criteria used for evaluating the outward signs of fertility of the male,
- Evaluate the internal reproductive organs for breeding soundness,
- Understand the value of the various factors used in evaluating semen,
- Appreciate the difficulties in developing a single breeding soundness evaluation system, and
- Assemble the facts and figures available to meet the need for breeding soundness evaluation under a specific condition.

It seems obvious that a method of selecting breeding stock should be developed and utilized to separate the good from the bad. There is no doubt that selection has been practiced to a degree from the beginning of time. In natural selection, if a sire is of low fertility there will be fewer offspring sired by him. With domestication, man has added his own selection pressure and eliminated nonbreeders as he has observed a reduced number or absence of offspring from a particular sire. Refinement of technique has led us to a more exacting program involving predictive measures based on research and past experiences.

Much of our present knowledge on evaluation of breeding stock has accumulated since the early 1950s. Colorado and Texas were particularly concerned because of severe drought conditions and subsequent poor conception rates and fewer calves then available for sale. Surveys were conducted[37,46] and from the evaluation of semen from large numbers of bulls under varying circumstances it was found that between 80 and 90 percent of the bulls were considered satisfactory for breeding purposes and the remainder either sterile or of poor predicted fertility. Increased attention has since been directed toward more exacting measures of fertility estimates. A survey of 1127 examinations was made in Missouri in 1975 and the results were essentially the same as in Texas and Colorado 20 years earlier.[22]

This discussion of sire breeding soundness evaluation will again use the bull as the basic animal for discussion and differences will be pointed out as they occur in other species. General observations will be discussed first, followed by examination of reproductive organs, semen evaluation, and measures of libido.

GENERAL OBSERVATIONS

Masculine Traits

The male animal has certain characteristics that are designated as masculine. These are present primarily in response to testosterone and its activity in the body. These include the crest, muscling, behavior, and development of the reproductive organs. The presence of these characteristics tells us something about the testosterone level, therefore, and we can associate visual appraisal with libido, which is necessary for sexual activity.

Feet and Legs

In addition to these masculine traits, the sire should be examined for general conformation, with special emphasis on feet and legs (Fig. 5–1). Range animals are expected to travel some distances, and good feet and legs are essential. The postlegged condition causes pressure on the joints, resulting in pain and inability to mount. The sickle-hocked condition causes a tiring of the animal with increased travel and results in a lack of desire of the animal to mount. Narrow chest floor caused by the front legs being set close together prevents some sires from mounting larger females.

The feet should be examined for weak pasterns, damaged dew claws, and corns between the hooves. These are all painful and discourage mounting (Table 5–1).

Although the percentages do not appear high, the examination takes only a few seconds observation and may save undue concern later.

REPRODUCTIVE ORGANS

The penis, prepuce, and scrotal area can best be observed during electroejaculation because of reduced excitement and kicking of the animal. Internal organs should be

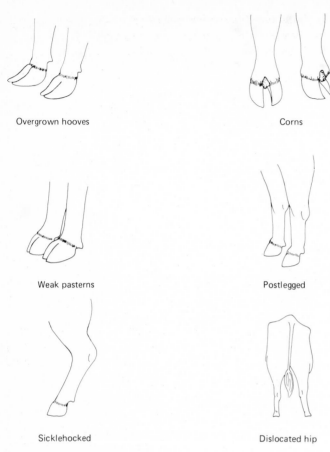

Figure 5-1 Locomotor defects.

examined if there is reason to suspect some difficulties as indicated by the semen examination. This may be done while the animal is still restrained in the chute.

Penis and Prepuce

During electrical stimulation, the penis is erected and extended, allowing examination of the glans and body of the penis as well as the prepuce as it unfolds over the penis. The glans should be observed for normal shape and size, rings of hair around the penis from mounting other bulls, damage due to scar tissue or lacerations, presence of a frenulum, and other malformations (Fig. 5–2).[69] The prepuce should also be examined for freedom of defects, and, in instances where the penis is not fully extended, the prepuce should be exposed by grasping the penis with a gauze pad and pulling the sheath posteriorly to make the entire prepuce visible. Palpation of the penis posterior to the scrotum will allow detection of injury, swelling, and scar tissue from previous damage. The opening in the prepuce sometimes restricts passage of the penis to the exterior; palpation of the orifice assists in this diagnosis.

Table 5-1   Defects of the Locomotor System in 10,940 Beef Bulls

Defect	Percent
Overgrown hooves, need trimming	3.0
Interdigital fibromas, corns	.8
Nonspecific lameness	.6
Foot rot	.3
Arthritis	.3
Luxation, dislocations	.2
Total defects	5.2

From Carroll et al.[11]

Upon erection and extension, the penis may be examined for deviations in any direction other than normal. The coiling of the terminal penis is normal and it usually straightens after several stimulations. Lateral and vertical deviations are rare. Growths on the penis, and any openings of the urethra other than normal, should be observed.

In 10,940 range bulls examined in Colorado,[11] 3.5 percent of the bulls had some abnormality of the penis and prepuce (Table 5–2).

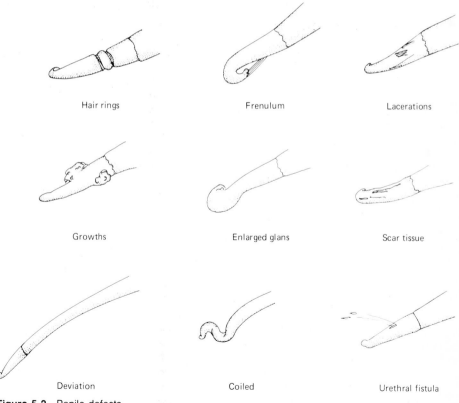

Hair rings   Frenulum   Lacerations

Growths   Enlarged glans   Scar tissue

Deviation   Coiled   Urethral fistula

Figure 5-2   Penile defects.

Table 5-2   Defects of the Penis and Prepuce in 10,940 Beef Bulls

Defect	Percent
Deviations, vertical, lateral	1.7
Neoplasms, growths, tumors	.9
Persistent penile frenulum	.5
Lacerations, cuts, tears	.2
Urethral fistulas	.2
Total defects	3.5

From Carroll et al.[11]

Scrotum

Initial observation of the scrotum and its contents should be made as the animal is standing normally without restraint or stress. The scrotum should be pendulous yet well suspended. If the neck of the scrotum is the same size as the testicular area, the testes are usually medium-sized and sometimes elongated. The cord may also be filled with fatty tissue. If the scrotum tapers to a point on the bottom, generally the testes will be small and the neck of the scrotum may be filled with fat.

The scrotum and its contents may be examined best as electrical stimulation begins. If palpation is delayed, the testes will be pulled closer to the body and feeling the individual segments becomes more difficult.

This is the best time to measure the circumference of the scrotum. Some data were presented in Chapter 1 as the testes were discussed; more will be said now about the procedure for measuring them. Any flexible tape may be used for measurement. A special flexible metal tape is available commercially. The testes should be pulled firmly into the base of the scrotum. Encircling the neck of the scrotum and milking downward accomplishes this easily. A loop of the tape is then slipped over the base of the scrotum and the greatest diameter of the entire scrotum with both testes is measured.[4]

Large numbers of bulls have been measured in Saskatchewan. These data indicate that beef bulls will rank satisfactorily 90 percent of the time if scrotal measurements are 41 cm (16 in) or over. If measurements are over 38 cm (15 in), over 80 percent will be satisfactory; if they measure 36 cm (14 in) or over, 70 percent will be satisfactory.[12]

Heavily fitted bulls may average 4 to 5 cm (2 in) greater than bulls in thin condition and 2 to 3 cm (1 in) greater than bulls in normal condition. Fat or overfinished bulls are often put on a starvation diet to remove the fat, and after a "let-down" period of 60 to 90 days the scrotal circumference may have decreased as much as 5 cm (2 in).

Breed, age, and weight, as well as condition must be considered when interpreting scrotal circumference measurements.[16] Table 5–3 is a composite of data that best illustrates these influencing factors.[52]

Several workers have related the scrotal circumference to sperm productivity.[31,72] Correlations between scrotal circumference and sperm output per week

Table 5-3   Scrotal Circumference of Bulls of Various Breeds and Ages

Breed	Number of bulls	Average age (mo)	Average scrotal circumference (cm)
English Beef	37	10.5	30.6
	36	12.0	32.7
	20	13.5	34.5
Angus	58	18.1	37.9
Angus	28	Mature	38.3
Hereford			
Horned	11	18.6	34.7
Polled	54	17.8	35.9
Aged	12	Mature	37.9
Shorthorn	13	Mature	40.3
Santa Gertrudis			
High gain	54	14.0	34.9
Medium gain	113	19.2	35.8
Medium gain	21	29.5	38.6
Charolais	30	16.5	34.3
	41	18.0	35.3
	71	20.5	35.0
	9	29.0	37.9
	3	Mature	39.0
Brahman		14	21.9
		14–17	27.4
		17–20	29.4
		20–23	31.4
		23–26	31.7
		26–30	33.5
		30–36	34.7
		36	36.7
Dairy breeds	8	13.4	31.7
Holstein	59	15.5	34.9
	54	21.5	37.1
	52	27.5	38.7
	54	33.5	39.3
	208	Mature	42.0
Dairy breeds	267	Mature	41.0
Jersey	41	Mature	38.5
Total 1354 w/o Brahman			Average 35.3 unweighted

Adapted from Morris.[52]

ranged from .81 in bulls 17 to 22 months of age to .40 in bulls 42 to 53 months of age. Evidently, measurements in younger bulls are more desirable and more reliable than those in older bulls.

The outer skin of the scrotum should be examined for indications of earlier damage such as scratches, punctures, lacerations, frostbite, and infection. Scar tissue, scabs on the surface, and thickened and firm walls of tissue are most common. Severe damage may retain the testes in the upper scrotal cavity next to the body, thereby depressing spermatogenesis through elevated temperature. Infections may be noted also, which in turn could cause a poor ejaculate immediately, but which in time would heal, allowing sperm production to return to normal.

The testes should be free in the scrotal sac without adhesions. The tone should be determined by palpation, and the distinction should be made between firm, live-feeling, normal testes and those having a meaty or muscular texture. Fibrous testes, which are found particularly in older bulls, should be identified since spermatogenic tissue has been replaced and production reduced in such instances. Soft, spongy testes indicate poor production and that the tubules are not full and turgid. The temperature of the testes should be noted also, as infection will cause fever.

The epididymis should be palpated in its entirety. Normality of size, tone, and location are important. Tumors or absence of the epididymis should be identified. Both would interfere with sperm passage. The tail of the epididymis is a good indication of sperm production since it stores sperm. Fullness and firmness, not hardness, should indicate abundant sperm. Soft or flaccid conditions may indicate poor production or overuse. The bulging tail of the epididymis should be visible even without palpation (Fig. 5–3). Infection and inflammation (epididymitis) would cause fever in this area, and usually this will be accompanied by swelling.

The deferent duct and the spermatic cord should also be palpated for normality to detect swollen area, growths, and absence of segments.

A summary of the incidence of these defects is given in Table 5–4. It should be recognized that although there are many things to observe in the form of defects, this only takes a few seconds of the semen collecting procedure. Defects of this nature account for about one-fifth of the population tested for breeding soundness.

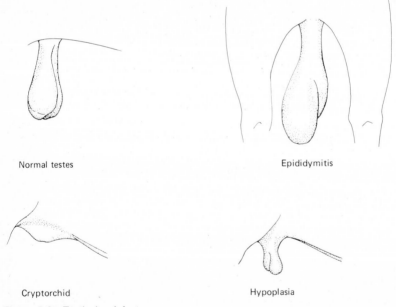

Normal testes   Epididymitis

Cryptorchid   Hypoplasia

Figure 5-3 Testicular defects.

Table 5-4   Defects of the Testes and Epididymides of 10,940 Beef Bulls

Defect	Percent
Small testes, hypoplasia	8.8
Soft testes	7.4
Abnormal shape of testes	1.0
Fibrosis, hard testes	.4
Cryptorchid	.1
Epididymal tumors, abscesses, granulomas	.5
Epididymitis, inflammation	.4
Segmental aplasia or hypoplasia	.2
Total defects	18.8

From Carroll et al.[11]

INTERNAL ORGANS

The ampullae, vesicular glands, prostate, urethral area, and the internal pudendal rings should be palpated per rectum for normality. Apparently, the greatest difficulty lies in the vesicular glands,[11] where infection causes enlargement or hardness. This difficulty may also be noticed by the presence of white blood cells in the ejaculates. Examination of the inguinal ring reveals whether the testes have an open passageway back into the abdominal cavity or if in fact a testis has not descended (cryptorchid). Table 5–5 gives some data to emphasize the importance of this examination. Observe that 7.4 percent of the physical defects were internal and probably would only be discovered by palpation.

Other researchers have shown no obvious relationship between palpable characteristics of the genital organs and fertility.[8]

SEMEN EVALUATION

Evaluation of semen is conducted to determine the usefulness of a sire or of a particular ejaculate. It may be used to predict the sire's value as a breeding animal under pasture conditions, handmating conditions, or for artificial insemination.

Semen evaluation should not be confused with fertility testing since the latter

Table 5-5   Defects of the Internal Genital Organs of 7,359 Beef Bulls

Defect	Percent
Enlarged vesicular glands	4.6
Vesiculitis, inflammation	2.5
Scrotal hernia	.2
Enlarged inguinal rings	.1
Total defects	7.4

From Carroll et al.[11]

is measured by breeding and conception followed by a viable offspring. It has been suggested that our best test of semen fertility is actual conception rates under field conditions,[15] and no one can argue with that.

Criteria that are used in evaluation will be discussed first, followed by some tests of questionable value, and then actual evaluation methods will be discussed as a part of breeding soundness. Melrose[49] presented a good review of various criteria.

A sample record sheet for semen evaluation is given in Table 5–6.

CRITERIA

Total Number of Viable Sperm

The "good" cells are the ones that count. This is determined by multiplying the volume of the ejaculate X the concentration per unit volume X the percent living cells X the percent normal cells.

Volume. The volume is measured directly in the collecting container. A graduated collecting tube facilitates rapid measurement in the case of the bull, ram, and stallion. The thermos used to collect the boar necessitates pouring the ejaculate into a second container for measurement. Remember, temperature change is critical: sperm are damaged and killed by sudden drops in temperature.

Volume varies considerably between individual animals and breeds; however, some general figures are needed to talk in terms of what might be expected. Bulls produce between 5 and 15 ml of semen per ejaculate (Table 5–7). Usually, dairy bulls fall in the upper range and beef bulls in the lower range. Volume is rather meaningless for comparison with other collections when collecting with the electroejaculator (EE), but may be used in determining total sperm per ejaculate when multiplied by concentration.

Total sperm is not as variable between collections made with artificial vagina as between the AV collection and EE.

The ram produces .8 to 1.2 ml of very concentrated sperm; the boar, 150 to 200 ml of dilute semen; the stallion, 40 to 100 ml of dilute semen; and man produces 2 to 6 ml of dilute semen. The jack produces 40 to 60 ml per ejaculate.

The volume of semen is reduced with multiple ejaculates in stallions according to some researchers,[56] while others showed no reduction in bulls.[28] Season influences volume in bulls, with a reduction in the winter and the largest volumes in the spring.[59]

In one analysis of human male fertility, pregnancy rate was significantly lower when the volume was below 2 ml.[45]

Concentration The number of sperm per unit volume is necessary since this determines, with volume, the total number of cells present in the ejaculate. Although the relationship between concentration and fertility is reported as being low, we must realize that if no sperm are present the male is sterile and that at some point the animal will be of questionable fertility, while at another concentration fertility should be high. It is on this basis that concentration becomes important, then.

Table 5-6. Semen Evaluation

Owner _____

Address _____

Method of Collection:
Artificial Vagina _____
Electrical Stimulation _____
Recovery _____

Date	Animal no.	Breed	Age	Ejac. no.	Vol. ml	Appearance	Motility %	RFM	Morphology % abnormal	Rating S-Q-C	Conc. $\times 10^6$/ml	Total live cells	Erection

Research with range bulls has yielded a correlation coefficient of .96 between number of sperm and fertility.[43] We can eliminate those males that produce little or no sperm and make use of those with satisfactory production.

Concentration is determined in a number of ways. Some will be applicable under certain circumstances while not under others.

Visual observation Field evaluation of concentration may be accomplished by observing the opacity of the sample in the collecting tube. Concentration is classified as good, fair, or poor.

Good samples will appear creamy and thick for the bull and ram (Fig. 5–4). The sperm will be boiling and have a pearly appearance. It is as if the sperm are moving like schools of fish in the test tube. The boar and stallion have less concentration, and the sample will appear less opaque.

Fair samples of semen will appear thin and have a greyish cast. They will look like skimmed milk. No swirling motion will be observed.

Poor samples will have a very thin appearance because only a few sperm are present.

Contaminants may be present in some samples. Care should always be taken to obtain a very clean sample, but hair and dirt from the underline may fall into the collecting apparatus. Flecks of debri are easily discernible in the light-colored sample, and such samples should not be used for breeding purposes. Cleaning the underline and clipping the preputial hairs will help eliminate this contaminant.

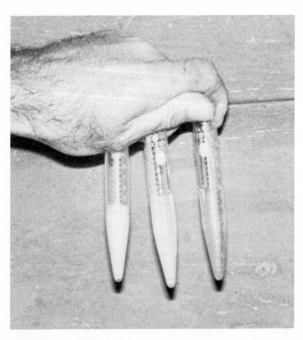

Figure 5-4 Good, fair, and poor concentrations of bull semen.

White blood cells or pus may be ejaculated by diseased animals. These cells may come from the testes, epididymides, accessory glands, or urethra. Examination by a veterinarian is certainly in order if such cells are observed. These cells will cause a flaky, clotted, or very thick appearance and will adhere to the collecting tube when it is tilted.

Red blood cells will cause a pinkish tint in the ejaculate. These may come from a damaged penis, and the penis should be carefully examined and treated accordingly. There may be a tearing of the raphe or scraping of the penis during collections or prior bleeding. The cells may also originate in the reproductive tract itself. The sample may be utilized if a very few cells are present.

Urine in the sample will cause a yellow discoloration and give a characteristic odor. It is detrimental to the life of the sperm, and the sample may be used for evaluation but not for breeding purposes. Urination frequently results from prolonged stimulation with the electroejaculator. If urine is observed in the ejaculate it is best to discard the sample and make a second collection.

Yellow-colored ejaculates sometimes appear without apparent reason. The pigment has been identified as riboflavin and apparently is heritable since in one instance eight bulls were examined and six of these were first-, second-, or third-generation offspring of a single sire.[71] The color fades upon exposure to sunlight and apparently is not detrimental to sperm livability.

Epithelial cells that are sloughed or rubbed from the prepuce and penis are sometimes found in the ejaculate. These may be particularly numerous if the ejaculate is collected as drippings from the sheath rather than from the extended penis.

Hemacytometer Where a limited number of samples is to be evaluated, concentration may be measured with a hemacytometer (Fig. 5–5). The following procedure is described for use of a diluting pipette and a hemacytometer. This procedure is

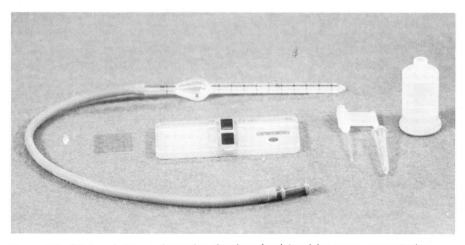

Figure 5-5 Diluting pipettes and counting chambers for determining sperm concentration.

applicable for veterinarians or ranchers wishing to determine exact numbers of sperm.

1 The semen sample should be thoroughly mixed by gently swirling the container prior to evaluation.
2 Dilution
   a Immerse the tip of the pipette until the desired level of semen is drawn into it. Commercial standard-volume pipettes with capillary tubes are available or the standard blood-diluting pipette may be used to form a 1 : 200 dilution.
   b Any excess semen on the outside of the tube should be removed so that a very exact amount is in the tube for dilution.
   c The reservoir containing the fixed amount of diluter is opened and a vacuum formed by exerting pressure on its sides.
   d Insert and seat the pipette in the neck of the reservoir and siphon the semen from the capillary tube by releasing pressure on the reservoir. Rinse the pipette carefully several times to insure obtaining all the cells.
   e Place the index finger over the upper opening of the pipette and invert several times to mix the semen and diluent.
   f Remove and invert the pipette.
   g Place the reservoir in *hot* water for one minute to kill all the sperm.
   h Discard a few drops of diluted semen by squeezing the reservoir.
3 Prepare the hemacytometer (Fig. 5–6).
   a Locate the shiny surfaces in the middle of the slide. These have microscopic grids consisting of heavy lines dividing the field into 25 large squares. Within each of these squares are 16 smaller squares.
   b Notice that the cover slip does not touch the grid area when placed over the middle portion. This allows a space or chamber .1 mm deep and the grid is 1 mm square. Therefore a chamber is delineated with a volume of .1 cubic mm (mm^3).
4 Counting
   a Touch the tip of the diluting pipette to the angle formed by the cover slip and counting chamber and allow the area under the slip to fill with the diluted semen. Do not overfill.
   b Locate the counting area under low power (10x) magnification and then switch to high (450x) for counting.
   c It is not necessary to count every cell in every square. Count sperm in five large diagonal squares or the four corners and center large square. Count cells in the large squares including those lying on the lines on the bottom and right sides of the large squares only so that these will not be counted twice.
5 Calculations
   a You have counted the sperm in 1/50 mm^3 volume.
   b You have diluted the raw semen 1 : 200.
   c Therefore, the number of cells you counted multiplied by the volume fraction you counted multiplied by the dilution rate should equal the number of cells per cubic millimeter.

   $$X \times 50 \times 200 = 10,000 \ X/mm^3$$

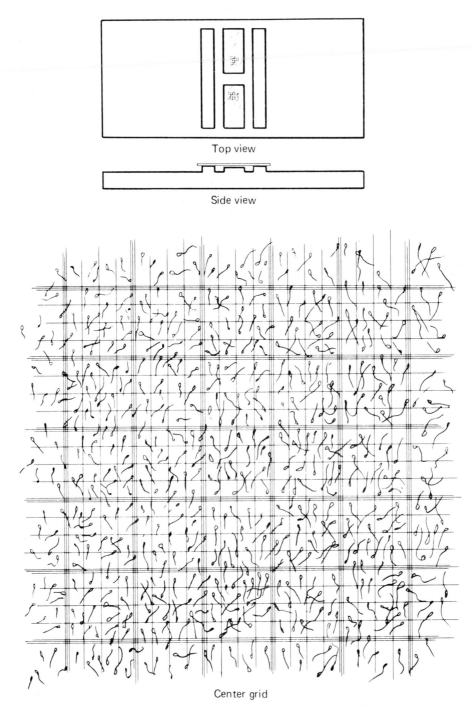

Top view

Side view

Center grid

Figure 5-6 Counting chamber and grid for determining sperm concentration.

d We normally express concentration in cubic centimeters, or milliliters, therefore we must multiply by 1000. Therefore, we have 10,000,000 X/cc. For a shortcut, simply add seven zeros to the number of sperm you counted and concentration per cc is determined.

e When counting samples of fair or poor concentration it may be necessary to use a lower dilution rate of 1:50 or 1:10 to guarantee a sufficient number of cells to count with accuracy. Calculations will change accordingly. Repeatability is high, .95, when experienced individuals conduct the measurement,[25] but repeatability is not so high with inexperienced personnel.

Optical density This method is used to measure density of a substance. The greater the opacity, or in our case concentration, the less light is allowed to pass through (Fig. 5–7). The photometric instrument is calculated by means of a hemacytometer and a given sample's concentration may be read directly from a prepared table relating light transmission to concentration.[27] There are numerous types of these instruments on the market and they will not be discussed here. Methods of calibration have been described by Foote.[26] Comparison of a Spectronic 20 photometer with the hemacytometer gives a high correlation (.95) with experience.[29]

Nephelometer (cloud measurer) This is similar to a photometer except it measures the light scattered by the sample rather than the transmitted light.

Packed Cell Volume This method consists of capillary tubes as are used in hematocrit measurements of the components of blood. It has been referred to as a spermatocrit value,[36] because sperm are drawn into a capillary tube and centrifuged to pack them into one end. A calibrated scale is developed and the concentration read directly from the scale according to the proportion that is sperm compared to the entire sample volume. The repeatability of this method is very high, .998,[25] and compares favorably with photoelectric methods.[3] Poultry sperm concentration has been compared between hemacytometer, optical density, and packed cell volume, and the correlations were .91 or better.[67]

Concentration of bull sperm ranges from 800×10^6 to 1200×10^6 cells per milliliter (Table 5–7). This is rather concentrated and yields a total of 4 to 18×10^9 sperm per ejaculate. This seems to be a very large number of cells when only one is needed to fertilize an ovum, but we know that many are lost along the way and many are needed for penetration of the egg cell mass.

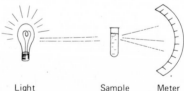

Light   Sample   Meter

Figure 5-7 Optical density measurement.

Table 5-7   Semen Characteristics

	Bull	Ram	Boar	Stallion	Man
Volume					
ml/ejaculate	5–15	.8–1.2	150–200	40–100	2–6
Concentration					
millions (10^6)/ml	800–1,200	2,000–3,000	200–300	200–500	50–150
billions (10^9)/ejaculate	4–18	1.6–3.6	30–60	8–50	.1–.9
Motility					
% live cells	75	95	70	70	65
Morphology					
% normal	95	95	90	90	60
pH	6.3–6.9	5.9–7.3	7.3–7.9	7.2–7.8	7.1–7.5

Concentration of sperm per milliliter and total sperm per ejaculate are 2 to 3 $\times 10^9$ and 1.6 to 3.6 $\times 10^9$ for the ram; 200 to 300 $\times 10^6$ and 30 to 60 $\times 10^9$ for the boar; 200 to 500 $\times 10^6$ and 8 to 50 $\times 10^9$ for the stallion; and 50 to 150 $\times 10^6$ and 100 to 900 $\times 10^6$ for man, respectively. The jack has a concentration of 170 to 400 $\times 10^6$/ml and total concentration of 7 to 24 $\times 10^9$ sperm.

Concentration is greater in first ejaculates than in succeeding ones, so that even though the volume stays the same, the total available number of sperm is lower.[28] Daily collection of semen from dairy bulls is not detrimental to fertility, and the number of useable sperm is increased[30] over a given time.

When concentration falls below 20 $\times 10^6$ in man, there is a significant drop in pregnancy rate.[45]

Concentration alone has not been determined to be highly correlated with fertility[73] in cattle; however, fertility has been shown to decrease when ejaculates contained less than 16 $\times 10^9$ sperm.[43]

Centrifugation for the purpose of concentrating sperm has little effect on motility in stallion semen as long as seminal plasma is above 10 percent, but fertility is lowered in bull semen following centrifugation.[57]

Motility   Motility is expressed as the percent moving or living cells. These cells may be moving in any direction at any speed. Direction is accounted for in the overall evaluation by the morphology observation, because abnormal cells will not normally swim in a forward direction. Some researchers use the term "progressive motility," which incorporates direction with rate, while others use a separate measure for "rate of forward movement."

Visual Evaluation   A fair degree of motility can be attained by viewing the collecting tube and observing the swirling or boiling motion of the sperm. Even this movement is difficult to see in the sparse samples.

Microscopic Evaluation   The best method for observation is by the microscope at a power of approximately 200 magnification. Lower magnification (100x) gives a view of a larger field, but the sperm are too small to study individually and one can only study swirling motions. High magnification (450x) restricts the field severely and few sperm may be seen without moving the field of vision numerous times. It has the advantage of giving a more detailed view of individual cells for a study of morphology.

Visual Some evaluators prefer to place a drop of raw semen on the microscope slide and study the mass movement of the sperm. This is a crude method that does not account for the dead cells being moved by the live ones. A cover slip may or may not be used. A hanging drop may be used.

It is much more desirable to observe individual cells for motility, and this necessitates extension of the ejaculate with some physiological solution to prolong life of the cells. Again, be sure temperature changes are gradual and when mixing an extender with the sperm be sure that the temperatures are the same. Dilute by adding the extender a drop at a time to a drop of semen on the slide to a point where the cells may swim freely. Some poorly concentrated ejaculates will need no extension. Have the extended semen at 37°C (99°F) for observation. Cooling will decrease motility and heat may cause a burst of speed.

An individual may be trained to quickly evaluate percent motility by focusing the microscope on a field and quickly observing 10 sperm. Differentiate between those moving and those lying still. Move quickly to another field and observe another 10 sperm. Repeat this procedure until a total of 100 sperm has been observed. This 100 will be composed of a certain number of moving and a certain number of dead ones. The number of moving or live cells is therefore the percent motility. With repeated evaluations of this nature, one can reach a point whereby a quick scan of the slide will produce an evaluation similar to that resulting from the laborious task of counting individual cells. Most of the motility evaluations used today are visual measurements.

A word of caution should be given concerning boar semen. Motility decreases rapidly in the absence of oxygen.[23] The sample must be either read quickly following collection, oxygenated, or examined in a hanging-drop manner.

Live-dead staining It has been shown that live spermatozoa will resist supravital stains while dead ones will absorb the stain. This offers a simple method of counting, and therefore determining, the percent live sperm in a specimen.

There are several stains that may be utilized. Most are mixtures of eosin and a counterstain. Two widely accepted stains are the Eosin-Nigrosin Stain[65] and the Eosin-Fast Green FCF stain. Their formulas follow.

Eosin-Nigrosin Stain
    Eosin B: 1 gram
    Nigrosin: 5 grams
    3 percent sodium citrate (dihydrate): 100 ml
    Mix stains with citrate.
    Remains stable for over 1 year but should be refrigerated to prevent bacterial
        growth.

Eosin-Fast Green FCF
  Fast green FCF: 2 grams
  Eosin B (bluish): 0.8 grams
  M/8 phosphate buffer (pH 7.3–7.4): 100 ml
    Buffer is prepared from 22 gm Na_2HPO_4 in 500 ml distilled water and 8.5 gm KH_2PO_4 in 500 ml distilled water.
  Add the eosin to the fast green–phosphate buffer, bring to a boil and filter.
  Storage life is 4 to 5 years.

The slide is prepared by placing a drop of mixed semen on a warm microscope slide to which is added a drop or two of the stain. The two are mixed thoroughly but quickly to prevent death and staining of cells. A second slide is touched to the drop and drawn across the first slide to form a thin smear. The slide is then immediately dried in hot air or over a flame.

Examination of the slide reveals a background of the green or nigrosin stain with sperm heads appearing as pink-stained bodies or heads that are clear or slightly colored similar to the background. The clear heads indicate live cells at the time of staining and the stained ones indicate dead ones. Simple mathematics yield percent live or motile sperm for the specimen.

The slide will deteriorate, particularly in a damp atmosphere, and if there is a need to come back for an evaluation later the slides should be stored in a desiccator or drying oven at low temperature.

The slightly lower counts determined when using the live-dead stain indicate that death followed by staining of some cells occurs in preparation when compared to visual appraisal. Differences have been noted between the ends of stained slides by as much as 12 percent, which also indicates death during preparation of the slide. [5] Speed is of utmost importance in preparation, and accuracy in counting is also very important.

Some individuals have experienced difficulty in staining sperm that have been exposed to glycerol. Congo red instead of eosin may alleviate this problem. [9]

The Eosin-Fast green FCF stain has given good results in semen from the bull, ram, stallion, and man, but results from most stains have been erratic with boar semen. [48] Other combinations with eosin have given very acceptable results. Live-dead stains are also very helpful in studying morphology of the sperm.

Cinematography (motion picture) This method removes some of the subjectivity of the visual evaluation method. It entails the use of time-lapse photography that shows the pathway or movement of the motile sperm (Fig. 5–8). The motile sperm make tracks similar to the seed head of barley or wheat or the pattern formed by an ice skater. [21]

A comparison has been made with counts made on a hemacytometer, where grid lines are available to assist in counting, visual estimates, and photographic methods. The results are in Table 5–8. Differences between progressive motility scores of hemacytometer and photographic versus visual were significantly different. It appears that some dead cells were counted as moving in the visual method.

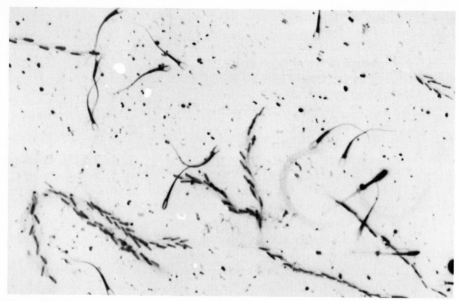

Figure 5-8 Cinematographic measurement of sperm motility. *(Courtesy F. I. Elliott, ABS.)*

Bumping of dead cells is very difficult to ascertain unless dilution is sufficient, and this could be the reason.

When costs are compared, the photographic method requires more labor and materials. Reportedly, 7.5 specimens can be evaluated visually in one man-hour compared to 5 specimens by the photographic method.

The method has been used successfully in evaluating human semen,[40] bull semen,[21] and stallion semen.[7]

Cinematography has also been used to determine the speed of sperm movement. Estimates using this method show that stallion sperm swim 50 μm/sec[7] and human sperm swim 44 μm/sec.[40] Speed of bull sperm measured by the sperm crossing a grid line in a given time was 114 μm/sec,[51] and the speed of those swimming from a limited circle in a given time was 117 μm/second.[58]

Motility of sperm for the various species is presented as a general figure rather than an exact one in Table 5–6. Percent motile sperm in bulls should approximate 75; ram, 95; boar, 70; stallion, 70; and man, 65.

Table 5-8 Comparison of Methods to Assess Motility of Bovine Spermatozoa

Method		Mean
Hemacytometer	% total motility	34.6
	% progressive motility	25.1
Visual estimate	% progressive motility	34.8
Photographic	% progressive motility	25.7

From Elliott et al.[21]

Opinions concerning the usefulness of motility in predicting fertility appear to vary considerably among researchers. Some feel that there is a definite relationship in bulls,[17,42,44,47,50,53] stallions,[6] and rams,[19] while others found no correlation in bulls.[15,43,73] Two workers determined a correlation coefficient of .003 but found that semen containing under 50 percent motility gave questionable fertility, while semen with 50 to 90 percent live sperm yielded satisfactory fertility.[43]

Morphology (form study) The normal spermatozoon was described in Chapter 2. Anything deviating from that description may be termed abnormal. A morphological study separates the two types and results in a percent normal evaluation.

Spermatozoa may be examined by means of a bright field microscope. Under bright field conditions and no stain, the light source must be of low intensity to differentiate the cells. Observation is best made at high power magnification (450 or over). Stained slides assist greatly in differentiating abnormal cell types from normal using bright field microscopy.

Phase contrast microscopy is much more satisfactory. It is possible to reflect light off the sides of the sperm cells, thereby giving a three-dimensional effect with much greater clarification of the components of the cell. Oil immersion may also be used for higher magnification.

Differential-interference-contrast microscopes give excellent resolution at high magnifications and are used especially for the study of the acrosomal formation. Because of expense, the phase microscope and differential-interference-contrast microscope are mostly used in research laboratories or the larger breeding organizations.

The abnormalities are commonly divided into two classes—primary and secondary. They will be discussed by this classification.

Primary abnormalities These are abnormalities that are of testicular origin. Presumably something went wrong in the spermatogenic process and was not corrected in passage through the duct system (Fig. 5–9).

Head These sperm have some irregularity in the shape of the head:

1 pyriform or pear-shaped
2 round
3 elongated or slender
4 microcephalic or small
5 macrocephalic or giant
6 double or twin
7 abnormal acrosome

The first seven types of head abnormalities are self-explanatory by their descriptive names. The abnormal acrosome should be explained because of the tremendous amount of current interest.

The acrosome was earlier described as a double-walled membrane covering the anterior head of the spermatozoon. It has a peculiar configuration, the acrosomal

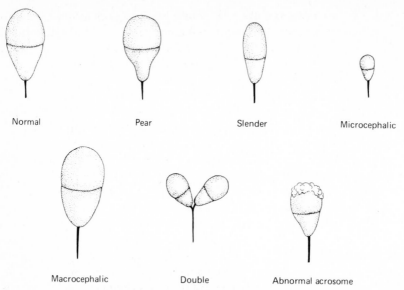

Normal   Pear   Slender   Microcephalic

Macrocephalic   Double   Abnormal acrosome

Figure 5-9   Primary abnormalities of the sperm head.

ridge, folding across the apical edge of the sperm (Fig. 5–10). The integrity of the acrosome is correlated with fertility and apparently is the best measure of fertility at the present time. A study of acrosomes showed a correlation of .80 and .81 between intact acrosomes and fertility following incubation of sperm for 2 and 10 hours, respectively. Motility at the beginning of incubation had a correlation coefficient of .56 in comparison.[62]

The acrosome deteriorates gradually and begins with a swelling of the anterior portion, deterioration, and loss of the anterior portion. The presence of the apical ridge is the criterion most used to evaluate the integrity of the acrosome.

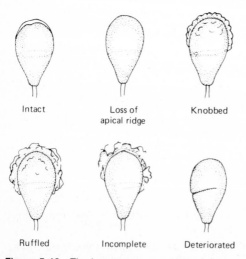

Intact   Loss of   Knobbed
                 apical ridge

Ruffled   Incomplete   Deteriorated

Figure 5-10   The intact acrosome and stages of deterioration.

Acrosomes have been described as knobbed, ruffled, and incomplete.[61] The acrosomal condition also appears to be inherited.[60] Although most work has been done on bull sperm, research on the acrosome of the boar indicates formation continues in the sperm's progress through the epididymis where it reduces its dimensions and changes its shape.[41]

Select Sires, one of the major AI organizations, collects over 30 bulls a day for semen processing, and acrosomal evaluation becomes a prolonged exercise, so they chose to evaluate by motility and examine acrosomes on questionable samples only. Of 428 ejaculates examined for motility they chose to further evaluate 247 for intact acrosomes. This was 57.7 percent. Of these, 127 or 52 percent were below their standards and were reevaluated, resulting in 79 being culled. These 79 that were culled comprised 18.4 percent of the samples. This was a faster method and appeared to work satisfactorily for them.[47]

Midpiece

1 bent or kinked at right angle
2 twin or double
3 enlarged or swollen
4 off-center attachment or abaxial

These are the most common defects (Fig. 5–11), but there may be numerous deviations from some self-explanatory types. The most common are the bent tails, and some researchers assume that the abaxial tail attachment is normal.

Tail

1 coiled or curled
2 double tail

The coiled tail is the most common abnormality of the tail and in fact of the entire sperm (Fig. 5–11). The coil may begin at the base of the head and encircle it or be a coil at the terminal tail. It is a tight coil in most instances and should not be confused with cold-shock sperm. Sperm that are cold shocked will curl their tail rather uniformly in a gradual manner. It will form a crescent and rarely curl more than 180°. As has been said numerous times earlier, be sure to maintain a constant temperature or change it gradually.

A rancher in the Panhandle of Texas called the author and asked for advice concerning his herd sires. A reproductive consultant evaluated semen of his bulls and he recommended that the rancher cull 16 out of 23 bulls examined. This rancher couldn't believe this many were no good. After some discussion, the following facts came to light. It was in the middle of winter and the Panhandle can get very cold at that time of year. The collecting tube was not protected following electroejacula-

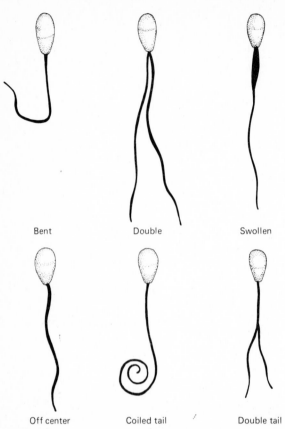

Bent   Double   Swollen

Off center   Coiled tail   Double tail

Figure 5-11 Primary abnormalities of the sperm midpiece and tail.

tion and the microscope was set up on the tailgate of the pickup. It is no wonder the sperm coiled their tails and died. It was suggested that he have the bulls rechecked with temperature control at collection and evaluation. This was done and he happily reported one cull bull and two questionable ones. Temperature is important!

Secondary abnormalities Secondary abnormalities are thought to occur in the duct system after leaving the seminiferous tubules and testis proper. It should be noticed that these are of a deteriorating sort (Fig. 5–12):

1 detached heads
2 protoplasmic droplet on the neck or tail
3 shoehook tail
4 loose cap from the head

Detached heads usually occur in handling. The sample should not be shaken vigorously. Heads may be lost in smearing slides for staining.

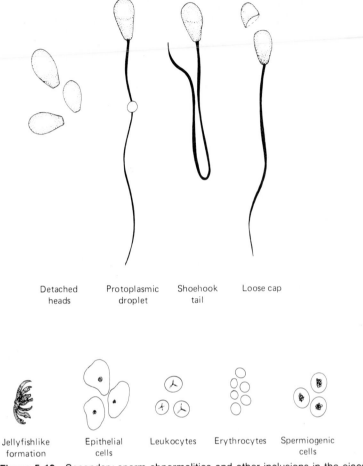

Detached heads   Protoplasmic droplet   Shoehook tail   Loose cap

Jellyfishlike formation   Epithelial cells   Leukocytes   Erythrocytes   Spermiogenic cells

Figure 5-12 Secondary sperm abnormalities and other inclusions in the ejaculate.

Protoplasmic droplets indicate sperm being ejaculated before completing maturation. Perhaps the male is being overused and needs a rest.

Other infrequent inclusions

1. medusa or jellyfishlike formations
2. epithelial cells
3. leukocytes
4. erythrocytes
5. primordial or developing spermiogenic cells

The presence of any of these inclusions indicates some upset in the reproductive tract, and a veterinarian with experience in reproductive disorders should be contacted.

Other methods of classification have been and are being used. Primary and secondary abnormalities have been used by others to denote abnormalities of the head and abnormalities of the remainder of the cell. Some researchers do not differentiate by primary and secondary but by individual abnormalities. The end results are about the same, as most are concerned with total abnormalities. Some may divide out immature cells with protoplasmic droplets, as these denote overuse of the sire in most instances and indicate a stage of normal maturation.

There is a greater relationship between the percent normal cells and fertility than any other single criterion.[11,17,50] One set of data showed the conception rate to be 66 percent for 10 bulls with 10 to 20 percent abnormalities, 62 percent for 2 bulls between 20 and 30 percent, and 61 percent for 5 bulls with 30 to 45 percent abnormalities.[53] A level of 23 percent or more abnormal cells seemed to depress conception. There appears to be a relationship between bent or broken tails and death of the sperm in the epididymis.[1] Number of normal cells per insemination is related to conception.[68] Abnormal cells do not appear related to age, body weight, season, or feed supplementation.[59] Semen is discarded by Curtiss Breeding Service if abnormalities are over 25 percent[24] or if either protoplasmic droplets or head abnormalities exceed 12 percent. Data on stallions are not as definite in relating abnormalities to fertility.[18] The only criterion shown to be related to the percent of swine ova shed represented by embryos is percent normal cells.[63,64]

Normal figures for percent normal sperm in the respective species are 95 percent for the bull and ram, 90 percent for the boar and stallion, and 60 percent for man.

The author is not convinced that there is a big problem with abnormalities, since he has collected semen from thousands of bulls of all breeds, ages, and locations in Texas and has found less than a dozen with abnormalities over 20 percent. This does not take away from the relationship of normality to fertility.

Other tests

Respiratory activity The methylene blue reduction test is used to measure metabolic activity according to oxygen utilization by the sperm. The relative time required for the reduction of the blue color by the sperm indicates the number or concentration and activity or motility of a sample.[33] Very slow, over 10-minute, reduction time would indicate very poor quality semen which should not be used.

A measure of oxygen consumption falls off as the reaction proceeds, which is apparently due to an irreversible decay within the sperm itself and not a result of the medium. This method is not widely used but may be used to compare the merits of various extenders.[70]

pH A measure of the acidic or basic condition of the ejaculate yields some information concerning the quality of the sample. pH is also a measure of metabolic activity of the sperm. As sperm age, there is a production of lactic acid from glycolysis; the accumulation of this acid reduces the pH. Motility of the sperm decreases as pH decreases. This test is used to a limited extent. Ranges for the various species are given in Table 5–7.

Cold shock Relative vigor of the sperm may be determined by exposing it to unfavorable conditions such as cold. Percentage live sperm should be determined before and after shocking a small portion of the diluted sample in a 0°C (32°F) waterbath for 10 minutes. The greater number of sperm that are motile upon examination post–cold shock, the more viable the sample.

Incubation Placing samples of semen at an elevated temperature (46 to 48°C, 115 to 118°F) and studying the length of livability yields an estimate of the viability and therefore fertility and storage capacity.

LABORATORY SCORING SYSTEM

There are numerous evaluation systems in use at the present time for the bull. An effort has been made to standardize these systems so that evaluations will be meaningful to more people. The Society for Theriogenology has led in this standardization procedure, and its standards will be discussed first (Society for Theriogenology, Hastings, Nebraska).

There are three scores for the breeding soundness of bulls: satisfactory, questionable, and unsatisfactory. These scores are based on scrotal circumference, percent abnormal cells, and motility. The evaluations for these criteria are presented in Tables 5–9, 5–10, 5–11, and 5–12, and the final score evaluation in Table 5–13.

Figure 5–13 is the back and front of the form used by the Society for Theriogenology and lists the criteria previously discussed.

Table 5–14 presents a summary of the criteria, score assessment, and final classification.

Table 5-9   Scrotal Circumference (cm) Classification for Bulls

Classification	Age (mo)				Score
	12 to 14	15 to 20	21 to 30	Over 30	
Good	>35	>37	>39	>40	40
Fair	30–35	31–37	32–39	33–40	24
Poor	<30	<31	<32	<33	10

Table 5-10   Percent Abnormal Sperm Classification for Bulls

Classification	Primary	Total	Score
Very good	<10	<25	40
Good	10–19	26–39	24
Fair	20–29	40–59	10
Poor	>29	>59	3

Table 5-11   Motility Classification for Bulls

Classification	Gross	Individual	Score
Very good	Rapid swirling	Rapid linear	20
Good	Slower swirling	Moderately fast linear	12
Fair	Shaky	Slow linear to erratic	10
Poor	Flickers	Very slow, often erratic	3

Table 5-12   The Society of Theriogenology Scoring Evaluation for Breeding
Soundness in Bulls

Criterion	Maximum score
Scrotal circumference	40
Percent abnormal cells	40
Motility	20

Table 5-13   Laboratory Classification Categories for Breeding Soundness in Bulls

Classification	Score
Satisfactory	>60
Questionable	30–60
Unsatisfactory	<30

FIELD EVALUATION

Field evaluation of bulls for breeding soundness varies mainly in terms of exactness
of measurement, but from the practical results over many years of use this seems
to be sufficient. Very few bulls that have been evaluated in the field as satisfactory
have failed to perform as predicted.

The evaluation is based on visual appraisal, scrotal size and tone, concentration,
motility, and morphology of sperm.

Visual Appraisal

The prospective sire should be observed for physical soundness as described earlier.

Scrotal Size and Tone

These criteria are estimated by palpating the scrotum and its contents.

Size   Size is determined by relativity. The entire scrotum is palpated and scored
according to the expected overall size in proportion to the sire's age (Table 5–14).
Sires with underdeveloped (hypoplastic) testes would not be satisfactory, and extremely large (hyperplastic) testes should be scored according to expected damage
by bruising or injury.

Society For Theriogenology
(American Veterinary Society for the Study of Breeding Soundness)
Association Bldg. 9th and Minnesota Hastings, Nebraska 68901
NCR PAPER - No Carbon Required.

Owner:

Date: Case No.:

Date of previous exam.:_____
Case No. of previous exam.:_____
Classification:_____

Address

Bull:
Name

Birth Date:

Breed:

Reg. No. Tattoo Horn Brand Ear Tag Hide Brand Other

Remarks relative to breeding history, calf production, breeding efficiency of family, herd management, etc.

Classification: Interpretation of data resulting from this examination would indicate, to the best of my knowledge, that this bull is a:

Satisfactory potential breeder_____Questionable potential breeder_____Unsatisfactory breeder_____

Remarks: **Unless otherwise indicated below this bull has been examined only for physical soundness and quality of semen. No special diagnostic tests were made for possible venereal disease or other infection.**

_____
Veterinarian

Member: Society for Theriogenology

BE SURE TO REMOVE BLANK TISSUE BEFORE FILLING OUT THIS SIDE.

CHARACTERISTICS	Ejaculates 1	2	3
Scrotal Circumference cm.			
Morphology % Primary Abnormalities			
% Secondary Abnormalities			
% Total Abnormalities			
Spheroids/ H.P. Field			
Non-germinal Cellular Material			
WBC RBC Epithelial Cells			
Scrotal Circumference Score			
Morphology Score			
Motility Score			
TOTAL SCORE			

CLASSIFICATION of SEMEN QUALITY
Check One (✓)
Satisfactory_____
Questionable_____
Unsatisfactory_____

PHYSICAL EXAMINATION
General Condition
Opthalmic
Feet and Legs
Reproductive
Testes
Epididymes
Vasa Deferentia
Spermatic Cord
Penis
Prepuce
RECTAL EXAM.
Vesicular Glands
Inguinal Rings
Vasa Deferentia
Viscera and Omentum

CLASSIFICATION of PHYSICAL CONDITION
Check One (✓)
Satisfactory_____
Questionable_____
Unsatisfactory_____

COLLECTION METHOD
Check One (✓) EE._____
AV._____Massage_____
Erection_____
Protrusion_____
Ejaculation_____

Indicate final classification on front of card. Be sure to remove blank before filling out other side.

INFORMATION TABLES TO BE USED IN COMPUTING SCORES

SCORING CRITERIA		Very Good	Good	Fair	Poor
Scrotal	12-14 mos.	>34 cm	30-34	<30	<30
Circum.	15-20 mos.	>36 cm	31-36	<31	<31
by Age	21-30 mos.	>38 cm	32-38	<32	<32
	over 31 mos.	>39 cm	34-39	<34	<34
SCORE FOR SCROTAL CIRCUMFERENCE:		40	24	10	10
SEMEN MORPHOLOGY Primary Abnormalities		<10	10-19	20-29	>29
Total Abnormalities		<25	26-39	40-59	>59
SCORE FOR MORPHOLOGY		40	24	10	3

	GROSS MOTILITY	RAPID SWIRLING	SLOWER SWIRLING	GENERALIZED OSCILLATION	SPORADIC OSCILLATION
Individual		Rapid Linear	Moderate Linear	Slow Linear To Erratic	Very Slow To Erratic
SCORE FOR MOTILITY:		20	12	10	3

OTHER TESTS IF USED

Libido

Mating Ability

Cytogenetic and Other Special Tests

Other

REMARKS

Figure 5-13 Sire evaluation form of the Society for Theriogenology.

Table 5-14   Breeding Soundness Evaluation and Scoring

Criterion	Very good	Good	Fair	Poor
Scrotal circumference (cm)				
Age (mo)				
12–14	>35	30–35	<30	<30
15–20	>37	31–37	<31	<31
21–30	>39	32–39	<32	<32
30	>40	33–40	<33	<33
Score	40	24	10	10
Sperm abnormalities (%)				
Primary	<10	10–19	20–29	>29
Total abnormalities	<25	26–39	40–59	>59
Score	40	24	10	3
Motility				
Individual	Rapid linear	Moderate linear	Slow linear	Very slow
Gross	Vigorous swirls	Slow swirls	Shaky	Flickers
Score	20	12	10	3
Total score	100	60	30	16

Classification: Satisfactory—>60
                 Questionable—30 through 59
                 Unsatisfactory—<30

Texture The turgidity or firmness of the testes is determined by palpation, as are the contents of the spermatic cord and the tail of the epididymis. Extreme softness or hardness is undesirable, as are infiltration of fatty tissue and fullness of the spermatic cord.

Total The combination of size and texture yields a score of satisfactory, questionable, or unsatisfactory, of a more subjective measure than actual measurements.

Concentration

Visual evaluation of raw semen in the collecting tube is all that is used in the field. It is classified as good, fair, or poor.

> *Good* The ejaculate is milky to creamy in color with a swirling motion.
> *Fair* Some cloudiness or thin milky appearance is visible.
> *Poor* The fluid is clear or very thin in appearance.

Motility

Sperm motility is measured under the microscope. A thin sample of semen should be viewed. This may be obtained by mixing with a physiological solution or by placing a drop of semen on the slide and quickly slinging the slide so that the semen passes off the slide leaving a film. The uncovered slide may be examined immediately without placing a cover slip over it. Speed is very important so that the sperm do not die. A visual appraisal of several areas on the slide yields an approximation of the percent living cells. If more time is desired, dilution should be made and a cover slip should be used.

Morphology

The shape and size of the sperm are determined on the same slide used for motility. The cells on the outer edges of the semen smear die first and may be observed, as they slow down in movement, for any abnormalities of the entire structures and the various components. This is expressed as a percent abnormal cells.

FINAL EVALUATION

Any single deficiency may cause elimination of an animal from the breeding group. For instance, if no sperm are present there is no measure of anything else; if all sperm are dead there is no fertility; if all sperm move backwards fertility is close to zero; if the testes are one-half normal size then sperm production is greatly reduced. Combinations of the criteria yield classifications of satisfactory, questionable, or unsatisfactory and are given in Table 5–15.

A single semen collection and evaluation may be used to predict breeding efficiency if the sample is satisfactory. If the sample is questionable or unsatisfactory, then multiple samples should be evaluated either at the same time or after a period of rest.[34] Only when the evaluator feels he has obtained the best possible sample should a bull be culled.

It has been suggested that the proportion of infertile rams in the sheep population is approximately 10 percent.[20]

Evaluation of the ram has been primarily on semen characteristics very similar to those for the bull. Visual appraisal and scrotal examination have been utilized, but fewer records are available for scrutiny. The two criteria most highly related to fertility in the ram are motility and morphology.[39] Indexes have been developed utilizing these criteria, and the correlations with fertility are high: .76 and .73. The indexes formulated by Hulet and Ercanbrack are presented here.

Table 5-15 Field Classification of Criteria (Minimum) for Breeding Soundness in Bulls

Criterion	Satisfactory	Questionable	Unsatisfactory
Scrotum and contents	Normal Firm	Slightly hypoplastic or hyperplastic, soft or hard	Hypoplastic or hyperplastic, very soft or hard
Concentration	Good	Fair	Poor
Motility percent	>50	30–50	<30
Abnormals percent	<15	15–25	>25

Index A = 174–17.19 (pH) + .28 (% live normal) − .08 (% abnormal) − .2 (% abnormal necks)

Index B = 217 − 4.38 (motility score) − 18.89 (pH) − .19 (% abnormal) − .14 (% abnormal necks)

A satisfactory sample should have a minimum of 50 percent motility and less than 20 percent abnormal cells with a good concentration of sperm.[20]

Infertile rams may cause problems in the breeding programs under the following circumstances:

1   Too few fertile rams remain to satisfactorily breed the entire flock,
2   Infertile "boss" rams will prevent fertile rams from breeding, and
3   In large range areas where rams collect a harem of 50 to 60 ewes, these would be left unbred.

Boar semen evaluation follows a pattern similar to that of the bull and ram. Volume is not very important unless there is drastic deviation from the normal 250 ml per ejaculate. Frequent ejaculation will lower volume per ejaculate; therefore, breeding history of the boar should be considered. Motility should be at least 50 percent before a boar is used for breeding.[35] When motility is rated on progressive movement from 1 to 10, a boar's semen should rank at least 5 before considering use. In Anderson's[2] review of the literature, 30 percent abnormalities was suggested as a breaking point for selection.

Since boars are used primarily in handmating breeding programs, it is relatively easy to keep track of their semen picture by frequent microscopic examination.

Recommendations for acceptable stallion ejaculates to insure fertility have been developed, but they are not as explicit as for the other domestic animals.[55,66] Acceptable total sperm range from 800×10^6 to 9×10^9 with motility of 40 to 95 percent and normal sperm from 65 to 75 percent. Bielanski[6] classified stallions as useful or doubtful and the semen was required to pass at least two of the criteria: volume of 16 ml, 40 percent motile sperm, minimum concentration of 50×10^6/ml, and survival time of 12 hours.

BREEDING CAPACITY TESTS

Libido and the capability of completing the mating act can only be measured by actual testing of the male. He must have access to an estrous female, desire to mate, and be physically able to mount and serve her.[13]

One group of 548 bulls was examined for breeding soundness according to visual appraisal, scrotal evaluation, and semen evaluation.[10] Sixty-five were culled because of locomotor abnormalities, genital abnormalities, and semen examination. When the bulls were subjected to a breeding capacity test another 48 were culled because 16 had locomotor abnormalities, 15 had genital abnormalities, and 17 exhibited poor serving capacity. These 48, or 9 percent, of the animals would have been designated satisfactory without the breeding capacity test.

Apparently there is no relationship between libido and semen production; therefore, it is very important to test for both factors. Heretofore, the evaluation of libido has been by visual evaluation of the masculine traits of a male caused by testosterone, which is also responsible for libido.

One test devised to test libido of the bull was confinement of a bull in a small pen with a cow restrained in a stanchion.[54] Sixty 12-to-15-month-old Angus bulls were tested and 18 satisfactorily mounted and served a cow in a test period of 5 minutes. Thirty bulls attempted mounts while the other 30 exhibited poor libido.

Other workers prepared heifers by bringing them into estrus with hormones. Each bull was allowed to enter a pen containing one of the estrous heifers. The bull was allowed 5 minutes with the heifer and observed for sexual activity. Each bull was tested twice, and only the best score was retained.[14] A group of 56 bulls was tested this way and then used in controlled mating trials. The correlation was .13 based on semen score and .32 based on libido when compared to pregnancy rate.

A report from Australia states that the serving capacity of bulls measured by their reaction to immobilized cows for 1 hour gives an accurate prediction of the mating capacity on pasture.[10] It was pointed out, however, that some false or misleading values may be gleaned from the tests. One bull with short penile protrusion had difficulty making contact and intromission unless the mount cows were restrained. If they were restrained, his capacity was equal to or better than most of the bulls. His actual breeding performance was highly correlated with his breeding difficulties. Subjecting bulls to two tests instead of one evidently does not increase accuracy of prediction.

It should be stated that all research is not so positive in relating libido to fertility.[8] Some workers have found no obvious relationship between libido and fertility.

A review of sexual behavior related to germ cell output in farm animals is given by Hale and Almquist.[32]

WHEN TO EVALUATE SIRES

Sires may be evaluated at any number of times and as often as desired. Some of the advantages and disadvantages need to be enumerated.

Just Prior to the Breeding Season

This time may be within a week of turning the male with a group of females for a season of breeding. The main advantage here is that the evaluation indicates breeding ability at the time nearest the time of use. Nothing should go wrong between the test and actual mating. Another advantage is that the males are usually gathered at this time anyway for observation before turning them out, so unnecessary labor and stress are eliminated.

The main disadvantage lies in the procurement of replacements. If several sires are unsatisfactory it may be difficult to find sires of the desired quality to replace them. This is probably the time other producers are turning out their herd sires as well. This problem may be alleviated to some extent by retaining a few spares to fill the gap caused by unsatisfactory males.

When Sires Are Plentiful

Evaluation during the off-season when sires are plentiful offers an excellent opportunity to purchase new sires and replacements. Prices should be best at this time also.

The disadvantage with this time is that the sire selected for breeding may injure himself or become ill between the time of evaluation and the breeding season. Fortunately this is not a frequent happening, but when it does happen the livestockman finds himself in a dilemma and has to search for replacements at an undesirable time.

During the Breeding Season

A few livestockmen would like to know if their sire is keeping his sperm production up while breeding the herd. Evaluation may be made after 3 to 4 weeks of the breeding season have elapsed. By this time all females should have been in estrus and the sire afforded the opportunity of breeding each. The presence of poor-quality semen at this time as indicated by poor concentration and the presence of a large number of immature cells would indicate overuse. The sire should then be removed and rested while a replacement picks up the slack. The sire should be returned to a smaller group of females so that he will be capable of maintaining his sperm production to equal the need.

End of the Breeding Season

Although this time is of little value to current breeding, it does afford the livestock manager an opportunity to eliminate any undesirable sires so they will not be carried over several months without any return to the economy. Normal breeding seasons for cattle, for instance, are 3 months long. Elimination of a poor bull at the end of the season eliminates the cost of feed and care for the 9-month period before the next season.

When in Question

If females continue to recycle, indicating they are not bred, then the sire that is supposed to be breeding them should be checked. This could be done at any time the manager desires and adjustments made at that time.

SUMMARY

Many criteria have been discussed relating to evaluating the potential of a herd sire. Even though single factors are not considered to be highly correlated with fertility, a combination of these factors is very important.

The importance of the various areas of evaluation make the end result even more significant, e.g., locomotor defects, 5.2 percent; penile defects, 3.5 percent; scrotal contents, 18.8 percent; internal organ defects, 7.4 percent for a total of 34.9 percent. Based on these figures, approximately one-third of our bulls could be culled or at least separated for medication or correction of defects. Semen evaluation indicates that between 10 and 20 percent of our bulls are either unsatisfactory or questionable.

Breeding capacity tests are still in the developmental stage but certainly indicate the incapacity of some bulls to complete the mating act.

Better methods will be forthcoming, and until there are better methods it is hoped that these suggestions will be of value.

WHAT DID YOU LEARN?

1 Why is evaluation of feet and legs important to reproduction?
2 When examining the scrotum and its contents, what should be specifically observed?
3 What internal reproductive organs are most defective?
4 What four main criteria are used in semen evaluation?
5 Which of the four criteria is most highly correlated with fertility?
6 What is the difference between primary and secondary sperm morphological defects?
7 What is an indicator of sire overuse?
8 What are hypoplastic testes?
9 Devise your own method for testing breeding ability based on libido and physical capability.
10 When do you think is the best time to evaluate a potential sire? Why?

REFERENCES

1 Amann, R. P. and J. O. Almquist. 1962. Reproductive capacity of dairy bulls. VII. Morphology of epididymal sperm. *J. Dairy Sci.* 45:1516–1526.
2 Anderson, J. 1945. *The Semen of Animals and its Use for Artificial Insemination.* Imperial Bureau Animal Breeding and Genetics, London.
3 Arscott, G. H. and R. V. Kuhns. 1969. Packed sperm volume versus density as a measure of semen concentration. *Poultry Sci.* 48:1126–1127.
4 Ball, L. 1976. Electroejaculation and semen evaluation of bulls. In *A Compilation of Current Information on Breeding Soundness Evaluation and Related Subjects.* Rev. ed. The Soc. for Therio. VII.
5 Ball, L., L. D. Nelson, J. W. Furman, and G. E. Seidel, Jr. 1974. Semen collection and evaluation of bulls for breeding soundness. Presented at the Ann. Mtg. of AVSSBS. Pp. 1–27.
6 Bielanski, W. 1956. Results of extensive researches of the semen of stallions. *Proc. 3rd Int. Congr. on Anim. Reprod. and A.I.* 3:85–87.
7 ————. 1975. The evaluation of stallion semen in aspects of fertility control and its use for artificial insemination. *J. Reprod. Fert. Suppl.* 23:19–24.
8 Bishop, M. W. H., R. C. Campbell, J. L. Hancock, and A. Walton. 1954. Semen characteristics and fertility in the bull. *J. Agri. Sci.* 44:227–248.

9 Blackshaw, A. W. March 1958. The effects of glycerol on the supra-vital staining of spermatozoa. *Australian Vet. J.* Pp. 71–76.

10 Blockey, M. A. deB. 1975. Studies on the social and sexual behaviour of bulls. Ph.D. thesis, Univ. of Melbourne, Victoria, Australia. Pp. 1–230.

11 Carroll, E. J., L. Ball, and J. A. Scott. 1963. Breeding soundness in bulls: A summary of 10,490 examinations. *J.A.V.M.A.* 142: 1105–1111.

12 Cates, W. F. 1976. Observations on scrotal circumference and its relationship to classification of bulls. In *A Compilation of Current Information on Breeding Soundness Evaluation and Related Subjects.* Rev. ed. The Soc. for Therio. VII.

13 Chenoweth, P. J. 1977. Libido and mating behavior in the bull. Beef Cattle Section, Texas Anim. Agr. Conf., College Station, Texas. Pp. 16–1, 16–7.

14 Chenoweth, P. J. and H. G. Osborne. 1975. Breed differences in the reproductive function of young beef bulls in central Queensland. *Australian Vet. J.* 51:405–406.

15 Clarke, R. H., G. H. O'Neill, R. W. Hewetson, and B. J. Thompson. 1973. The predictability of fertility from semen scores. *Australian Vet. J.* 49:498–499.

16 Coulter, G. H. and R. H. Foote. 1977. Relationship of body weight to testicular size and consistency in growing Holstein bulls. *J. Anim. Sci.* 44:1076–1079.

17 Cupps, P. T., R. C. Laben, and S. W. Mead. 1952. The relation of certain semen-quality tests to breeding efficiency and characteristics of semen from low-fertility bulls before and after hormone injection. *J. Dairy Sci.* 36:422–426.

18 Dott, H. M. 1975. Morphology of stallion spermatozoa. *J. Reprod. Fert. Suppl.* 23:41–46.

19 Edgar, D. G. 1959. Examination of rams for fertility. *New Zealand Vet. J.* 7:61–63.

20 ———. 1963. The place of ram testing in the sheep industry. *New Zealand Vet. J.* 11:113–115.

21 Elliott, F. I., J. K. Sherman, E. J. Elliott, and J. J. Sullivan. April 1973. A photographic method of measuring percentage of progressively motile sperm cells using dark-field microscopy. Presented at the VIII Internat. Symp. on Zootechny, Milan, Italy.

22 Elmore, R. G., C. J. Bierschwal, C. E. Martin, and R. S. Youngquist. 1975. A summary of 1127 breeding soundness examinations in beef bulls. *Therio.* 3:209–218.

23 First, N. L. 1968. Collection, evaluation and insemination of boar semen. *Proc. 2nd Tech. Conf. on A.I. and Reprod.* Pp. 52–54.

24 Fleming, W. N., T. T. Olar, and J. R. Mitchell. 1976. Techniques for evaluation of frozen bovine semen at Curtiss Breeding Service. *Proc. 6th Tech. Conf. on A.I. and Reprod.* Pp. 88–90.

25 Foote, R. H. 1958. Estimation of bull sperm concentration by packed cell volume. *J. Dairy Sci.* 41:1109–1110.

26 ———. 1968. Standards for sperm concentration: Polystyrene latex particles as an aid in quality control. *Proc. 2nd Tech. Conf. on AI and Reprod.* Pp. 95–97.

27 ———. 1972. How to measure sperm cell concentration by turbidity (optical density). *Proc. 4th Tech. Conf. on AI and Reprod.* Pp. 57–61.

28 Foster, J., J. O. Almquist, and R. C. Martig. 1970. Reproductive capacity of beef bulls. IV. Changes in sexual behavior and semen characteristics among successive ejaculations. *J. Anim. Sci.* 30:245–252.

29 Haag, F. M. 1959. Determination of the approximate sperm concentration of horse semen with the aid of spectrophotometer. *J.A.V.M.A.* 134:314–316.

30 Hafs, H. D., R. S. Hoyt, and R. W. Bratton. 1959. Libido, sperm characteristics, sperm output, and fertility of mature dairy bulls ejaculated daily or weekly for thirty-two weeks. *J. Dairy Sci.* 42:626–636.

31 Hahn, J., R. H. Foote, and G. E. Seidel, Jr. 1963. Testicular growth and related sperm output in dairy bulls. *J. Anim. Sci.* 29:41–47.

32 Hale, E. B. and J. O. Almquist. 1960. Relation of sexual behavior to germ cell output in farm animals. *J. Dairy Sci. Suppl.* 43:145–169.

33 Herman, H. A. and F. W. Madden. 1949. *The Artificial Insemination of Dairy Cattle.* Lucas Bros., Columbia, Missouri.

34 Herman, H. A. and E. W. Swanson. 1941. Variations in dairy bull semen with respect to its use in artificial insemination. Univ. of Missouri, *Agri. Exp. Sta. Res. Bull. 326.* Pp. 1–82.

35 Herrick, J. B. and H. L. Self. 1962. *Evaluation of Fertility in the Bull and Boar.* Iowa State University Press, Ames.

36 Hickman, C. G. 1958. Spermatocrit values in facilitating the estimation of spermatozoa concentrations. *J. Dairy Sci.* 41:318–319.

37 Hill, H. J., L. C. Faulkner, and E. J. Carroll. 1959. Theory of evaluating bulls as to breeding soundness. *J.A.V.M.A.* 135:318–320.

38 Hulet, C. V. and S. K. Ercanbrack. 1962. A fertility index for rams. *J. Anim. Sci.* 21:489–493.

39 Hulet, G. V., W. C. Foote, and R. L. Blackwell. 1965. Relationship of semen quality and fertility in the ram to fecundity in the ewe. *J. Reprod. Fert.* 9:311–315.

40 Janick, J. and J. MacLeod. 1970. The measurement of human spermatozoan motility. *Fert. and Steril.* 21:140–146.

41 Jones, R. C. 1971. Studies of the structure of the head of boar spermatozoa from the epididymis. *J. Reprod. Fert. Suppl.* 13:51–64.

42 Larson, Lester L. Spring 1960. Semen collection and its evaluation in the bull. *Southwestern Vet.* Pp. 187–196.

43 Lasley, J. F. and R. Bogart. 1943. Some factors influencing reproductive efficiency of range cattle under artificial and natural breeding conditions. Univ. of Missouri, *Agri. Exp. Sta. Res. Bull. 376.* Pp. 1–56.

44 Linford, Eileen, F. A. Glover, C. Bishop, and D. L. Stewart. 1976. The relationship between semen evaluation methods and fertility in the bull. *J. Reprod. Fert.* 47:283–291.

45 MacLeod, J. and R. Z. Gold. 1958. An analysis of human male fertility. *Int. J. Fert.* 3:382–388.

46 Maddox, L. A., Jr., R. O. Berry, A. M. Sorensen, Jr., and U.D. Thompson. 1959. Testing bulls for fertility. Tex. A&M Univ., *Tex. Agr. Exp. Sta. and Tex. Agr. Ext. Serv. Bull. 924.* Pp. 1–8.

47 Marshall, C. and L. Frey. 1976. Semen evaluation at Select Sires. *Proc. 6th Tech. Conf. on A.I. and Reprod.* Pp. 91–95.

48 Mayer, D. T., C. D. Squires, R. Bogart, and M. M. Oloufa. 1951. The technique for characterizing mammalian spermatozoa as dead or living by differential staining. *J. Anim. Sci.* 10:227–235.

49 Melrose, D. R. 1962. Artificial insemination in cattle. In J. P. Maule, ed. *The Semen of Animals and Artificial Insemination.* Commonwealth Agr. Bureaux, England. Pp. 2–181.

50 Mercier, E. and G. W. Salisbury. 1946. The effects of season on the spermatogenic activity and fertility of dairy bulls used in artificial insemination. *Cornell Vet.* 36:301–311.

51 Moeller, A. N. and N. L. VanDemark. 1955. In vitro speeds of bovine spermatozoa. *Fertil. and Steril.* 6:506–512.

52 Morris, D. L. 1977. Breeding soundness evaluation in the bull. *Proc. Food Anim. Med. Conf.,* Texas A&M Univ., College Station. Pp. 66–99.

53 Munro, I. B. 1961. Bovine semen characteristics and fertility. *J. Reprod. Fert.* 2:513–515.

54 Osborne, H. G., L. G. Williams, and D. B. Galloway. 1971. A test for libido and serving ability in beef bulls. *Australian Vet. J.* 47:465–467.

55 Pickett, B. W. 1968. Collection and evaluation of stallion semen. *Proc. 2nd Tech. Conf. on AI and Reprod.* Pp. 80–87.

56 Pickett, B. W., L. C. Faulkner, G. E. Seidel, Jr., W. E. Berndtson, and J. L. Voss. 1976. Reproductive physiology of the stallion. VI. Seminal and behavioral characteristics. *J. Anim. Sci.* 43:617–625.

57 Pickett, B. W., J. J. Sullivan, W. W. Byers, M. M. Pace, and E. E. Remmenga. 1975. Effect of centrifugation and seminal plasma on motility and fertility of stallion and bull spermatozoa. *Fertil. and Steril.* 26:167–174.

58 Rothschild, Lord. 1953. A new method of measuring sperm speeds. *Nature* 171:512–513.

59 Ruttle, J. L., Z. Ezaz, and E. J. Sceery. 1975. Some factors influencing semen characteristics in range bulls. *J. Anim. Sci.* 41:1069–1076.

60 Saacke, R. G. and R. P. Amann. 1966. Inherited abnormal acrosomal caps of bull spermatozoa. *J. Anim. Sci.* 25:929. (Abstr.)

61 Saacke, R. G., R. P. Amann, and C. E. Marshall. 1968. Acrosomal cap abnormalities of sperm from subfertile bulls. *J. Anim. Sci.* 27:1391–1400.

62 Saacke, R. G. and J. M. White. 1972. Semen quality tests and their relationship to fertility. *Proc. 4th Tech. Conf. on A.I. and Reprod.* Pp. 22–27.

63 Singleton, W. L. and D. R. Shelby. 1967. Variation between boars in semen characteristics and fertility. *J. Anim. Sci.* 26:1499.

64 Singleton, W. L. and D. R. Shelby. 1972. Variation among boars in semen characteristics and fertility. *J. Anim. Sci.* 34:762–766.

65 Swanson, E. W. and H. J. Bearden. 1951. An eosin-nigrosis stain for differentiating live and dead bovine spermatozoa. *J. Anim. Sci.* 10:981–987.

66 Swire, P. W. 1962. Artificial insemination in other animals: Artificial insemination in mule production. In J. P. Maule, ed. *The Semen of Animals and Artificial Insemination.* Commonwealth Agr. Bureaux, England. Pp. 298–303.

67 Taneja, G. C. and R. S. Gowe. 1969. Spermatozoa concentration in the semen of two breeds of fowl estimated by three different methods. *Poultry Sci.* 40:608–615.

68 Trimberger, G. W. and H. P. Davis. 1942. The relation of morphology to fertility in bull semen. *J. Dairy Sci.* 25:692–693.

69 Walker, D. F. 1972. Diagnosis of infertility in the bull. *J.A.V.M.A.* 161:1288–1290.

70 Walton, A. 1939. Respiratory activity of the spermatozoon as an index of activity and fertilising capacity. Presented at Celebrazioni Spallanzaniane, Regia Universita di Pavia, Italy.

71 White, I. G. and G. J. Lincoln. 1958. Riboflavin in yellow semen. *Nature* 182:667–668.

72 Willett, E. L. and J. I. Ohms. 1957. Measurement of testicular size and its relation to production of spermatozoa by bulls. *J. Dairy Sci.* 40:1559.

73 Wiltbank, J. N., W. W. Rowden, and J. E. Ingalls. 1965. Relationship between measures of semen quality and fertility in bulls mated under natural conditions. *Nebraska Agri. Exp. Sta. Res. Bull. 224.* Pp. 3–19.

CHAPTER 6

Semen Production, Processing, and Storage

When you have completed this chapter, you should be able to:

- Discuss the efficacy of using fresh semen in a breeding program,
- Know the fate of unejaculated sperm,
- Appreciate the values of various means of processing semen,
- Know the constituents of a semen extender,
- Calculate semen extension for fresh and frozen semen processing, and
- Relate the advantages and disadvantages of the various methods of packaging semen.

SPERM PRODUCTION

The production of sperm in adequate amounts is of utmost importance. The relationship between size of the testes and sperm production was mentioned in an earlier chapter. Let us pursue sperm production further at this time.

The seminiferous tubules are constantly producing spermatozoa. This production rate apparently is rather uniform. It has been concluded that testis histology and spermatogenesis are not affected by ejaculation frequency, rate of sperm removal by collection, or vasectomy.[7] Numerous methods have been utilized in determining reserve supply and rate of production. Most of the collections of semen have been made with the artificial vagina.

Stimulation

Sexual stimulation apparently affects ease of collection as well as volume and concentration of sperm. This stimulation may be accomplished in several ways. The bull may be brought into the presence of a teaser animal, which may be a cow in estrus or a mount animal (Fig. 6–1). Best response is usually to a cow in estrus. The bull may be allowed to watch other bulls mount and serve. Introduction of a new teaser animal may stimulate a lethargic bull or the bull may be taken away from the teaser and brought back. It must be realized that each animal is an individual with his own desires and abilities.

The use of false mounting and restraint is not as beneficial in beef bulls as in dairy bulls. One false mount followed by 5 minutes of active restraint in one research program did not significantly affect the percent motile sperm nor total sperm output.[34]

Teasing in the boar[109] and stallion[94] results in increased volume but does not change the number of sperm ejaculated.

Frequency of Collection

Exhaustion trials have been used extensively to try to determine the sperm-producing potential of a bull. Many trials have compared collection once a week with

Figure 6-1 Bulls with teasers. *(Courtesy of Central Ohio Breeding Association.)*

collection six times a week. One group of yearling Charolais bulls produced 5×10^9 sperm when collected once a week compared to 14×10^9 when ejaculated six times weekly. As these yearling bulls grew to 2 years of age, the once-a-week-collected bulls produced 11.2×10^9 compared to the six-times-a-week bulls with 33.6×10^9. The more frequently ejaculated bulls produced smaller ejaculate volumes but total sperm and total motile sperm were greater per week.[4,5]

In another trial, a group of Holstein bulls was collected twice a week at varying ages. Age and sperm output per week were 17 to 22 months, 28.4×10^9; 34 to 42 months, 41.5×10^9; 42 to 53 months, 38.0×10^9; 59 to 69 months, 42.7×10^9; and over 70 months, 28.2×10^9.[47] This indicates that bulls should be used between 2 and 6 years of age for maximum semen production.

It has been suggested that bulls may be ejaculated daily for extended periods of time without depleting the sperm supply—at least up to 8 months.[45] Comparisons were given of conception rates to one service of 70 percent for semen collected once a week and 73 percent for bulls collected once a day. Fresh semen therefore could be supplied in sufficient quantity to conduct a satisfactory breeding program.

Extragonadal sperm reserve determined from numerous trials has been summarized as 70×10^9 for sexually rested mature bulls.[15] In addition to rate of production, it has been calculated that each gram of testis produces a minimum of nearly 3×10^6 sperm per day or 20×10^6 per week.[21] Correlations between weight of testes and epididymides and sperm production are about .8, but season causes so much variation that predictability is poor. There is no accurate prediction by age, weight, or epididymal sperm reserve.[8]

Repeated ejaculates from boars over a 20-day period at intervals of 4 days, 2 days, and daily yielded total sperm per ejaculate of 54.9×10^9, 39.5×10^9, and 23.7×10^9, respectively.[39] This suggests that boars may be collected every other day satisfactorily. Depletion trials suggest that the boar produces about 15.5×10^9 sperm daily[116] and, also, only sperm from the caudal epididymis are ejaculated during depletion. Pregnancy rates were actually greater when sows were inseminated with semen collected every day compared to that collected every 3 days (83 vs. 70 percent).[117] Daily sperm production has been measured histologically in boar testes, and estimates range from 16.5×10^9 to 17.8×10^9.[115] This only points out the fact that boars are capable of breeding more sows than we have heretofore believed.

The daily sperm production by the stallion is considerably less than for the boar. Histological studies yielded approximately 8×10^9 sperm produced daily. Sperm per gram of tissue was estimated at 20×10^6.[38] Depletion trials have yielded as many as 21×10^9 sperm when stallions were allowed to mount and ejaculate until a lapse of 30 minutes following the last ejaculation.[20] Seven stallions averaged 23 ejaculates.

Stallions collected three or six times a week yielded comparable numbers of sperm per week after extragonadal reserves were stabilized—35.2×10^9, 35.3×10^9 —and were greater than 11.4×10^9 for the single collection.[92] This indicates the practicality of using a collection schedule of alternate days when inseminating mares.

Most of the extragonadal sperm reserve is in the caudal epididymis of the stallion.[37] The epididymis is reported to contain 88 percent of the reserve, of which

61 percent is in the caudal portion. There are sufficient sperm in the deferent ducts and ampullae to account for a single ejaculate.

Testicular measurements are not good criteria for determining sperm capacity in the stallion, but attention should be given to extremes in size and texture.[37]

The effects of season on the stallion's sperm production have not been clearly shown. Some researchers relate day length to production, but no clear effect on total sperm is available. Even the same workers have reported differences in their observations.[87,91]

FATE OF SPERM

Since the male produces billions of sperm, of which only a portion is used for breeding, what is the fate of the remainder?

Bull sperm have been studied in the various segments of the reproductive system,[103] and apparently those sperm in the cranial epididymis are mostly normal, but as degeneration occurs, the mitochondrial sheath swells and finally is destroyed, followed by loss of the sperm head. Most of the decapitated sperm are removed in the caudal epididymis by macrophages that are phagocytic in action. Other studies have revealed a possible phagocytosis in the efferent ductules.[26]

Sperm may be eliminated in a number of ways by the ram,[58,59] who may spontaneously ejaculate small amounts, which are sprayed on the wool underline. Resorption and phagocytosis in the various ducts is very nominal if at all, and about 80 percent of the sperm output has been measured in the urine.

Most of the available literature insinuates, without actually proving, that sperm are lost throughout the duct system by phagocytosis and the majority is lost in urination.

SIRE SELECTION

To extend the usefulness of outstanding sires, methods of adding media to the limited ejaculate volume to prolong life and methods of processing the semen for prolonged storage have been developed.

A bull in natural service may breed 25 cows per year for a lifetime of approximately 8 years for a total of possibly 200 offspring. Through collection, processing, and storing semen where the bull is collected twice weekly over an 8-year period and each collection extended to breed approximately 200 cows, simple calculation yields 166,400 potential breedings. This is almost 1000 times what is expected from natural service, and these figures are conservative.

The potential of the sire through semen extension therefore makes it mandatory that strict selection procedures be adhered to in planning a breeding program.

Cattle producers, both dairy and beef, make greater use of semen extension and artificial insemination than producers of any other class of livestock. Selection is very exacting among the major breeding organizations, and many individual dairymen and ranchers are very exacting in their selection also.

Young Sire Selection

One method of selecting young sires is to study the records of all related individuals for the desired traits and plan a mating between a desirable sire and a desirable dam. Availability of Dairy Herd Improvement (DHI) records and knowledge of heritability estimates for the various traits such as milk production, solids-not-fat production, milkfat production, desirability of the udder, feet and legs, calving ease, and longevity help in the selection of the parents for the planned mating.

Beef cattle traits are not as well defined in our records, but more and more information is becoming available. Heretofore we have had birth weight, weaning weight, average daily gain, feed conversion, and limited carcass data. We are now accumulating records of calving ease and electronic measures of loin eye muscles and fat covering.

Once the selected young sire is born he is placed with other similar prospects and fed for optimum growth to reach puberty at an early age. Records are kept on him throughout this growing period for gain, feed conversion, and conformation. His health is monitored continually, and every effort is made to get the maximum from this valuable young male.

Once puberty is reached, semen is collected, evaluated, and processed. Only high-quality semen is utilized, and most of the processed semen is shipped to technicians for breeding in numerous herds to sample this potential young sire. A proportion of the semen is retained at the breeding center and banked for future use.

Most young sires will then be placed with similar bulls and maintained until their proof starts coming in on records of conception and production. This will be approximately 3 years in dairy cattle because of a gestation time of 9 months for the offspring, 12 months to reach puberty and breed, 9 months gestation, and 10 months for lactation. Therefore, the hopeful young sire must wait for his proof before a decision can be made on his future. A few very outstanding prospects may be placed in limited use immediately. These are the exceptional ones.

As proof accumulates, a decision is made as to whether the selected bull goes into production or is culled and sold for ground beef. The attrition rate is high.

Mature Sire Selection

Mature sires are selected upon their records of performance. One of the difficulties in the selection of older sires is that most of the records will have been made in only one or two herds and perhaps under selective conditions. The sire will also be older and have a limited remaining productive life.

Most individual livestock producers select their sires as mature sires, however, because of the limited data available on younger animals.

Once the sire is selected, a decision must be made as to the use and procedure for processing semen.

NONRETURN RATES

Before we discuss semen processing it is necessary to understand conception data related to artificial insemination. Breeding results are usually reported as nonreturn rates (NR). This is basing conception on the fact that the female has not returned to estrus for rebreeding in a given period of time and is assumed, therefore, to be pregnant.

The days related to the nonreturn rate originated from the reports of artificial breeding technicians to their breeding organizations each month. They reported, for registration purposes, a form complete with identification of the cow, bull, date, and name of the technician, at least. These reports were made monthly and from them it was possible to calculate the nonreturn rate at 30-day intervals. Nonreturn rates at 30 to 60 days are usually high, 80 to 85 percent. A 60–90 NR is lower because some cows have been identified in estrus for rebreeding that perhaps were missed on the last heat check. Some early embryonic mortality may also have occurred and the cow recycled. The 60–90 NR is the assumed standard in artificial insemination circles and, unless stated otherwise, nonreturn figures will be based on 60–90 NR. A normal 60–90 NR is 70 to 75 percent.

These NR figures are also based on the first service, so that repeat breeding livestock will not be considered in subsequent reports. The greater the time span before calculation, usually the lower the NR.

PROCESSING BULL SEMEN
Liquid or Frozen

If the semen is to be used on a limited basis, and particularly by one or two individuals, then liquid semen may be the method to employ. The term "liquid" indicates that the semen remains in a liquid state at all times. The cattleman may collect and extend the bull's semen and store it in his home refrigerator at 4°C (39°F) for approximately 3 days and still maintain good fertilizing capacity. Raw semen, even though cooled, will maintain viability for only 1 or 2 days.

Some other limitations include a need for the sire to be in relatively close proximity and to have experienced personnel collecting and extending the ejaculate.

It should be remembered that frozen semen has only been with us since the early 1950s; prior to that time all semen was processed and utilized in the liquid state. Under those circumstances, semen was shipped hundreds of miles to technicians who then had to use it in only a couple of days. This resulted in the use of approximately one-third of the potential breeding power.

Refrigerated liquid semen is the most economical method if an individual wants to use a particular available sire on a limited number of cows within a short time. Liquid semen should not be discounted too severely because of its short life.

The ability to maintain semen quality at environmental temperatures for extended periods of time would alleviate many of the problems associated with refrigeration. Underdeveloped countries could especially benefit. Numerous studies have been conducted with success but the projected usefulness has not materialized.

One of these extenders for bull semen is called the IVT (Illini Variable Temperature), because it was developed in Illinois and maintains sperm viability under variable temperatures.[119] Semen stored through 6 days yielded a 60–90 NR Of 75.7 percent compared to the use of egg yolk–citrate storage for 3 days yielding 66.9 percent NR.[119] Other reports have shown 60–90 NR of 69 percent at 1 day of storage, 45 percent at 2 days, 33 percent at 3 days, 26 percent at 4 days, 25 percent at 5 days, and 21 percent at 6 days[27] and 38–78 NR of 75.8 percent at 1 day, 81.6 percent at 2 days, 77.7 percent at 3 days, and 62.3 percent at 4 days.[63]

The basis for the extended life of the sperm is the use of carbon dioxide to depress motility and conserve energy of the cells.

Other extenders utilizing coconut milk have also been developed for nonrefrigerated storage.[78] Malmberg and Israelsson[61] used coconut water extender (CWE) and obtained better conception from semen 1 to 4 days old stored at 15 to 25°C (59 to 77°F) than from frozen semen in straws. The split-ejaculate technique was used. Conception rates were 66.2 percent for CWE and 63.7 percent for frozen semen at 84-day pregnancy checks. Over 3000 cows were in each trial. They also used some semen for as long as 7 days with conception rates of 39.1 percent determined at 84 days. Other trials with coconut milk extenders (CME) have yielded NR rates from 55 to 72 percent.[77,79,80]

IVT extender has also been used for boar semen with somewhat varying results up to day 5 of storage. Conception rates were 76.5 percent when 2×10^9 sperm per insemination were used.[14]

"Frozen" semen is that extended ejaculate which can be stored for an indefinite period of time. It is not unusual to hear of someone using semen that is over 10 years old from a sire who is dead and gone. The semen must be stored at very cold temperatures; the most common storage medium today is liquid nitrogen, which maintains a storage temperature of –196°C (–320°F). Other methods of storage are mechanical (–110°C, –166°F) and dry ice and alcohol (–79°C, –110°F).

The disadvantages of the liquid nitrogen method of storage include a refrigerator, which is an expensive oversize thermos, and a source of refrigerant. Part of the disadvantages are overcome by the availability of rental refrigerators, commonly called nitrogen tanks, from the semen-producing organization from which one purchases the semen, and availability of nitrogen from the same organization for keeping the tank charged. The nitrogen expands and evaporates to cool the contents of the tank and therefore is lost and must be replaced.

Semen may also be frozen in pellet form where less extender is used; storage is thereby increased by about three times. Conception rates are similar if not slightly better than with straws and ampules.

Extenders for liquid semen The extender should be formulated shortly before collection of the semen, cooled to 4°C (39°F), and stored until needed. The extender for liquid semen is composed of a source of *nutrients, a buffer, antibacterial agents,* and sometimes *glycerol.*

Nutrient The nutrient portion may be from numerous sources. The most common is egg yolk. The egg yolk should be carefully separated from the other constituents of the egg, since they are detrimental to sperm survival. Milk is a rather common medium but must be heated to a temperature of 92 to 95°C (198°F) for 10 minutes to destroy the enzymes detrimental to sperm livability.[6,118] Other sources are coconut milk, reconstituted dried buttermilk, and duck egg yolk.

Buffer The buffer acts to neutralize the waste products released by the sperm as metabolism takes place. It particularly neutralizes the lactic acid released. The most common buffer is 2.9 percent sodium citrate solution. Sodium phosphate may be used also.

Antibacterial agents These agents have a dual purpose: they are present to destroy disease organisms and to reduce metabolism of the sperm. Many agents have been tried, and there is probably more literature on this one subject than any other relating to semen processing. Just imagine all the antibiotics and antibacterial agents available and calculate the number of possible combinations and you will understand the reason for numerous articles in the journals. Through these many trials, penicillin and streptomycin have been accepted as the standard additions. A combination of the two controls bacterial growth in the majority of cases.

Glycerol Presence of glycerol in milk extenders has yielded improved conception rates over just milk; 3 percent better on day 1, 5 percent on day 2, 8 percent on day 3 and 11 percent on day 4.[3]

Example

> Make up an egg yolk citrate extender for liquid semen.
> 40% egg yolk
> 60% 2.9% sodium citrate
> Mix thoroughly and add
> 500 units penicillin/ml
> 1 mg streptomycin/ml

This extender is usually designated as EYC (egg yolk citrate).

Extenders for frozen semen. In addition to the three above constituents in liquid semen, a fourth is needed for freezing and storage—an antifreeze.

Antifreeze If sperm are frozen without some antifreeze being present they will all rupture and die. Crystalline formation is in the shape of sharp spines or needles which form and puncture the sperm. The antifreeze causes a change in ice crystal formation so that freezing occurs as a sheet rather than needles. The sperm survive this process and remain viable.

The most common antifreeze is glycerol, which may range in concentration of the final extended semen from 6 to 12 percent. Addition of glycerol to the semen is critical. It must be very gradual. Rapid addition will destroy the sperm.

Example
   Make up extender for frozen semen.

   20% egg yolk
   80% 2.9% sodium citrate
   Mix thoroughly and add
   500 units penicillin/ml
   1 mg streptomycin/ml

   Divide the EYC into two halves and add 15 percent glycerol to one half (EYCG).
   When the EYC is added to the semen first, there is no glycerol present. The EYCG is then added gradually to yield a final percentage of 7.5 glycerol, which is optimum for further processing.

Collection

Now that we have some preliminaries behind us, collection and processing will be discussed.

Method The AV is generally used in the large breeding centers. The electroejaculator is used on those that refuse to serve the AV—crippled, aged, and low libido bulls. Other methods are very seldom used.

Frequency Major bull studs will collect two or three times a week and usually collect two ejaculates at about 10 to 15 minute intervals. This should yield 10 to 30 ml of concentrated sperm for processing.

Evaluation

The collected semen should immediately be placed in a container the same temperature as the semen. A glass or beaker of warm water will furnish a warm jacket that will insulate against cold shock and cool down gradually when placed in a cool atmosphere. The volume should be read directly from the collecting tube. Motility should be calculated immediately thereafter. Then a sample should be taken for determining concentration. After the sample is taken, extender should be warmed and added at a ratio of one part semen to four parts extender. This helps preserve and protect it against cold shock in the next few minutes. Concentration is then determined by any of the methods described earlier. The major bull studs will use some sort of light density meter.

Calculation and Extension

The next step is to calculate the number of units of extended semen that may be processed from the evaluation information. The unit, regardless of volume, should contain 10 million motile normal cells at the time of insemination.[22,114] Some research shows that as low as 5 million cells may be sufficient.[113] Liquid semen is used almost immediately; therefore, extension is calculated to put 10 million viable cells into each unit. When freezing semen in straws, it is expected that one-third of the sperm will be killed in the processing, freezing, and thawing, so 15 million viable sperm are placed in each unit to obtain 10 million for insemination following thawing. One-half of the sperm are expected to be killed when processed in glass ampules; therefore, 20 million viable sperm should be used in calculating extension.

Liquid The number of viable cells is determined by multiplying the number of milliliters of semen by the concentration per milliliter by the percent motile by the percent normal.

Volume (ml) X Concentration/ml X % Motile X % Normal = Total viable cells.

The total viable cells divided by the number of viable cells needed at insemination equals the number of units of extended semen.

$$\frac{\text{Total viable cells}}{\text{No. viable cells/insemination}} = \text{units of extended semen}$$

The units of extended semen is the same as the number of potential inseminations.

Example

Volume—7 ml
Concentration—1×10^9/ml
Motility—70%
Normality—90%

Formula:

$$\frac{\text{Vol} \times \text{Conc} \times \% \text{ Motile} \times \% \text{ Normal}}{10 \times 10^6} = \text{units}$$

$$\frac{7 \times 1 \times 10^9 \times .7 \times .9}{10 \times 10^6} = 441 \text{ units}$$

Therefore, we could possibly breed 441 cows to the single ejaculate.

No mention has been made of volume other than that of the ejaculate. Volume per insemination is not nearly as important as the number of live normal cells. If we wish to use 1 ml of extended liquid semen for insemination, which is common, then unit and milliliter are synonymous. However, we could use only .5 ml per insemination; in this instance .5 ml and unit become synonymous. The volume of the unit determines the amount of added extender, and the unit must always have 10 million viable cells present. Please remember this!

Let us assume that we will use 1 ml volume per insemination. The total volume of extended semen would be 441 milliliters. Subtract the volume of semen (7 ml) from 441 and we see that 434 ml of extender are needed. A 40 percent egg yolk, 60 percent citrate extender was given earlier.

Example

1 ml dosage $\times$ 441 units = 441 ml extended semen
441 ml extended semen $-$ 7 ml semen = 434 ml extender
174 ml egg yolk $+$ 260 ml citrate = 434 ml EYC
Add 441 $\times$ 500 units penicillin/ml = 220,500 units penicillin
Add 441 $\times$ 1 mg streptomycin/ml = 441 mg streptomycin

The extender should be added to the cooled semen gradually. Both extender and semen should be at refrigerator temperature at this time, 4°C (39°F). Swirl the container gently to mix the semen and extender thoroughly. The semen may be divided into smaller containers for ease in handling and to preserve the mixture from rapid changes in temperature later. The extended semen may be used immediately, but be sure to keep the remainder refrigerated.

If it is known that fewer cows than the potential number calculated are to be bred in the next 3 days, then a lower extension rate may be used, which would insure an adequate number of sperm per insemination. The above calculations are for maximum usage.

Frozen Now is a good time to talk about the various forms in which semen is frozen. Straws are now the most popular container in the United States and perhaps the world. They are replacing glass ampules, which have been in use for many years. Pellets are used widely in Europe and the Scandinavian countries. Freeze-dry methods are being experimented with presently.

Straws Straws are thin-walled plastic tubes of different dimensions. The most popular straw currently has a capacity of .5 ml and is 13.5 mm long and 3 mm inside diameter. These are commonly called the French or Canadian straws. A .25 ml "ministraw"[23] is the same length but of smaller diameter and is slightly more difficult to handle. One end of the straw contains a plug made of two fibrous plugs with a small section of polyvinyl powder between them. This allows air to be syphoned through it to draw extended semen into the straw. Moisture of the semen wets the powder, forming a seal.

Other straws are on the market, and an American Continental and Minitub contain about .3 ml and are sealed by plastic or metal plugs on each end. They are the same diameter as the .5 ml straws.

Ampules Glass ampules look like miniature coke bottles. The most common ampules contain 1 ml or .5 ml. After the ampule is filled, the tip is melted in a flame and the glass becomes molten and seals the ampule. Most ampules are prescored;

that is, the neck has been scratched so that the top may be broken off without difficulty at the time of use.

Pellets A pellet is a frozen drop of extended concentrated semen. The drop of semen is placed in a depression of solid carbon dioxide (dry ice) and freezing is immediate. There is no container for the semen. Molds and other freezing media may be used. The volume is approximately .1 ml.

Freeze-dry Research is striving to perfect a method of freezing under vacuum to form a dry powdered sperm. Some foods are preserved this way now.

Others Many containers have been used, some with good success and others with poor success. Among these are freezing in a catheter, in a syringe, in plastic ampules, polybulbs, capillary tubes, and surely there are others that have been tried.

The same calculation steps are necessary for frozen semen as for liquid with some addition. The number of viable sperm per unit before freezing in straws must be 15 million, or one and one-half the number used in processing liquid semen. This is needed to offset mortality of sperm during processing and thawing. The other factor is the antifreeze. Glycerol must be added to 6 to 12 percent by volume to insure satisfactory freezing. Less percent egg yolk is needed because the period of metabolism of the sperm is shortened.

Example (for straws)

Volume—6 ml
Concentration—$.9 \times 10^9$/ml
Motility—80%
Normality—80%

Formula:

$$\frac{\text{Vol} \times \text{Conc} \times \% \text{ Motile} \times \% \text{ Normal}}{15 \times 10^6} = \text{units}$$

$$\frac{6 \times .9 \times 10^9 \times .8 \times .8}{15 \times 10^6} = 230 \text{ units}$$

We could potentially breed 230 cows to this single ejaculate. Our actual number and our potential number of breedings should be the same since we should have no wastage of the frozen semen.

Again, it should be emphasized that volume has not been mentioned, only the number of potential breedings, and each unit will have 10 million viable sperm when thawed for insemination. Most semen is now processed in .5 ml straws, so let us determine the volume of extender needed using 20 percent egg yolk.

Example

.5 ml straw $\times$ 230 units = 115 ml extended semen
115 ml – 6 ml semen = 109 ml extender
22 ml egg yolk + 87 ml citrate = 109 ml EYC
Add 115 $\times$ 500 units penicillin/ml = 57,500 units penicillin
Add 115 $\times$ 1 mg streptomycin/ml = 115 mg streptomycin
115 ml extended semen $\times$ 7.5% glycerol = 8.6 ml glycerol
109 ml EYC – 8.6 ml glycerol = 100 ml EYC needed

The EYC is divided into two equal parts and one half (50 ml) is added to the semen. Temperature should be the same for semen and EYC. The 8.6 ml glycerol is added to the other half (50 ml) of EYC and mixed to form egg yolk citrate glycerol (EYCG). The EYCG is then mixed gradually with the extended semen to give the final 115 ml of extended semen with 7.5% glycerol.

The gradual mixing of the EYCG with the EYC semen portion may be accomplished by adding 10 percent of the EYCG and mixing thoroughly by swirling, waiting 20 minutes, adding 20 percent of the EYCG and mixing, waiting 20 minutes, adding 30 percent EYCG and mixing, waiting 20 minutes, and adding the remaining 40 percent of the EYCG and mixing. This alleviates shocking and killing the sperm with high concentrations of glycerol. Other methods of mixing may be utilized. A constant drip and mixing works very well.

The above calculations have been for freezing in .5 ml straws. If 1 ml ampules are used, the volume of extended semen would be greater but the required number of viable sperm per unit would remain the same. We would then put 20 million viable sperm into 1 ml before freezing to obtain 10 million in the 1 ml extended semen upon thawing. Smaller (.5 ml) ampules may be used also, with consideration given to the different volume per unit.

Processing Straws and Ampules

Equilibration After the semen and constituents are mixed, the extended semen must be allowed to equalize so that the sperm will be well protected during the freezing process. This is a period called equilibration and may range from 2 to 6 hours. Shorter times are better than longer times.[29,42]

Labeling All semen looks alike, and it is necessary to read the labels carefully to determine identification. Color coding the semen helps the inseminator to identify breeds quickly. A drop of nontoxic vegetable dye is added to the extended semen. When the straw or ampule is viewed, the breed is automatically identified. Table 6–1 lists the system now in use for dairy and major beef breeds. Each breed is also coded by initials for further identification. These are under the direction of the National Association of Animal Breeders (NAAB).[71]

The uniform identification on the semen package includes a number assigned to the semen-producing organization by NAAB and USDA/ARS, followed by the breed code, and a four-digit bull number. Following this identification system, the BOOTMAKER Holstein bull owned by American Breeders Service would carry the label 29 H1881, and the semen would be green.

The semen-producing business may place other information on the container, but it is somewhat restricted by space and the size of the letters and numbers. The date and batch of semen are usually added to those listed above.

The technician should be cautioned that there are many units of semen still being used that have an old label that does not fit this format. Be sure to record the exact label when using a unit.

During the equilibration time, the containers for the semen may be labeled. This may be done any time prior to this, but at this time one knows exactly how many units will be frozen. Labeling of straws is possible by means of prepared rubber

Table 6-1   Color Code and Breed Code for Dairy and Major Beef Breeds

Dairy breed	Color	Breed code
Guernsey	Yellow	G
Holstein	Green	H
Jersey	Red	J
Brown Swiss	Brown	B
Milking Shorthorn	Lime	M

For a period of time, no coloring was used for the beef breeds, but as of February 1, 1976, the semen of the major beef breeds has been colored as follows:

Beef breed	Color	Breed code
Angus	Orange	AN
Red Angus	Magenta Red	AR
Blonde d'Aquitaine	Yellow	BD
Beef Friesian	Yellow	BF
Brangus	Pink Orange	BN
Brahman	Pink Orange	BR
Chianina	Purple	CA
Charolais	Pink Rose	CH
Gelbvieh	Peach	GV
Hays Converter	Yellow	HC
Hereford	Nut Brown	HH
Polled Hereford	Nut Brown	HP
Limousin	Bright Red	LM
Maine-Anjou	Dull Purple	MA
Meuse-Rhine-Issel	Yellow	MI
Marchigiana	Yellow	MR
Norwegian Red	Yellow	NR
Pinzgauer	Yellow Orange	PZ
Romagnola	Yellow	RN
Santa Gertrudis	Blue	SG
Simmental	Lime Green	SM
Shorthorn	Brilliant Purple	SS
Tarentaise	Pink Rose	TA

stamps with the necessary information. Rolling the straws over the inked stamps may be feasible when only a few are to be labeled, but when hundreds are to be processed an automatic labeler should be considered.

Labeling of ampules may be conducted by hand, but the same problems arise with large numbers as with straws.

Filling Straws may be filled by syphoning the extended semen into them by vacuum. Ampules may be filled with a syringe fitted with a plastic tube, which is inserted through the neck of the ampule and used to fill the lower portion. Care should be taken to refrain from touching any semen to the neck when entering or retracting the tube, because this will interfere with sealing later. Semiautomatic and automatic fillers are available (Fig. 6–2).

Sealing Straws may be sealed with small plastic plugs or polyvinyl powder, or hermetically sealed. It is important in filling to leave a small open portion of the straw for sealing and expansion.

Ampules are flame sealed. Care should be taken to keep the ampules upright so that semen will not touch the heated neck and seal. Semiautomatic and automatic sealers are available.

Freezing Straws are spread on a rack for vapor freezing (Fig. 6–3). This allows the vapors to encircle the entire straw and yield a uniform freezing of the entire batch in less than 5 minutes.[52]

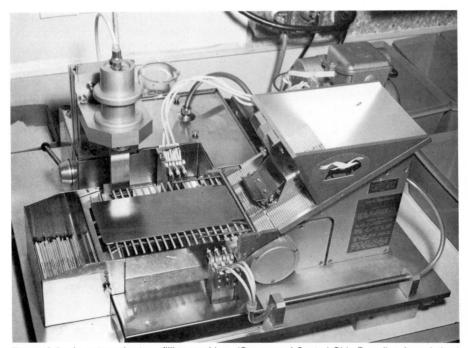

Figure 6-2   An automatic straw filling machine. *(Courtesy of Central Ohio Breeding Association.)*

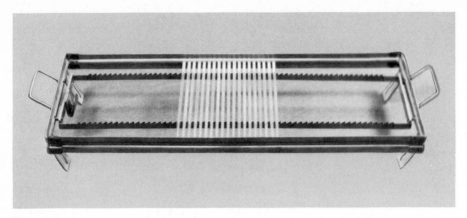

Figure 6-3 Straws on a rack for vapor freezing.

Ampules are placed on metal canes that have clips for individual ampules. Rajamannan[100] spin-froze semen in ampules for faster uniform freezing and slightly increased recovery of motile sperm.

A relatively simple vapor freezer is available that allows the prepared containers to be lowered into liquid nitrogen vapor and finally into liquid nitrogen itself. The process is gradual so that the initial drop in temperature is slow; the rate accelerates as the racks approach the liquid nitrogen in the bottom of the freezer.

After submersion in the liquid nitrogen for 10 minutes the straws are immediately placed in goblets of liquid nitrogen on canes and into canisters in a liquid nitrogen refrigerator. The transfer must be rapid to eliminate thawing of the frozen straws.

Ampules and their canes are transferred to canisters in a liquid nitrogen refrigerator for storage.

The actual freezing of the sperm when properly manipulated has little effect on the ultrastructure of the cells as shown through electron microscopy.[49]

Processing Pellets

Another method of freezing bull semen results in a frozen pellet. The extender is composed of an egg yolk–glycerol–carbohydrate combination with a ratio of approximately one part semen to three parts extender. Extenders are commonly composed of 20 percent egg yolk, 4.7 percent glycerol, and 75.3 percent carbohydrate solution. The carbohydrate may be glucose, mannose, lactose, stachyose, raffinose, or a combination of these.[68]

The pellets are usually frozen on a block of dry ice into which small depressions have been melted.[70] The volume of each drop of extended semen may vary from .013 to .2 ml, and they form a solid pellet almost immediately when the drop is placed in the depression. The pellets are then shaken from the block and transferred to metal tubes for storage. These are filled with pellets followed by a brass weight to keep them from floating from the container. The tubes are then placed immediately into canisters in a liquid nitrogen refrigerator.

Modifications of the freezing technique utilize aluminum blocks or metal plates with small depressions, or plastic molds in conjunction with liquid nitrogen vapor.

Labeling of pellets is difficult, but small strips may be placed in the depressions and one end frozen into the pellet. Most pellets are not labeled individually but the canes containing them are labeled.

Freeze-Dry Processing

An even more innovative method of preserving sperm is freeze-drying. Although this is still in the experimental stage,[19,43] some few offspring have been born to semen of this type. The sample is frozen under a vacuum which dehydrates it and allows reconstitution.

GENERAL

Do not forget temperature. The entire procedure for processing semen is dependent on gradual changes in temperature and the elimination of shock either by adding constituents or submitting the sperm to changes in environmental temperatures. Pelleting is the exception.

Advantages and Disadvantages of Packaging Methods

There have been many comparisons of the packages we have just discussed. Regardless of the package, the major factor in the final analysis is "How well did the semen bring about conception?" In other words, what yields the best nonreturn rate? Let us discuss advantages and disadvantages of each and make some comparisons.[16,25,41,57,89,112]

Straws

Advantages

1 Greater recovery following processing and thawing.
2 Slightly increased conception over ampules.
3 Less storage space required.
4 Cost of straw more economical than glass.
5 No exploding ampules.
6 Complete evacuation of straw at time of insemination, using all sperm.
7 Uniform freezing because of shape and size.
8 Quick thaw.

Disadvantages

1   Transfer time is very critical to prevent thawing.
2   Labeling is smaller.
3   Splitting or blowing end plugs.
4   Still in developmental stages, needs standardization.

Ampules

Advantages

1   Many outstanding sires already collected and stored.
2   Inseminator more familiar with ampule, handling, thawing.
3   Transfer between storage units less critical.
4   Easier to read labels.
5   Larger and easier to handle.
6   Sanitary package.

Disadvantages

1   Need more storage space.
2   More time needed for thawing.
3   Greater sperm loss in processing and thawing.
4   Improperly sealed ampules explode.
5   Slightly lower conception rates.
6   Approximately 15 to 20 percent of the sperm left in the ampule.

Pellet

Advantages

1   Production technique quick and simple.
2   Glycerolization can be avoided.
3   Less storage required than straws.
4   Low cost of equipment.
5   Greater live sperm recovery.

Disadvantages

1   Labeling very difficult.[57]
2   Chips may relocate on other pellets or packages.
3   Bacterial contamination.
4   Lacks automation.
5   Clumsy to handle.
6   Quick thaw when exposed.
7   Need separate extender when thawed.

Freeze-Dry

Advantages

    1 Storage problems almost eliminated.
    2 Transportation by mail.

Disadvantages

    1 Low conception rates, still experimental.

Conception

Table 6–2 is a compilation of data from several trials relating to the various packages used. Some are split ejaculates where half the ejaculate was processed in one manner and half in another. These are the best types of trials; however, others have been included to increase numbers. Although overall differences are small, pellets appear very favorable, followed by straws and then ampules. The combination of high

Table 6-2   Conception Rate (%) Related to Type of Semen Package

No. inseminations	Fresh	Straw	Ampule	Pellet	Source
388,923		68.8	67.3		31
2,808		63.5	57.9	69.7	66
574		54.0	32.0		67
204		58.0	44.0		67
161,151			69.1		30
176,293		67.7			30
4,034	66.9		60.4		65
2,234	75.9		63.1		65
—		69.0	67.5		56
Split ejaculates					
3,474	65.9				
2,839				65.7	64
2,937		66.1			
4,191				66.7	40
4,107		67.8			
1,993		68.5			2
1,872				59.0	
9,680		67.5			46
9,633			67.6		
7,168		61.1			46
7,108			65.5		
103,744	65.0				12
78,455				70.0	

conception rates and other advantages are the reasons straws have become the standard method for packaging semen.

Storage

Table 6–3 compares the storage of various types of packages for frozen semen.

PROCESSING RAM SEMEN

Semen from the ram resembles that of the bull, and because of this most of the early extenders were of the same composition. One comparison was made between egg yolk–glucose–citrate and heated cow's milk showing little difference between the two.[105,106] The semen was used within 3 to 5 hours of collection, and conception rates on a single service were 68.4 and 65.9, respectively, compared to undiluted semen conception of 71.2. Duration of storage was critical, with a decrease of 10 percent conception for each 24 hours storage. Other trials are comparable in maintaining livability.[120]

The concentration of ram semen per insemination has been studied extensively, [51,54,105] and an accepted figure is 50×10^6 live normal cells per insemination in a volume of .1 ml to 1 milliliter. This means that most ejaculates may be extended 1:4, and if .1 ml is used per ewe, 40 ewes could be inseminated per ejaculate. Extension rates over 1:10 have resulted in poor conception rates.[1]

Example

Make up extender for liquid semen.
Homogenized milk
1000 units penicillin/ml
Heat milk to 95°C (203°F) for 10 minutes.
Ejaculate information:
Volume—1 ml
Concentration—2200×10^6/ml
Motility—90%
Normality—90%
Formula:

Table 6-3   Storage Space Required by Various Packaging Methods for Frozen Semen

Package (unit)	Units/2½ in sq. canister	Units/cubic foot	Nitrogen (ml) displacement of 1,000 units
Pipets (5 mm O.D.)	150	3,700	5,562
Ampules (1 ml on canes)	150	3,700	3,104
.5 ml straws (French)	1,030	25,550	854
.25 ml straws (French)	1,960	48,450	396
Pellets (in tubes)	3,600	59,200	167

From Rajamannan.[101]

$$\frac{\text{Vol} \times \text{Conc} \times \% \text{ Motile} \times \% \text{ Normal}}{50 \times 10^6} = \text{Units}$$

$$\frac{1 \times 2200 \times 10^6 \times .9 \times .9}{50 \times 10^6} = 35 \text{ units}$$

Therefore, we could possibly breed 35 ewes to the single ejaculate. If .1 ml volume were used, the 1 ml ejaculate would be extended with 2.5 ml extender to yield 3.5 ml extended semen to breed the 35 ewes.

Freezing of ram semen has been accomplished in ampules, straws, and pellets. Many of the early trials resulted in very low conception rates,[32,54,111] but improvements have been and are still being made.

Results from breeding with frozen semen in straws have been encouraging. Little loss is apparent over long term storage.[107] Lambing rates from semen stored 5 years has been reported as 49.3 percent on a single service and 58 percent on double inseminations.[107] Another report shows semen frozen under the best conditions to have fertilizing ability similar to that of fresh semen.[24,104]

Semen frozen in ampules is about equal to that frozen in straws.[122]

Numerous research programs include dilution for processing and reconcentrating the sperm before insemination. There doesn't seem to be any critical difference as long as the optimal number of cells is maintained.[120] It has also been proposed that the semen be washed and centrifuged for recovery.[48] This seems to be unnecessary.

Pelleting is also a popular method for processing ram semen.[35] The most common extender was developed by Nagase and Niwa[69] and consists of 25 percent egg yolk, 71.5 percent lactose (11 percent solution), and 3.5 percent glycerol. Equilibration time is 2 hours.

A limited amount of work has been conducted on processing goat semen, and it has been successfully frozen in ampules using sterile skimmed milk and 7 percent glycerol with a 2-hour equilibration time.[11]

PROCESSING BOAR SEMEN

The semen of the boar has been processed and stored at room temperature, at 5°C, and in the frozen state. The volume of fluid in the ejaculate makes it necessary to concentrate for freezing, and this area still requires considerable research for a feasible method to be available.

A number of researchers have shown that the concentration of sperm must be 2×10^9 or greater per insemination.[10,14,55,60,76,96] Concentrations have ranged from 2×10^9 to 10×10^9 per insemination and conception rates from 32 to 71.5 percent.

Since the volume of the ejaculate measures near 200 ml and concentration approximately 200×10^6/ml, the total number of cells is about 40×10^9. If 5×10^9 sperm are used per insemination, as is common, only 8 sows may be inseminated per ejaculate. By using 2×10^9 sperm this may be increased to 20 sows.

Age of the sperm influences conception; therefore, storage methods are needed for long-term use without decreased potency.[86,95] Liquid semen processed and stored in the refrigerator at 5°C (41°F) has given results of 90 percent on day 1, 92 percent on day 2, and dropped to 50 percent on day 3.[9]

Several extenders for liquid semen have been developed.[28,33] The extender given here was developed by Foley and others at Purdue and may be used for storage at 15°C (59°F) or 5°C (39°F). If storage is to be for several days, the egg yolk is added.

Foley's extender for boar semen:

1.3 g glucose
1.4 g sodium citrate
.029 g potassium chloride
.15 g sodium bicarbonate
.3 g streptomycin
10,000 IU penicillin
100 ml distilled water
Mix ingredients thoroughly.
10% egg yolk should be added for storage.

The filtered semen is evaluated and the total number of live normal cells determined. This is divided by the concentration per insemination to determine how many potential breedings may be conducted and also to determine the amount of extender needed.

$$\frac{\text{Vol} \times \text{Conc} \times \% \text{ Motile} \times \% \text{ Normal}}{5 \times 10^9} = \text{potential breedings or units}$$

Example

Volume—150 ml
Concentration—200 $\times$ 10^6/ml
Motility—70%
Normality—90%
Formula:

$$\frac{\text{Vol} \times \text{Conc} \times \% \text{ Motile} \times \% \text{ Normal}}{5 \times 10^9}$$

$$\frac{150 \times 200 \times 10^6 \times .7 \times .9}{5 \times 10^9} = 3.8 \text{ or } 4 \text{ units}$$

The semen is then extended 1:3, and four sows may be bred with this particular sample. A better sample would breed a greater number. If the semen is not used immediately the egg yolk (10 percent) should be added.

Most of the frozen semen processing has been accomplished by using the pelleting method.[83,84,97,98,99, 110] The BF5 extender developed by Pursel and Johnson[98] is given here.

BF5 Extender

    1.2 g Tes-N-Tris (hydroxymethyl) methyl 2 aminoethane sulfonic acid
    .2 g Tris (hydroxymethyl) aminomethane
    3.2 g Dextrose, anhydrous
    20 ml Egg yolk
    .5 ml Orvus ES Paste (Proctor and Gamble, Cincinnati, Ohio)
    Bring to 100 ml with distilled water.

Centrifuge at 12,000 g for 10 minutes and decant extender. Cool the ejaculate to room temperature (22°C, 72°F). Determine concentration and separate into centrifuge tubes with aliquots of 6×10^9 sperm. Centrifuge and aspirate the accessory fluids. Resuspend to a volume of 5 ml with BF5 extender. Cool gradually to 5°C (41°F). Gradually add 5 ml of the extender containing 2% glycerol to each tube. Freeze immediately on dry ice in .15 to .2 ml pellets and transfer to liquid nitrogen for storage.

Conception rates to frozen semen have varied under different conditions but ranges are reported from 37 percent (farrowed) to 85 percent (gilts with fertilized ova).

PROCESSING STALLION SEMEN

The semen of stallions has been used for many years in the raw state to inseminate a mare already bred by the stallion or to breed two or three mares that are in estrus the same day. Extension for storage of liquid semen prolongs the useful life for 2 to 3 days. Freezing the semen removes the time limits.

Conception rates following breeding with diluted semen within 2 to 8 hours has yielded high conception rates (67 percent) compared to very low or no conception when stored longer.[72] Other workers maintained good conception with other extenders; 67.4 percent with milk or cream-gel and 78.9 percent for natural breeding in one trial;[50] and 75.0 percent with tris, 95.8 percent with cream-gel, and 91.7 percent with raw semen in another trial.[93] Numerous other extenders have been used successfully —powdered buttermilk and glucose[17,18] and evaporated milk and glucose—but data are not as available.

Following is the formula for the cream-gelatin extender that is very popular presently.

Cream-Gelatin Extender

    88.7 ml half-and-half cream
    1.3 g Knox gelatin
    10.0 ml distilled water
    1000 units penicillin/ml
    1 mg dihydrostreptomycin/ml
    200 units Polymixin B/ml
    Heat cream to 95°C (203°F) for 2 to 4 minutes.
    Autoclave gelatin in 10 ml water.

Mix hot cream with gelatin.
Cool and add antibiotics.

In practice most of the extended semen has resulted from proportions of one part raw semen to one to four parts extender.[50] This is usually sufficient to breed the number of mares currently in estrus, and no exacting concentration per insemination is calculated. Exacting trials to determine number of viable sperm needed per insemination for optimum conception are lacking. Concentrations of 500×10^6 in a volume of 10 to 30 ml is a common unit.[90,93] Concentration of 100×10^6 sperm in raw semen has equaled 500×10^6 in conception in one trial.[88] Low numbers of sperm (40, 80, and 160×10^6) have been used in testing frozen semen, but comparisons are difficult to make since conception rates ranged from 5 to 35 percent. The difficulty may have been in numbers or in processing.[85]

If 500×10^6 motile sperm are used per insemination then 23 mares may be bred from a single normal ejaculate.

Example

Volume—60 ml
Concentration—300×10^6/ml
Motility—70%
Normality—90%

$$\frac{\text{Vol} \times \text{Conc} \times \% \text{ Motile} \times \% \text{ Normal}}{500 \times 10^6} = \text{units}$$

$$\frac{60 \times 300 \times 10^6 \times .7 \times .9}{500 \times 10^6} = 23 \text{ units}$$

Stallion semen has been frozen in ampules, straws, and pellets. Recovery rates have been approximately 60 to 80 percent and some even better.[72]

Semen is usually centrifuged and the seminal fluids discarded and replaced with the extender. This affords greater immediate livability and storage.[102] Apparently the high sodium chloride content of seminal fluids is detrimental during freezing.

One of the extenders giving the best conception rate was reported by Nishikawa and Shinomiya[74] and is presented here. This may be used for processing in ampules or straws.

The colloidal substance is filtered from the semen with several layers of gauze and then extender 1 is added at a ratio of 7:3. The extended semen is centrifuged at 600 to 800 g for 10 minutes. The fluid portion is discarded leaving 2 to 4 ml of concentrated sperm. This is again extended with the same volume of extender 1. An equal volume of extender 2 is then added and the extended semen may be ampuled or put into straws before vapor freezing.[74,75] Apparently, equilibration is not necessary.[73]

Semen has been frozen in pellets with good recovery; however, conception rates are not reported as high as those resulting from straws. Oshida et al.[81] developed

HF-20 Extender

	First extender	Second extender
Glucose	5%	First extender
Lactose	.3	plus 10% glycerol
Na-citrate	.3	
Na-phosphate	.05	
K-Na-tartrate	.05	
Egg yolk	2.5–5.0	
Penicillin	250 μ/ml	
Streptomycin	250 mg/ml	

the following formula and bred 98 mares with a conception rate of 34.7 percent. Five stallions were used and rates varied from 11.1 to 66.6 percent, so the effect of the stallion must be considered.

The semen is prediluted 1:1 with 5 percent glucose containing 5 percent egg yolk. The mixture is centrifuged 20 minutes at 1300 *g* and the supernatant discarded. The above extender is then added at a ratio of 1:2 or 1:3 and equilibrated for 2 to 3 hours. Pellets of .2 ml are then frozen on dry ice and transferred to liquid nitrogen for storage. Conception rates of 35 to 60 percent have been reported in various breeds of horses.[82]

PROCESSING HUMAN SEMEN

The semen of man appears to demand less critical processing than domestic animals. Extenders have been based on those used for the bull, with few modifications. Apparently the study of human sperm constituents and their physiology has not attracted extensive research. It therefore appears fortunate that many extenders and methods do actually work.

Fresh or liquid semen is usually used without extension because the demand for breeding numerous women to one man is not the purpose. The purpose is to bring about a single pregnancy in the most definitive manner.

Frozen semen allows banking of semen, particularly by those men who plan to be vasectomized. Successful storage has produced viable sperm 10 years after processing.[36,108] Loss of motility was minimal, 0 to 30 percent, and figures of 7 abnormalities out of 571 births or about 1 percent abnormal progeny was far lower than the 6 percent average in the population. Abortions also were lower—50 of 621 pregnancies versus 10 to 15 percent in the general population.

Extender		
Yolk	10%	
Glycerol	5.5	
Sugar medium	84.5	
7.5% Glucose		30%
10% Lactose		40%
18% Raffinose		30%

One method of extending and freezing man's semen consists of an extender of 28 percent egg yolk and 72 percent citrate/fructose/glycerol buffer.[44] This buffer is 28 percent glycerol. The semen and buffer are mixed gradually after the semen liquefies. The ampules are then equilibrated for 30 minutes and then frozen in liquid nitrogen vapor.

Another method consists of allowing the semen to liquefy at room temperature and then placing it in a protective medium. The extender consists of 20 percent egg yolk, 14 percent glycerol, and 66 percent glucose/sodium citrate solution. Penicillin, streptomycin, and glycine are added and the solution heated at 56°C (133°F) for 30 minutes and adjusted to a pH of 7.2 to 7.4. Semen is then mixed with the extender and placed in glass ampules and frozen in a biological freezer.[13] Pregnancies have occurred in 42.6 percent of the cases compared to 69 percent where fresh semen was used.

CONCLUSION

The brief descriptions given in this chapter give only generalities for processing semen. Exacting procedures should be sought by the individual seriously considering processing semen. Numerous semen businesses are worldwide in scope and process millions of units of frozen semen annually. Their reputation is tested every time they sell a unit, and therefore quality is a must with them. Experienced personnel, mechanized processing, and standardized procedures yield quality. Semen from tested and proven sires is available from them, and the reader is directed to the National Association of Animal Breeders for names and addresses of these companies.

Custom freezing services are available for the individual who feels he has an outstanding sire and wishes to use him through an artificial insemination program.

WHAT DID YOU LEARN?

1 What method of selecting sires is most beneficial? Why?
2 When is liquid semen use advantageous?
3 What does 60–90 NR mean? What is normal for dairy cattle?
4 What four components are present in the extender used for freezing bull semen?
5 Discuss the types of packages for processed semen.
6 Calculate the number of potential breedings from the following bull ejaculate using frozen straws as the method of processing.
   Volume—9 ml
   Concentration—800 X 10^6/ml
   Motility—80%
   Normality—95%
7 How many viable sperm are needed to inseminate a sow?
8 Why aren't pellets more popular?

9 Which conserves storage space—straws or ampules?
10 Where could you obtain the addresses of the larger semen processing businesses or a local custom processor?

REFERENCES

1   Aamdal, J. and K. Anderson. 1968. Freezing of ram semen in straws. *Proc. 6th Int. Congr. on Anim. Reprod. and A.I.* 2:977–981.
2   Adler, H. C., C. Jespersen, J. H. Meding, and N. O. Rasbech. 1968. Breeding efficiency of bull semen frozen in straws and in pellets. *Proc. 6th Int. Congr. on Anim. Reprod. and A.I.* 2:981–983.
3   Almquist, J. O. 1959. Efficient, low cost results using milk-glycerol diluent. *A.I. Digest* 7:11–14, 27.
4   Almquist, J. O., R. J. Branas, and K. A. Barber. 1976. Postpuberal changes in semen production of Charolais bulls ejaculated at high frequency and the relation between testicular measurements and sperm output. *J. Anim. Sci.* 42:670–676.
5   Almquist, J. O. and D. C. Cunningham. 1967. Reproductive capacity of beef bulls. I. Postpuberal changes in semen production at different ejaculation frequencies. *J. Anim. Sci.* 26:174–181.
6   Almquist, J. O., R. J. Flipse, and D. L. Thacker. 1954. Diluters for bovine semen. IV. Fertility of bovine spermatozoa in heated homogenized milk and skim milk. *J. Dairy Sci.* 37:1303–1307.
7   Amann, R. P. 1962. Reproductive capacity of dairy bulls. III. The effect of ejaculation frequency, unilateral vasectomy, and age on spermatogenesis. *Amer. J. Anat.* 110:49–67.
8   ———. 1970. Sperm production rates. In Johnson, Gomes, and VanDemark, eds. *The Testis.* Vol. I. Academic Press, New York. Ch. 7, pp. 433–482.
9   Arhipovec, A. I. 1959. Artificial insemination of sows with stored semen. *Anim. Breed. Abstr.* 27:438.
10 Baker, R. D., P. J. Dziuk, and H. W. Norton. 1968. Effect of volume of semen, number of sperm and drugs on transport of sperm in artificially inseminated gilts. *J. Anim. Sci.* 27:88–93.
11 Barker, C. A. V. 1968. The preparation of dairy goat semen for freezing. *Proc. 6th Int. Congr. on Anim. Reprod. and A.I.* 2:1611–1612.
12 Barriere, J. 1968. Economical and technical efficiency of pellet freezing of bull semen. *Proc. 6th Int. Congr. on Anim. Reprod. and A.I.* 2:993–996.
13 Behrman, S. J. and D. R. Ackerman. 1969. Freeze preservation of human sperm. *Amer. J. Obstet. and Gynecol.* 103:654–661.
14 Bennett, G. H., C. O'Hagan, and D. L. Stewart. 1968. The effect of length of storage time and numbers of spermatozoa on the fertility of diluted boar semen. *Proc. 6th Int. Congr. on Anim. Reprod. and A.I.* 2:997–1000.
15 Berndtson, W. E. 1977. Methods for quantifying mammalian spermatogenesis: A review. *J. Anim. Sci.* 44:818–833.
16 Berndtson, W. E., B. W. Pickett, and C. D. Rugg. 1976. Procedures for field handling of bovine semen in plastic straws. *Proc. 6th Tech. Conf. on A.I. and Reprod.* Pp. 51–60.
17 Berry, R. O. 1958. Diluters for stallion semen. *Southwestern Vet.* 11:199–200.

18 Berry, R. O. and P. J. Gazder. 1960. The viability of stallion spermatozoa as influenced by storage media and by antibiotics. *Southwestern Vet.* 13:217–220

19 Bialy, G. and V. R. Smith. 1957. Freeze-drying of bovine spermatozoa. *J. Dairy Sci.* 40:739–745.

20 Bielanski, W. and S. Wierzbowski. 1961. "Depletion test" in stallions. *Proc. 4th Int. Congr. on Anim. Reprod. and A.I.* 2:279–282.

21 Boyd, L. J. and N. L. VanDemark. 1957. Spermatogenic capacity of the male bovine. I. A measurement technique. *J. Dairy Sci.* 40:689–697.

22 Bratton, R. W., R. H. Foote, and C. R. Henderson. 1954. The relationship between fertility and the number of spermatozoa inseminated. *J. Dairy Sci.* 37:1353–1356.

23 Cassou, R. 1968. Miniaturization of straws. *Proc. 6th Int. Congr. on Anim. Reprod. and A.I.* 2:1009–1012.

24 Colas, G. 1975. Effect of initial freezing temperature, addition of glycerol and dilution on the survival and fertilizing ability of deep-frozen ram semen. *J. Reprod. Fert.* 42:277–285.

25 Coulter, G. H. and R. H. Foote. 1977. Effects of package, extender, and light on stored frozen bull spermatozoa. *J. Dairy Sci.* 60:1428–1432.

26 Crabo, B., B. Gustafsson, L. Nicander, and A. R. Rao. 1971. Subnormal testicular function in a bull concealed by phagocytosis of abnormal spermatozoa in the efferent ductules. *J. Reprod. Fert.* 26:393–396.

27 Dunn, H. O. and R. H. Foote. 1958. Fertility of bull semen stored at room temperature for six days. *J. Dairy Sci.* 41:732. (Abstr.)

28 Dziuk, P. J. 1958. Dilution and storage of boar semen. *J. Anim. Sci.* 17:548–553.

29 Ennen, B. D., W. E. Berndtson, R. G. Mortimer, and B. W. Pickett. 1976. Effect of processing procedures on motility of bovine spermatozoa frozen in .25-ml straws. *J. Anim. Sci.* 43:651–656.

30 Filseth, O. 1969. Conception rates using the French straw. *Buskap. Avdratt.* 21:165. *Anim. Breed. Abstr.* 38-1349.

31 ———. 1970. Conception rates using the French straw. *Buskap Avdratt* 22:25. *Anim. Breed. Abstr.* 38-3638.

32 First, N. L., A. Sevinge, and H. A. Henneman. 1961. Fertility of frozen and unfrozen ram semen. *J. Anim. Sci.* 20:79–84.

33 Foley, C. W., C. J. Heindreich, and H. W. Jones. 1963. The development of procedures and diluents capable of extending the viability of swine spermatozoa. *Res. Prog. Rep.,* no. 72, Purdue Univ.

34 Foster, J., J. O. Almquist, and R. C. Martig. 1970. Reproductive capacity of beef bulls. IV. Changes in sexual behavior and semen characteristics among successive ejaculations. *J. Anim. Sci.* 30:245–252.

35 Fraser, A. F. 1968. Progress in the artificial insemination of sheep with frozen semen. *Proc. 6th Int. Congr. on Anim. Reprod. and A.I.* 2:1033–1035.

36 Freund, M. and J. Wiederman. 1964. Recovery of large numbers of motile spermatozoa in diluted human semen after storage of –85°C for periods of up to ten months. *Bull. N.Y. Acad. Med.* 40:72.

37 Gebauer, M. R., B. W. Pickett, J. L. Voss, and E. E. Swierstra. 1974. Reproductive physiology of the stallion: Daily sperm output and testicular measurements. *J.A.V.M.A.* 165:711–713.

38 Gebauer, M. R., B. W. Pickett, and E. E. Swierstra. 1974. Reproductive physiology of the stallion. III. Extra-gonadal transit time and sperm reserves. *J. Anim. Sci.* 39:737–742.

39 Gerrits, R. J., E. F. Graham, and C. L. Cole. 1962. Effect of collection interval on the characteristics of the ejaculate of the boar. *J. Anim. Sci.* 21:1022. (Abstr.)

40 Goffaux, M. 1968. Fertility of bull semen frozen according to 2 different techniques, one involving pellets, the other straws. *Proc. 6th Int. Congr. on Anim. Reprod. and A.I.* 2:1041–1043.

41 Graham, E. F. 1966. Comments on freezing spermatozoa. *Proc. 1st Tech. Conf. on A.I. and Reprod.* Pp. 45–56.

42 Graham, E. F., W. E. Erickson, and N. D. Bayley. 1957. Effect of glycerol equilibration on frozen bovine spermatozoa. *J. Dairy Sci.* 40:510–515.

43 Graham, E. F., E. V. Larson, and B. G. Crabo. 1974. Freezing and freeze-drying bovine spermatozoa. *Proc. 6th Tech. Conf. on A.I. and Reprod.* pp. 14–20.

44 Greep, R. O. 1975. Reproductive physiology. In T. D. Glover, ed. *Recent Progress in the Study of Male Reproductive Physiology. MTP International Review of Science.* 8:263–267.

45 Hafs, H. D., R. S. Hoyt, and R. W. Bratton. 1959. Libido, sperm characteristics, sperm output and fertility of mature dairy bulls ejaculated daily or weekly for thirty-two weeks. *J. Dairy Sci.* 42:626–636.

46 Hahn, R., B. Cassou, and K. Eibl. 1969. A comparison of straws and ampules in the freezing of bull semen. Dtsch. Tieraerztl. Wochenschr. 76:346–350.

47 Hahn, J., R. H. Foote, and G. E. Seidel, Jr. 1969. Testicular growth and related sperm output in dairy bulls. *J. Anim. Sci.* 29:41–47

48 Harrison, R. A. P. 1976. A highly efficient method for washing mammalian spermatozoa. *J. Reprod. Fert.* 48:347–353.

49 Healey, P. 1969. Effect of freezing on the ultrastructure of the spermatozoon of some domestic animals. *J. Reprod. Fert.* 18:21–27.

50 Hughes, J. P. and R. G. Loy. 1970. Artificial insemination in the equine: A comparison of natural breeding and artificial insemination of mares using semen from six stallions. *Cornell Vet.* 60:463–475.

51 Inskeep, E. K. and C. E. Cooke. 1968. Artificial insemination and preservation of semen. *Proc. Symposium on Physiology of Reprod. in Sheep,* Oklahoma State Univ., Stillwater. Pp. 162–180.

52 Jondet, R. 1968. Four years of rapid freezing of bull semen in liquid nitrogen vapor. *Proc. 6th Int. Congr. on Anim. Reprod. and A.I.* 2:1057–1059.

53 ———. 1972. Adaptation to 0.20 ml. straws of the vertical freezing method in the liquid nitrogen vapour phase. *Proc. 7th Int. Congr. on Anim. Reprod. and A.I.* 2:1350–1351.

54 Jones, R. C., I. C. A. Martin, and K. R. Lapwood. 1969. Studies of the artificial insemination of sheep: The effects on fertility of diluting ram semen, stage of oestrus of the ewe at insemination, and injection of synthetic oxytocin. *Australian J. Agr. Res.* 20:141–150.

55 Licon, M. A. 1971. Effect of age and concentration of sperm on conception rate and litter size in swine. M.S. thesis, Texas A&M Univ., College Station.

56 Linares, I. A. 1969. A comparison of the methods of freezing semen in straws and ampules for artificial insemination. *Zootec. Vet.* 24:181–187.

57 Lindstrom, U., B. G. Holmstrom, and L. Jokinen. 1972. Pellets: Experiences and results of storage over 3 years. *Proc. 7th Int. Congr. on Anim. Reprod. and A.I.* 2:1427–1435.

58 Lino, B. F. and A. W. H. Braden. 1972. Output of spermatozoa in rams. I. Relationship with testicular output of spermatozoa and the effect of ejaculations. *Australia J. Biol. Sci.* 25:351–358.

59   Lino, B. G., A. W. H. Braden, and K. E. Turnbull. 1967. Fate of unejaculated sper-
     matozoa. *Nature* 213:594–595.
60   Madden, D. H. L. 1961. A method of obtaining high fertility level with the artificial
     insemination of farm pigs. *Proc. 4th Int. Congr. on Anim. Reprod. and A.I.* 4:851–854.
61   Malmberg, G. and R. Israelsson. 1972. A comparison of breeding efficiency of semen
     preserved at room temperature and deep frozen semen. *Proc. 7th Int. Congr. on Anim.
     Reprod. and A.I.* 2:1384–1387.
62   McCall, J. P., Jr. and A. M. Sorensen, Jr. 1971. Evaporated milk as an extender for
     stallion semen. *A.I. Digest* 19:8–10.
63   McFee, A. F., L. J. Boyd, and E. W. Swanson. 1958. A comparison of two diluents in
     single-service glass ampules for routine artificial insemination of cattle. *J. Dairy Sci.*
     41:732. (Abstr.)
64   Meding, J. H. 1970. Fertilizing efficiency of bull semen frozen in straws or pellets.
     Arsberetn. Inst. Sterilitetsforsk. K. Vet.–og Landbohojsk. Pp. 249–288.
65   Molinari, G., M. Valpreda, and R. Maletto. 1968. Observations on the fertility of semen
     stored at 5°C and frozen semen. *Proc. 6th Int. Congr. on Anim. Reprod. and A.I.*
     2:1099–1101.
66   Morales, J. R. and O. Duverger. 1967. Three different techniques for freezing of cattle
     semen and their conception results. *Zootecnia y sanidad animal en Cuba.* Havana,
     Cuba: Instituto del Libro. pp. 33–36.
67   Mortimer, R. G., W. E. Berndtson, B. W. Pickett, and L. Ball. 1976. Fertility of frozen
     bovine spermatozoa packaged in continental straws or ampules. *J. Dairy Sci.* 59:1595–
     1598.
68   Nagase, H. and E. F. Graham. 1964. Pelleted semen: Comparison of different extenders
     and processes on fertility of bovine spermatozoa. *Proc. 5th Int. Congr. on Anim. Reprod.
     and A.I.* 4:387–391.
69   Nagase, H. and T. Niwa. 1963. Studies on deep-freezing technique for bull semen. III.
     Deep-freezing of bull semen in tablet form. *Jap. J. Anim. Reprod.* 9:73.
70   ———. 1964. Deep freezing bull semen in concentrated pellet form. I. Factors affecting
     survival of spermatozoa. *Proc. 5th Int. Congr. On Anim. Reprod. and A.I.* 4:410–415.
71   National Association of Animal Breeders, Box 1033, Columbia, Missouri 65201.
72   Nishikawa, Y. 1975. Studies on the preservation of raw and frozen horse semen. *J.
     Reprod. Fert. Suppl.* 23:99–104.
73   Nishikawa, Y., A. Iritani, and S. Shinomiya. 1972. Studies on the protective effects of
     egg yolk and glycerol on the freezability of horse spermatozoa. *Proc. 7th Int. Congr.
     on Anim. Reprod. and A.I.* 2:1546–1549.
74   Nishikawa, Y. and S. Shinomiya. 1972. Freezability of horse spermatozoa in the non-
     breeding season. *Proc. 7th Int. Congr. on Anim. Reprod. and A.I.* 1:1540–1543.
75   Nishikawa, Y., Y. Waide and S. Shinomiya. 1968. Studies on deep freezing of horse
     spermatozoa. *Proc. 6th Int. Congr. on Anim. Reprod. and A.I.* 2:1589–1591.
76   Niwa, T. 1961. Researches and practices in the artificial insemination of pigs. *Proc. 4th
     Int. Congr. on Anim. Reprod. and A.I.* 1:83–115.
77   Norman, C. 1972. Comparison of motility and fertilizing capacity of buffalo and cattle
     sperm preserved at ambient temperatures in coconut milk extender (CME). *Proc. 7th
     Int. Congr. on Anim. Reprod. and A.I.* 2:1312–1314.
78   Norman, C., C. E. Johnson, and I. D. Porterfield. 1958. Livability of bovine sper-
     matozoa at room temperatures in a coconut milk–citrate–calcium carbonate diluent.
     J. Dairy Sci. 47:733. (Abstr.)
79   Norman, C., N. H. Joshi, A. Khan, and A. V. Rai. 1968. Conservation of buffalo semen

at room temperature in coconut milk extender (CME). *Proc. 7th Int. Congr. on Anim. Reprod. and A.I.* 2:1115–1117.

80 Norman, C., Y. Udagawa, M. Biedma, O. Bojanovich, D. Grove, T. N. Docker, A. V. Arevalo, N. H. Joshi, and A. V. Rai. 1968. Advancement of artificial insemination programs in developing countries through the use of coconut milk extender (CME). *Proc. 7th Int. Congr. on Anim. Reprod. and A.I.* 2:1119–1121.

81 Oshida, H., S. Horiuchi, H. Takahashi, T. Tomizuka, and H. Nagase. 1968. Fertility of frozen stallion semen and some factors affecting to it. *Proc. 6th Int. Congr. on Anim. Reprod. and A.I.* 2:1597–1599.

82 Oshida, H., T. Tomizuka, J. Masaki, A. Hanada, and H. Nagase. 1972. Some observations on freezing of stallion semen. *Proc. 7th Int. Congr. on Anim. Reprod. and A.I.* 2:1535–1537.

83 Osinowo, O. and S. Salamon. 1976. Examination of some processing methods for freezing boar semen. *Australian J. Biol. Sci.* 29:325–333.

84 ———. 1976. Fertility test of frozen boar semen. *Australian J. Biol. Sci.* 29:335–339.

85 Pace, M. M. and J. J. Sullivan. 1975. Effect of timing of insemination, numbers of spermatozoa and extender components on the pregnancy rate in mares inseminated with frozen stallion semen. *J. Reprod. Fert. Suppl.* 23:115–121.

86 Paredis, F. and M. Vandeplassche. 1961. Effect of initial motility, number and age of spermatozoa on farrowing rate and litter size. *Proc. 4th Int. Congr. on Anim. Reprod. and A.I.* 4:828–831.

87 Pickett, B. W. 1970. Seasonal variation of stallion semen. *Proc. 3rd Tech. Conf. on A.I. and Reprod.* Pp. 52–59.

88 Pickett, B. W., D. G. Back, L. D. Burwash, and J. L. Voss. 1974. The effect of extenders, spermatozoal numbers and rectal palpation on equine fertility. *Proc. 5th Tech. Conf. on A.I. and Reprod.* Pp. 47–58.

89 Pickett, B. W., W. E. Berndtson, and J. J. Sullivan. 1976. Techniques for processing and packaging bovine semen. *Proc. 6th Tech. Conf. on A.I. and Reprod.* Pp. 23–29.

90 Pickett, B. W., L. D. Burwash, J. L. Voss, and D. G. Back. 1975. Effect of seminal extenders on equine fertility. *J. Anim. Sci.* 40:1136–1143.

91 Pickett, B. W., L. C. Faulkner, and J. L. Voss. 1975. Effect of season on some characteristics of stallion semen. *J. Reprod. Fert. Suppl.* 23:25–28.

92 Pickett, B. W., J. J. Sullivan, and G. E. Seidel, Jr. 1975. Reproductive physiology of the stallion. V. Effect of frequency of ejaculation on seminal characteristics and spermatozoal output. *J. Anim. Sci.* 40:917–923.

93 Pickett, B. W. and J. L. Voss. 1975. The effect of semen extenders and sperm number on mare fertility. *J. Reprod. Fert. Suppl.* 23:95–98.

94 ———. 1973. Reproductive management of the stallion. *Colo. State Univ. Exp. Sta. Gen. Series* 934.

95 Polge, C. 1956. The development of an artificial insemination service for pigs. *Anim. Breed. Abstr.* 24:209.

96 ———. 1956. Artificial insemination of pigs. *Vet. Rec.* 68:62.

97 Pursel, V. G. and L. A. Johnson. 1971. Procedure for the preservation of boar spermatozoa by freezing. *Agr. Res. Ser.* 44-227. Pp. 1–5.

98 ———. 1975. Freezing of boar spermatozoa: Fertilizing capacity with concentrated semen and a new thawing procedure. *J. Anim. Sci.* 40:99–102.

99 ———. 1976. Frozen boar spermatozoa: Methods of thawing pellets. *J. Anim. Sci.* 42:927–931.

100 Rajamannan, A. H. J. 1968. Spin freezing of semen. *Proc. 6th Int. Congr. on Anim. Reprod. and A.I.* 2:1145–1147.

101 ———. 1970. A method of packaging semen—the straw. *Proc. 3rd Tech. Conf. on A.I. and Reprod.* Pp. 49–51.

102 Rajamannan, A. H. J., R. Zemjanis, and J. Ellery. 1968. Freezing and fertility studies with stallion semen. *Proc. 6th Int. Congr. on Anim. Reprod. and A.I.* 2:1601–1604.

103 Roussel, J. D., O. T. Stallcup, and C. R. Austin. 1967. Selective phagocytosis of spermatozoa in the epididymis of bulls, rabbits and monkeys. *Fertil. and Steril.* 18:509–515.

104 Sainsbury, R. W. 1968. Freezing of ram semen in Cassou straws. *Proc. 6th Int. Congr. on Anim. Reprod. and A.I.* 2:1151–1152.

105 Salamon, S. and T. J. Robinson. 1962. Studies on the artificial insemination of Merino sheep. I. The effects of frequency and season of insemination, age of the ewe, rams, and milk diluents on lambing performance. *Australian J. Agri. Res.* 13:52–68.

106 ———. 1962. Studies on the artificial insemination of Merino sheep. II. The effects of semen diluents and storage on lambing performance. *Australian J. Agri. Res.* 13:271–281.

107 Salamon, S. and D. Visser. 1974. Fertility of ram spermatozoa frozen-stored for 5 years. *J. Reprod. Fert.* 37:433–435.

108 Sherman, J. K. 1973. Synopsis of the use of frozen human semen since 1964: State of the art of human semen banking. *Fertil. and Steril.* 24:397–412.

109 Signoret, J. P. 1970. Swine behavior in reproduction. In *Effect of Disease and Stress on Reproductive Efficiency in Swine.* Proc. Symp. sponsored by the National Pork Prod. Council, Federal Ext. Sv., Univ. Nebraska Coop. Ext. Sv., Iowa State Univ. Vet. Med. Res. Inst. and the Agr. Res. Sv. of U.S.D.A.

110 Singleton, Wayne L. 1975. New developments in using frozen boar semen. Swine Short Course, Texas Animal Agriculture Conference, Texas A&M Univ., College Station. Mimeo.

111 Smith, J. F., R. T. S. Boys, H. Drost, and S. G. Willson. 1975. A. I. of sheep with frozen semen. *Proc. of the New Zealand Soc. of Anim. Prod.* 35:71–77.

112 Sorensen, A. M., Jr. 1972. Straws vs. ampules—which way? *Proc. 21st and 22nd Beef Cattle Short Course,* Texas A&M Univ., College Station. Pp. 128–137.

113 Stewart, D. L. and G. H. Bennett. 1968. The minimum number of spermatozoa per frozen semen insemination compatible with normal fertility in cattle. *Proc. 6th Int. Congr. on Anim. Reprod. and A.I.* 2:1167–1170.

114 Sullivan, J. J. 1970. Sperm numbers required for optimum breeding efficiency in cattle. *Proc. 3rd Tech. Conf. on A.I. and Reprod.* Pp. 36–43.

115 Swierstra, E. E. 1968. A comparison of spermatozoa production and spermatozoa output of Yorkshire and Lacombe boars. *J. Reprod. Fertil.* 17:459–469.

116 ———. 1971. Sperm production of boars as measured from epididymal sperm reserves and quantitative testicular histology. *J. Reprod. Fertil.* 27:91–99.

117 ——— and G. W. Dyck. 1976. Influence of the boar and ejaculation frequency on pregnancy rate and embryonic survival in swine. *J. Anim. Sci.* 42:455–460.

118 Thacker, D. L. and J. O. Almquist. 1953. Diluters for bovine semen. I. Fertility and motility of bovine spermatozoa in boiled milk. *J. Dairy Sci.* 36:173–180.

119 VanDemark, N. L. and U. D. Sharma. 1957. Preliminary fertility results from the preservation of bovine semen at room temperatures. *Proc. Ann. Mtg., Amer. Dairy Sci. Assn.* Pp. 438–439.

120 Visser, D. and S. Salamon. 1974. Fertility following inseminations with frozen-thawed reconcentrated and unconcentrated ram semen. *Australian J. Biol. Sci.* 27:423–425.

121 Watson, P. F. and I. C. A. Martin. 1973. The response of ram spermatozoa to preparations of egg yolk in semen diluents during storage at 5 or –196°C. *Australian J. Biol. Sci.* 26:927–935.

122 ———. 1975. Effects of egg yolk, glycerol and the freezing rate on the viability and acrosomal structures of frozen ram spermatozoa. *Australian J. Biol. Sci.* 28:153–159.

Macroscopic Female Functional Anatomy

When you have completed this chapter you should be able to:

- Trace the ovum from its beginning to the exterior,
- Distinguish anatomical differences in anatomy of the reproductive system among species,
- Identify the structures on the ovary and relate them to their function,
- Classify the uteri of different species according to configuration, and
- Understand some of the effects on conception due to anomalies of the reproductive system and available corrective measures.

The female anatomy section will be presented like that of the male, i.e., the germ cell will be traced from its origin to the exterior. The cow will be used as the base animal with differences discussed for other classes of livestock and the woman.

The female germ cell is called the ovum and grows in the ovary until its release into the oviduct. Fertilization occurs in the oviduct and the fertilized ovum passes into the uterus for growth and development. The ovum, which has now developed into a fetus, passes through the cervix, vagina, vestibule, and vulva to the outside (Fig. 7–1). Now let us discuss each of these structures and its function, again using the cow as the base animal (Figs. 7–2, 7–3, 7–4, 7–5, 7–6).

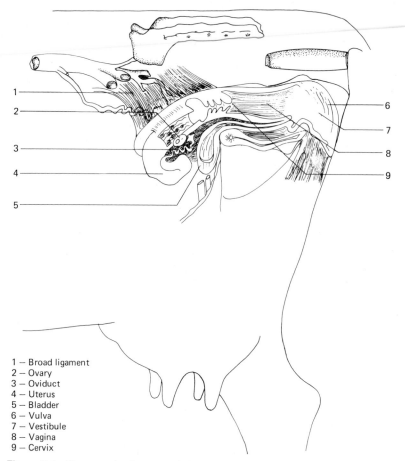

1 — Broad ligament
2 — Ovary
3 — Oviduct
4 — Uterus
5 — Bladder
6 — Vulva
7 — Vestibule
8 — Vagina
9 — Cervix

Figure 7-1 The reproductive tract of the cow.

OVARY (Ovaries: Egg Source)

The ovaries of the cow are oval in shape and located in the peritoneal cavity at the face of the pelvic arch. They are lateral and about on level with the middle of the pelvic opening (Fig. 7–1). The position is dictated by numerous factors. The rumen of the cow is located on the animal's left side. An enlarged rumen may displace the entire reproductive tract to the right side. It may also push it into the pelvic cavity proper. The reproductive tract stretches and relaxes with age so that, generally speaking, the whole system will lie lower in the caudal peritoneal cavity. The main support comes from the mesovarium of the broad ligament.

Support

The *broad ligament* (Fig. 7–2/1) supports the reproductive tract. The *mesovarium* (Fig. 7–2/2) is the cranial portion and is a peritoneal fold that originates on the

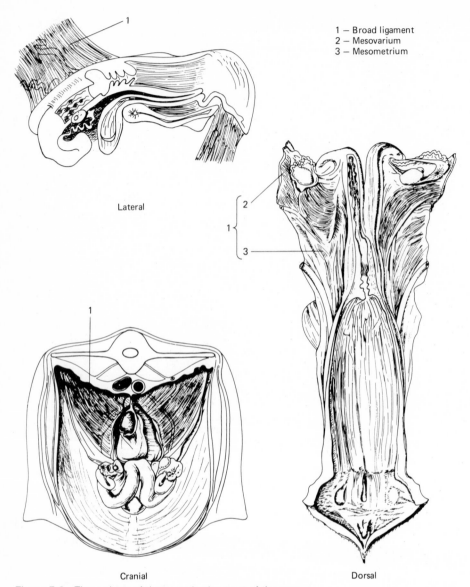

1 — Broad ligament
2 — Mesovarium
3 — Mesometrium

Lateral

Cranial   Dorsal

Figure 7-2   Three views of the reproductive tract of the cow.

lateral walls of the pelvic cavity and attaches to the hilus of the ovary and continues into the *mesometrium* (Fig. 7–2/3) supporting the uterus. The ovary is anchored in place by the *proper ligament,* which is also a portion of the broad ligament. The arteries, veins, lymphatics, and nerves of the ovary are located in these ligaments. The ovarian artery branches off the aorta to supply the ovary. Additional blood supply is derived from branches of the uterine artery.

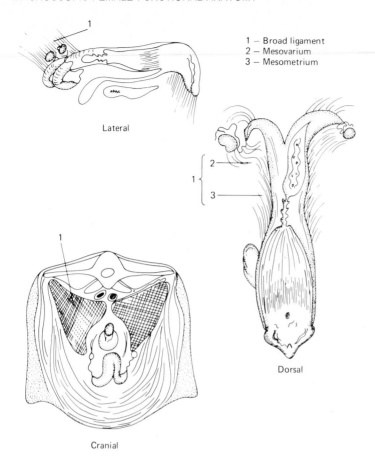

1 — Broad ligament
2 — Mesovarium
3 — Mesometrium

Lateral

Dorsal

Cranial

Figure 7-3   Three views of the reproductive tract of the ewe.

The ovary of the cow is oval and slightly flattened (Fig. 7–7). It measures approximately 30 to 40 mm (1.5 in) X 20 to 30 mm (1 in) X 10 to 20 mm (.6 in) (Table 7–1) and the size is affected greatly by the stage of the reproductive cycle. Each weighs 6 to 20 grams. The ovary has four characteristic structures on it: follicle, corpus hemorrhagicum, corpus luteum, and corpus albicans.[23]

Follicle (Follicles: Little Bag)

The follicle will vary in size from 6 to 20 mm (.5 in) and appear as a clear blister bulging on the surface of the ovary (Fig. 7–7/1). Many will be embedded to a large extent and appear as a clear area on the surface. These follicles grow from microscopic cells and are twofold in purpose: they produce or contain the growing ovum and produce and store the female excitatory hormone called estrogen. Upon matura-

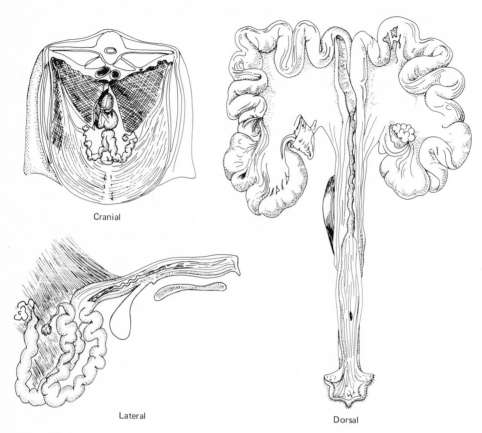

Cranial

Lateral

Dorsal

Figure 7-4 Three views of the reproductive tract of the sow.

tion the follicle ruptures to release the ovum to be picked up by the oviduct and moved on through the remainder of the system. A single follicle ruptures every three weeks.

Corpus Hemorrhagicum (Corpora Hemorrhagica: Body Bloodclot)

The rupture point on the follicle everts on the surface as the follicle collapses and a small hemorrhage occurs. This results in a fluffy tissue that is red in color and is called the corpus hemorrhagicum (CH). The CH is short-lived and develops into a corpus luteum in two to three days.

Corpus Luteum (Corpora Lutea: Body Yellow)

The cells lining the CH change in shape and content and multiply to develop a mass of cells that have a yellow pigment, therefore the name yellow body. These cells

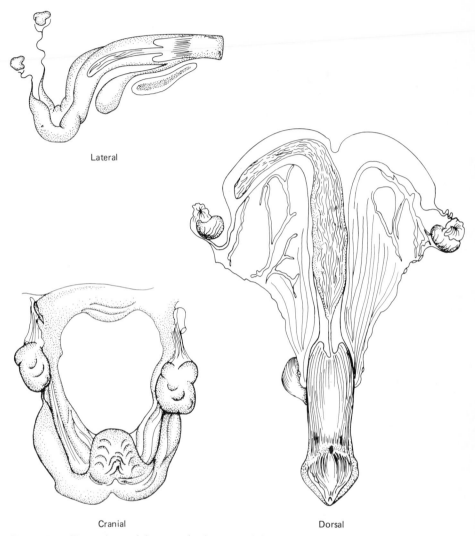

Lateral

Cranial   Dorsal

Figure 7-5 Three views of the reproductive tract of the mare.

multiply until they fill the cavity of the ruptured follicle. The size of the corpus luteum (CL) will be very similar in size to the old follicle. The main difference will be in the protrusion of a teatlike structure at the point of rupture called a papillum (Fig. 7–7/3). The color is not always yellow[11] but may range from a light yellow to brick red. The cells may not completely fill the cavity and leave a pool of fluid in the center of the CL. This apparently is normal. The CL has a single purpose—to produce a second female sex hormone called progesterone, which quiets the reproductive system and maintains pregnancy.

The lifespan of the CL related to healthy cells producing progesterone is ap-

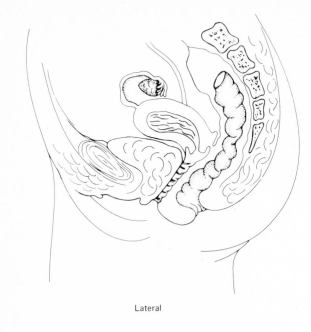

Lateral

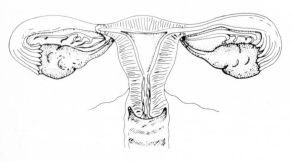

Frontal

Figure 7-6 Frontal and lateral view of the reproduction tract of the woman.

proximately 12 days, and the cell mass itself may remain several more days before degenerating and disappearing. The CL of pregnancy persists throughout gestation in the cow.

Corpus Albicans (Corpora Albicantia: Body White)

The degenerating CL is invaded by connective tissue and the cell components are broken down and resorbed by the tissue. Remaining is a scar consisting of the connective tissue, which appears as a white area at the site of the CL papillum. All corpora albicantia (CA) are not white but might be shades of yellow to brick red. The scar may remain for months. There is no known function besides removal of the luteal tissue and returning the ovary to its normal shape, size, and function.

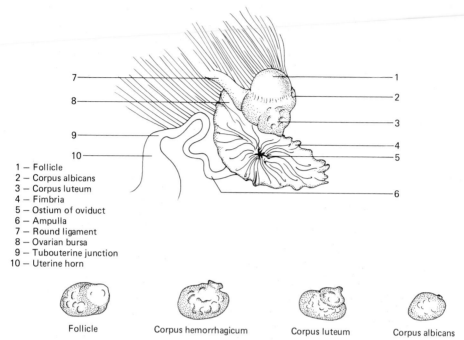

1 — Follicle
2 — Corpus albicans
3 — Corpus luteum
4 — Fimbria
5 — Ostium of oviduct
6 — Ampulla
7 — Round ligament
8 — Ovarian bursa
9 — Tubouterine junction
10 — Uterine horn

Follicle   Corpus hemorrhagicum   Corpus luteum   Corpus albicans

Figure 7-7   Ovary and surrounding structures of the cow.

The ovaries of the ewe appear as miniature cow ovaries with the exception of the number of follicles, CH, CL, and CA (Fig. 7–8). The ewe releases two and sometimes three ova at the time of ovulation, therefore there may be two or three follicles protruding followed by multiple CH, CL, and CA. The structures, support, and function are the same as those of the cow. The ovaries measure 5 to 20 mm (.5 in) X 4 to 12 mm (.3 in) X 4 to 12 mm (.3 in). The bursa or sac surrounding the ovary is deeper and more distinct. The doe (goat) is similar to the ewe.[19]

The ovary of the sow (Fig. 7–9) is best described as looking like a cluster of grapes. The ovaries are oval, measuring 30 to 50 mm (1.5 in) long and 20 to 30 mm (1 in) across. There are multiple follicles present, and when these rupture nearly all at one time there form multiple CH, CL, and CA. As many as 8 to 15 may be counted on a single ovary. Follicles are not as transparent as in the ruminants. There is a pink or red cast to the follicles and there are very few embedded follicles. They protrude very distinctly on the surface. When rupture occurs there is a definite coning or pointing of the rupture point and no papillum forms as in the cow and ewe. The corpus luteum then appears as a conical body and is dark red in color.

The sow ovary lacks the support of the cow and ewe. The mesovarium is long, the proper ligament is not as tightly attached, and the ovaries lie loosely in the peritoneal cavity similar to the intestines.

Mare ovaries are bean or kidney shaped (Fig. 7–10). They are 60 to 80 mm (3 in) X 25 to 40 (1.5 in) X 20 to 30 mm (1 in), and a distinct depression or fossa is

Table 7-1 Comparative Anatomy of the Female Reproductive System (Nonpregnant)

Structure	Cow	Ewe	Sow	Mare	Woman
Ovary					
shape	almond	almond	grape cluster	kidney	almond
length (mm)	35	15	40	70	30
width (mm)	25	10	25	35	20
thickness (mm)	15	10	25	25	10
weight per ovary av (gm)	6–20	3–4	3–10	40–80	5–15
mature follicle (no.)	1–2	1–4	10–30	1–2	1–2
mature follicle size (mm)	6–20	5–10	8–12	15–50	10–15
corpus luteum size (mm)	8–26	6–12	10–15	10–30	10–12
papillum on CL	yes	yes	no	no	slight
Oviduct					
length (cm)	20	17	20	25	10
Uterus					
type	bipartite	bipartite	bicornuate	bipartite	simplex
horn length (cm)	25–45	10–12	40–140	15–25	—
body length (cm)	2–4	1–2	3–5	15–20	5
lining	caruncles	caruncles	folds	folds	folds
Cervix					
length (cm)	5–10	4–10	10–24	7–8	2
outside diameter (cm)	2–4	1–2	2–3	3–4	2
folds	annular	annular	bumps and grooves	longitudinal	longitudinal
Vagina					
length (cm)	24–30	10–14	10–24	15–30	8
Hymen	slight	prominent	prominent	prominent	prominent
Vestibule (cm)	10–12	2–3	6–8	10–12	none

Numerous factors may affect measurements: age, breed, parity, and nutrition.
Measurements are based on several references.[1, 5, 6, 7, 8, 9, 10, 11, 14, 15, 20, 21, 25, 27]

present on the lesser curvature. They are firm to the touch, and several follicles may be present on the ovaries measuring up to 3 or 4 cm (1.5 in), although only one usually ruptures at ovulation. Ovulation occurs in the ovulation fossa,[3] and the ovum passes into the oviduct, which lies over this area. The corpus hemorrhagicum is not prominent and does not form a papillum as the corpus luteum develops. This makes it difficult to distinguish structures easily by palpation per rectum. The corpus albicans forms as in other species.

The ovaries lie in a position similar to those of the cow. The distance forward is greater and they lie very near the kidneys and more lateral. The mesovarium and proper ligament resemble those of the cow, and the ovarian bursa formed by these ligaments is rather shallow.

The human ovaries are oval and flattened 30 to 40 X 20 X 10 mm (1.5 X .8 X .4 in) (Fig. 7–11). They have numerous developing follicles embedded and on the surface. One ovum is shed at a time, so the corpora lutea are limited. The ovaries are supported lateral to the uterus in the pelvic opening by the suspensory ligaments and to the uterus by the ovarian ligaments, which are parts of the broad ligaments.

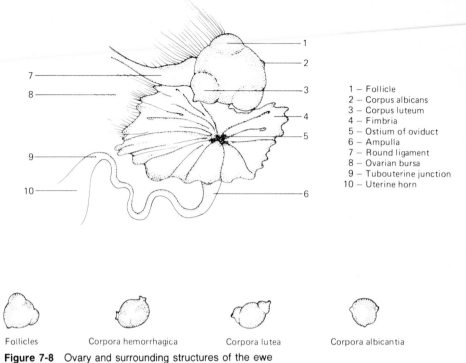

1 – Follicle
2 – Corpus albicans
3 – Corpus luteum
4 – Fimbria
5 – Ostium of oviduct
6 – Ampulla
7 – Round ligament
8 – Ovarian bursa
9 – Tubouterine junction
10 – Uterine horn

Follicles   Corpora hemorrhagica   Corpora lutea   Corpora albicantia

Figure 7-8   Ovary and surrounding structures of the ewe

Because of the upright stance of the woman, the orientation must be shifted approximately 90 degrees from that of the domestic animals (Fig. 7–6).

The cow and mare are large enough that the ovaries may be palpated per rectum. With some experience an individual may identify the various structures, and in fact that is how much of our research data are derived. The follicles are usually very turgid and feel like marbles on the surface. Follicles as small as 4 to 5 mm (.2 in) may be distinguished in some animals. The number and size is determined in this manner, and growth of the follicle may be charted by repeated palpation. When the follicle of the cow or mare reaches its optimum size it will soften and feel rather spongy prior to ovulation.

The corpus hemorrhagicum is not easily distinguished from the mass of the ovary except for a few hours following ovulation. If routine palpation is being conducted and ovulation is charted, then the probability of finding a CH is enhanced. The cavity may be probed with the finger, but it fills quickly with luteal cells and is on its way to forming a corpus luteum. The CH of the mare is in the ovulation fossa.

The corpus luteum is distinguished in the cow by the prominent papillum. This forms quickly and may be felt about 2 days after ovulation. It may still be rather soft, and, as time advances, it becomes firmer so that it has a thicker, firmer feel, like muscle, than the blister texture of a follicle. The papillum is not always present.

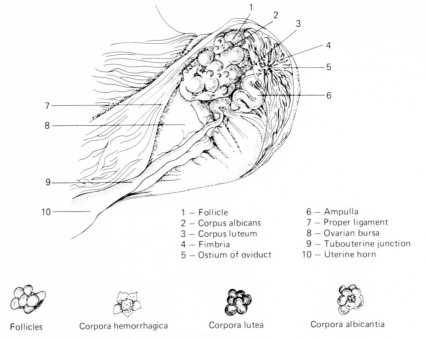

1 — Follicle   6 — Ampulla
2 — Corpus albicans   7 — Proper ligament
3 — Corpus luteum   8 — Ovarian bursa
4 — Fimbria   9 — Tubouterine junction
5 — Ostium of oviduct   10 — Uterine horn

Follicles   Corpora hemorrhagica   Corpora lutea   Corpora albicantia

Figure 7-9 Ovary and surrounding structures of the sow.

The CL of the mare does not form a papillum, and identification is dependent to a large extent on texture and location. It forms in the ovulation fossa, but as it fills the old follicular cavity it pushes into the body of the ovary.[21]

The corpus albicans is identifiable only in its early stages and may be traced only by repeated, frequent palpations.

Abnormalities may also be identified. Cystic follicles develop as a follicle fails to rupture and continues to grow. They may reach sizes much larger than the ovary itself. Persistent CL, although rare, may be identified by repeated palpations. Multiple ovulations stimulation in preparation for embryo transfers may be felt. Absence of any activity on the ovary of noncycling animals helps in making decisions for disposal.

Palpation per rectum in the sow has been practiced on a very limited scale. It takes a large sow and a small arm.

Other observations of the ovaries of most animals have been made through the use of a laparoscope.[23] This instrument allows observation via a lighted tube and manipulation of the ovaries by a probe or per rectum. The method is becoming very popular.

OVIDUCT (Oviducts: Egg Tube)

The oviduct may also be called the uterine tube, salpinx, or fallopian tube. The oviduct of the cow is a small tube 2 mm (.1 in) in diameter and 15 to 25 cm (6 in)

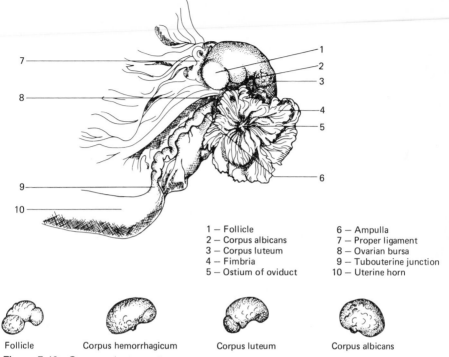

1 — Follicle	6 — Ampulla
2 — Corpus albicans	7 — Proper ligament
3 — Corpus luteum	8 — Ovarian bursa
4 — Fimbria	9 — Tubouterine junction
5 — Ostium of oviduct	10 — Uterine horn

Follicle   Corpus hemorrhagicum   Corpus luteum   Corpus albicans

Figure 7-10   Ovary and surrounding structures of the mare.

long. It is curving in configuration as it passes from the opening in the ovarian bursa near the ovary to the tubouterine junction at the uterine end. It functions as the site of fertilization and as a passageway for the fertilized ovum into the uterus.

Support

The *mesosalpinx* is a portion of the broad ligament that is continuous with the mesovarium and supports the oviduct. The oviduct is rather coiled and embedded in the thin mesosalpinx. Blood is supplied to the oviduct via branches from the uterine artery, which originates at the aorta.

The oviduct is divided into the infundibulum, ampulla, isthmus, and tubouterine portions from the terminal end to the uterus, in order. The latter is actually a junction only, but because of its importance in sperm transport it will be treated as a portion of the oviduct.

Infundibulum (Infundibulae: Funnel)

The terminal portion of the oviduct is called the infundibulum and is structured to receive the ovum following ovulation. The filmy terminal membrane is called the *fimbriated end* of the oviduct because of the fringed border. This portion normally

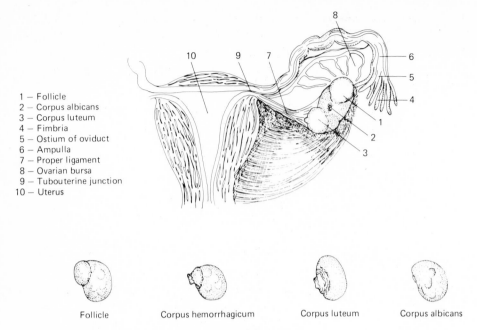

1 — Follicle
2 — Corpus albicans
3 — Corpus luteum
4 — Fimbria
5 — Ostium of oviduct
6 — Ampulla
7 — Proper ligament
8 — Ovarian bursa
9 — Tubouterine junction
10 — Uterus

Follicle   Corpus hemorrhagicum   Corpus luteum   Corpus albicans

Figure 7-11   Ovary and surrounding structures of the woman.

lies closely over the ovary, almost completely engulfing it with the thin membrane. It is attached to the interior of the ovarian bursa.

Ampulla (Ampullae: Jug)

The infundibulum forms a funnel-like structure as it enters the tubular portion of the oviduct, and this area is called the ampulla. It is a passageway for the ovum and the location of union of the sperm and ovum.

Isthmus (Isthmi: Narrow Part)

This segment coils cranially, medially, and finally laterally before joining the uterus. The diameter is rather uniform throughout its length and it is embedded in the mesosalpinx.

Tubouterine Junction (Womb Tube)

The oviduct enlarges quickly into the uterus. The valvelike interior somewhat limits flow of fluid from the uterus into the oviduct yet allows relatively free passage from the oviduct into the uterus. In swine, the tubouterine junction constricts during estrus, until ovulation, thereby concentrating sperm in preparation for fertilization.[17,22]

The major difference in the oviduct of the ewe and cow is that the ewe has a very tortuous tube and the length is long (15 to 20 cm, 4.4 to 5.8 in) compared to the size of the animal. It has a greater constriction at the tubouterine junction and the internal valve is better developed.

The oviduct of the sow is very tortuous and the infundibulum, which lies on the inner surface of the bursa, almost completely engulfs the ovary. The oviduct is 14 to 28 cm (5 in) long and tapers gradually into the uterus.

The oviduct of the mare flares abruptly into the infundibulum, which is thicker than in the other species and less distended, so that it covers only the fossa area of the ovary without covering the remainder. The entire oviduct is 20 to 30 cm (7 in) long and is tortuous as it courses through the mesosalpinx and joins the uterus bluntly.

The oviduct of the woman is about 10 cm (4 in) long and much straighter than in domestic animals. The ampullar area is much longer in proportion and is thin walled. As in other females, the oviduct is supported by the mesosalpinx. The free isthmus is rather short because this portion penetrates the thick wall of the uterus and there is a greater area of tubouterine oviduct.

Some abnormalities of the oviduct are very important. The occurrence of hydrosalpinx and salpingitis in cattle interferes with fertility.[26] Hydrosalpinx means that there are sacs of fluid in the oviduct. These may be formed in the tube proper or be closely related so that the pressure occludes passage of the sperm and ova. Salpingitis is the word for inflammation of the oviduct and may cause a sealing or restriction that may act the same as hydrosalpinx. The first condition is not usually considered to be correctable and there are doubts about the latter. Palpation of the structure per rectum may permit identification of the condition but many times the formations are very small.

UTERUS (Uteri: Womb)

Uteri are given a designation according to their shape (Table 7–1). *Bipartite* uteri have two distinct horns or cornua and a relatively large body; *bicornuate* uteri have two long horns and a proportionately small body; and *simplex* uteri have a single rounded body without horns.

The uterus is composed of the uterine horns, a body, and the cervix. Because of the different structure of the cervix, it is commonly considered a separate organ and will be described as such here. The two horns and body are continuous and will be discussed as a single structure.

Position and Structure

The uterus of the cow is located cranially to the pelvic opening with the cervix lying in the pelvic cavity. The uterus is on level with the floor of the pelvis and coils downward as it moves cranially. The cow uterus is a *bipartite* (two-part) uterus; the body measures 3 cm (1.2 in) and each horn is 40 cm (16 in) long. The diameter of the midhorn is 3 cm (1.2 in) and tapers as the oviduct is approached. The peritoneal covering of the body of the uterus causes it to appear much longer than it is. *Intercornual ligaments* attach the two cornua in the area of the body. The cornua course cranially and form spirals as they pass ventrally, caudally, and dorsally supported by the broad ligament (Fig. 7–2). The tips of the horns fold back on themselves in an S shape.

Support

The broad ligaments are attached dorsolaterally in the pelvic cavity and dorsally in the peritoneal cavity. That portion attached to the lateral border of the cornua and body is called the *mesometrium* (mid-uterus). Muscle fibers in the suspensory ligaments indicate an active role in positioning and moving the uterus. The *round ligament* is found in the lateral folds of the mesometrium and assists in holding the uterus in position. Vascular support is via the uterine artery, which originates at the aorta and also branches to supply the ovary, oviduct, cervix, and vagina.

Internal Structure

The uterus is lined with longitudinal folds. On and in these folds are located numerous rounded prominences called *caruncles* (flesh growth). These serve as points of attachments of the placenta during pregnancy for the exchange of nutrients and waste. There are approximately 200 located in an irregular fashion throughout the two horns and body. They measure 10 to 15 mm (.4 to .6 in) in diameter in the nonpregnant cow.

The ewe has a uterus very similar to the cow's, only smaller. The horns are 10 mm (.4 in) in diameter and 15 cm (6 in) long. The body is relatively long (2 cm, .8 in). Suspension is very similar to the cow, and caruncles line the uterus. The caruncles characteristically have a depression in the center and a pigment of gray or black. The pigment may be found in animals of all ages and usually disappears during pregnancy.

The uterus of the sow is very long. Each horn measures 100 cm (40 in) and appears very similar to the intestines. The broad ligament is very extensive and gives little support when compared to that of the ruminant females. The body is 5 cm (2 in) long and the uterus is *bicornuate* (two-horned). The uterus contains many folds internally and there are no caruncles present. The placenta attaches over the entire surface during pregnancy.

The uterus of the mare is more flaccid than those of the other three species. The horns are about the same length as the body, which is 25 cm (10 in). The diameter of the mid-horn is 3 cm (1.2 in) and the size is maintained rather uniformly throughout the length of the horns. It is a *bipartite* uterus with a prominent body. The uterus is suspended by the broad ligaments that attach forward and dorsally in the sublumbar area as well as to the lateral pelvic wall. The ligaments allow the uterine horns to sag in the middle, so that the body and tips of the horns are on level and the midportion is lower. This makes palpation more difficult than with the coiled horns of the cow. The flaccid condition is also detrimental to palpation. The interior of the uterus contains longitudinal folds without caruncles.

The *simplex* uterus of the woman is pear-shaped with the oviducts attached laterally at the upper curvature. The uterus is held upright in the abdominal cavity by the paired broad ligaments, which attach laterally to the interior pelvis, and the round ligaments, which pass anteriorly to the abdominal wall. There are also four uterosacral ligaments which attach the uterus to the posterior pelvic wall. The uterus measures 8 cm (3 in) long, 5 cm (2 in) wide, and 2.5 cm (1 in) thick. These measurements include the cervix. Relaxation or damage to the poor support may allow the uterus to fold and, because of the distorted position, interfere with conception and/or pregnancy.

The uterus serves as a passageway for actively transporting sperm to the oviduct following copulation and later becomes the incubator for developing the fetus. It secretes fluids to bathe the sperm first and later supplies nourishment for the embryo prior to attachment. At parturition the uterus contracts to expel the fetus.

The uterus of the cow and mare may be palpated per rectum to determine abnormal conditions as well as pregnancy. Pregnancy will be discussed in detail later. The uterus of the cow has a relatively firm texture, particularly during estrus. The texture is of muscle and is much firmer than the flaccid uterus of the mare. The uterus of the mare must sometimes be traced from the more prominent cervix. Pyometra, which is pus or leucocytes in the uterus, may be observed as a thick fluid to plastic feel. The cells fill the cavity in an effort to remove the existing cause of infection. Sometimes a cloudy exudate will be observed dripping from the vulva. A veterinarian certainly should be called if such is observed. Metritis or endometritis is infection of the uterus and causes a thickening of the uterine wall and enlargement of the entire structure. Immediate attention is mandatory in such instances.

CERVIX (Cervices: Neck)

The cervix is a firm portion of the tract when compared to the uterus on one side and the vagina on the other (Fig. 7–12). It is usually easily found in palpation and may be used as a point of orientation. The term "neck" from which it was derived is very descriptive, for the cervix of the cow closely resembles the skinned neck of a turkey or chicken when felt. The cervix is composed of a large amount of connective tissue and some muscle. It is approximately 8 cm (3 in) long and 2 cm (.8 in) in diameter. Cervices of young heifers will naturally be smaller than those of older cows.

Cows with some Zebu breeding will commonly have larger cervices than European cattle. It is not unusual to palpate cervices that are 15 cm (6 in) long and 6 cm (2.4 in) in diameter. Even young heifers may have large cervices, so it is not injury in calving that causes the enlargement, as some may think. The cervix may still function normally and may be penetrated easily during artificial insemination.

Longitudinal folds line the cervix. These form prominent ridges that encircle the interior and may be three or four in number, one behind the other, or may form an irregular spiral. These are commonly spoken of as being annular in configuration. The ridges are slanted caudally as if to prevent the entrance of any foreign material into the uterus. Secretory cells line the base of the crypts.[16]

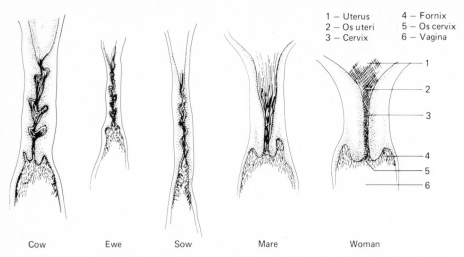

1 — Uterus   4 — Fornix
2 — Os uteri   5 — Os cervix
3 — Cervix   6 — Vagina

Cow   Ewe   Sow   Mare   Woman

Figure 7-12 Cervices of the cow, ewe, sow, mare, amd woman.

The cranial cervix blends gradually into the body of the uterus, and the caudal cervix extends into the vagina so as to form a circular depression, the *fornix,* around the protruding cervix. The os of the cervix appears as a rosette.

The functions of the cervix are (1) to act as a passageway for sperm following breeding, by opening and secreting thin fluid, (2) sealing following breeding to maintain the uterus in an undisturbed state, and (3) opening and lubricating the canal for birth of the young.

The cervix is penetrated during artificial insemination in order to deposit the semen in the proper place. Not all cervices are normal in shape and size; insemination is therefore difficult. Some of the common difficulties are L, V, or S-shaped cervices. The muscular and connective tissue walls give great rigidity to the structure and attempt to maintain the cervix in its original position. It is possible in some instances to traverse this tortuous canal, but is impossible in other cases. The crooked cervix does not seem to interfere at birth.

The ewe has a miniature cervix structured like that of the cow. The circular folds are much more distinct and may number six or seven. The intravaginal portion extends further and lies closer to the floor than in the cow. The cervix measures 1 cm (.4 in) in diameter and 5 cm (2 in) long.

The cervix of the sow is long and firm (20 cm, 8 in). It extends from the floor of the pelvic cavity into the peritoneal cavity. It is lined with an irregular series of prominences and opposing depressions that fit closely together. The size is greater in mid-cervix and becomes smaller at each end. There is a blending of the cervix with the body of the uterus and with the cranial vagina so that no protrusion or fornix exists. The corkscrew glans penis of the boar penetrates the cervix during copulation; this is the only domestic animal in which this happens.

The cervical canal of the mare has its distinguishing feature. It consists of numerous tall longitudinal folds that provide little protection to penetration. The cervix opens as much as 2 cm (.8 in) during estrus, and by use of a speculum and light one may observe the internal cervix and body of the uterus. The stallion ejaculates directly into the cervix and hence into the uterus at copulation. The intravaginal cervix is very prominent, extending 2 to 3 cm (.8 to 1.2 in) when the mare is in estrus.[13] One of the difficulties encountered in the mare at the time of estrus is a drooping or relaxing of the protruding cervix into the cranial vagina. Under these circumstances, the penis of the stallion closes these folds tightly during copulation preventing passage of the sperm into the cervix and hence the uterus. This condition may be observed by using a speculum and observing the protruding folds during estrus. The difficulty is best overcome by using artificial insemination. The catheter is used to lift the drooping folds and pass the semen on into the cervix and uterus.

Sealing of the cervix depends to a large extent on the production of thick tenacious mucus when the mare is not in estrus. The cervix is approximately 3 cm (1.2 in) in diameter and 8 cm (3.1 in) long and is firm enough to be palpated and used as a point of orientation, since the soft uterus is sometimes difficult to palpate.

The cervix of the woman is more closely associated with the uterus than in domestic animals. Constriction of this area is not as great. The cervix is about 2 cm (.8 in) in diameter and 2 cm (.8 in) long. The interior consists of longitudinal folds, and there is a distinct protrusion into the vagina. The cervix enters the vagina at an angle so that the posterior fornix is much deeper than the anterior portion (Fig. 7–6).

VAGINA (Vaginae: Sheath)

The vagina is the copulatory organ of the female. It receives the penis during copulation and is the receptacle for the semen deposited by the bull and ram. The boar and stallion deposit semen directly into the cervix. The vagina of the cow extends from the cervix to a point cranial to the urethral orifice and is 30 cm (12 in) long. The walls are muscular and usually collapsed. The organ is covered with the peritoneum, which forms the rectovaginal pouch dorsally allowing penetration through the cranial dorsal wall of the vagina into the peritoneal cavity. This approach is used for ovariectomy, insemination, and embryo transfer in some instances.

The cranial vagina forms a deep fornix (1 cm, .4 in) around the intravaginal portion of the cervix. This area is a problem to some inseminating technicians as the catheter misses the os cervix and is stopped by the deep fornix. The catheter must be retracted slightly and realigned with the os.

The caudal border of the vagina is the *site of the hymen* (membrane). This is composed of a ring of scar tissue in the wall at the junction of the vagina and vestibule and is a vestige of a wall of tissue in the embryo separating the internal and external structures during development. The hymen usually has degenerated; however, instances of an intact hymen have been noted and these may be severed with little difficulty mechanically or they are usually torn during the initial copulation. A small amount of bleeding may follow.

Occasionally a cow will have a prolapse of the vagina. This usually precedes parturition when the pelvic musculature relaxes and the cow has some preparturient contractions of the uterine musculature and abdominal muscles. This forces the vagina to turn inside out. Sometimes this may be even more severe with prolapse of the cervix and the uterus at the time of birth. A competent veterinarian should be contacted and the everted tissue kept as clean as possible until it can be replaced. Heavy sutures are placed across the vulva with enough room left for urination, and the stitches or lacing are released before parturition.[18] Prolapse in other species is relatively rare.

The vagina of the ewe is similar, but smaller. The sow vagina is 10 cm (4 in) long and has a rather definite annular fold at the site of the hymen. There is no fornix at the tapering junction with the cervix.

The mare vagina is 15 cm (6 in) long and forms a deep fornix around the intravaginal part of the cervix. A rather prominent fold is on the floor at the junction with the vestibule, and a persistent hymen is more common in the mare than other domestic animals.

The vagina is approximately 8 cm (3.1 in) long in the woman. There is a distinct fornix surrounding the intravaginal cervix, which protrudes 1 cm (.4 in). The vagina opens directly into the vulvar area, since the genital and urinary systems are separate entities in the woman.

VESTIBULE (Vestibules: Antechamber)

The vestibule begins at the site of the hymen and extends to the lips of the vulva. This area is truly urogenital since it is a part of both systems. In the floor of the cranial vestibule is the *suburethral diverticulum* (under-canal to turn aside). This blind pocket is 2 cm (.8 in) long and 2 cm (.8 in) deep. The opening into the urethra is in the dorsal wall, and the pocket extends cranially beneath it (Fig. 7–2). The suburethral diverticulum is of no particular known use but it is a trap to the inseminator in breeding and to the researcher or veterinarian wishing to catheterize the bladder.

Vestibular glands are located in the walls of the vestibule and open on the floor just caudal and lateral to the urethral orifice. The vestibule acts as an entrance and passage to the vagina, and the glands lubricate it during copulation and birth.

The vestibule of the sheep and associated glands are similar to those of the cow. The suburethral diverticulum is absent.

The sow possesses a small suburethral diverticulum and minor vestibular glands. The mare does not have a suburethral diverticulum and has only minor vestibular glands for lubrication. The vestibule is absent in the woman.

VULVA AND CLITORIS (Vulvas: Lips, Clitori)

The vulva composes the external genitalia of the female (Fig. 7–13). In the cow there is a *labium* (lip) on each side, which is equivalent to the labia minora in the woman.

The two lips join ventrally in a commissure and are covered with fine hair on the lips and long coarser hair at the base. Parting of the ventral commissure reveals the glans clitoris. The clitoris is the homologue (that is, came from the same embryonic source) of the penis in the male. The body of the clitoris is in the floor of the vulva, and only the glans is visible in a small preputial pocket. The clitoris is not considered an excitatory organ in the cow, although recent research has linked clitoral massage to slightly increased conception through artificial insemination.

The vulva functions only as an entrance to the reproductive internal organs. Selection of cattle should include observation of the vulva for appearance and location. The vulva should be of a size and shape that is normal for the breed of cattle. Underdeveloped, or hypotropic, vulvas indicate a hormonal deficiency in the reproductive system, and cattle with this type should not be selected for breeding stock. The vulva of European breeds is usually rather firm and close fitting when compared to the loose, pendulous vulva of cattle carrying some degree of Zebu breeding.

Pneumovagina is commonly called windsucking and means air in the vagina. Stock with relaxed lips of the vulva and particularly weakened support of the vagina exhibit this condition.[28] When air is sucked into the vagina, dust and airborne bacteria may enter and infection result.[24] The condition is not usually corrected in the cow. The pneumovagina condition in the mare is more serious because of the open condition of the cervix during estrus. Restricting the vulvar opening is usually accomplished by a surgical procedure named Caslick's.[4] This entails cutting a thin strip of tissue from the inner lips of the vulva and suturing these together leaving an approximately 1-inch opening at the base for urination. The opening may require enlarging for breeding, although artificial insemination may be employed to circumvent the restriction. The vulva usually tears at the time of parturition, although many instances have been observed where copulation and parturition have not interfered with the sealed portion.

Three areas of constriction of the reproductive tract afford protection to the

1 — Anus	6 — Ventral commissure
2 — Dorsal commissure	7 — Labia majora
3 — Labium	8 — Labia minora
4 — Vulvar opening	9 — Urethral orifice
5 — Clitoris	10 — Vagina

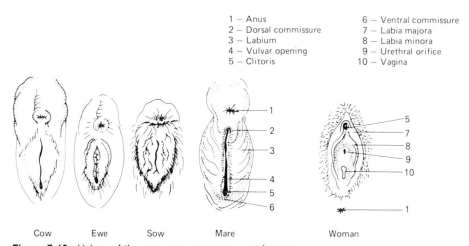

Cow   Ewe   Sow   Mare   Woman

Figure 7-13   Vulvas of the cow, ewe, sow, mare, and woman.

delicate endometrium.[3] These are the lips of the vulva forming a valvelike closure, the circular muscles just inside the vulvar opening, and the os cervix. All of these must function properly in any class of livestock to properly afford a suitable environment.

The position of the vulva is also important. The vulvar opening should be vertical. Some cows have the vulva between the tuber ischiadica (pin bones) and even horizontal in position. Passage of feces during defecation is across the vulvar opening, and debri will fall into the vulva and vestibule, interfering with conception by contamination. The position also causes great difficulty for the bull in searching for the vulvar opening during coitus.

The labia of the ewe are sometimes divided slightly into minor and major lips. The lips are more prominent when the ewe is in estrus. The clitoris is well hidden in the ventral commissure.

The sow possesses a rather distinctive vulva because of its shape. The lips are wrinkled and come to a point at the ventral commissure. When the sow is in estrus the labia become turgid with fluid and the fullness and pointed condition are used by swine producers in detecting sows in estrus. The clitoris is small exteriorly but may be 8 cm (3.1 in) in length under the floor of the vestibule.

The vulva and clitoris of the mare are also different from the other species. The vulva is composed of thick rounded labia and the ventral commissure is curving or rounded rather than coming to a point. The clitoris is very prominent, as the glans is darkly pigmented and is located in a deep fossa in the area of the ventral commissure. During estrus, the vulva opens and closes in a winking fashion exposing the internal surfaces of the labia and the clitoris. This is especially true following urination or teasing by the stallion.

There are two distinct labia in the woman: the labia minora, inside, and the labia majora, outside. The labia minora are closely associated with the vagina and are devoid of hair. The labia majora are larger and more protective and covered by hair on the exposed surfaces. The clitoris is located anterior to the urethra and is surrounded by the labia minora. It responds during sexual excitement, as does the penis of the male, by becoming turgid; and in all probability it contributes to orgasm in the woman.

WHAT DID YOU LEARN?

1 Describe to someone who knows nothing of anatomy the distinguishing features of the ovaries of the cow, sow, and mare.
2 Where is estrogen produced?
3 From what is a corpus hemorrhagicum derived?
4 What does "corpus albicans" mean literally?
5 Distinguish between the cervices of the ewe, sow, and woman.
6 Which animal(s) does (do) not have a suburethral diverticulum?
7 What does bipartite mean? In what animal(s) is it found?
8 What artery supplies the cervix?
9 What is pneumovagina?
10 Where is the fornix located?

REFERENCES

1 Basmajian, John V. 1975. *Grant's Method of Anatomy.* 9th ed. Williams & Wilkins, Baltimore. Pp. 290–297.

2 Bergin, W. C. and W. D. Shipley. 1968. Genital health in the mare—I: observations concerning the ovulation fossa. *Vet. Med./Small Anim. Clinician* 63:362–365.

3 ———. 1968. Genital health in the mare—II: the vulva. *Vet. Med./Small Anim. Clinician* 63:447–450.

4 Caslick, E. A. 1937. The vulva and vulvo-vaginal orifice and its relation to genital health of the Thoroughbred mare. *Cornell Vet.* 27:178–186.

5 Clemente, C. D. 1975. *Anatomy: A Regional Atlas of the Human Body.* Lea & Febiger, Philadelphia.

6 Cowan, F. T. and J. W. Macpherson. 1966. The reproductive tract of the porcine female (a biometrical study). *Can. J. of Comp. Med. Vet. Sci.* 30:107–108.

7 Crouch, J. E. 1974. *Functional Human Anatomy.* Lea & Febiger, Philadelphia. Pp. 448–463.

8 Crouch, J. E. and J. R. McClintic. 1971. *Human Anatomy and Physiology.* John Wiley & Sons, New York.

9 Drennan, W. G. and J. W. Macpherson. 1966. The reproductive tract of bovine slaughter heifers (a biometrical study). *Can. J. of Comp. Med. Vet. Sci.* 30:224–227.

10 Edwards, M. J. 1965. Observations on the anatomy of the reproductive organs of cows with special reference to those features sought during examination *per rectum. New Zealand Vet. J.* 13:25–37.

11 Elder, Cecil. 1925. Studies of the corpus luteum. *J.A.V.M.A.* 67:349–363.

12 Frandson, R. D. 1965. *Anatomy and Physiology of Farm Animals.* Lea & Febiger, Philadelphia.

13 Hafez, E. S. E. 1972. Functional anatomy of the cervix uteri and domestic animals and primates. *Proc. 7th Int. Congr. on Anim. Reprod. and A.I.* 2:2304–2307.

14 ———. 1974. *Reproduction in Farm Animals.* Lea & Febiger, Philadelphia. P. 37.

15 Hancock, J. L. 1962. The clinical features of the reproductive organs of pregnant and non-pregnant cattle. *Vet. Rec.* 74:646–652.

16 Herrick, J. B. 1951. The cytological changes in the cervical mucosa of the cow (Bos taurus) throughout the estrous cycle. *Amer. J. Vet. Res.* 12:276–281.

17 Hunter, R. H. F. 1972. Utero-tubal function, sperm transport and polyspermic fertilization in pigs. *Proc. 7th Int. Congr. on Anim. Reprod. and A.I.* 2:1177–1180.

18 Johansen, R. D. 1968. Repair of prolapsed vagina in the cow. *Vet. Med./Small Anim. Clinician* 63:252–256.

19 Lyngset, O. 1968. Studies on reproduction in the goat. I. The normal genital organs of the nonpregnant goat. *Acta Vet. Scand.* 9:208–222.

20 McDonald, L. E. 1975. *Veterinary Endocrinology and Reproduction.* Lea & Febiger, Philadelphia. P. 251.

21 McNutt, G. W. 1924. The corpus luteum of the ox ovary in relation to the estrous cycle. *J.A.V.M.A.* 65:556–583.

22 Rigby, J. P. 1965. The structure of the uterotubal junction of the sow. *J. Anat.* 99:416.

23 Seeger, K. 1977. Laparoscopic investigation of the bovine ovary. *Vet. Med./Small Anim. Clinician* 72:1037–1044.

24 Shipley, W. D. and W. C. Bergin. 1968. Genital health in the mare—III: pneumovagina. *Vet. Med./Small Anim. Clinician* 63:699–702.

25 Steinbach, J. and D. Smidt. 1970. Cyclical phenomena in the female genital tract of swine —histological observations. *J. Anim. Sci.* 30:573–577.

26 Tanabe, T. Y. and J. O. Almquist. 1967. The nature of subfertility in the dairy heifer. III. Gross genital abnormalities. *Pennsylvania Agric. Exp. Sta. Bull. 736.*

27 Warszawsky, L. F., W. G. Parker, N. L. First, and O. J. Ginther. 1972. Gross changes of internal genitalia during the estrous cycle in the mare. *Amer. J. Vet. Res.* 33:19–26.

28 Wempe, W. W. 1968. Observations and opinions on breeding and obstetrical problems in the cow. *Vet. Med./Small Anim. Clinician* 63:1151–1153.

CHAPTER 8

Microscopic Female Functional Anatomy

When you have completed this chapter you should be able to:

- Distinguish between a follicle, corpus hemorrhagicum, corpus luteum, corpus albicans, and an atretic follicle,
- Enumerate the steps in follicular growth,
- Relate cell divisions during oogenesis, and
- Understand the relationship of cell type to function in the oviduct, uterus, cervix, vagina, vestibule, and vulva.

The female reproductive tract, like that of the male, is concerned with the production of germ cells and hormones. In addition, the female system is responsible for providing a point of fertilization and an incubator for developing the young followed by expulsion of that young. The cellular construction of these many organs are therefore varied in type and functions to bring about this multitude of activities.

OVARY

The ovary is composed of two rather specific areas, the medulla and the cortex covered by the tunica albuginea and the superficial epithelium.

Medulla (Middle)

The middle portion of the ovary is composed of connective tissue supporting the spiral vascular system and nerves. These enter the ovary from the mesovarium through the attachment called the *hilus.*

Cortex (Cortices: Bark)

Surrounding the medulla is dense stroma of connective tissue in which are located the various components of the germ cell throughout its life, and subsequent structures (Fig. 8–1). Included here are the follicles, corpora hemorrhagica, corpora lutea, corpora albicantia, and atretic follicles. It is the site of female sex hormone production. The cortex and medulla are reversed in the mare.[9] The medulla on the outside of the mare makes up the structural tissue, and the follicles are produced in the central cortex. The follicles grow and protrude through the medullar portion so they may be palpated on the surface. They move toward the ovulation fossa with maturity and rupture at that point.

Superficial Epithelium

The superficial epithelium on the surface of the ovary may be cuboidal or rounded in the very young animal; with age, the cells become flattened. There is no continued generation of oocytes from what was called the germinal epithelium. The oocytes are present deeper in the ovary at birth and are not increased in number after birth.[21] Under the superficial epithelium is the tunica albuginea.

Tunica Albuginea (White Coat)

This thin coat of connective tissue is the outer support of the ovarian structure. It is organized early in the life of the animal and can actually be called a structure in the pig at 3 months of age.[15] The area of oocytes and follicular development lies beneath the tunica albuginea.

Follicle (Follicles: Little Bag)

The oocytes are apparently present at birth. In the human it is estimated that there are as many as 400,000. The estimate for ovaries of the sow are up to 80,000. Aged cows of 14 to 15 years have as many as 24,000 oocytes present.[13] If one assumes only one ovum developing each cycle then there are many more than could ever reach maturity. In the cow there are approximately 12 follicles that die during maturation for every one that reaches the point of ovulation. Without a doubt there are enough oocytes at birth to last a lifetime. Figure 8–2 shows the changes in proportion of the various types of follicles postnatally.[12]

Each oocyte measures approximately 20 μm in diameter. The oocytes, located in the cortex just beneath the tunica albuginea, begin to differentiate so that one becomes surrounded by a single layer of squamous-type follicular cells.[15] Many more

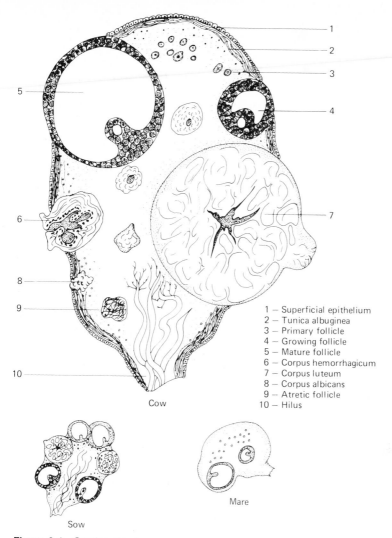

1 — Superficial epithelium
2 — Tunica albuginea
3 — Primary follicle
4 — Growing follicle
5 — Mature follicle
6 — Corpus hemorrhagicum
7 — Corpus luteum
8 — Corpus albicans
9 — Atretic follicle
10 — Hilus

Cow

Sow

Mare

Figure 8-1 Ovarian structures.

die at this time. This developing oocyte is called a *primary follicle* because of the single layer of cells surrounding it. In truth, this is not yet a follicle, but it will later form a cavity and become one (Fig. 8–3). It measures about 40 μm in diameter.

The follicular cells multiply and form two layers of cells around the oocyte. The structure is then called a *secondary follicle.* Other layers of cuboidal cells will form so that there is a mass of cells surrounding the developing oocyte. The ovum will measure 80 μm at this time, and the entire follicle will be about 120 μm in diameter. The structure during this time is designated a *growing follicle,* and the term is used as the follicular cells continue to multiply and separate to form fluid-filled areas. These unite to form the cavity of the follicle called the *antrum.* The granular-

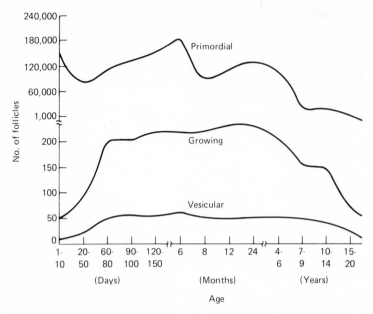

Figure 8-2 Changes in follicular types postnatally in the bovine. *(Adapted from Erickson.[12])*

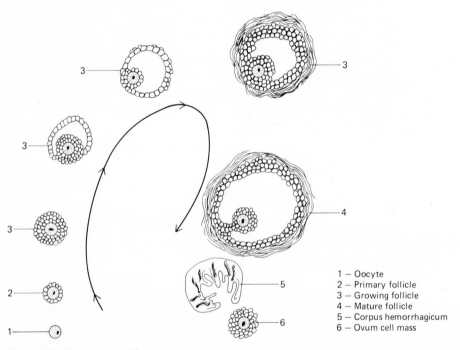

1 — Oocyte
2 — Primary follicle
3 — Growing follicle
4 — Mature follicle
5 — Corpus hemorrhagicum
6 — Ovum cell mass

Figure 8-3 Follicular growth.

appearing follicular cells lining the follicle are called the *stratum granulosum* and become stratified into 5 to 10 layers of cells. This area is avascular.[36] The oocyte becomes the *primary oocyte* during this stage, and the *zona pellucida* forms immediately surrounding it.

The zona pellucida is secreted by the oocyte and the granulosa cells immediately surrounding it. In late antral stage the granulosa cells elongate adjacent to the zona and form the *corona radiata.*

During the growing period there is organization of the stroma cells to form a spindle-shaped epithelioid cell layer around the granulosa cells.[24] These are called the *tunica interna* (coat-inside) and together with the granulosa cells produce the female excitatory hormone, estrogen.

Other stromal cells form spindle-shaped cells mixed with connective tissue cells to form another supportive layer for the follicle. These are called the *tunica externa* (coat-outside). No other function than support is known for this area. They are very vascular,[35] so the support is nutrient as well as physical.

The *mature follicle* is the end product as depicted in Figure 8–4. It is sometimes called the Graafian follicle. It has migrated internally as growth pressure has been exerted from the outer cortex and then externally so that it protrudes distinctly on the surface. It appears much as a blister on the ovary as it stretches the stratum granulosum, theca folliculi, tunica albuginea, and superficial epithelium on the bulging surface. The mature follicle of the cow reaches 10 to 20 mm and may be palpated per rectum as a bulging blister. Follicles of the ewe measure 5 to 10 mm, 8 to 15 mm for the sow, and 20 to 40 mm for the mare.

Internally the ovum is developing surrounded by cells of the granulosum called

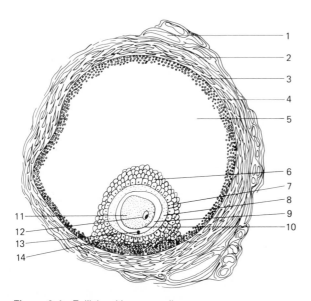

1 — Stroma
2 — Tunica externa
3 — Tunica interna
4 — Stratum granulosum
5 — Antrum
6 — Cumulus oophorus
7 — Corona radiata
8 — Zona pellucida
9 — Perivitelline space
10 — Vitelline membrane
11 — Vitellus
12 — Nucleus
13 — Polar body
14 — Hillock

Figure 8-4   Follicle with ovum cell mass.

the *cumulus oophorus*. This ovum cell mass is continuous with the granulosum until ovulation, when the mass is expelled.

Ovum Cell Mass The mound of granulosa cells supporting the ovum in the antrum is called the *hillock*. The outer cells of the ovum cell mass are designated *cumulus oophorus* (little mound-egg-to bear) because of the shape. Beneath this cloud of cells is a layer of elongated cells arranged perpendicular to the ovum as if they are radiating from it. These are called the *corona radiata* (crown radiate). These cells send minute processes into the underlying *zona pellucida* (area-shine through) and penetrate into the space surrounding the ovum where they possibly assist in nutrient exchange.

The zona pellucida is a translucent membrane directly around the ovum. It is protective in nature, as will be discussed in the section on fertilization. The *vitelline membrane* (yolk-film) covers the ovum and structurally holds the vitellus or cytoplasm in its shell.

It is during this maturation stage that the primary oocyte divides to form the secondary oocyte and first polar body. It remains thus until ovulation. The secondary oocyte is 120 to 200 μm in diameter.

Ovulation Ovulation, or rupture of the follicle and release of the ovum, occurs as the follicle reaches maturity and the wall deteriorates. The follicle becomes very turgid during the latter growth stages, and several hours before ovulation it becomes soft. This is apparently due to stretching and necrosis of the wall.[27] The follicle bulges to form a stigma or conelike projection, and rupture occurs at this point. The thin follicular fluid passes out followed by the egg cell mass which detaches from the degenerating granulosa cells. The mass is usually located opposite the stigma but may be at other locations.

The egg cell mass moves into the open point and temporarily plugs the opening. A sudden release of the mass from this constriction allows the ovum and its surrounding cells to be free in the infundibular portion of the oviduct.

The follicle ruptures at any point on the ovaries of the cow and ewe (Fig. 8–5). Only one ruptures at a time in the cow, while two may rupture in the ewe. The sow's ovaries are covered with follicles, and each stigma forms a distinct cone shape on the surface. The follicle of the mare develops in the centrally located cortex and migrates into the area of the ovulation fossa[1] where the ovulations occur.[5,32] Ovulation may occur on either ovary, and there is no apparent alternation of activity from one side to the other. A slightly larger proportion of ovulations occur on the right ovary in the cow,[2] ewe,[6] and mare, while the reverse is true in the sow.

Oogenesis (Egg Production) The development of the *oogonia* occurs prenatally as the germinal epithelial cells divide and invade the cortex. Multiplication continues and results in numerous *oocytes* under the tunica albuginea at the time of birth or shortly thereafter.[21] The greatest differences in the development of the ovum when contrasted with sperm are the large amount of cytoplasm, round shape, and lack of motility.

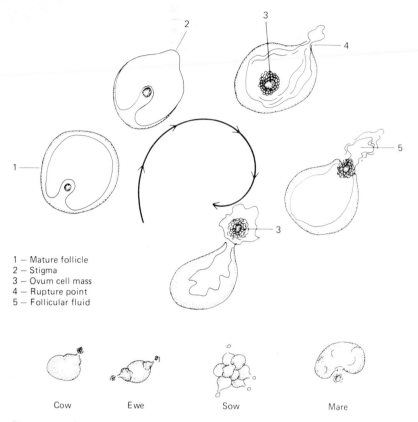

1 — Mature follicle
2 — Stigma
3 — Ovum cell mass
4 — Rupture point
5 — Follicular fluid

Cow   Ewe   Sow   Mare

Figure 8-5 Ovulation.

As the female reaches puberty, the circulating gonadotropic hormones cause a continued cell division that is completed by at least one follicle each time the female displays a desire for mating. The *primary oocyte* divides in an uneven fashion to produce two daughter cells (Fig. 8–6). The genetic makeup is retained in each daughter cell but the majority of the cytoplasm goes to one cell, the *secondary oocyte*, while the other cell is almost entirely a nucleus and is called the *first polar body*. The polar body is expelled from the ovum proper into the *perivitelline space* where it remains.[3]

The secondary oocyte begins its stages of development just before or at the time of ovulation and passes through prophase into metaphase where it stops in the cow, ewe, and sow until fertilization. The ovum progresses to the primary oocyte stage in the mare. Upon fertilization, the secondary oocyte continues its division to expel a *second polar body* and form a resulting fertilized ovum. Reduction of the chromosome number has occurred from the primary oocyte with 2N complement to 1N in the female pronucleus. The first polar body may also divide so that there may be two or three polar bodies in the perivitelline space following fertilization. If fertilization does not occur, the secondary oocyte in its metaphase division deteriorates and

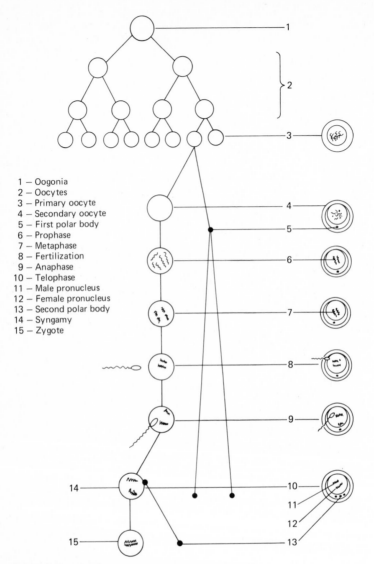

1 — Oogonia
2 — Oocytes
3 — Primary oocyte
4 — Secondary oocyte
5 — First polar body
6 — Prophase
7 — Metaphase
8 — Fertilization
9 — Anaphase
10 — Telophase
11 — Male pronucleus
12 — Female pronucleus
13 — Second polar body
14 — Syngamy
15 — Zygote

Figure 8-6 Oogenesis.

is absorbed in the wall of the reproductive tract or could possibly pass to the exterior. Fertilization will be discussed further in a later chapter.

Atretic Follicles (Dead Bag)

Many follicles begin development but die and deteriorate as they progress. This may occur at any stage from the oocyte to the mature follicle. Following death of the ovum, the cytoplasm shrinks, the zona pellucida thickens and fragments, and the follicle, if one exists, deteriorates[25,26] and is invaded by connective tissue cells of the surrounding stroma (Fig. 8–7). These cells engulf the ovum, and gradually the substance of the cell is replaced by a scar of dense connective tissue.[29] The scar will persist for months.

Corpus Hemorrhagicum (Corpora Hemorrhagica: Body-Blood)

As ovulation progresses, there is a collapse of the follicle with an enfolding of the walls.[22] Little if any hemorrhage occurs in the cow, ewe, and sow, but there is considerable bleeding in the mare. The ruptured follicle takes on a bloody appearance and hence its name at this time, corpus hemorrhagicum (CH). The period of the CH is brief and there is no clearcut time when it is considered finished. It lasts about 2 or 3 days.

Corpus Luteum (Corpora Lutea: Body-Yellow)

The corpus hemorrhagicum gradually fills with luteal or yellow cells.[8] These cells are derived from the stratum granulosum and the tunica interna and contain lipid droplets. The cavity continues to fill until the corpus luteum (CL) is equal to or larger in size than the follicle whose place it took. The CL of the cow and ewe has a distinct papillum or teatlike projection at the point of follicular rupture.[10] The luteal cells push out and protrude from the area in a characteristic manner. The papillum is palpable per rectum and its growth may be monitored. Color ranges from yellow to brick red and may not be used to distinguish age.[11]

The growth phase of the CL continues for about 10 days and then it is maintained for 3 or 4 more days before regression begins.

The CL of the sow develops quickly and only the color helps differentiate

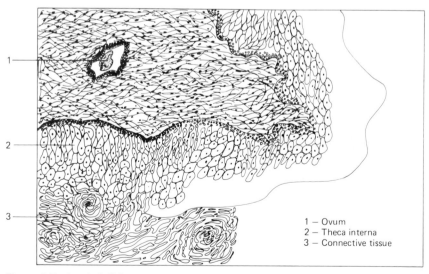

Figure 8-7   Atretic follicles.

between the CL and follicles.[37] The CL is a deep red color and lacks a papillum. The mare's CL is harder to palpate than the cow's because the consistency is softer and no papillum develops. It is also deeply seated in the fossa of the ovary. Its color is usually a pale yellow. The cells of the CL are derived from granulosa and tunica interna cells. Those of granulosa origin are of large, rounded configuration, while those of tunica interna origin are smaller and rounded. The cells become mixed with growth and development so there is no clear demarcation between them. The large cells may be 40 μm in diameter and assume a polyhedral shape with growth and crowding.

The luteal cells secrete progesterone, which prepares for and maintains pregnancy (Fig. 8–8). The CL of pregnancy remains viable for varying lengths of time in different species. This will be discussed in the section on pregnancy.

Corpus Albicans (Corpora Albicantia: Body-White)

Regression of the corpus luteum is very rapid. The cells shrink, become vacuolated, lose their granulation, and disintegrate in about 3 days' time. With this death, there is invasion of the structure by connective tissue cells and finally the CL is replaced and called a corpus albicans (CA). Most are white scars but many may be seen as red or brown dots on the ovarian surface. The structure shrinks so that immediately at the beginning of its life it looks similar to a small CL but within about 2 months only a small scar is visible. There is no known substance produced by the CA.

Cystic Follicles

Some follicles fail to rupture for some unknown reason. Speculations can be made placing the blame on low hormone concentration, thick follicular walls, or upset hormone patterns. The follicle wall thickens with extremely dense theca folliculi layers and fully organized granulosa (Fig. 8–9). Many cystic follicles form luteal cells

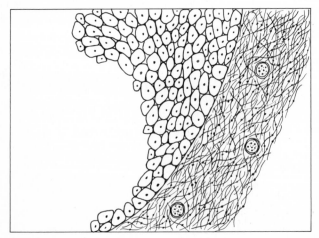

Figure 8-8 Corpus Luteum.

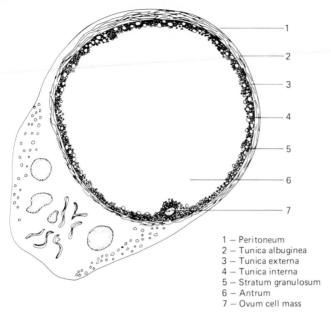

1 — Peritoneum
2 — Tunica albuginea
3 — Tunica externa
4 — Tunica interna
5 — Stratum granulosum
6 — Antrum
7 — Ovum cell mass

Figure 8-9 Cystic follicle.

in the walls and take on the structure and function of the corpus luteum. These are commonly called luteinized follicles.[20]

The majority of follicles continue to produce estrogen, telling the female to remain in estrus.

Hilus (Pit)

This is the connection of the ovary to the mesovarium. It is through this area that the vascular, nerve, and lymphatic structures pass to supply the ovary. The vascularity of the ovary changes drastically under the cyclic hormonal stimuli.

OVIDUCT

Serosa (Serous Membrane)

The outer covering of the oviduct is the *serosa* and is a continuation of the peritoneum as it covers the internal organs. It is a shiny tough connective tissue for the purpose of support, covered by a single layer of cuboidal epithelium (Fig. 8–10).

Muscularis (Muscle Coat)

Under the serosa is the *muscularis,* which is a layer of muscle that is very thin at the infundibular end and thickens as it approaches the uterus. Two layers develop, with the outer layer oriented longitudinally and the inner in a circular direction. These muscles are active particularly during the estrous portion of the cycle and

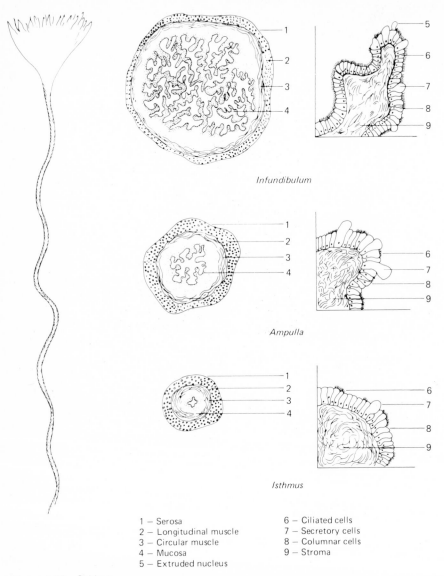

1 — Serosa   6 — Ciliated cells
2 — Longitudinal muscle   7 — Secretory cells
3 — Circular muscle   8 — Columnar cells
4 — Mucosa   9 — Stroma
5 — Extruded nucleus

Figure 8-10 Oviduct.

cause peristaltic-antiperistaltic movement to assist in moving the sperm to the point of fertilization in the upper oviduct and also to assist movement of the ovum into the tubular structure. The muscle structure of the oviduct apparently functions separately from the muscles of the uterus. The muscles are relatively inactive when the female is not under the estrogenic influence.

Mucosa (Mucous Layer)

Lining the oviduct is the *mucosa,* which is very folded longitudinally and covered with ciliated columnar, nonciliated columnar, and secretory cells.[30] The columnar cells also have microvilli on the surface. The folds are very thin and branching with secondary and tertiary folds in the infundibulum, surrounded by a thin muscularis. As the tubouterine junction is approached, the folds become less tortuous and the musculature thickens.[29] The mucosa is supported by the lamina propria, which is connective tissue with many reticular fibers. The mucosa consists mainly of ciliated columnar epithelium and secretory cells in the infundibulum.[18] The many ciliated cells have active hairlike appendages that beat in a wavelike manner toward the uterus. They stand very erect during estrus.[30] If you can imagine the movement of a field of wheat swaying in the breeze then you have a picture of the surface of the infundibulum and ampulla during estrus. The activity decreases as the female becomes anestrous. The number of ciliated cells decreases so that the tubouterine segment has few ciliated cells but many nonciliated cells.

The secretory cells are most numerous in the infundibular portion and are highly secretory during estrus. The fluid produced by these cells serves as a medium for the active sperm cells and the floating ovum. The cells are usually goblet shaped with the secretory portion bulging on the surface until rupture and release occurs. The cells then repair and continue production. The number of secretory cells decreases as the tubouterine junction is approached, where they are replaced by nonciliated columnar epithelium.

The nonciliated cells appear relatively inactive except for periods of rapid multiplication when they assume a pseudostratified appearance and some of the nuclei are extruded into the lumen.[23,29] Their number increases near the tubouterine junction.

UTERUS

The uterine wall consists of three distinct layers: perimetrium, myometrium, and endometrium (Fig. 8–11).

Perimetrium (Around-Womb)

The serosal covering of the uterus is a continuation of the peritioneal covering of the oviduct. It attaches to the broad ligament through the connective tissue elements for support.

Myometrium (Muscle-Womb)

Like the oviduct muscularis, the uterine muscles are layered with an inner circular and an outer longitudinal one. They intertwine to some extent to form a network of fibers. These are very active under the influence of estrogen at the time of estrus to move the sperm up the tract. There is a kneading motion that results in a churning of the internal fluids and subsequent transport of the sperm. The fibers become quiescent during the luteal or progesterone portion of the cycle to allow attachment of the embryonic membranes and pregnancy to continue.

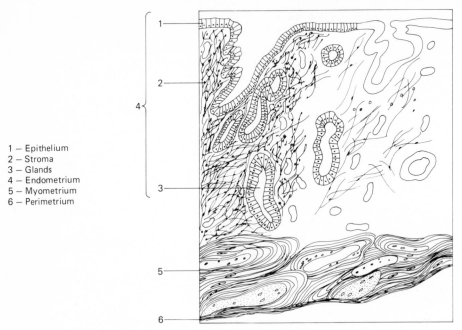

1 — Epithelium
2 — Stroma
3 — Glands
4 — Endometrium
5 — Myometrium
6 — Perimetrium

Figure 8-11 Uterus of the cow.

Endometrium (Inner-Womb)

The endometrium is composed of the stroma, containing the vascular system and glands, and the epithelium. It may make up two-thirds of the thickness of the uterine wall.[16] The glands are well developed and spiral in shape. Few are present prepuberally and growth is very rapid upon the onset of puberty and hormone activity (Fig.

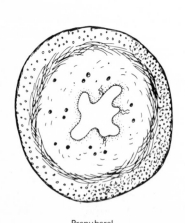

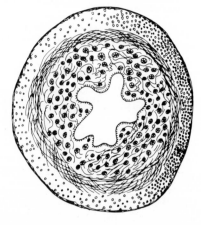

Prepuberal   Postpuberal

Figure 8-12 Uteri of heifers pre- and postpuberal.

8–12). They open onto the surface only between the caruncles of the cow and ewe but may open at any point in the sow, mare, and woman. The secretory cells are mostly pyramidal in shape, as they are broader near the basement membrane and taper toward the lumen. Secretion occurs primarily in response to progesterone when pregnancy is assumed, and the early developing embryo is bathed in the uterine milk produced by the glands.

The epithelium is mostly columnar epithelium. Few ciliated columnar cells are found near the tubouterine area, but these largely disappear as the body is approached.[29] Pseudostratified columnar epithelial cells are present during times of rapid proliferation[25] in the cow, sow, and ewe. The same cells cover the caruncles as are on the intercaruncular spaces. The glandular openings are lined by a mixture of the secretory cells and columnar cells. The uterine epithelium grows rapidly during the luteal phase and sloughs to some extent when progesterone decreases. This is particularly true in women where menstruation occurs. Even some of the glandular tissue sloughs at this time and must rebuild during the ensuing cycle.

CERVIX

The peritoneal fold continues over the cervix to form the serosa. The thickened wall is composed of connective tissue and several layers of circular muscle fibers and an outer longitudinal layer. The prominent folds protruding into the lumen are covered with columnar cells that are mostly ciliated.[33] The cells vary in height during the cycle.[31] The cilia beat in the direction of the vagina. The movement of fluids is also in that direction, so that during estrus when the sperm are attempting to penetrate the cervix, mucous secretion is at its highest and ciliary action is also greatest. The sperm orient themselves against the current and manage to pass into the uterus and on to the point of fertilization. The ciliated cells are most dense on the surface of the folds[28] and may reach 50 percent of total cells in sheep and goats.[17] They are replaced by secretory cells (Fig. 8–13) in the walls and base of the folds or crypts.[4] The secretory cells are very irregular in shape because of the various angles of the folds and are most active during estrus. They are densely covered with microvilli.[34] The mucus is very thin at this time. As the luteal phase occurs, the mucus becomes thick and tenacious and of a lesser amount. The cervix has no true glands, but it does have a large secretory surface in the crypts.[19]

VAGINA

The serosa, muscularis, and mucosal layers are all present in the vagina. The peritoneal fold covers the cranial vagina and then folds back to line the peritoneal cavity. The muscularis consists of an inner circular layer and an outer longitudinal layer continuous over the cervix and vagina. The pig has an inner longitudinal layer also. The protruding cervix is covered with columnar cells that change rather abruptly into stratified squamous epithelium. This is a rather drastic change in cell type and

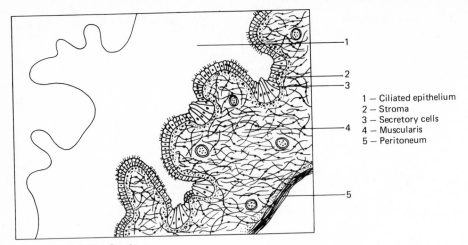

1 — Ciliated epithelium
2 — Stroma
3 — Secretory cells
4 — Muscularis
5 — Peritoneum

Figure 8-13 Cervix.

forms a weak cellular union. Disruption of cell growth here leads to cervical carcinoma. For this reason it is common to cauterize the cervical os following birth of the firstborn in women. Scar tissue forms and protects the area.

The stratified squamous cells form irregular papilla into the underlying stroma (Fig. 8–14). The vagina is nonsecretory except in the cow, where some secretory cells are interspersed near the cervical os. Cornification of the stratified squamous cells is less in the cow than other species. Sloughing of the surface epithelium occurs during estrus when protection is most needed. A smear of vaginal cells may be used

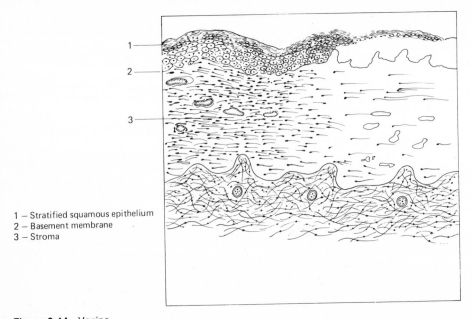

1 — Stratified squamous epithelium
2 — Basement membrane
3 — Stroma

Figure 8-14 Vagina.

to identify the stage of the estrous cycle in laboratory animals with short cycles. They are not dependable in large animals except in broad time intervals.[14]

HYMEN

The site of the hymen is recognizable only as a thickened area of mucosa lining separating the vagina and vestibule.

VESTIBULE

The vestibule is similar to the vagina except for the presence of vestibular glands in the ventral wall which open lateral and caudal to the suburethral diverticulum (Fig. 8–15). These glands are most active at estrus to lubricate the entrance in preparation for copulation. The major vestibular glands are present in the cow and sometimes in the sheep, while the minor vestibular glands are present in the sheep and pig.

VULVA

The vulva contains a small amount of muscle tissue, sebaceous and sweat glands, fat, and connective tissue in its walls. The inner and outer surfaces are covered with thick stratified squamous epithelium for protection (Fig. 8–16). Hairs and hair follicles are present on the exterior surface.

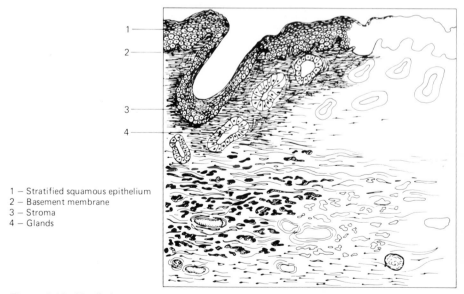

1 – Stratified squamous epithelium
2 – Basement membrane
3 – Stroma
4 – Glands

Figure 8-15 Vestibule.

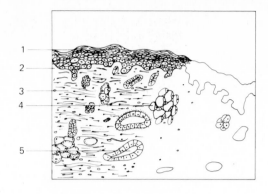

1 — Stratified squamous epithelium
2 — Basement membrane
3 — Stroma
4 — Fat cells
5 — Glands

Figure 8-16   Vulva.

CLITORIS

The clitoris contains cavernous tissue similar to the penis of the male. The covering epithelium is stratified squamous.

WHAT DID YOU LEARN?

1 Where are the majority of oocytes located at birth?
2 What is a mature follicle? Describe its components.
3 How may one distinguish between a follicle and a corpus luteum by palpation per rectum in the cow?
4 How would one tell that a follicle is about to ovulate in the mare by palpation?
5 What is a papillum?
6 What types of cells are found in the oviduct?
7 Where do endometrial glands open in the cow?
8 When is the myometrium most active?
9 What type of epithelium is found in the crypts of the cervix? When are they most active?
10 Why is stratified squamous epithelium needed in the vagina?

REFERENCES

1 Allen, W. E. 1974. The palpability of the corpus luteum in Welsh pony mares. *Equine Vet. J.* 6:25–27.
2 Asdell, S. A., J. deAlba, and S. J. Roberts. 1949. Studies of the estrous cycle in dairy cattle: Cycle length, size of corpus luteum and endometrial changes. *Cornell Vet.* 39:389–402.
3 Baker, R. D., K. S. Mellish, and D. H. Segal. 1969. First polar body formation and ovulation in gilts. *J. Anim. Sci.* 29:183–184.
4 Basmajian, John V. 1975. *Grant's Method of Anatomy.* 9th ed. Williams & Wilkins, Baltimore. Pp. 290–297.
5 Bergin, W. C. and W. D. Shipley. 1968. Genital health in the mare—I: observations concerning the ovulation fossa. *Vet. Med./Small Anim. Clinician* 63:362–365.

6   Casida, L. E., C. O. Woody, and A. L. Pope. 1966. Inequality in function of the right
    and left ovaries and uterine horns of the ewe. *J. Anim. Sci.* 25:1169–1171.
7   Constantinides, P. 1974. *Functional Electronic Histology.* Elsevier, New York. Pp. 133–
    142.
8   Dellman, H. 1971. *Veterinary Histology: An Outline Text–Atlas.* Lea & Febiger, Philadel-
    phia. Pp. 209–226.
9   Dellman, H. and E. M. Brown. 1976. *Textbook of Veterinary Histology.* Lea & Febiger.
    Philadelphia. Pp. 321–349.
10 Edwards, M. J. 1965. Observations on the anatomy of the reproductive organs of cows
    with special reference to those features sought during examination *per rectum. New
    Zealand Vet. J.* 13:25–37.
11 Elder, Cecil. 1925. Studies of the corpus luteum. *J.A.V.M.A.* 67:349–363.
12 Erickson, B. H. 1966. Development and senescence of the postnatal bovine ovary. *J.
    Anim. Sci.* 25:800–805.
13 Erickson, B. H., R. A. Reynolds, and R. L. Murphree. 1976. Ovarian characteristics and
    reproductive performance of the aged cow. *Biol. Reprod.* 15:555–560.
14 Ghannam, S. A. M., J. J. Bosc, and F. D. DuBuisson. 1972. Examination of vagina
    epithelium of the sheep and its use in pregnancy diagnosis. *Amer. J. Vet. Res.* 33:1175–
    1185.
15 Hadek, R. and R. Getty. 1959. Age-change studies of the ovary of the domesticated pig.
    Amer. J. Vet. Res. 20:578–584.
16 ———. 1959. The changing morphology in the uterus of the growing pig. *Amer. J. Vet.
    Res.* 20:573–577.
17 Hafez, E. S. E. 1972. Functional anatomy of the cervix uteri in domestic animals and
    primates. *Proc. 7th Int. Congr. on Anim. Reprod. and A.I.* 2:2304–2307.
18 Hafez, E. S. E. and H. Kanagawa. 1973. Scanning electron microscopy of bovine repro-
    ductive tract in female. *Cornell Vet.* 63:469–482.
19 Herrick, J. B. 1951. The cytological changes in the cervical mucosa of the cow (Bos
    taurus) throughout the estrous cycle. *Amer. J. Vet. Res.* 12:276–281.
20 MacKenzie, A. J. and T. N. Edey. 1975. The fate of large "cystic" ovarian follicles in
    sheep. *J. Reprod. Fert.* 43:393–394.
21 Mauleon, P. and J. C. Mariana. 1977. Oogenesis and folliculogenesis In H. H. Cole and
    P. T. Cupps, eds. *Reproduction in Domestic Animals.* Academic Press, New York. Pp.
    175–202.
22 McNutt, G. W. 1924. The corpus luteum of the ox ovary in relation to the estrous cycle.
    J.A.V.M.A. 65:556–583.
23 Nayak, R. K. and T. H. Brinsfield. 1973. Fine structure of infundibular epithelium in
    the mare. *J. Anim. Sci.* 37:322. (Abstr.)
24 O'Shea, J. D. 1973. The ultrastructure origin and fate of the theca externa of ovarian
    follicles in the sheep. *Res. Vet. Sci.* 14:273–278.
25 Palmer, W. M., H. S. Teague, and W. G. Venzke. 1965. Histological changes in the
    reproductive tract of the sow during lactation and early postweaning. *J. Anim. Sci.*
    24:1117–1125.
26 Peluso, J. J., R. W. Steger, and E. S. E. Hafez. 1977. Surface ultrastructural changes in
    granulosa cells of atretic follicles. *Biol. Reprod.* 16:600–604.
27 Rondell, P. 1970. Biophysical aspects of ovulation. *Biol. Reprod. Suppl.* 2:64–89.
28 Smidt, D., W. Endell, and W. Holtz. 1972. Histophysiology of the parturient cervix in
    the pig. *Proc. 7th Int. Congr. on Anim. Reprod. and A.I.* 2:2294–2301.
29 Sorensen, A. M., W. Hansel, W. H. Hough, D. T. Armstrong, K. McEntee, and R. W.
    Bratton. 1959. Causes and prevention of reproductive failures in dairy cattle. I. Influence

of underfeeding and overfeeding on growth and development of Holstein heifers. *Cornell Univ. Agr. Exp. Sta. Bull. 936.* Pp. 1–51.

30   Stalhaim, O. H. V., J. E. Gallagher, and B. L. Deyoe. 1975. Scanning electron microscopy of the bovine, equine, porcine and caprine uterine tube (oviduct). *Amer. J. Vet. Res.* 36:1069–1075.

31   Steinbach, J. and D. Smidt. 1970. Cyclical phenomena in the female genital tract of swine —histological observations. *J. Anim. Sci.* 30:573–577.

32   Witherspoon, D. M. and R. B. Talbot. 1970. Ovulation site in the mare. *J.A.V.M.A.* 157:1452–1459.

33   Wordinger, R. J., J. B. Ramsey, J. F. Dickey, and J. R. Hill, Jr. 1973. On the presence of a ciliated columnar epithelial cell type within the bovine cervical mucosa. *J. Anim. Sci.* 36:936–940.

34   Wu, A. S. H. and F. Stormshak. 1976. Ultrastructure of ovine cervical epithelium. *J. Anim. Sci.* 43:311. (Abstr.)

35   Yamashita, T. 1960. Histological studies on the ovaries of sows. III. On the elastic fibers of the wall of blood vessels in various histological structures. *Jap. J. Vet. Res.* 8:221–238.

36   ———. 1961. Histological studies of the ovaries of sows. IV. Stereographical study of the vascular arrangement in the various structures of ovaries by use of neoprene latex casting specimens. *Jap. J. Vet. Res.* 9:31–45.

37   ———. 1962. Histological studies on the ovaries of sows. V. Histological observations of the various corpora lutea in the ovaries of sows which have definite histories of parturition. *Jap. J. Vet. Res.* 10:1–24.

CHAPTER 9

Hormones and Puberty
in the Female

When you have completed this chapter you should be able to:

- Identify the hormones originating in the hypothalamus, hypophysis, and the gonads related to female reproduction,
- Associate the various hormones with their resulting target organs,
- Discuss the four factors related to puberty,
- Recite ages and ranges for onset of puberty, and
- Understand some of the effects of hormones, genetics, nutrition, and environment on the manifestation of puberty.

HORMONES

As was described in Chapter 3, there are three specific sources of hormones: the hypothalamus, hypophysis, and gonads.[5]

Hypothalamic Hormones

The hypothalamic hormones related to female reproduction are *Gonadotropic Releasing Hormone* (GNRH), *Prolactin Inhibitory Hormone* (PIH), and *Oxytocin.*

Gonadotropic Releasing Hormone (GNRH) This is considered to be the source of both the FSHRH and LHRH substances.[6,29,30] It is of interest that the 1977 Nobel Prize for Physiology or Medicine was awarded to Andrew Schally and Roger Guillemin for their work on hypothalamic hormones.[21] There is still question as to the source of two separate hormones. GNRH has been observed in numerous areas of the hypothalamus[2,14,24,25,32,36,40] from which it follows the neurons into the adenohypophysis where its influence results in production and secretion of FSH and LH by the basophilic cells of the adenohypophysis.[5,17]

Prolactin Inhibitory Hormone PIH is produced by the hypothalamus and restricts the production and release of prolactin from the adenohypophysis. The flow of the hormone from the hypothalamus is via neural pathways, and the action is on the cells of the adenohypophysis to inhibit production and release of prolactin.

Oxytocin Oxytocin is produced by the supraoptic and paraventricular nuclei of the hypothalamus and flows by neural pathways into the neurohypophysis where it is stored. There is no releasing hormone associated with this hormone. Upon the proper stimulus for milk letdown or contraction of the myometrium during parturition, oxytocin is released from the neurohypophysis.

Hypophyseal Hormones

Hormones of the hypophysis are divided into those of the adenohypophysis and the neurohypophysis.

Adenohypophysis The glandular adenohypophysis secretes and releases FSH and LH, two glycoproteins.

Follicle stimulating hormone FSH is produced by the blue-staining basophilic cells and passes through the cell walls and between the cells to enter the vascular bed of the adenohypophysis and thence to the circulation of the body and its target organ.

FSH has the ovary as its main target in the female. Its name is self-explanatory. It stimulates growth of the follicle to the stage of maturity. There is a multiplication of cells and accumulation of fluid in the follicle, which is rich in estrogen.

Luteinizing hormone LH is produced by the same type cells as FSH and enters the bloodstream in a like manner. Its target organ is the follicle on the ovary. LH peaks in blood concentration and this peak is followed by ovulation. During and following ovulation LH is active in initiating a change that may be noted in the granulosa and theca folliculi cells as they change shape and begin to fill with lipoid substance, which gives them a characteristic yellow color. As the cells continue to grow they produce the second female sex hormone, progesterone.

Prolactin PRL is of acidophilic cell origin and stimulates the CL in its development and maintenance in some species. It is receiving a great deal of attention by researchers in the cow at the present time. Prolactin is a polypeptide.

Neurohypophysis *Oxytocin* is *stored* here but is produced in the hypothalamus.

Gonadal Hormones

The ovary produces two hormones: estrogen from the follicle and progesterone from the corpus luteum.

Follicular hormones *Estrogen* is a collective term for the steroid hormones that are the preparatory or excitatory hormones of the female. It includes *estradiol,* which is the natural product of the granulosa cells and the theca interna of the follicle. There are two other estrogenic hormones: *estrone,* which is a secretory product, and *estriol,* which is an excretory product.

Progestogens include progesterone and pregnanediol. *Progesterone* is produced by the luteal cells of the corpus luteum that have developed from the granulosa and internal theca folliculi cells.

Hormones of the female are not as easily related to growth of the primary sex organs, accessory glands, and secondary sex characteristics as those of the male. They will therefore be discussed in subsequent chapters as they are related to puberty and to the estrous cycle and the multitude of changes that occur in the reproductive structures and in estrus.

PUBERTY

Puberty in the female is much more clearly exhibited than in the male. It is defined similarly to the male as that time when conception is possible, physically and physiologically. Puberty has been defined in other ways, and the reader should determine the definition of the author before making comparisons. Some individuals consider the presence of mature follicles that maintain themselves, or the presence of a corpus luteum, as indicating puberty. These structures sometimes develop in an anestrous situation, which means the female does not show signs of estrus. She therefore will not breed. Others depend strictly on signs of estrus, and ovulation may not occur in every instance.

One of the reasons that puberty is so important in the female is that this is the beginning of her reproductive life, and the earlier it can begin, the more offspring she may produce in her lifetime. This means that a heifer bred to calve as a 2-year-old will have one more calf than one bred to calve at 3 years of age. Also, cows that calve early the first time exposed tend to continue to breed early in later years. Seasonal effects on other classes of livestock somewhat offset this advantage in the cow; however, the early puberty gilt will have an advantage in number of litters produced.

Table 9–1 gives the reader some figures to keep in mind while reading this chapter, and it must be realized that there are so many factors affecting puberty that it is very difficult to place exact numbers with accuracy.

The same factors that were discussed as relating to puberty in the male exist in the female: hormones, genetics, nutrition, and environment.

Table 9-1 Age and Weight at Puberty for Females

Female	Age		Weight	
	Months	Range	Kg (lb)	Range
Heifer	11	7–18	300 (661)	200 (441)–450 (992)
Ewe	7	6–9	45 (99)	40 (88)–50 (110)
Gilt	7	5–8	77 (170)	73 (160)–82 (180)
Filly	14	10–24		
Girl	13	12–16		

HORMONES

Interaction of the various hormones of the hypothalamus and pituitary stimulate the ovaries to respond by producing the ovum accompanied by libido. The level of GNRH and FSH prior to and during the first estrous cycle shows little change in concentrations.[11]

The heifer exhibits a definite change in LH during the prepubertal period and at puberty. A priming peak of LH occurs about 10 days before estrus, and then a peak of about the same magnitude at estrus. This peak is necessary in the second instance for ovulation, and until more knowledge becomes available the earlier peak can only be classified as a priming peak.

Progesterone levels are very low in the newborn and appear to rise, followed by LH peaks, as puberty approaches.

Induction of estrus in prepubertal heifers has met with mixed success. Heifers averaging 8.5 months of age and 249 kg (549 lb) were treated with progestogens and estrogens, and although the number showing estrus and ovulating within a limited number of days was greater than controls, there was no significant difference in pregnancy rate.[35] Thus estrus may be effected but fertility is still lacking. Other work[12] showed some success in heifers of Angus and Hereford X Charolais breeding, 12 to 14 months of age, and averaging 278 kg (513 lb). Estrus and conception were markedly improved by treatments including estrogen and progesterone. Many details must be solved, but there is hope for inducing puberty.

Apparently the reproductive tract of the prepubertal female is ready to respond to hormone stimuli even from birth. Induced ovulation has been accomplished in prepubertal females by injecting PMSG and HCG.[23] This affords an avenue for the use of embryo transfer from prepubertal females. Over 100,000 primordial follicles are present in the prepubertal heifer.[9]

Genetic Factors

The genetic influence is most noticeable in purebred and crossbred females. Puberty is usually accepted as being delayed with inbreeding and shortened with crossbreeding. Limited numbers of straightbred cattle and crosses between the various breeds show that the crossbreds usually reach puberty at an age intermediate between the two parent breeds.[19,26] Others have found sire influences on age at puberty in cattle to be significant.[1,27]

The breed effect on age at puberty is well demonstrated by comparing smaller breeds with larger breeds.[18,22] Laster and the researchers at Nebraska found that the cattle in their program separated into three distinct groups. Jersey crosses reached puberty much earlier and Charolais crosses later than the medium-sized breeds— Hereford X Angus and South Devon, Limousin and Simmental crosses. The Jersey crosses averaged 322 days at puberty compared to a range of 364 to 415 days for the other breed crosses. Comparable weights at puberty were 219 kg (483 lb) for Jersey crosses and 266 to 303 kg (586 to 668 lb) for other crosses.

Sheep breeds differ considerably in age and weight at puberty as shown by Finn crosses cycling as early as 219 days and 40 kg (88 lb) compared to Rambouillet crosses at 238 days and 44 kg (97 lb) and purebred lines of 245 days and 45 kg (99 lb).[8]

Purebred gilts of Poland China and Chester White breeds reached puberty at 204 days of age compared to crossbred gilts at 182 days.[42] Seemingly, the purebreds are a little slower in reaching puberty than crosses, and the smaller breeds reach puberty before the larger, slower-maturing breeds. These statements must be weighed in relation to the effects of hormones, nutrition, and environment in making any accurate statement on an age or weight at puberty.

Nutritional Factors

The majority of research related to puberty has been in the nutritional area. Man can change this factor more easily than any other. Underfeeding will prolong the time to puberty, and overfeeding will shorten it. The effect of nutrition is intertwined with the other factors and must be considered largely as an environmental effect. The responsiveness of the animal depends upon its genetic potential.

Heifers have been submitted to high, medium, and low levels of nutrition with regard to energy, and the response of Holstein heifers is shown in Figures 9–1 through 9–4.[37] These figures are representative of other similar experiments.[34,41] Growth of the skeleton takes place first, and it is evident that the low-level ration of 60 percent recommended nutrients was not sufficient for optimum growth, while the normal level and high levels were sufficient. Ages at puberty for the three groups were 262 days for the high level, 344 days for the medium level, and over 504 days for those on the low level. It is interesting to note that ages for the heifers ranged from 203 to 560 days and weights ranged from 179 kg (394 lb) to 424 kg (934 lb). Thus the extremes in nutrition regimes can be appreciated as they affect factors related to puberty.

The effect of nutrition on age at puberty in swine is rather confusing. Some researchers have shown an older age at estrus associated with high levels of nutrition,[4,13,31] while others showed a delay in puberty associated with restricted feeding.[3,15,28,42] Sorensen et al.[38] found very little difference in age or weight at puberty in Duroc, Hampshire, and Poland China gilts fed high and low levels of energy (93 or 55 therms/100 lb free choice). Age favored high energy by 2 days (298 vs. 210); weight was heavier in the high-energy group (187 vs. 161). Again, it must be said that response is extremely variable.

Age at puberty in girls has made a spectacular decline over the last 100 years,

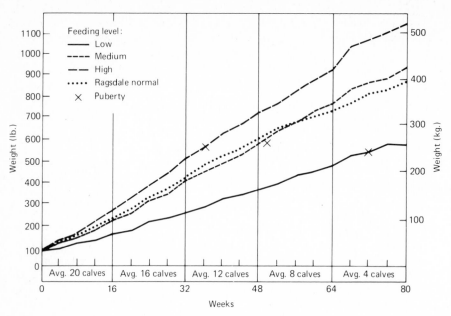

Figure 9-1   Average body weight of Holstein heifers on various feed levels related to puberty.

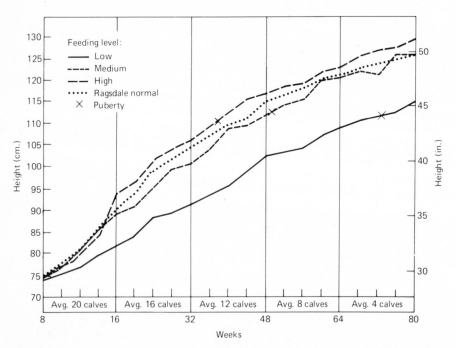

Figure 9-2   Average height at withers of Holstein heifers on various feed levels as related to puberty.

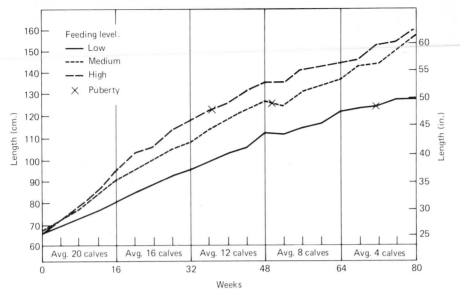

Figure 9-3 Average length of Holstein heifers on various feed levels related to puberty.

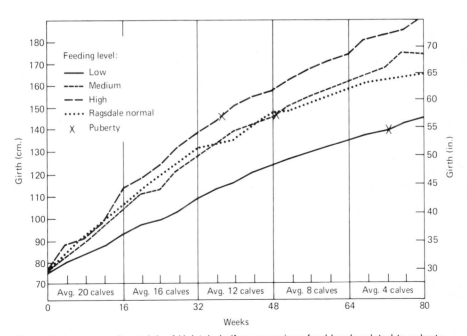

Figure 9-4 Average heartgirth of Holstein heifers on various feed levels related to puberty.

so that the mean age at menarche is now about 13 years.[33] This is probably influenced more by nutrition than any other factor.

Environmental Factors

Stress conditions, whether of temperature, humidity, or nutrition, will delay attainment of puberty. Santa Gertrudis, Brahman, and Shorthorn calves were raised under controlled temperatures of 10°C (50°F) or 27°C (80°F) from one month of age until puberty at the University of Missouri.[7] The high-temperature groups (Brahman and Shorthorn) grew at a more rapid rate but reached puberty at a later date than the lower-temperature heifers. The Santa Gertrudis were not affected to any extent. A third group of similar heifers was placed in open environment and reached puberty before the two temperature groups. For comparison, the Brahman at 10°C (50°F) reached puberty at 307 days, Santa Gertrudis at 290 days, and the Shorthorn at 303 days. Corresponding weights were 261, 295, and 263 kg (575, 650, 580 lb). Thus, either temperature or confinement delayed puberty.

The time of birth of lambs greatly influences puberty. Ewe lambs born in the spring of the year may be mature enough to breed in the winter season, whereas those born late in the season, summer or fall, will probably not reach puberty until the following year.[10,39] This means that age at puberty may range from 115 days to almost a year.

Gilts born in the fall tend to reach puberty earlier than those born in the spring.[20,37] Breed of the gilts may interact with season of birth as shown by a group of Chester White gilts born in the spring that reached puberty 12 days earlier than fall-farrowed gilts, while in the same experiment Poland China gilts were just the opposite—fall-born gilts reached puberty 13 days before spring-born gilts.[42]

Fillies born in the spring of the year will not reach puberty until the following spring at about 12 months of age. Those born in the fall and winter will also reach puberty in the spring and will be approximately 18 months of age.

Another environmental effect shortening the age at puberty is the presence of the male. This has been demonstrated in both sheep and swine, and there are indications that it applies in cattle and horses as well.

Close confinement of swine has hastened puberty when compared to gilts maintained in open lots.[16] Apparently swine are stimulated by the presence of other females.

WHAT DID YOU LEARN?

1 What is the source of GNRH and what is its target organ?
2 What change in hormone nomenclature is there in the female when compared to the male hypophyseal hormones?
3 What is the function of FSH?
4 Define puberty in the female.
5 Why would one want to shorten the prepubertal interval?
6 Give the "average" age and weight at puberty for the heifer, ewe, gilt, filly, and girl.

7 How can we practically use the fact that the ovary is responsive to hormones prepubertally?

8 Which would you expect to reach puberty first—a Jersey or a Holstein, a Shetland or a Clydesdale?

9 What factor governs onset of puberty the most?

10 Do you think you could select livestock for late maturity?

REFERENCES

1 Arije, G. F. and J. N. Wiltbank. 1971. Age and weight at puberty in Hereford heifers. *J. Anim. Sci.* 33:401–406.

2 Baker, B. L., W. C. Dermody, and J. R. Reel. 1974. Localization of luteinizing hormone-releasing hormone in the mammalian hypothalamus. *Amer. J. Anat.* 139:129–132.

3 Burger, J. F. 1952. Sex physiology of pigs. *Onderstepoort J. Vet. Res. Suppl.* 2:41–86.

4 Christian, R. E. and J. C. Nofziger. 1952. Puberty and other reproductive phenomena in gilts as affected by plane of nutrition. *J. Anim. Sci.* 11:789. (Abstr.)

5 Convey, E. M. 1973. Neuroendocrine relationships in farm animals: A review. *J. Anim. Sci.* 37:745–757.

6 Crighton, D. B. 1973. Review of releasing hormones in domestic animals. *Vet. Rec.* 93:254.

7 Dale, H. E., A. C. Ragsdale, and C. S. Cheng. 1959. Effect of constant environmental temperatures, 50° and 80°F, on appearance of puberty in beef calves. *J. Anim. Sci.* 18:1363–1366.

8 Dickerson, G. E. and D. B. Laster. 1975. Breed, heterosis and environmental influences on growth and puberty in ewe lambs. *J. Anim. Sci.* 41:1–9.

9 Erickson, B. H. 1966. Development and senescence of the postnatal bovine ovary. *J. Anim. Sci.* 25:800–805.

10 Foote, W. C., N. Sefidbakht, and M. A. Madsen. 1970. Puberal estrus and ovulation and subsequent estrous cycle patterns in the ewe. *J. Anim. Sci.* 30:86–90.

11 Gonzalez-Padilla, E., R. Ruiz, D. LeFever, A. Denham, and J. N. Wiltbank. 1975. Puberty in beef heifers. III. Induction of fertile estrus. *J. Anim. Sci.* 40:1110–1118.

12 Gonzalez-Padilla, E., J. N. Wiltbank, and G. D. Niswender. 1975. Puberty in beef heifers. I. The interrelationship between pituitary, hypothalamic and ovarian hormones. *J. Anim. Sci.* 40:1091–1104.

13 Gossett, J. W. and A. M. Sorensen, Jr. 1959. The effects of two levels of energy and seasons on reproductive phenomena of gilts. *J. Anim. Sci.* 18:40–47.

14 Gross, D. S. 1976. Distribution of gonadotropin-releasing hormone in the mouse brain as revealed by immunohistochemistry. *Endocrinol.* 98:1408–1417.

15 Haines, C. E., A. C. Warnick, and H. D. Wallace. 1959. The effect of two levels of energy intake on reproductive phenomena in Duroc Jersey gilts. *J. Anim. Sci.* 18:347–354.

16 Jensen, A. H., J. T. Yen, M. M. Gehring, D. H. Baker, D. E. Becker, and G. B. Harmon. 1970. Effects of space restriction and management on pre- and post-puberal response of female swine. *J. Anim. Sci.* 31:745–750.

17 Jubb, K. V. and K. McEntee. 1955. Observations on the bovine pituitary glands. I. Review of literature on the general problem of adenohypophyseal functional cytology. *Cornell Vet.* 45:576–592.

18 Laster, D. B., G. M. Smith, and K. E. Gregory. 1976. Characterization of biological types of cattle. IV. Postweaning growth and puberty of heifers. *J. Anim. Sci.* 43:63–70.

19 Long, C. R., T. G. Jenkins, and T. S. Stewart. 1977. Results of cattle research. *Technical Report 77–1,* Texas Agr. Exp. Sta., College Station. Pp. 33–59.

20 Mavrogenis, A. P. and O. W. Robison. 1976. Factors affecting puberty in swine. *J. Anim. Sci.* 42:1251–1255.

21 Meites, J. 1977. The 1977 Nobel Prize in physiology or medicine. *Science* 198:594–596.

22 Morrow, D. A., L. V. Swanson, and H. D. Hafs. 1970. Estrous and ovarian activity in pubertal heifers. *J. Anim. Sci.* 31:232. (Abstr.)

23 Murray, F. A. 1976. Reproduction in the near-pubertal gilt. *J. Anim. Sci.* 43:298. (Abstr.)

24 Palkovits, M., A. Arimura, M. Brownstein, A. V. Schally, and J. M. Saaverda. 1974. Luteinizing hormone-releasing hormone (LH-RH) content of the hypothalamic nuclei in rat. *Endocrinol.* 95:554–558.

25 Pelletier, G., R. Leclerc, and D. Dube. 1976. Immunohistochemical localization of hypothalamic hormones. *J. Histochem. and Cytochem.* 24:864–871.

26 Pleasants, A. B., G. K. Hight, and R. A. Barton. 1975. Onset of puberty in Angus, Friesian, Friesian X Angus, and Friesian X Jersey heifers. *Proc. New Zealand Soc. Anim. Prod.* 35:97–102.

27 Reynolds, W. L., T. M. DeRouen, and J. W. High, Jr. 1963. The age and weight at puberty of Angus, Brahman and Zebu cross heifers. *J. Anim. Sci.* 22:243. (Abstr.)

28 Robertson, G. L., L. E. Casida, R. H. Grummer, and A. B. Chapman. 1951. Some feeding and management factors affecting age at puberty and related phenomena in Chester White and Poland China gilts. *J. Anim. Sci.* 10:841–866.

29 Schally, A. V., A. Arimura, and A. J. Kastin. 1973. Hypothalamic regulatory hormones. *Science* 179:341–350.

30 Schally, A. V., A. Arimura, A. J. Kastin, H. Matsuo, Y. Baba, T. W. Redding, R. M. G. Nair, L. Debeljuk, and W. F. White. 1971. Gonadotropin-releasing hormone: One polypeptide regulates secretion of luteinizing and follicle-stimulating hormones. *Science* 173:1036–1038.

31 Self, H. L., R. H. Grummer, and L. E. Casida. 1955. The effects of various sequences of full and limited feeding on the reproductive phenomena in Chester White and Poland China gilts. *J. Anim. Sci.* 14:573–592.

32 Setalo, G., S. Vigh, A. V. Schally, A. Arimura, and B. Ferko. 1975. LH-RH-containing neural elements in the rat hypothalamus. *Endocrinol.* 96:135–142.

33 Short, R. V. 1973. Man, the changing animal. In E. M. Coutinho and F. Fuchs, eds. *Physiology and Genetics of Reproduction.* Part A. Plenum Press, New York. Pp. 3–15.

34 Short, R. E. and R. A. Bellows. 1971. Relationships among weight gains, age at puberty and reproductive performance in heifers. *J. Anim. Sci.* 32:127–131.

35 Short, R. E., R. A. Bellows, J. B. Carr, R. B. Staigmiller, and R. D. Randel. 1976. Induced or synchronized puberty in heifers. *J. Anim. Sci.* 43:1254–1258.

36 Silverman, A. J., J. L. Antunes, M. Ferin, and E. Z. Zimmerman. 1977. The distribution of luteinizing-releasing hormone (LHRH) in the hypothalamus of the Rhesus monkey: Light microscopic studies using immunoperoxidase technique. *Endocrinol.* 101:134–142.

37 Sorensen, A. M., W. Hansel, W. H. Hough, D. T. Armstrong, K. McEntee, and R. W. Bratton. 1959. Causes and prevention of reproductive failures in dairy cattle. I. Influence of underfeeding and overfeeding on growth and development of Holstein heifers. *Cornell Univ. Agr. Exp. Sta. Bull. 936,* pp. 16–31.

38 Sorensen, A. M., W. B. Thomas, and J. W. Gossett. 1961. A further study of the influence of level of energy intake and season on reproductive performance of gilts. *J. Anim. Sci.* 20:347–349.

39 Watson, R. H. and L. C. Gamble. 1961. Puberty in the Merino ewe with special reference to the influence of season of birth upon its occurrence. *Australian J. Agr. Res.* 12:124–138.

40 Wheaton, J. E., L. Krulich, and S. M. McCann. 1975. Localization of luteinizing hormone-releasing hormone in the preoptic area and hypothalamus of the rat using radioimmunoassay. *Endocrinol.* 97:30–38.

41 Wiltbank, J. N., C. W. Kasson, and J. E. Ingalls. 1969. Puberty in crossbred and straightbred beef heifers on two levels of feed. *J. Anim. Sci.* 29:602–605.

42 Zimmerman, D. R., H. G. Spies, E. M. Rigor, H. L. Self, and L. E. Casida. 1960. The effect of restricted feeding, crossbreeding and season of birth on age at puberty in swine. *J. Anim. Sci.* 19:687–694.

Estrus and the Estrous Cycle

When you have completed this chapter you should be able to:

- Enumerate the symptoms of estrus in the various species,
- Understand the broad meaning of proestrus, estrus, metestrus, diestrus, and anestrus,
- Relate the hormonal pathways to initiate activities of various glands and organs of the body,
- Relate specific hormones to specific responses from target organs, and
- Trace the growth of ovarian structures through an estrous cycle.

ESTRUS (Desire)

Estrus is that time during which the female will accept the services of the male. This period is cyclical in nature, and the length of the period and cycle vary among species. Estrus is also called "heat" because of the excitement of the animal at this time. It is brought about by estrogen, the female excitatory hormone. Estrus will first be discussed for each animal, and then the cyclic activities will be outlined. Understand that "estrus" is a noun and "estrous" is an adjective.

Cow

The cow is considered a polyestrous animal because she cycles continuously. Season or climate affecting other animals is not as critical in the cow. There are seasons of greater fertility in the spring and fall months, but cyclic activity and estrus itself are affected more by nutrition and stage of lactation than by season.

The length of estrus in the cow is approximately 16 hours (Table 10-1), and cycle length is 21 days. Extensive research has been conducted on estrus and the estrous cycle because of the importance of breeding at the correct time. Most of the early research dealt with dairy cattle and particularly cattle in the northeast and midwest United States. Now, data are available on beef cattle as well, and for all over the world. Table 10–1 summarizes some of the many reports on length of estrus at numerous locations. Reports from Kenya[4] and Florida[82] were based on Zebu cattle, and these and other data show that cattle with Zebu breeding such as the Brahman, Santa Gertrudis, and crossbreds will have shorter estrous periods than other breeds of cattle.

It is during this period of libido or sexual urge that the female will exhibit certain symptoms indicating her receptivity to the male.[58,98,114] The bull depends on these symptoms and so does the livestock producer who wishes to breed her artificially or by handmating at a specific time.

Symptoms

1 She will stand to be mounted by other animals (Fig. 10–1). These may be the bull, young bull calves, teaser animals, or other cows. The cow is somewhat homosexual in activity and this helps the observer to determine estrus. *This is the ultimate symptom of her being ready for breeding.*

Table 10-1   Estrous Duration in Cows

Reference source	Duration of estrus (hr)	Type cattle	Method of detection	Location
4	4.8	Beef	—	Kenya
7	17.1	Dairy	Teasers	Wisconsin
10	13.4	Beef	HMD, Teasers	Queensland
14	12.4	Dairy	Visual, Teasers	Texas
22	11.36	Friesian	Visual	Kenya
23	14.2	Beef and dairy	Visual	Queensland
43	11.9	Dairy	Visual	Louisiana
44	17.0	—	—	England
46	18.6	Dairy	—	New York
60	18.0	—	—	—
65	12.6	Beef	Teaser, Visual	Texas
82	6.7	Beef	—	Florida
108	16.9	Dairy	Visual	Nebraska
113	23.5	Dairy	Visual, Teasers	Texas
115	21.1	Beef	—	Nebraska
116	21.0	Beef	—	Nebraska
116	19.2	Beef	—	Nebraska

Figure 10-1   Cow exhibiting estrus by standing to be mounted.

2   She will attempt to mount other cows. When a cow does this, she should be observed to see if she will allow others to mount her. The cow doing the mounting may not be in estrus but may only be attracted by one that is in estrus. Watch these cows further.

3   Mucus may be smeared on the buttocks. This mucus originates in the cervix and will drip or stream from the vulva where the swinging tail will spread it. It may glisten in the light. This indicates the cow may be approaching estrus, be in estrus, or have just passed estrus. Mucus may be present 3 or 4 days from the actual period of acceptance so it should only be used as an indicator for further close observation.

4   She will usually be nervous. This is evidenced by refusing to eat, walking more than usual, reduced milk production, butting, bellowing, and, in general, an excited behavior. Pedometers were attached to the rear leg of dairy cows to measure physical activity during the estrous cycle,[26,59] and activity as measured by steps taken in a given period increased from two to four times during estrus as compared to the other periods of the cycle.

5   She will seek the bull and stay near him as estrus approaches and during ˙estrus.

6   Rubbed tailhead or mud on the hips indicates she has been ridden and was, or is, in estrus.

7   Chin resting on her rump by other cows, tail raising, licking the vulva, and excessive urination may be noted. Cows are somewhat nocturnal in estrous behavior. The greatest proportion show signs of estrus from evening until mid-morning.[10,31,58,65,66] The greatest concentration of cycles with the strongest symptoms are in the spring months[10,81] when the pastures turn green, the days get longer, and nutrition is generally improved.

Many observations have been made of other factors affecting estrus. Temperature has been measured without much success in predicting estrus or ovulation, as is possible in the human.[12,65] Electrical resistance of vaginal or cervical mucus has been attempted to determine estrus. Most instruments measure resistance in ohms, and although some changes are expressed, the reliability is not great enough to make the measurement feasible.[61] Cattle were bred when ohm readings were between 20 and 25 with 89 percent conception compared to 78 percent at 26 to 30 and 50 percent at 31 to 35. Perhaps further trials will indicate that it is feasible.

Smears of cervico-vaginal mucus have been studied as a possible measure of estrous activity.[3,13,37,74] The height of mucous crystallization extends from 2 to 3 days proestrus to 2 to 3 days postestrus and therefore is not exacting enough. There is an apparent increase in sodium chloride content of the mucus under the influence of estrogen, and as the progestational period of the cycle is manifest, the content lowers and crystallization is minimized.[90]

Monitoring the estrous cycle may be done by studying the progesterone level in blood or milk. There is a drop at the time of estrus; however, it is not abrupt enough to give any exacting time for estrus or ovulation.[28,97] Prolactin is high before ovulation and reaches minimal levels around the time of ovulation.[95] This may be useful in research but has little practical application. Peak levels of estradiol are reached on the day before estrus, and this may also have research significance.[97]

It is relatively common for cattle to show a small amount of blood on the vulva or buttocks about 2 to 4 days postestrus. This is not associated with whether the cow conceived at the breeding, as many people have believed. It results from a diffuse-type hemorrhage in the intercaruncular spaces, and this blood and a small amount of cellular debri find their way to the exterior.[47,111] It is a normal response to the drop in estrogen which has caused rapid growth of the endometrium and is then suddenly lowered drastically following estrus.

Ewe

The ewe is a seasonally polyestrous female. She cycles normally at 17-day intervals from mid-fall to early spring. The breed influences estrous activity to some extent. Fine-wool breeds of Rambouillet and Merino usually cycle year-round. The coarse-wool or mutton breeds follow the seasonally polyestrous pattern with an anestrous period from early spring until fall. If Rambouillet ewes are placed on a year-round breeding program, those lambing in the spring will return to estrus earlier than those lambing at other seasons.[30] The average time lapse is about 50 days. Those not lambing in the spring will take almost 100 days and must usually be held until the next breeding season.

Figure 10–2 gives the percent ewes in estrus when Rambouillet ewes were taken from two different locations and subjected to Texas hill country environment,[91] and indicates the influence of length of daylight on percent animals showing estrus.

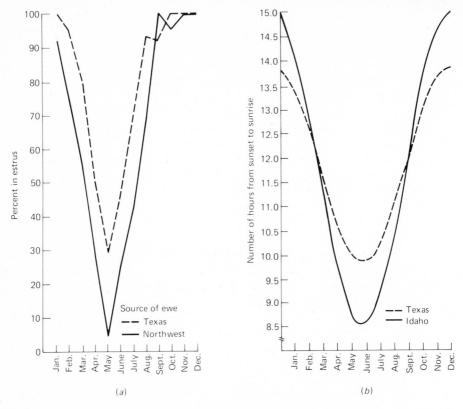

Figure 10-2   Influence of the season and daylight length on percent Rambouillet ewes in estrus. *(Shelton and Hulet.[91])*

Experimentally, estrous manifestation can be controlled, but it is not feasible under existing management conditions.

One of the significant developments in sheep breeding has been the introduction of the Landrace breed of Finnish origin. These are commonly called Finn sheep. They are noted primarily for early sexual maturity, shorter gestation, and their ability to produce multiple lambs; as well, they are supposedly polyestrous year-round. Crossing Finn sheep with Rambouillets yields higher ovulation rates, but the animals are seasonally polyestrus to a greater extent than the Rambouillets.[92]

The ewe will accept the ram for about 30 hours, and her cycle duration is 17 days. Although there is less demand for knowing when estrus occurs in the ewe compared to other species, the symptoms are needed in instances of artificial insemination. Some of the available data are summarized in Table 10–2. The longer Finn sheep estrus may be related to the increased fertility of the breed and should be further investigated.[76] There is also considerable variation between the ewe lambs and the mature ewes. As the ewe continues to cycle, the period of estrus lengthens and the cycle stays very nearly the same.

Table 10-2 Estrous Duration in Ewes

Reference source	Duration of estrus (hr)	Type sheep	Location
29	28.8	American breeds	U.S.
40	45	Dorset horn ewes	—
40	22.5	Blackface mountain ewes	—
41	32	Suffolk lambs	—
56	15.7	American breeds	U.S.
76	72	Finnsheep ewes	Sweden
85	30	Common breeds	—
96	18.7	Romney Marsh lambs	New Zealand
96	27.6	Romney Marsh ewes	New Zealand

Symptoms

1 She will stand to be mounted by the ram, teasers, or other ewes. The ewe is not as homosexual in nature as the cow but will attract attention when in estrus.

2 She will search out the ram.[56]

3 The vulva will swell slightly as edema occurs in the lips. This is fluid retention due to estrogen.

4 She will be nervous and walk the fence, bleating for her mate.

5 Characteristic of the ewe is a vibrating movement of the tail in the presence of the ram. The dock, or cutoff tail, will move rapidly from side to side. This action has been copied when attempting to artificially collect semen from a ram that is not particularly interested. It attracts his attention quickly, and ejaculation usually follows.

Methods of hormone assays have shown an increase in estradiol proestrus from 0 to 8 hours and a basal progesterone level by 12 hours proestrus.[79] These are of research significance but not of practical value at the present.

Vaginal smears have been used to characterize the period of estrus. There is a preponderance of squamous cells during estrus followed by cornified cells and neutrophils in metestrus, but the changes are not definite enough for reliably predicting estrus.[36,89]

The presence of the ram influences the expressions of estrus in a positive manner. Ewes separated from rams so they cannot hear, smell, or see them have more erratic estrous activity than those with rams in closer proximity. The closer the association, the more positive the response.

Sow

The sow is polyestrous. Her estrous period lasts approximately 44 hours, and cyclic activity occurs every 21 days. Swine producers use handmating methods where the sow is taken to the boar or vice versa, and it is necessary to be familiar with estrous symptoms. Artificial insemination is not widespread in swine but advances are being made. Table 10–3 summarizes some of the estrous data in swine.

Table 10-3 Estrous Behavior in Sows

Reference source	Duration of estrus (hr)	Type swine	Location
1	43	Crossbred	Oklahoma
5	22–48	Mixed breed	Iowa
110	66	Mixed breed	Wisconsin
110	20	Mixed breed	Wisconsin
110	84	Mixed breed	Wisconsin
110	52.8	Mixed breed	Wisconsin
120	50.6	Crossbred	Nebraska

Symptoms

1 The sow will stand to be mounted by the boar, teasers, or sometimes other sows. Like the others,[93] this is the only true symptom. The producer may place his hands on the loin or rump area and press down without the sow moving away (Fig. 10–3).

2 She will be nervous and move about a great deal, grunting and eating very little.

3 Some sows will attempt to mount other females.

4 Little mucus will be present on the vulva.

5 Characteristic of the sow is the swollen vulva (Fig. 10–4). It becomes engorged with blood and fluid and protrudes markedly. The producer who observes his herd daily will pick this up quickly.

Sounds of a grunting boar during courtship and mating helps stimulate estrous response.

Climatic conditions are critical for the sow. High temperatures will cause shortened estrous periods, and waiting to breed on the second day of estrus, as is rather common, may result in the sow refusing to accept the boar.

Mare

The mare is considered to be seasonally polyestrous, although some will cycle during all seasons. Mares generally begin cycling with erratic cycles in January, and it may

Figure 10-3 Sow in estrus responding to pressure.

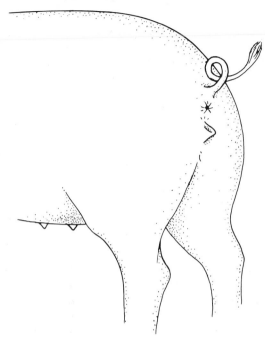

Figure 10-4 Swollen vulva of a sow in estrus.

be March before normal cycles are manifest. Conception during this time is not the best, but the pressure of registration of ages by a January 1 date forces many breeders to attempt mating at this time. Horses are registered as of January 1 regardless of their birth date, and in order to have the strongest, fastest, or largest horse in competition it is important that the foal be dropped as close to January 1 as possible. This means the mare should be bred around February 1.

The better breeding season is from March through July when the mares are cycling with greater regularity and conception is much improved. The length of estrus in the mare is considerably longer than in the other species. It lasts approximately 6 days (Table 10–4), and the cycle is 21 days. The mare is excited during this period of time, but she will only accept the stallion for about 2 days. Perhaps we need to reexamine our definition of estrus for the mare. Most mares are teased with a stallion or gelding to determine the time for breeding. He is restrained by a lead or separated from the mare by a barrier of some sort. A simple structure may be built in the center of a corral to restrict him while the mares circulate freely around him. He can see, smell, hear, and touch the mares without being able to make sexual contact.

Symptoms

1 The mare will stand to be mounted by the stallion or teaser. Sometimes other mares will mount or attempt to mount but this is not too common.

Table 10-4   Estrous Duration of Mares

Reference source	Duration of estrus (days)	Location
6	5	U.S.
9	6.8	Colorado
15	5.8–8.2	Colorado
38	5.2–8.3	Wisconsin
54	5.5	California
63	4–8	U.S.
73	5.2	Michigan
117	6	U.S.

2   Initial symptoms will be mostly nervousness on the part of the mare. She will walk a great deal and eat little.

3   She will then show more signs of interest in the stallion but resist any approaches on his part. Urination is frequent and this is most noticeable in the presence of other horses. She will kick at the stallion.

4   She becomes more nervous and may kick at the stallion but squats and urinates followed by a winking motion of the vulva in which the lips open and close exposing the internal lips and the clitoris.

5   Finally she becomes quieter in the presence of the stallion, raises her tail, squats, urinates, and winks the vulva (Fig. 10–5).[9,84,117]

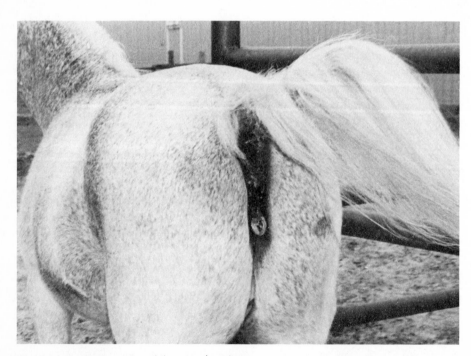

Figure 10-5   Winking vulva of the mare in estrus.

In a detailed study of reliability of the various symptoms, Back et al.[9] examined the relationship of winking, tail raising, squatting, urinating, kicking, ears back, squealing, and fence pushing and striking to estrous behavior. The conclusion was that winking and tail raising were the two most reliable criteria and, coupled with a lack of kicking, accounted for over three-fourths of the variation in behavior.

A method of detecting the time of ovulation, which may occur with or without estrus, is by palpation per rectum. The ovary may be felt for the presence of follicles and an estimate made of the time of ovulation.

Attempts to relate estrus and ovulation to pH, urinary protein, glucose,[53] temperature, vaginal smears, and cervical mucus have not been exacting enough to be meaningful. There are changes that occur, but they are gradual and without a definite peak of activity.

Woman

There is no period in the cycle of the woman that corresponds to estrus in the domestic animals. The cyclic pattern is based upon menstruation and is called the menstrual cycle. This is of 28 days duration and will be covered in more detail later in this chapter.

ESTROUS CYCLE

Physiological activities of the female reproductive system are cyclical in nature. Because of the outer manifestations of the excitatory preparation going on inside the female, this is called the estrous cycle. The cycle is interrupted, or elongated, by pregnancy or some abnormal situation. Data pertinent to the cycle are given in Table 10–5 and should be referred to from time to time through the remainder of this chapter.

The cyclic pattern is controlled by hormones circulating in the female's blood and the reaction to these hormones at the target organs. The cycle of each species will be discussed with relation to the hypothalamic, hypophyseal, and ovarian hormones, and structural changes in the ovary and uterus.

Various events occur on particular days. For the purposes of this discussion the beginning of estrus is considered the beginning of the estrous cycle; therefore, day 1 begins as estrus begins. Some literature follows this pattern, while other experts will consider the onset of estrus as beginning day 0.

The estrous cycle may be conveniently broken into periods designated proestrus, estrus, metestrus, and diestrus, plus a period of anestrus in some species.

Table 10-5 Reproductive Phenomena of Domestic Females

	Cow	Ewe	Sow	Mare
Estrous duration (hours)	16	30	44	6 (days)
Ovulation time after beginning of estrus (hours)	30	26	38	5 (days)
Estrous cycle duration (days)	21	17	21	21

₃ (Before Desire)

₃d of proestrus is one of preparation for mating. The entire system is in a ₁development and excitement. Estrogen is rising at this time and is primarily responsible for the changes.

Estrus (Desire)

The animal is very excited inside and out, and this is the only time she will accept the male. Estrogen is very high. Ovulation occurs at this time in most species. The cow is an exception.

Metestrus (After Desire)

Estrogen is low, progesterone is low, and the animal is recovering from the excitement of breeding and preparing for pregnancy.

Diestrus (Between Desire)

Progesterone is high and the animal is in a quiescent period between the periods of sexual excitement.

Anestrus (Without Desire)

This term may refer to an animal that does not show libido for an extended period of time, such as is present in the seasonally polyestrous species that cycle normally for a period of time and then have an extended period of inactivity. Or, it may refer to a short-term situation such as the period of expected estrus when ovulation occurs but no outward signs are manifest. This would be an anestrous ovulation. Many references refer to this as a "silent heat," but in truth, if it is silent, no one knows that it happens.

Cow

Hypothalamic Hormone Gonadotropic releasing hormone (GNRH) is being studied in more detail as assay systems are being developed; therefore, the preliminary comments made here may well be out of date by the time they are published. Hopefully the general trends and principles will remain relatively stable.

GNRH, secreted by the hypothalamus and stimulating FSH and LH release[17] from the adenohypophysis, rises in proestrus, peaks during estrus, and decreases toward the end of metestrus. It stays low during diestrus before rising again in proestrus (Fig. 10–6).

This would indicate stimulation of FSH and LH before, during, and shortly after estrus.

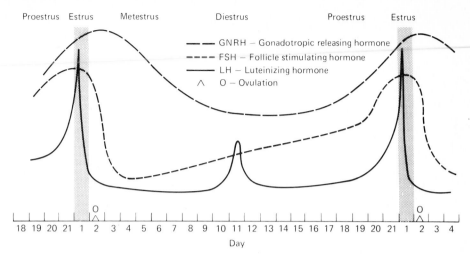

Figure 10-6 Hypothalamic and hypophyseal hormones in the estrous cycle of the cow. *(Adapted from Hackett and Hafs[39]; Hansel et al.[48]; Robinson.[87])*

Hypophyseal hormones hormones

Follicle stimulating hormone (FSH) FSH is secreted by the adenohypophysis in response to GNRH and in turn stimulates growth of follicles on the ovary and production of estrogen. FSH is present in the blood and begins to rise on day 4 to 6. It continues to rise and stimulates follicular growth throughout most of the remainder of the cycle.[39] It would seem that the level would continue to increase until ovulation, and perhaps as other data become available this will be shown.

Luteinizing hormone (LH) LH is also secreted by cells of the adenohypophysis in response to GNRH. Its purpose is to cause rupture of the follicle and begin growth of the corpus luteum. It reaches a very sharp peak at the beginning of estrus,[70] and ovulation occurs approximately 30 hours later (Fig. 10–6).

Ovarian Structures The ovarian structures change in a cyclic manner, with new growth and death of the structures occurring every 21 days. The follicle, corpus hemorrhagicum, corpus luteum, and corpus albicans function in each normal cycle (Fig. 10–7).

Follicle The follicle begins its development in the embryonic life of the animal as an oocyte. After puberty, selected oocytes are stimulated each cycle to grow to maturity, and one of these usually ruptures, releasing the ovum. This growth is under the influence of FSH. Many follicles start growing each cycle from the dormant oocytes. Some follicles will die during the process at any stage of development and become atretic follicles. These will regress and be resorbed by the ovary. Other follicles will grow and reach sizes of 4 to 15 mm and then become atretic. Palpation of the ovaries in proestrus may reveal several rather large follicles.

One of these follicles, or perhaps two in rare instances, will become mature.

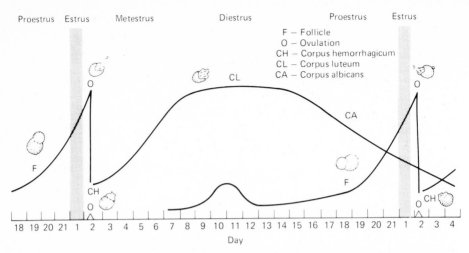

Figure 10-7 Ovarian structures in the estrous cycle of the cow. *(Adapted from Hancock[45] and McNutt.[67])*

There is no known reason for a specific one to be chosen for ovulation. After ovulation, the other follicles will become atretic or lie dormant, possibly for the next cycle. The most rapid growth of the follicle is in the late proestrous and estrous periods. It is not necessarily the largest follicle prior to this time that makes the rapid growth and ruptures. The chosen follicle is stimulated by LH to bring about ovulation, and the ruptured follicle forms the corpus hemorrhagicum.

It is during the growth of these follicles that estrogen is being produced by the granulosa and tunica interna cells. The larger and more abundant the follicles, the greater amount of estrogen present (Fig. 10–8).

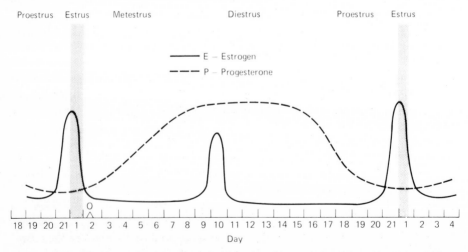

Figure 10-8 Estrogen (E) and progesterone (P) in the estrous cycle of the cow. *(Adapted from Hansel et al.[48]; Robinson[87]; Geschwind[35]; Smith et al.[97]; Stabenfeldt.[104])*

Corpus hemorrhagicum (CH) The CH develops immediately in the cavity of the ruptured follicle. This would occur about 30 hours from the beginning of estrus, and the period of the CH lasts about 2 days. The change is so gradual into the corpus luteum that a definite ending of the CH is difficult to ascertain.

Corpus luteum (CL) The CL develops gradually from the lining cells of the follicle and reaches its mature size around 8 to 10 days from the beginning of estrus. The cells produce progesterone approximately in proportion to the size of the CL, and therefore the curve of progesterone activity follows the growth of the CL closely. The life of the CL is about 12 days; therefore, at 16 to 17 days of the cycle there is a death of the cells and a rapid drop in progesterone. The cells do not reduce in size as rapidly as their progesterone content decreases.

Corpus albicans (CA) The CA is also a gradually acquired structure because of the slow demise of the CL. It gradually changes in size as the cells lyse and are resorbed into the ovary. A CA may be discerned in the ovary many months following its inception.

In the cyclic pattern shown in Figure 10–7 it should be noticed that the ovary will repeat its production of other follicles followed by CH, CL, and CA over and over until pregnancy occurs or reproductive life terminates for one reason or another. The ovaries may or may not alternate in activity.

Gonadal hormones The two gonadal hormone groups are the estrogens and progestogens. The hormone levels of estrogens have been assayed separately and collectively and will be referred to here as the entire complex. More and more research is now separating the estrogens into estradiol, estrone, and estriol,[68] and these terms may be used in specific instances.

Estrogen Estrogen is produced primarily by the follicle, and more specifically by the granulosa and tunica interna cells. This production is in response to FSH stimulation of the follicle to grow. Figure 10–7 shows the changes in estrogen level, and, as would be expected, the hormone concentration corresponds to the size of the follicle, with its greatest potency at the beginning of estrus.[32] Estrogen is responsible for libido and for preparation of the entire reproductive system for conception (Fig. 10–7). The mid-cycle peak of estrogen corresponds to the numerous accounts of short cycles reported and is probably high enough in some cows to result in estrus.[64]

Hormone interaction Estrogen acts as a triggering mechanism for the release of LH. This can be seen by comparing the peak of estrogen with the immediate subsequent release of LH. It also interacts with its parent hormone, FSH. This is accomplished via two pathways, neural and humoral. The neural pathway conducts a message to the hypothalamus and thence to the adenohypophysis to slow down its secretion of FSH. If there is not enough estrogen being produced for the balance to be maintained, no depressing signal is sent; if too much is being produced, the signal is sent. The humoral pathway is via the blood system to the adenohypophysis

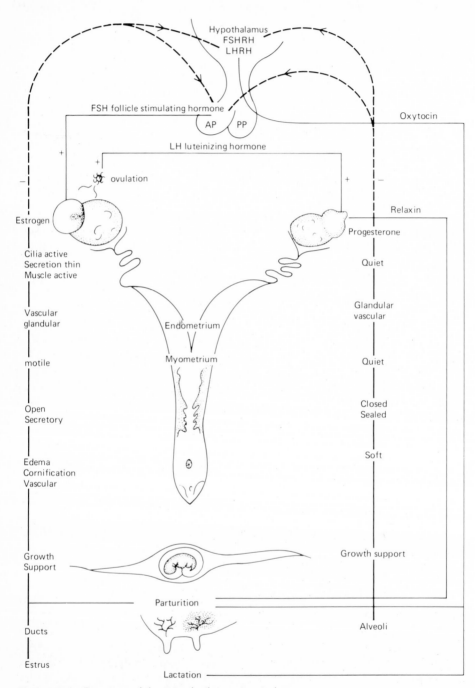

Figure 10-9 Response of the reproductive system to hormones.

where FSH is produced. As in the neural system, the balance-counterbalance system again comes into play.

Oviduct The ciliated cells of the oviduct are very active under the influence of estrogen. The long filaments stand erect at the beginning of estrus and later in estrus beat in a rhythmic manner to sweep the ovum into the oviduct to the ampulla for fertilization.[106] This movement is assisted by the copious secretion of fluids by the secretory cells. This thin, abundant fluid acts as a medium for both the free-floating, nonmotile ovum and the swimming sperm coming up the tract.

The muscularis is also active in an effort to churn the contents of the tube, assisting in movement of the sperm and ovum.

Uterus The columnar epithelium begins growth and becomes pseudostratified as the cells vie for position on the crowded surface. They are tallest in proestrus and estrus.[8] Within the endometrium the glandular components are beginning to grow as they are stimulated by the much increased vascular growth. All of this is in preparation for a fertilized ovum and the role of nourishment played by the uterine glands (Fig. 10–10).

The myometrium is very active as it contracts and relaxes in a peristaltic-antiperistaltic manner to help move the sperm through the uterus.

Cervix During this period of excitement under the influence of estrogen, the cervix assists in every way it can to pass the sperm from the point of deposition at the mouth of the cervix into the uterus.[75] The cervix opens to allow easier passage. The mucus cells in the crypts become very secretory and rupture to release mucus.[52] Most of the mucus seen passing from the vulva of a cow in estrus originates in the cervix. Crystalline patterns of mucus are very marked.[37] The few cilia that

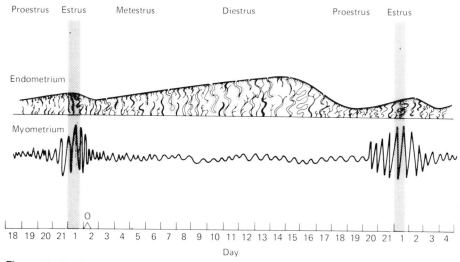

Figure 10-10 Cyclic changes in the endometrium and myometrium of the cow.

beat toward the os cervix,[42] and if any current results, it tends to orient toward the point of fertilization.

gina and vestibule The stratified squamous epithelium grows rapidly as estrogen increases, so that multiple layers of cells are present to resist the abrasion of the penis during copulation. Also at this time, the vaginal surface is moistened.

Vulva The surface of the vulva changes little, but there is retention of fluids in the tissue and increased vascularization resulting in some slight swelling.

Libido Estrogen is responsible for the sexual urge; the response becomes more intense as estrogen increases and less intense with its disappearance.

Mammary system The mammary system is composed of ducts for passage, and alveoli for milk production. The duct system is stimulated by estrogen so that there is an increase in numbers, length, and overall size of the ducts. This occurs in each cycle as estrogen increases.

Growth The point of growth of the long bones is the epiphysial plate. This point is depressed by estrogen so that mature intact females will be smaller than ovariectomized females.

Progesterone The period of excitement and preparation is followed by progesterone and a period of quiet for the development of a fertilized ovum. If fertilization does not occur, the system recognizes this and repeats the cycle for another opportunity.

Progesterone is produced by the luteal cells of the corpus luteum. These cells become functional on day 3 or 4 of the cycle and increase in numbers and production of progesterone until about day 8.[105] This level is maintained until day 16, at which time they will regress; progesterone levels will subsequently decrease sharply,[32] so that cells that were maintained by the higher progesterone levels are suddenly without support and die.

The quieting effect of progesterone is manifest throughout the reproductive system as everything prepares for pregnancy.

Hormonal interaction Progesterone acts like estrogen in maintaining a balance within the system. A neurohumoral inhibition takes place as progesterone reaches optimum production levels with the neural pathway to the hypothalamus and GNRH and the humoral system directly to the adenohypophysis for depressing LH production.[18]

Oviduct Ovulation is past, sperm passage is over, and there is no longer a need for the high level of activity exhibited in the estrous phase. Progesterone causes a slowing of ciliary action but not complete cessation. Mucus is secreted in lesser amounts and of thicker consistency. Muscle cells relax, so motility is decreased. The fertilized ovum is in the oviduct for about 4 days, so there is still a need for some activity to move it into the uterus during the early stages of progesterone production.

Uterus There is continued activity, particularly in the endometrium. Surface epithelium continues to proliferate. The vascular bed continues its growth and supports the rapidly growing glandular components so that they increase in size and numbers and produce a milky secretion to bathe the fertilized ovum during its early life. Height of cells and secretion increase up to the eighth day.[8]

The myometrium is quiet during the progestational phase of the cycle.

Cervix The open cervix closes by contracting the many folds. The mucous-secreting cells produce a very thick tenacious mucus that seals the cervix. Crystalline formation of this mucus is lacking, indicating an absence of salts at this time. The cilia are constricted by large amounts of mucin in adjoining cells.[118]

Vagina and vestibule The time of abrasion is past, so the cells slough in the early stages of progesterone dominance, and cornified or dead cells will be flushed from the surface. Growth is slower, and a thinner wall of stratified squamous epithelium is present.

Vulva The vulva loses the fluids back into the circulatory system and shrinks somewhat.

Libido There is no sign of sexual desire when the system is under the influence of progesterone.

Mammary system The alveoli are stimulated by progesterone so that the milk-secreting units grow and further develop the udder in conjunction with the ducts stimulated by estrogen.

So, the two gonadal hormones work together in a very logical sequence of (1) preparation under the influence of estrogen and (2) maintenance of pregnancy under the influence of progesterone.

The discussion of the estrous cycle has been based on changes of different hormones or structures related to the entire cycle. If the cycle is divided, as was done earlier, into proestrus, estrus, metestrus, and diestrus, one can see the relationship of the estrogenic phase to proestrus and estrus and the progestational phase to metestrus and diestrus, and the interaction of numerous hormones at a certain period (Fig. 10–11).

Ewe

The reproductive cycle of the ewe is of 17 (14 to 20) days' duration. Similar activities take place as in the cow. Fig. 10–12 depicts the hormonal and structural changes.

It is simpler to point out differences from the cow than to elaborate on each change. First, the cycle is shorter. The estrous period itself, however, is longer—30 (24 to 36) hours—and ovulation occurs in the latter part of estrus, approximately 24 to 27 hours from the beginning of estrus.[85] The life of the CL is from day 4 to 14, and there is a rapid degeneration at that time.[33]

The hormonal activities follow the same pattern, and uterine responses are the

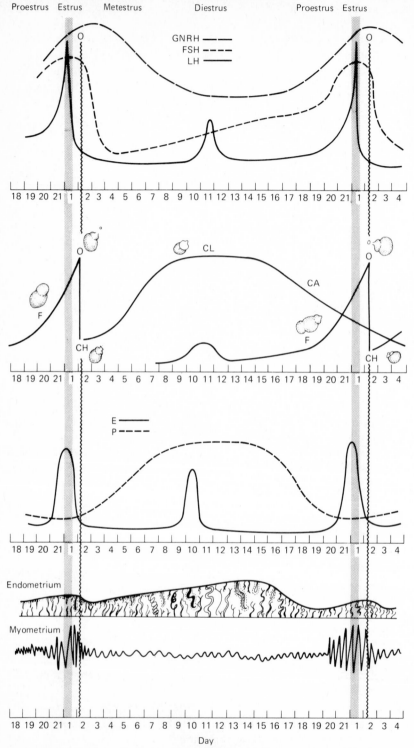

Figure 10-11 Hormones, ovarian structures, and uterine activity during the estrous cycle of the cow.

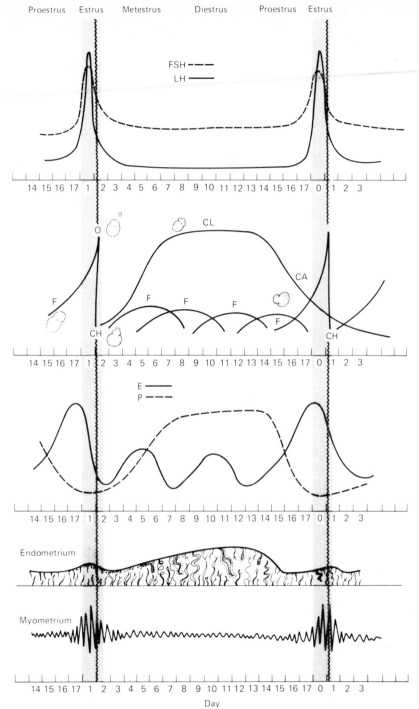

Figure 10-12 Hormones, ovarian structures, and uterine activity during the estrous cycle of the ewe. *(Adapted from Pant et al.[79]; Geschwind[35]; Robertson[85]; Smith et al.[96]; Cummings[20]; Hansel et al.[48]; Robertson.[86])*

same. Follicular development varies in that there are relatively large (5 mm) follicles throughout the cycle. These will grow and regress so that there is nearly always one follicle of this size. Changes in the oviducal cell components are less. Ciliated cells and secretory cells are there in about the same proportions throughout the cycle.[71] Vaginal epithelial cells are more cornified during estrus than in the cow, but there are still no definite changes to associate with specific days of estrus or ovulation.[36]

Sow

The period of estrus in the sow is 48 hours (46 to 50), and the cycle occurs every 21 days (18 to 24). A major difference lies in the fact that multiple ova are produced and ovulated. The follicles develop throughout the cycle and may become atretic at any stage. The large number of follicles (12 to 20) are shown in Figure 10–13 in the various stages of development.[1] The development of the structures may be followed in conjunction with Figure 10–14 to see the interaction of the stimulating hormones and the relationship to the production of gonadal hormones.

Figure 10–13/1 shows one ovary just prior to ovulation. FSH has stimulated growth, and now the follicles, under the influence of LH, have softened slightly in preparation for rupture. The ovaries rupture and form the CH in Figure 10–13/2, and the CH begin the transformation to CL. There is little hormonal activity at the time of rupture and shortly thereafter. The corpus luteum is formed fully by the time of Figure 10–13/9, and the luteal cells are secreting high levels of progesterone at this time (Fig. 10–14). The CL are maintained until a rapid decline starting about day 15 (Fig. 10–13/16), and the ovary becomes slightly smaller as the CL shrink and follicles begin their enlargement. The new follicles grow as influenced by FSH and prepare again for the surge of LH to bring about ovulation.

Ovulation occurs in the latter phase of estrus, about 35 to 40 hours after beginning of estrus and the LH peak.[24,94] The number of cystic follicles is much greater in swine than in other species[19] and accounts for most of the reproductive abnormalities. They are difficult to diagnose and treat.

Ovulation occurs over a period of 1 to 4 hours and is influenced by mating, so that sows mated ovulate about 4 hours earlier and for periods almost 3 hours shorter than sows not mated.[94]

Estrus is exhibited by sows within a few days postpartum. This is nonfertile for all practical purposes. It usually occurs within one week and is not accompanied by ovulation.[110] Estrous length may last from 20 to 84 hours.

Flushing sows is a rather common practice in swine breeding. This entails a program of increased nutrients for a week or less in an attempt to have more ova produced. The data from research are in conflict,[21] and it appears to be a matter of condition of the sows when flushing begins. Those in good condition will probably not respond as readily as those in poor condition.

The cyclic changes in epithelium throughout the reproductive tract follow a similar pattern to the cow and ewe.[107,119]

The oviducts are constricted during estrus, and the large volume of sperm

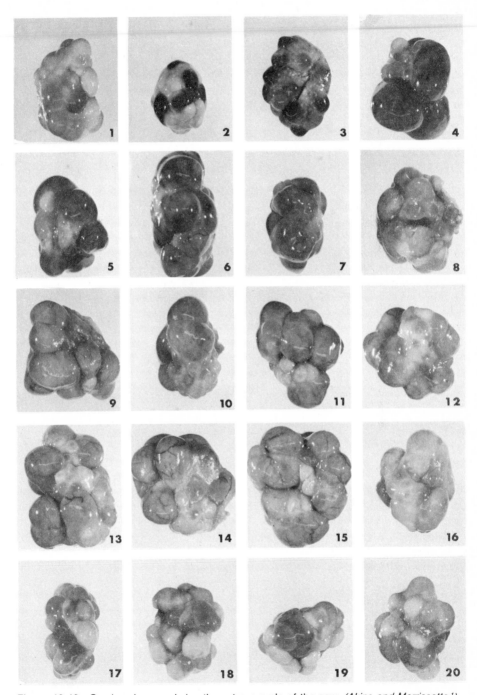

Figure 10-13 Ovarian changes during the estrous cycle of the sow. *(Akins and Morrissette.[1])*

ejaculated by the boar is trapped in the uterine horns and body. The sperm is very concentrated at the tubouterine junction.[57,83] The musculature relaxes about the time of ovulation, allowing the sperm to pass on to the point of fertilization.

Selection for the number of ova released has given some favorable response.[49] Gilts selected over eight generations were examined and the CL on the ovaries were counted. The results were 16.2, 13.0; 15.9, 13.4; 17.0, 13.4; and 17.2, 14.3 for selected and control groups of sows. It is feasibile, then, to select for larger litters.

Mare

There are so many differences between the mare and the other species that it demands more detailed discussion. The mare is very erratic in her cycles, length of estrus, and hormone levels. At times she even ovulates without regard for the other factors. It has been said that the only thing normal about the mare is her being abnormal.

Estrus may range from 1 day to 10 or more in the late winter and early spring. Cycles may be as variable, with ranges from 2 to 3 days to 30 or 40. Once the mare settles down in the spring, most cycles will be around 21 days and most estrous periods will be between 4 and 6 days. Ovulation usually occurs 24 hours before termination of estrus,[63] but since we cannot count backwards, this is of little use to us.

The hormones circulating in the blood of the mare also follow some peculiar patterns (Fig. 10–15). Note that FSH has a second peak on about day 15; the other domestic animals do not have this.[25] In response, a number of follicles are present at this time, and sometimes one will rupture.[11] The first rise in FSH does not seem to fit ovulation because it is still rising postovulation. Miller et al., working with pony mares, failed to show the peak at estrus.[69]

LH peaks after ovulation and therefore must be questioned as the causative factor of ovulation as has been shown in other species.[34,73,102,112]

Numerous follicles grow in preparation for estrus and ovulation.[6,99] It is not until very near ovulation that a single follicle increases quickly and softens.[63] Growth usually occurs two days before ovulation, and softness one day before. Not all mature follicles will soften, and some that soften will subsequently harden again before ovulation.[84,117] The follicles may be palpated on any portion of the ovary, but ovulation will occur in the fossa.[6] The CH forms quickly and appears more as a hemorrhage than in the other species.

The CL forms quickly and may be palpated in the early stages as a soft depression in the fossa. It is discernible for about a week but varies from 1 day to 14 or 16.[2,54] It becomes firm as it matures and feels much like the remainder of the ovary as a result.

Because of the rapid changes in structures and related activity the cycle is commonly divided into a period of "estrus" and a period of "diestrus," meaning that there are periods of excitement separated by periods of inactivity.[6] Figure 10–15 is headed with periods of proestrus and metestrus to remain uniform with the other species cycles. Proestrus has been placed within the accepted period of estrus because

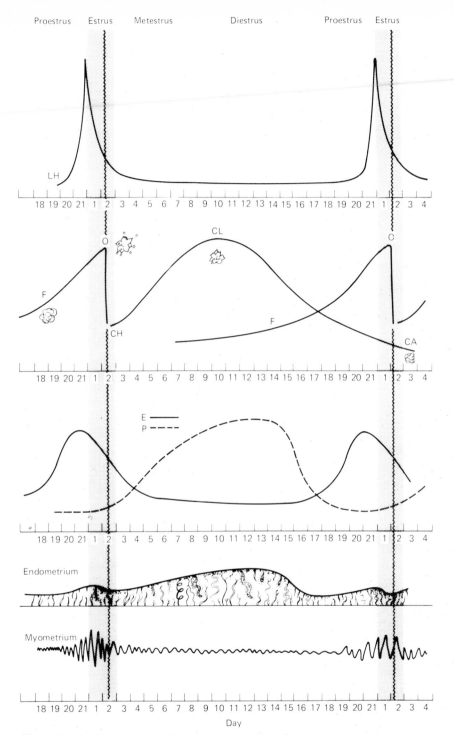

Figure 10-14 Hormones, ovarian structures, and uterine activity during the estrous cycle of the sow. *(Adapted from Anderson[5]; Hansel et al.[48]; Hendricks et al.[50]; Niswender et al.[72]; Palmer et al.[78]; Stabenfeldt et al.[105]; and Stenbach and Schmidt.[107])*

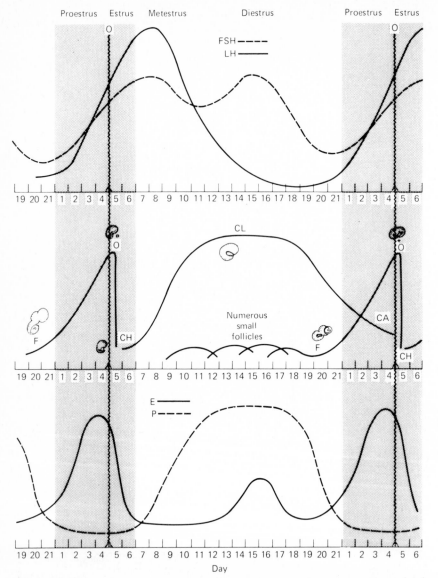

Figure 10-15 Hormones and ovarian structures during the estrous cycle of the mare. *(Adapted from Evans and Irvine[25]; Geschwind et al.[34]; Hughes et al.[34]; Noden et al.[73]; Palmer and Jousset[77]; Pattison et al.[80]; Stabenfeldt et al.[104]; Stabenfeldt and Hughes[102]; Whitmore et al.z[12]; Stabenfeldt et al.[103])*

the early part of this period coincides with the type of preparation seen in other species. Follicles are growing and the tract is being prepared for ovulation and fertilization.

During proestrus mucus is secreted by the cervix and may be seen on the vulva. Examination of the vagina and cervix will reveal a pale dull appearance.[55,62] As estrus approaches, the walls of the vagina appear shiny and transparent so that the blood vessels are visible. Epithelial changes are only slight.[63] The cervix becomes edematous, and soft folds may protrude distinctly into the cranial vagina.[42,102] Sometimes there will be more tone during estrus, but this condition is not dependable.

Metestrus is shortened by the rapid changes in the CL formation and function. Realize that there are only 15 days between the end of estrus and the beginning of the next cycle as compared to 20 in the cow.

The mare has the capability of recognizing a fertilized ovum while it is still in the oviduct. This is shown by the retention of unfertilized ova in the oviduct while the fertilized ova pass on into the uterus.[104] Oviducts have been flushed in cycling mares with multiple ova recovered in the absence of recent signs of ovulation on the ovary.

Woman

The cyclic pattern of the woman is essentially the same as for domestic animals except there is no period of estrus and there is a period of menstruation. Menstruation is the noticeable cyclic function, and the cycle is therefore called the *menstrual cycle.* Menstruation is a period when the uterine lining is sloughed and the cellular debri and blood are passed to the exterior. The cycle is normally 28 days long,[16] and ovulation commonly occurs on day 13.

Figure 10–16 outlines changes occurring in the menstrual cycle. FSH rises to stimulate growth of follicles. The FSH dips before ovulation and then rises sharply as does LH just prior to ovulation.[35] This peak is little different from other species, but the dip preceding it cannot be explained.

The ovaries respond in the follicular phase by the development of a single follicle and numerous others that become atretic. Estrogen rises as the follicles grow and reaches a peak about one day before ovulation, which triggers the LH secretion with subsequent ovulation. Estrogen drops quickly as ovulation occurs.

The CH and CL form quickly, and the CL begins its secretion of progesterone as in other species. The factor that differs at this point is the secretion of estrogen by the CL also. It rises a little slower than progesterone and then decreases as the corpus luteum regresses rapidly from day 21 to day 28.

The interaction of both estrogen and progesterone with FSH and LH is similar in the woman to other species. Inhibition occurs as before. The estrogen during the luteal phase apparently is not potent enough to completely depress follicular growth, but the major growth occurs after regression of the CL just prior to ovulation.

Major changes during the cycle take place in the uterus and particularly the endometrium. Estrogen primes the endometrium by stimulating growth of the vascular bed. Progesterone then stimulates the rapid growth of the glands. As the CL regresses, there is a rapid fall in estrogen and progesterone, and the endometrial lining, which by this time is highly developed, begins to die from lack of nourishment. The lining disintegrates and begins to slough. The blood vessels expel blood into the lumen, and the mixture of the two is passed through the cervix and vagina to the exterior. This *menstrual flow* usually lasts 3 to 5 days. The endometrial lining repairs itself and the flow ceases. The ensuing repair and growth under the influence of estrogen is termed the *proliferative phase.* This lasts until ovulation.

Following ovulation and formation of the CL, progesterone and estrogen continue the growth; this phase is called the *secretory phase,* at which point the cycle is completed.

Therefore, the follicular phase is synonymous with menstrual flow and the proliferative phase and the luteal phase are the same as the secretory phase.

There are several other differences in the effects of the female hormones not seen in domestic species. Estrogen is responsible for the pattern of pubic hair growth, although the actual growth is stimulated by androgens. The changes in vaginal epithelium are much more marked and may be used to determine the phase of the cycle. Progesterone is responsible for a rise in body temperature, and temperature charts are sometimes used as a means to control pregnancy. Figure 10–16 shows the temperature pattern. The pattern is too erratic to use for predictive purposes of ovulation.

WHAT DID YOU LEARN?

1   What is the sign of estrus common to all species, and the only true sign?
2   What sign of estrus is peculiar to the ewe?
3   How long is estrus in the sow? In the cow?
4   What happens to the ovary during proestrus in the cow?
5   When does LH peak in the estrous cycle of the ewe?
6   When does ovulation occur in the mare?
7   List differences between the mare estrous cycle and that of the cow.
8   What is the condition of the endometrium during the progestational phase of the cycle?
9   Describe the activity of the oviduct at the time of ovulation.
10   How does the menstrual cycle differ from the estrous cycle?

REFERENCES

1   Akins, E. L. and M. C. Morrissette. 1968. Gross ovarian changes during the estrous cycle of swine. *Amer. J. Vet. Res.* 29:1953–1957.
2   Allen, W. E. 1974. The palpability of the corpus luteum in Welsh pony mares. *Equine Vet. J.* 6:25–27.
3   Alliston, C. W., T. B. Patterson, and L. C. Ulberg. 1958. Crystallization patterns of cervical mucus as related to estrus in beef cattle. *J. Anim. Sci.* 17:322–325.
4   Anderson, J. 1944. The periodicity and duration of oestrus in Zebu and grade cattle. *J. Agr. Sci.* 34:57–72.
5   Anderson, L. L. 1966. Pituitary-ovarian-uterine relationships in pigs. *J. Reprod. Fert. Suppl.* 1:21–32.
6   Arthur, G. H. 1969. The ovary of the mare in health and disease. *Equine Vet. J.* 1:153–156.
7   Aschbacher, P. W., V. R. Smith, and W. H. Stone. 1956. Observations on fertility following insemination at three stages of the same estrus. *J. Anim. Sci.* 15:952–958.

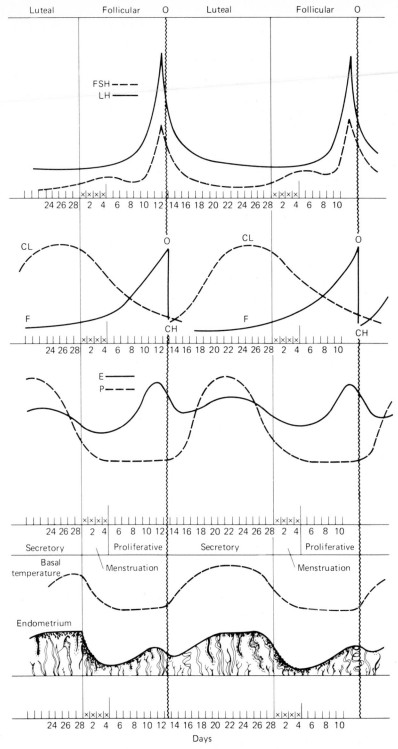

Figure 10-16 Hormone, ovarian structure and system changes during the menstrual cycle of the woman. *(Adapted from Hartenstein[50]; Ross et al.[88]; and Vander et al.[109])*

8   Asdell, S. A., J. deAlba, and S. J. Roberts. 1949. Studies on the estrous cycle of dairy cattle: Cycle length, size of corpus luteum, and endometrial changes. *Cornell Vet.* 39:389–402.

9   Back, D. G., B. W. Pickett, J. L. Voss, and G. E. Seidel, Jr. 1974. Observations on the sexual behavior of nonlactating mares. *J.A.V.M.A.* 165:717–720.

10   Baker, A. A. 1967. The pattern of oestrous behaviour in Sahiwal-Shorthorn heifers in South Eastern Queensland. *Australian Vet. J.* 43:140–144.

11   Berwyn-Jones, M. D. and C. H. G. Irvine. 1974. Induction of luteolysis and oestrus in mares with a synthetic prostaglandin analogue (ICI 81008). *New Zealand Vet. J.* 22:107–110.

12   Bitman, J., J. F. Sykes, and T. R. Wrenn. 1957. Body temperature variations in dairy cattle during the estrus cycle and pregnancy. *J. Anim. Sci.* 16:1095. (Abstr.)

13   Bone, J. F. 1954. Crystallization patterns in vaginal and cervical mucus smears as related to bovine ovarian activity and pregnancy. *Amer. J. Vet. Res.* 15:542–547.

14   Broadway, J. L. 1973. Optimum time for artificial insemination of the bovine species at various times of the year. M.S. thesis, Texas A&M Univ., College Station.

15   Burwash, L. D., B. W. Pickett, J. L. Voss, and D. G. Back. 1974. Relationship of duration of estrus to pregnancy rate in normally cycling, nonlactating mares. *J.A.V.-M.A.* 165:714–716.

16   Chiazze, L., Jr., F. T. Brayer, J. J. Macisco, Jr., M. P. Parker, and B. J. Duffy. 1968. The length and variability of the human menstrual cycle. *J.A.V.M.A.* 203:377–380.

17   Convey, E. M. 1973. Neuroendocrine relationships in farm animals: A review *J. Anim. Sci.* 37:745–757.

18   Convey, E. M., T. W. Beck, R. R. Neitzel, E. F. Bostwick, and H. D. Hafs. 1977. Negative feedback control of bovine serum luteinizing hormone (LH) concentration from completion of the preovulatory LH surge until resumption of luteal function. *J. Anim. Sci.* 46:792–796.

19   Cowan, F. T. and J. W. Macpherson. 1966. The reproductive tract of the porcine female (a biometrical study). *Can J. of Comp. Med. Vet. Sci.* 30:107–108.

20   Cumming, I. A. 1975. The ovine and bovine oestrous cycle. *J. Reprod. Fert.* 43:583–596.

21   Dailey, R. A., J. R. Clark, N. L. First, A. B. Chapman, and L. E. Casida. 1975. Effect of short-term "flushing" on follicular development at estrus and ovulation rate of gilts of different genetic groups. *J. Anim. Sci.* 41:842–847.

22   deVries, S., A. Osinga, and J. Zeinstra. 1972. The oestrus period and the oestrus cycle in Friesian milking cows in Kenya, as related to heat detection problems. *Proc. 7th Int. Congr. on Anim. Reprod. and A.I.* 1:383–387.

23   Donaldson, L. E., D. A. Little, and William Hansel. 1968. The duration of oestrus and the time of ovulation in cattle of three breed types with and without synchronisation of oestrus with a progestogen. *Australian Vet. J.* 44:364–366.

24   Dziuk, P. J. 1977. Reproduction in pigs. In H. H. Cole and P. T. Cupps, eds. *Reproduction in Domestic Animals.* 3rd ed. Academic Press, New York. Pp. 455–474.

25   Evans, M. J. and C. H. G. Irvine. 1973. Serum concentrations of FSH, LH and progesterone during the oestrous cycle and early pregnancy in the mare. *J. Reprod. Fert. Suppl.* 23:193–200.

26   Farris, E. J. 1954. Activity of dairy cows during estrus. *J.A.V.M.A.* 125:117–120.

27   ———. 1944. Comparison of patterns of cyclic activity of women and the female albino rat. *Anat. Rec.* 89:536. (Abstr.)

28   Foote, R. H., E. A. B. Oltenacu, and N. M. Munkenbeck. 1977. Estrus detection and

pregnancy rates monitored by milk progesterone. *J. Dairy Sci. Suppl.* 1:83. (Abstr.)

29 Foote, W. C., N. Sefidbakht, and M. A. Madsen. 1970. Puberal estrus and ovulation and subsequent estrous cycle patterns in the ewe. *J. Anim. Sci.* 30:86–90.

30 Gallagher, J. R. and M. Shelton. 1974. Influence of season on the return to estrus following lambing. *Tex. Agr. Exp. Sta. P.R.* 3284:7–8.

31 Garrett, W. R. 1977. Effect of seasonal variations and time of insemination on reproduction in Brahman females. M.S. thesis, Texas A&M Univ., College Station.

32 Garverick, H. A., R. E. Erb, and C. J. Callahan. 1970. Hormone levels during the bovine estrous cycle. *J. Anim. Sci.* 31:222. (Abstr.)

33 Gemmell, R. T., B. D. Stacy, and G. D. Thorburn. 1976. Morphology of the regressing corpus luteum in the ewe. *Biol. Reprod.* 14:270–279.

34 Geschwind, I. I., R. Dewey, J. P. Hughes, J. W. Evans, and G. H. Stabenfeldt. 1975. Plasma LH levels in the mare during the oestrus cycle. *J. Reprod. Fert. Suppl.* 23:207–212.

35 Geschwind, Irving I. 1972. Dynamics of pituitary gonadotropin secretion. *J. Anim. Sci. Suppl.* 1:19–38.

36 Ghannam, S. A. M., M. J. Bosc, and F. du Mesnil du Buisson. 1972. Examination of vaginal epithelium of the sheep and its use in pregnancy diagnosis. *Amer. J. Vet. Res.* 33:1175–1185.

37 Ghannam, S. A. M. and A. M. Sorensen, Jr. 1967. Early pregnancy diagnosis in the bovine. *J. Dairy Sci.* 50:562–568.

38 Ginther, O. J. 1974. Occurrence of anestrus, estrus, diestrus, and ovulation over a 12-month period of mares. *Amer. J. Vet. Res.* 35:1173–1179.

39 Hackett, A. J. and H. D. Hafs. 1969. Pituitary and hypothalamic endocrine changes during the bovine estrous cycle. *J. Anim. Sci.* 28:531–536.

40 Hafez, E. S. E. 1951. Mating behavior in sheep. *Nature* 167:777–778.

41 ———. 1952. Studies on the breeding season and reproduction of the ewe. Part 1. The breeding season in different environments. *J. Agr. Sci.* 42:189–199.

42 ———. 1972. Functional anatomy of the cervix uteri in domestic animals and primates. *Proc. 7th Int. Congr. on Anim. Reprod. and A.I.* 2:2304–2307.

43 Hall, J. G., C. Branton, and E. J. Stone. 1959. Estrus, estrous cycles, ovulation time, time of service and fertility of dairy cattle in Louisiana. *J. Dairy Sci.* 42:1086–1093.

44 Hammond, J. 1927. *The Physiology of Reproduction in the Cow.* Cambridge Univ. Press, London.

45 Hancock, J. L. 1962. The clinical features of the reproductive organs of pregnant and non-pregnant cattle. *Vet. Rec.* 74:646–652.

46 Hansel, W. and G. W. Trimberger. 1952. The effect of progesterone on ovulation time in dairy heifers. *J. Dairy Sci.* 35:65–70.

47 Hansel, W. and S. A. Asdell. 1952. The causes of bovine metestrous bleeding. *J. Anim. Sci.* 11:346–354.

48 Hansel, W., P. W. Concannon, and J. H. Lukaszewska. 1973. Corpora lutea of the large domestic animals. *Biol. Reprod.* 8:222–245.

49 Hansen, W. J., D. R. Zimmerman, and P. J. Cunningham. 1976. Selection for ovulation rate: Differences in successive estrous period. *J. Anim. Sci.* 43:287. (Abstr.)

50 Hartenstein, R. 1976. *Human Anatomy and Physiology: Principles and Applications.* D. Van Nostrand, New York. Pp. 223–238.

51 Henricks, D. M., H. D. Guthrie, and D. L. Handlin. 1972. Plasma estrogen, progesterone and luteinizing hormone levels during the estrous cycle in pigs. *Biol. Reprod.* 6:210–218.

52   Herrick, J. B. 1951. The cytological changes in the cervical mucosa of the cow (Bos taurus) throughout the estrous cycle. *Amer. J. Vet. Res.* 12:276–281.

53   Householder, D. D. 1973. Urinary and vaginal criteria for detecting ovulation in the mare. M.S. thesis, Texas A&M Univ., College Station.

54   Hughes, J. P., G. H. Stabenfeldt, and J. W. Evans. 1972. Estrous cycle and ovulation in the mare. *J.A.V.M.A.* 161:1367–1374.

55   ———. 1975. The oestrus cycle of the mare. *J. Reprod. Fert. Suppl.* 23:161–166.

56   Hulet, C. V., R. L. Blackwell, S. K. Ercanbrack, D. S. Price, and L. O. Wilson. 1962. Mating behavior of the ewe. *J. Anim. Sci.* 21:870–874.

57   Hunter, R. H. F. 1972. Utero-tubal function, sperm transport and polyspermic fertilization in pigs. *Proc. 7th Int. Congr. on Anim. Reprod. and A.I.* 2:1177–1180.

58   Huston, C. R. 1975. Heat signs. *Proc. 9th Conf. on A.I. of Beef Cattle,* Denver, Colo. Pp. 37–39.

59   Kiddy, C. A. 1977. Variation in physical activity as an indication of estrus in dairy cows. *J. Dairy Sci.* 60:235–248.

60   Lasley, J. F. 1968. Estrous cycles. In E. S. E. Hafez, ed. *Reproduction in Farm Animals.* 2nd ed. Lea & Febiger, Philadelphia. P. 83.

61   Leidl, W. and R. Stolla. 1976. Measurement of electric resistance of the vaginal mucus as an aid for heat detection. *Therio.* 6:237–249.

62   Lieux, P. 1970. Relationship between the appearance of the cervix and the heat cycle in the mare. *Vet. Med./Small Anim. Clinician* 65:879–886.

63   Loy, R. G. 1970. Management and other factors affecting breeding efficiency in mares. *Proc. 3rd Tech. Conf. on A.I. and Reprod.* Pp. 60–64.

64   Macmillan, K. L. and J. D. Watson. 1971. Short estrous cycles in New Zealand dairy cattle. *J. Dairy Sci.* 54:1526–1529.

65   Massey, J. M. 1974. Determination of ovulation from the onset of estrus in beef cows. M.S. thesis, Texas A&M Univ., College Station.

66   Mattner, P. E., J. M. George, and A. W. H. Braden. 1974. Herd mating activity in cattle. *J. Reprod. Fert.* 36:454–455.

67   McNutt, G. W. 1924. The corpus luteum of the ox ovary in relation to the estrous cycle. *J.A.V.M.A.* 65:556–597.

68   Mellin, T. N. and R. E. Erb. 1965. Estrogens in the bovine. *J. Dairy Sci.* 48:687–700.

69   Miller, K. F., L. J. Freedman, M. C. Garcia, and O. J. Ginther. 1977. FSH, LH and progesterone during the estrous cycle in mares. *Am. Soc. Anim. Sci. 1977 Mtg. Abstr. 472.* P. 188.

70   Mori, J., J. Masaki, K. Wakabayashi, T. Endo, and T. Hsoda. 1974. Serum luteinizing hormone levels in cattle under various reproductive states. *Therio.* 1:131–136.

71   Nayak, R. K. and T. H. Brinsfield. 1973. Fine structure of infundibular epithelium in the ewe. *J. Anim. Sci.* 37:322. (Abstr.)

72   Niswender, G. D., L. E. Reichert, Jr., and D. R. Zimmerman. 1970. Radioimmunoassay of serum levels of luteinizing hormone throughout the estrous cycle in pigs. *Endocrinol.* 87:576–580.

73   Noden, P. A., W. D. Oxender, and H. D. Hafs. 1975. The cycle of oestrus, ovulation and plasma level of hormones in the mare. *J. Reprod. Fert. Suppl.* 23:189–192.

74   Noonan, J. J., A. B. Schultze, and E. F. Ellington. 1975. Changes in bovine cervical and vaginal mucus during the estrous cycle and early pregnancy. *J. Anim. Sci.* 41:1084–1089.

75   Olds, D. and N. L. VanDemark. 1957. The behavior of spermatozoa in luminal fluids of bovine female genitalia. *Amer. J. Vet. Res.* 18:603–607.

76 Osborne, H. G. 1970. The duration and intensity of oestrus in Finnsheep. *Australian Vet. J.* 46:605.

77 Palmer, E. and B. Jousset. 1975. Urinary oestrogen and plasma progesterone levels in non-pregnant mares. *J. Reprod. Fert. Suppl.* 23:213–221.

78 Palmer, W. M., H. S. Teague, and W. G. Venzke. 1965. Histological changes in the reproductive tract of the sow during lactation and early postweaning. *J. Anim. Sci.* 24:1117–1125.

79 Pant, H. C., C. Hopkinson, and R. J. Fitzpatrick. 1972. Plasma oestradiol, progesterone and luteinizing hormone concentrations during the ovine oestrous cycle. *J. Reprod. Fert.* 31:501.

80 Pattison, M. L., C. L. Chen, and S. L. King. 1972. Determination of LH and estradiol-17β surge with reference to time of ovulation in mares. *Biol. Reprod.* 7:136. (Abstr.)

81 Plasse, D., A. C. Warnick, and M. Koger. 1968. Reproductive behavior of *Bos indicus* females in a subtropical environment. I. Puberty and ovulation frequency in Brahman and Brahman X British heifers. *J. Anim. Sci. Suppl.* 1:94–100.

82 ———. 1970. Reproductive behavior of *Bos indicus* females in a subtropical environment. IV. Length of estrous cycle, duration of estrus, time of ovulation, fertilization and embryo survival in grade Brahman heifers. *J. Anim. Sci.* 30:63–72.

83 Rigby, J. P. 1965. The structure of the uterotubal junction of the sow. *J. Anat.* 99:416.

84 Roberts, S. J. 1971. *Veterinary Obstetrics and Genital Diseases.* 2nd ed. Published by the author, Ithaca, N. Y. Pp. 512–529.

85 Robertson, H. A. 1977. Reproduction in the ewe and the goat. In H. H. Cole and P. T. Cupps, eds. *Reproduction in Domestic Animals.* 3rd ed. Academic Press, New York. Pp. 475–498.

86 Robertson, H. A. and A. M. Rakha. 1966. The sequence, time, and duration of the release of follicle-stimulating hormone and luteinizing hormone in relation to oestrus and to ovulation in the sheep. *J. Endocrinol.* 35:177–184.

87 Robinson, T. J. 1977. Reproduction in cattle. In H. H. Cole and P. T. Cupps, eds. *Reproduction in Domestic Animals.* 3rd ed. Academic Press, New York. Pp. 433–454.

88 Ross, G. T., C. M. Cargille, M. B. Lipsett, P. L. Rayford, J. R. Marshall, C. A. Strott, and D. Rodbard. 1970. Pituitary and gonadal hormones in women during spontaneous and induced ovulatory cycles. *Rec. Prog. Hormone Res.* 26:1–62.

89 Sanger, V. L., P. H. Engle, and D. S. Bell. 1958. The vaginal cytology of the ewe during the estrous cycle. *Amer. J. Vet. Res.* 19:283–287.

90 Scott B., G. W. Glover, and F. A. Glover. 1957. Crystallization patterns of sodium chloride in bovine (uterine) cervical mucus as related to its consistency. *Nature* 179:420.

91 Shelton, M., C. V. Hulet, J. R. Gallagher, and D. A. Price. 1973. Influence of season, location and source of ewe on estrus and ovulation rate of Rambouillet ewes. *Tex. Agr. Exp. Sta. P.R.* 3186B:26–28.

92 Shelton, M. and J. M. Klindt. 1976. Ovulation rate of Finnish Landrace X Rambouillet ewes. *Tex. Agr. Exp. Sta. P.R.* 3397:30–32.

93 Signoret, J. P. 1970. Reproductive behavior of pigs. *J. Reprod. Fert. Suppl.* 11:105–117.

94 Signoret, J. P., F. du Mesnit du Buisson, and P. Mauleon. 1972. Effect of mating on the onset and duration of ovulation in the sow. *J. Reprod. Fert.* 31:327–330.

95 Sinha, Y. N. and H. A. Tucker. 1969. Mammary development and pituitary prolactin level of heifers from birth through puberty and during the estrous cycle. *J. Dairy Sci.* 52:507–512.

96 Smith, J. F., H. Drost, R. J. Fairclough, A. J. Peterson, and H. R. Tervit. 1976. Effect

of age on peripheral levels of progesterone and oestradiol-17β, and duration of oestrus on Romney Marsh ewes. *New England J. Agr. Res.* 19:277–280.

97   Smith, J. F., R. J. Fairclough, E. Payne, and A. J. Peterson. 1975. Plasma hormone levels in the cow. *New Zealand J. Agr. Res.* 18:123–129.

98   Sorensen, A. M., Jr. 1975. Estrous detection in cattle. *Southwestern Vet.* 28:127–134.

99   Squires, E. L., R. H. Douglas, W. P. Staffenhagen, and O. J. Ginther. 1974. Ovarian changes during the estrous cycle and pregnancy in mares. *J. Anim. Sci.* 38:330–338.

100 Stabenfeldt, G. H. 1970. Recent advances in bovine reproductive physiology. *Bovine Pract.* 2:2–9.

101 Stabenfeldt, G. H., E. L. Akins, L. L. Ewing, and M. C. Morrissette. 1969. Peripheral plasma progesterone levels in pigs during the estrous cycle. *J. Reprod. Fert.* 20:433–449.

102 Stabenfeldt, G. H. and J. P. Hughes. 1977. Reproduction in horses. In H. H. Cole and P. T. Cupps, eds. *Reproduction in Domestic Animals.* 3rd ed. Academic Press, New York. Pp. 401–431.

103 Stabenfeldt, G. H., J. P. Hughes, J. W. Evans, and D. P. Neely. 1974. Spontaneous prolongation of luteal activity in the mare. *Equine Vet. J.* 6:158–163.

104 Stabenfeldt, G. H., J. P. Hughes, J. W. Evans, and I. I. Geschwind. 1975. Unique aspects of the reproductive cycle of the mare. *J. Reprod. Fert. Suppl.* 23:155–160.

105 Stabenfeldt, G. H., L. L. Ewing, and L. E. McDonald. 1969. Peripheral plasma progesterone levels during the bovine oestrous cycle. *J. Reprod. Fert.* 19:433–442.

106 Stalheim, O. H. V., J. E. Gallagher, and B. L. Deyoe. 1975. Scanning electron microscopy of the bovine, equine, porcine and caprine uterine tube (oviduct). *Amer. J. Vet. Res.* 36:1069–1075.

107 Steinbach, J. and D. Smidt. 1970. Cyclical phenomena in the female genital tract of swine—histological observations. *J. Anim. Sci.* 30:573–577.

108 Trimberger, G. W. 1944. Conception rate in dairy cattle by artificial insemination at various intervals before and after ovulation. *J. Dairy Sci.* 27:659–660. (Abstr.)

109 Vander, A. J., J. H. Sherman, and D. S. Luciano. 1975. *Human Physiology: The Mechanisms of Body Function.* McGraw-Hill, New York. Pp. 438–460.

110 Warnick, A. C., L. E. Casida, and R. H. Grummer. 1950. The occurrence of estrus and ovulation in postpartum sows. *J. Anim. Sci.* 9:66–72.

111 Weber, A. F., B. B. Morgan, and S. H. McNutt. 1948. A histological study of metorrhagia in the virgin heifer. *Amer. J. Anat.* 83:309–327.

112 Whitmore, H. L., B. C. Wentworth, and O. J. Ginther. 1973. Circulating concentrations of luteinizing hormone during estrous cycle of mares as determined by radioimmunoassay. *Amer. J. Vet. Res.* 34:631–636.

113 Williams, R. L. 1973. Meteorological factors affecting the length of the postestrus-preovulatory period in the dairy cow. M.S. thesis, Texas A&M Univ., College Station.

114 Williamson, N. B., R. S. Morris, D. C. Blood, C. M. Cannon, and P. J. Wright. 1972. A study of oestrous behaviour and oestrus detection methods in a large commercial dairy herd. 2. Oestrous signs and behaviour patterns. *Vet. Rec.* 91:58.

115 Wiltbank, J. N., A. C. Cook, R. E. Davis, and E. J. Warwick. 1957. The effect of different combinations of energy and protein on the occurrence of estrus, length of the estrous period, and time of ovulation in beef heifers. *J. Anim. Sci.* 16:1100. (Abstr.)

116 Wiltbank, J. N., R. P. Shumway, W. R. Parker, and D. R. Zimmerman. 1967. Duration of estrus, time of ovulation and fertilization rate in beef heifers synchronized with dehydroxyprogesterone acetophenide. *J. Anim. Sci.* 26:764–767.

117 Witherspoon, D. M. 1971. The oestrous cycle of the mare. *Equine Vet. J.* 3:114–117.

118 Wordinger, R. J., J. B. Ramsey, J. F. Dickey, and J. R. Hill, Jr. 1973. On the presence of a ciliated columnar epithelial cell type within the bovine cervical mucosa. *J. Anim. Sci.* 36:936–940.

119 Wu, A. S., S. D. Carlson, and N. L. First. 1976. Scanning electron microscopic study of the porcine oviduct and uterus. *J. Anim. Sci.* 42:804–809.

120 Zimmerman, D. R. and C. Naber. 1971. Influence of mating on ovulation time in the pig. *J. Anim. Sci.* 33:273. (Abstr.)

CHAPTER 11

Ovulation Control

When you have completed this chapter you should be able to:

- Enumerate and discuss the advantages and disadvantages of ovulation synchronization,
- Elaborate on the various compounds used for ovulation control for each class of livestock and the human,
- Differentiate between the action of progesterone, progestogens, and prostaglandins for ovulation control,
- Understand the need for two injections of prostaglandins to control ovulation,
- Describe a general plan for breeding sheep during anestrus,
- Outline a method for increasing number of pigs per litter,
- Discuss the general approach to superovulation of mares, and
- Appreciate the side effects of ovulation control in the woman.

Ovulation control has a number of advantages. By controlling ovulation in the prepuberal female, ova would be made available for conception earlier or for embryo transfer. Control of ovulation among breeding-age cattle would synchronize management and marketing. Control of postpartum breeding could shorten the interval to next parturition. These will be discussed for each animal to give the state of progress at the present time.

COW

Induced Ovulation Prepuberally

Calves approaching puberty may be stimulated to exhibit estrus and conceive. It is important to remember that these must be animals that are well developed and very near puberty.[107] There is no way of ascertaining exactly how much earlier this may be accomplished, as research has not given reliable answers yet. Most trials have entailed feeding progestogens, which are products having progesteronelike properties, or implanting progestogen pellets for a period of time. When the progestogen is removed some animals will come into estrus, ovulate, and conceive.

One advantage of advancing puberty is to shorten generation interval. Shorter generation intervals would enhance genetic selection. From a reproduction standpoint, the earlier such a program can be initiated, the better. We must realize other factors are concerned, however, such as size, calving ease of young stock, and rebreeding ability. (Fig. 11–1).

Shortening generation interval may have an optimistic future in embryo transfer. It has been demonstrated that calves may be superovulated at an early age and the ova flushed for transfer to mature females. This area is still in experimental stages but offers promise.

Synchronized Ovulation

Much of the literature talks about synchronized estrus, but in reality we are more interested in ovulation than in estrus, as will be seen in this discussion. "Synchronized" indicates grouping, and the purpose behind such a program is to group breeding, calving, and marketing.

A major factor or problem in artificial insemination is estrous detection. If this could be eliminated, many more livestock people would make use of AI. All of the methods discussed here and the many gimmicks devised by man still leave a great deal to be desired.

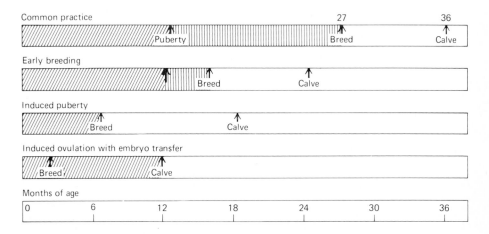

Figure 11-1 Possible shifting of calving dates to shorten generation intervals.

With our knowledge of hormones and their interactions and the response of the ovaries to these hormones, it seems feasible that a system could be devised to come up with a solution. Several hormones or hormonelike substances have been tried. These include progesterone, progestogens, estrogens, and prostaglandins.

Ovulation control, resulting in a high percent conception, offers a number of advantages to the stockman. It also has some disadvantages at the present time that will hopefully be overcome with research and more exacting methods.

Advantages

1 Reduces time spent checking estrus in an artificial insemination program. This is accomplished by synchronizing a large group of animals to exhibit estrus and/or ovulate at a specific time.

2 Reduces labor at the time of calving. Efforts can be concentrated for a shorter period of time.

3 Releases labor for other tasks that would be required for breeding.

4 Makes artificial insemination more feasible by reducing overall management problems.

5 Groups offspring for a more uniform calf crop to be marketed. Just imagine a group of steers from a common sire of proven genetic greatness born within a week of each other . . . and then sold concurrently.

6 Improves management practices. Cattle will be grouped, necessitating or at least allowing closer observation, better feeding practices, and improved herd health.

Disadvantages

1 Conception rates are low (35 to 45 percent). Most ranchers expect and should attain above 50 percent conception on first service.

2 Cost. No exact cost is available since *there is no synchronizing material on the market at the present time,* but the cost should not exceed $5 and $10 per head.

3 Concentrated labor would require pulling employees away from other jobs during these days.

4 Who wants a large number of cows dropping calves all at once?

Now let us look at some of the available synchronizing compounds and their uses.

Progesterone Progesterone is not available for ovulation control except by a veterinarian.

Injections A number of studies on ovulation control included injections of progesterone over an extended period. The object was to neutralize the CL and its natural production of progesterone and upon release from the hormone, the cycle should be rearranged (Fig. 11–2).

The response was fairly good, and although the procedure of injecting stock over a number of days was not feasible, at least the principle was sound. The

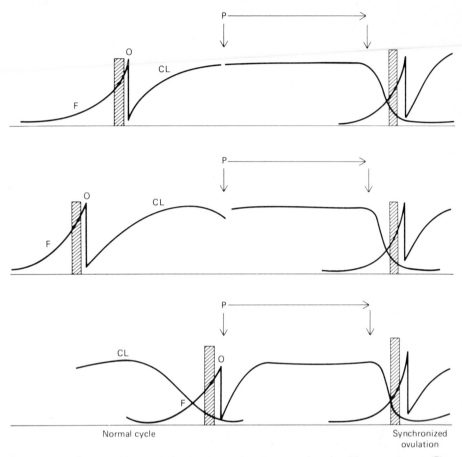

Figure 11-2 Synchronizing ovulation by depressing the normal cycle with progesterone (P) or progestogen for an extended period of time followed by release.

synthetic progestogens of greater potency and less expense then appeared to be the next step for study.

Intravaginal coils A relatively recent innovation has been to impregnate silastic rubber with progesterone and coat coils of spring steel with the material. These are coiled and placed in the cow's vagina past the site of the hymen and released. The pressure holds them in place very well—92 percent in cows and 98 percent in heifers.[79] The progesterone is released at a prescribed rate, and activity has been controlled very well with acceptable conception rates.

An example of this type of treatment is the research of Roche[80] in Ireland, where he used a program of progesterone-impregnated coils for 12 days preceded by injections of 5 mg estradiol benzoate and 50 mg progesterone intramuscularly on the day of insertion. Of the 156 heifers, 143 (93 percent) showed estrus between 2 and 6 days after removal. Of the 412 dairy cows, 379 (90 percent) were in estrus at the same time. Seventy-one percent were in estrus on the second day, and 17 percent on the third day, leaving 12 percent for the next 3 days. No difference existed in calving rates: treated, 53 percent and control, 45 percent. Similar trials have yielded similar results, and although the percentages seem low, consider that the treated are almost the same as the control statistics.[10] Breeding at 56 hours postremoval appears to be optimum for timed mating.[24]

Progestogens (Progesteronelike) Progestogens are not available at this time for ovulation control in cattle.

Oral When the progestogens were first used in the early 1950s there was an attempt to simulate the natural cycle as far as length was concerned. They were therefore fed for a period of 18 days and then removed with expected response in 3 days to mimic a 21-day cycle. It was possible to feed the material because of its passing through the stomach without being digested. Many trials were conducted with minor adjustments, and it was thought that success would come with the next trials. One trial was conducted in 1963 with Hereford heifers[96] in which a progestogen was fed for 18 days and random groups bred by AI or natural service. Of the 100 heifers treated, 75 percent were in estrus within 3 days after removal of the progestogen. The 100 control heifers bred under normal estrous checks and AI had a conception rate of 61 percent to first service compared to 33 percent for the treated AI group and 53 percent for the treated handmated group. Evidently the bulls did better than the technician using fresh liquid semen. Many trials had lower conception than this, while very few were higher. More recent work[72] showed high conception rates when bulls were placed with progestogen-synchronized heifers at ratios of 1:10, 1:15, and 1:25. Conception rates in two trials were 70, 69, and 81 and 90, 73, and 57, respectively. Bulls were observed to mate as many as 35 times in the 1:10 group. Trials with dairy cattle were no better.[62]

The next step was to shorten the feeding time to 16 days and then to 12 days without too much change in the other factors. Cattlemen were not satisfied with conception rates of 30 to 40 percent, which was normal. Neither were the researchers. Very few similar trials are conducted today.

One advantage of the oral method of administration is the ease of manipulation of the stock, but one disadvantage is that "boss" cows may keep others away from the feed, and a lowered progestogen level for even one day may upset the feeding program and the animal will "break through" in estrus before termination of the program.[91]

Implants Various implants have been devised. Some were cordlike with a sharp point to push under the skin with a portion left outside to assist in removal. Others were silastic rods placed under the skin which were removed surgically later. Some were barbed to retain them in the cervix or under the skin. The most recent is a small implant resembling a stilbestrol implant that is inserted at the base of the ear where it remains for 9 days. The insertion is accompanied by an injection of the same progestogen and estradiol valerate to destroy any existing corpus luteum producing progesterone. After 9 days a small incision is made over the implant and it is removed.[108]

Conception rates in cows are improved some over earlier trials. Five trials reported the following percent conceptions for treated and control cattle to first service: 33 vs. 54, 63 vs. 66, 56 vs. 60, 38 vs. 63, and 45 vs. 45.[107] Other cattle on the same regime yielded 43 percent and 32 percent in two trials.[48]

In a similarly planned trial, heifers were bred according to estrous detection, time-mated 48 hours after implant removal or 54 hours after implant removal. Conception rates were 65, 55, and 52 percent, respectively.

The advantages of implants are continued progestogen administration with a rapid increase when implanted and decrease when removed, and reduced handling of the animals. Disadvantages include the necessary, although minor, surgery and the possibility of leaving bits of the pellet when removing it.[91]

Intravaginal Sponges Pessaries of various designs and materials have been developed in an effort to devise an easier method of administration. These are mostly of a plastic foam material or sponge. The diameter is usually 10 cm (4 in) and about 6 to 7 cm (2.5 in) deep. A string is inserted for ease of removal. The sponge is usually a polyurethane foam and is impregnated with a progestogen to be released at a predetermined rate.[83,89]

The sponge is placed in the cranial vagina against the cervix, where it remains for the duration of the experiment. Losses were high in earlier trials[12,44] but seemingly have been reduced with larger sponges.[84]

Sponge treatments were used in conjunction with pregnant mare serum gonadotropin (PMSG) in 3- to 4-month-old calves to obtain superovulation. The average ovulations were 6.7, while those treated with PMSG alone only averaged one. Use of human chorionic gonadotropin (HCG) 5 days after PMSG yielded 16.2 ovulations 2 days later.[100] This indicates the usefulness of synchronization in conjunction with embryo transfer as a real possibility.

The advantages of sponges are the ease of application and continuous administration of the hormone. The main disadvantage is in the decline in dose rate over time.[91]

Others A daily pour-on method of doses in oil has been tried with results that require more testing.

Prostaglandins Three comprehensive reviews on prostaglandins are by Robinson,[77] Evans,[26] and Manns and Hafs.[60]

Prostaglandins are not available for ovulation control in cattle at this time.

Chemically, prostaglandins are variations of prostanoic acid, a 20-carbon fatty acid. The main natural prostaglandin being investigated presently is prostaglandin F_2 alpha ($PGF_2\alpha$). Several analogues, or compounds similar to $PGF_2\alpha$,, are being tested. One of the reasons for developing analogues is to separate the effects of the prostaglandins. The two effects that concern the reproduction researcher are smooth

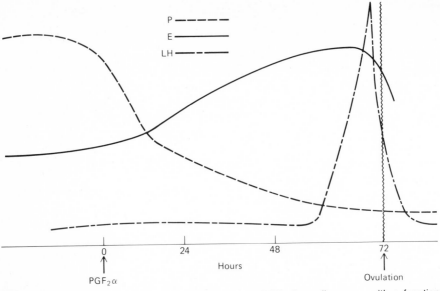

Figure 11-3 Hormonal changes following injection of $PGF_{2\alpha}$ in cycling cows with a functional corpus luteum.

muscle contraction and lysis, or death, of the corpus luteum. Hopefully the analogues will produce the latter without muscular contraction.

A mature functional corpus luteum may become nonfunctional within a matter of hours after injection of $PGF_2\alpha$. Progesterone, which is produced by the CL, will drop precipitously, and the cyclic pattern will be quickly upset (Fig. 11–3). It must be understood that the success of the use of $PGF_2\alpha$ is dependent upon the presence of a functional CL. It will have no effect on the developing CL before 5 days of age and no effect on the waning CL after about 16 days of age (Fig. 11–4).

In order to control ovulation, two injections of $PGF_2\alpha$ are given 10 to 12 days apart.[110] Any CL that are present will be eliminated by the first injection and new estrous cycles will be formed. However, those ovaries in the cycle between 5 days proestrus and 5 days postestrus will not be affected.[81] When the second injection is given, all females should have a CL present and following luteolysis the cycles should be synchronized with ovulation occurring in about 3 days (Fig. 11–4).[110]

Prostaglandins appear to be most exacting in their response, and working the cattle through the chutes for two injections does not seem unreasonable if the response is good. They also allow timed matings without estrous detection. Disadvantages lie in the necessity for the cow to have a functional CL, the inability of response of some females, and the cost, which has not yet been determined.[51]

$PGF_2\alpha$ or the analogues may be injected intramuscularly, in which case 20 to 30 mg is needed per injection. An intrauterine injection on the same side as ovulation occurred requires only 2 mg.[53] The response is the same, with luteolysis of the CL occurring concurrently. Evidently the reason for the higher dose intramuscularly is the short half-life of the substance. It is metabolized quickly once it gets into

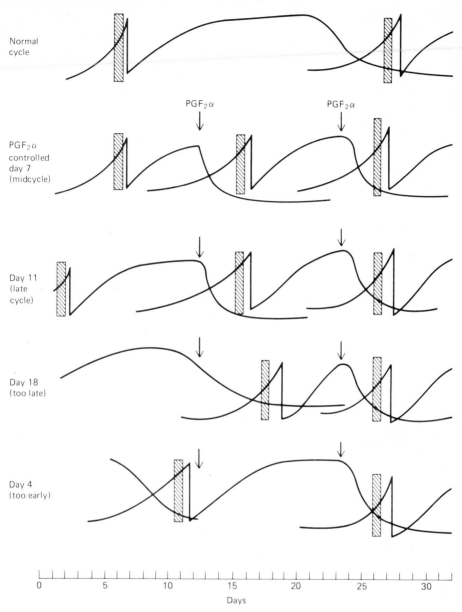

Figure 11-4 Synchronization of ovulation with two injections of $PGF_{2\alpha}$ 11 days apart at different stages of the estrous cycle in the cow.

circulation, and the half-life is estimated at 2 to 3 minutes, which means that approximately 90 percent is deactivated in a single passage through the body. The cost of the product and the manipulation of the livestock must be considered for the most feasible program.

Single or double injections Numerous trials have been conducted using a single injection. Cows coming in estrus have ranged from 55 percent for single to 69 percent for double injections 10 to 12 days apart.[92] Cost is an important factor, since under present conditions an injection of 30 mg $PGF_2\alpha$ may cost $30, and not many ranchers are interested at this price. Understandably, the analogues should be more economical.

We will surely see more research on similar compounds with more economical considerations involved.

Natural or analogue $PGF_2\alpha$ has given better synchronization in most instances than the analogues.[58,76,86,92] Analogue use has yielded conception rates of 33 to 40 percent.[85]

Timed insemination Being able to breed without the laborious estrous-checking regime would make a synchronization program much more attractive. In trials where animals were bred at 12, 72, 80, or 96 hours after the second $PGF_2\alpha$ injection, either singly or in combination, the conception rates were very acceptable, ranging from 47 to 69 percent.[64,101,104] Most trials have used a combination of 70 to 72 hours followed by insemination at 90 to 96 hours. Single inseminations have shown greatest promise at 74 or 80 hours.

Further research is needed and in fact is in progress toward developing a single set-time insemination that is equal to or greater than controlled insemination programs.

Gordon[36] has made comparisons between short-term progestogens and prostaglandins assuming equal response to the treatments in terms of conception. The ear implant is assumed to be the best approach with disadvantages in buildup of scar-tissue in the area of implantation and the asepsis necessary. Progestogens are now being used on a massive scale in human medicine and may therefore be more acceptable by the Food and Drug Administration. Cost is also in their favor.

Prostaglandins now appear to be the method of choice but must be considered in view of other uses and the stricter control of the product. There is a good possibility of its restriction to veterinary use or at least supervision. The cost is much greater per animal. The animal must have a functional corpus luteum for prostaglandin to be effective. Chances of causing abortions in cattle of unknown pregnancy may be detrimental to a breeding program.

With these pros and cons in mind we should all understand the need for further research and trials but look forward at the same time to an exciting step forward to control of livestock breeding.

Combination treatments $PGF_2\alpha$ has been combined with progestogens without improvement as shown in Table 11–1.[17]

The two products seem to act independently as well as in combination.

A combination of $PGF_2\alpha$ with releasing hormones has also been attempted, and no advantage was shown by the addition of LHRH/FSHRH stimulatory analogues. Control animals yielded conception to first insemination in 21 of 30 cows compared

Table 11-1 PGF$_2\alpha$ Alone or in Combination to Synchronize Ovulation in Cows

Treatment	Group	No. cows	Time of AI	% pregnant at 5 months
Progestogen implant	1	114	+48 to 72 hr	48.7
plus PGF$_2\alpha$	2	80	+56 hr	34.9
2 PGF$_2\alpha$ injections	1	102	+72 to 96 hr	37.7
	2	88	+80 hr	43.5

Adopted from Chupin et al.[17]

to PGF$_2\alpha$ with 26 of 30 and PGF$_2\alpha$ + analogues with 26 of 30 cows. This particular trial emphasizes the good response to PGF$_2\alpha$ as measured by conception.[14]

Many trials have combined progestogens with estradiol, and the major effect is the closer grouping of cattle in estrus with little if any change in conception.

The use of implants plus injection of the same progestogen has improved response slightly. This yields a high level of progestogen by injection followed by a constant level of release by the pellet. Luteolysis occurs more rapidly and response is improved.

Induced postpartum estrus Progestogens have been used to initiate postpartum estrus with mixed results. It should be remembered that there is no functional CL in the postpartum cow and therefore prostaglandins would be of no use.

Progestogens plus calf removal offer a possibility of inducing ovulation. Most research in this area has indicated good response after 100 days postpartum. The cow is given a progestogen injection and implant at the same time to destroy the existing CL if there is one. After 9 days the implant is removed and the calf is removed for 12 to 48 hours. The cow comes in estrus and is bred, after which the calf is returned.[108] Timed breeding at 48 to 54 hours after implant and calf removal showed some improvement over controls.[61] Pregnancies at 5, 25, and 46 days postbreeding for controls were 16, 73, and 92 percent and for progestogen plus calf removal, pregnancies were 61, 81, and 93 percent. It appears that a program of progestogen plus calf removal plus timed insemination offers a very important step in ovulation control in the lactating cow.

Presence of Gomer (teaser) bulls may affect conception rates by their presence[72] as shown by increased conception following progestrogen implants of 73 percent, compared to those without teaser bulls of 64 percent.

Attempts have also been made to clean the ovaries of major structures by rupturing follicles and expressing corpora lutea, thereby reducing ovarian effects at the beginning of treatment. Control (36 percent) and progestogen-treated (37 percent) heifers gave better conception than expressed plus progestogen (25 percent) heifers.[95]

Anestrous cows postpartum over 50 days and anestrous cows 50 days past the last estrus have been stimulated electrically with a bull probe with good success. Postpartum cows responded in 50 percent of the cases compared to 13 percent for controls; 43 percent of the anestrous cows following an estrus responded compared to 2 percent of the controls.[43]

Skipping the first estrus and breeding at the second estrus yields no better results than breeding at the first synchronized estrus,[94] and the grouping is much better at the first estrus.

EWE

Most synchronizing trials have been conducted outside the United States. A product called Synchromate is marketed by G. D. Searle and Company as a pessary or intravaginal sponge (Fig. 11–5).

The progestogen-impregnated pessary is placed in the anterior vagina against the cervix by placing the speculum in the vagina, inserting the pessary with the strings trailing, and pushing the pessary through the speculum with the plunger. The speculum and rod are removed and the pessary is in place with the strings extending past the vulva for use in later removal. The pessary is left in place for 14 days before removal.[88]

Ewes treated with pessaries have compared favorably with controls for conception, surpassing the controls in some instances.[18,78,106] Conception rates have ranged from 31 to 56 percent.[39,93]

Prostaglandins are not cleared for use, but research indicates very good response.[27] Injections of 125 μg 14 days apart have yielded 90 percent fertilization compared to 81 percent for controls.

SOW

No product is available for synchronizing breeding in swine at this time.

Research has not been extensive in swine because of the controlled management

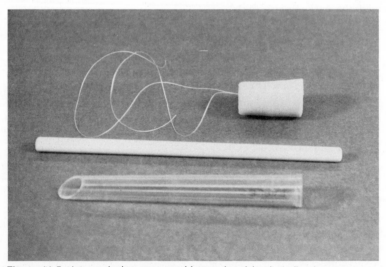

Figure 11-5   Intravaginal sponge used in synchronizing breeding in ewes.

conditions, and there doesn't appear to be a great deal of desire on the breeders' part to use synchronization.

Injected progesterone over a period of 13 to 18 days has been attempted[5] and resulted in lowered fertility and a greater number of cysts than in control gilts. Estrus was inhibited by the progesterone.

Progestogens have been fed at various levels for varying periods of time with poor results.[29,103] The first estrus was mostly infertile, although breeding at the second estrus gave good response. Cystic follicles developed in 58 percent of the treated gilts in one trial and is a very serious problem with progestogens.[33]

A synthetic product called ICI 33828 (methallibure) is a nonsteroidal inhibitor of gonadotropins and has been used in a feeding program of 20 days. Conception rates have been high and ovulation rates and number of embryos similar to control animals (11.6 vs. 12.8 ovulations and 10.6 vs. 10.5 embryos). The product offers promise,[31,73,74,98] but the malformation of some fetuses places doubts on its clearance for commercial use.[33,52]

Prostaglandins have been investigated[41,50] with luteal regression resulting and high fertilization rates (77 percent) of ova recovered from bred gilts. Further work will certainly follow in this area.

PMSG and HCG have been used in many combinations and concentrations with improved litter size through superovulation.[16] Day et al.[20] synchronized cycling gilts and young sows with 1200 IU PMSG followed by 1000 IU HCG three days later with equal conception to controls.

Sows do not normally cycle during lactation. Injections of PMSG and HCG have been used successfully to synchronize estrus and ovulation immediately following weaning.[90] Following is a time schedule that may be used for weaning pigs at 3 weeks and 6 weeks of age (Table 11–2).

MARES

Most of the breeding control research in mares has centered around prostaglandins, and these products are now available on the market for use in horses.

$PGF_2\alpha$, which is the natural product, was mentioned earlier as causing contraction of smooth muscles in addition to causing regression of the CL. This product has caused considerable sweating and some discomfort to the mares, and the analogues are being improved to attempt to remove this side effect.

Table 11-2 PMS-HCG Schedule for Synchronizing Ovulation Immediately Following Weaning in Sows

Weaning	3 weeks	6 weeks
PMS (1000 IU injected subcutaneously)	8 to 12 hr following weaning	8 to 12 hr following weaning
HCG (500 IU injected intramuscularly)	72 hr after PMS	56 hr after PMS
Inseminate all sows regardless of estrus	24 hr after HCG	24 hr after HCG

Adapted from Singleton, personal communications.

Dose levels of .25 mg PGF$_2\alpha$ did not cause sweating but did not give good control of estrus either. Higher levels of 1 to 10 mg given between days 6 and 9 after ovulation caused sweating in mares for 15 minutes to 2 hours with complete drying completed about 3 to 5 hours after injection. Rectal temperature dropped from .5 to 1.7°C between 30 minutes and 5 hours post-injection.[63] Numerous other trials have given similar results. Length of estrus and cyclic activity appear normal following prostaglandin injections.[70]

A prostaglandin analogue has been developed that has caused only a limited amount of sweating and has been successful in treating mares with persistent corpora lutea.[2] Cycling mares were injected with a single dose of 2 mg of the analogue between days 6 and 10 of the cycle with a resulting conception rate of 78 percent to the first breeding compared to 42 percent for control mares. Mares with persistent CL were treated similarly with a resulting conception rate of 67 vs. 46 percent for control mares. Other analogue trials have given favorable results.[55,109] As in any other animal, the presence of a functional CL is necessary, and there are many noncycling mares without a CL that will not respond.

GNRH alone has caused ovulation in seasonally anovulatory mares,[4] but it hardly seems worth the effort. Light must be controlled and injections made every 8 hours over a period of 14 days.

Saline infusion into the uterus of mares has given favorable estrus and ovulatory response.[1] There is little effect during anestrus, but diestrous mares respond in 16 days, and those infused between 5 and 9 days returned to estrus about 4 days earlier than normal. This treatment may also be useful for pseudopregnant mares.

WOMAN

Ovulation control in the woman has been directed more at contraception than at conception. However, the use of hormones in controlling ovulation and the menstrual cycle are very important to the healthy sex life of the woman.

Hormones are used clinically by physicians in much the same manner as described for our domestic animals. The cyclic activity is controlled by hormones as described in Chapter 10. The major control presently is the oral contraceptive, commonly called the pill. It is composed of estrogen and progestogen in varying combinations. Some consist of progesterone alone. The purpose is to control the cycle by maintaining levels of hormones until a scheduled time of release. There are usually 20 to 21 tablets taken for hormone control followed by 7 or 8 days without a tablet in order for menstruation to occur.

Induction of ovulation is usually obtained by one of two methods, clomiphene or gonadotropins.

Clomiphene is an antiestrogenic drug that increases plasma FSH and LH.[47] It is given to anovulatory women, and success has been very acceptable. Ovulations have resulted in 70 percent or more of the times and conception from 24 to 44 percent.[38,47,75] Response is not the same in every case, and the patients must be selected carefully. Side effects include multiple births.

Gonadotropins that are used as a source of FSH are usually human pituitary gonadotropin (HPG) and human menopausal gonadotropin (HMG) from urine of menopausal women. HCG is used as the source of LH, as well as HPG and HMG which are somewhat contaminated with LH. Combinations of these hormones have given good ovulation response and conception. Ovulations have ranged as high as 98 percent and pregnancies from 50 to 65 percent. Side effects include high rates of abortion (22 percent) and multiple births. Patients should be carefully screened by the physician before treatment.[47,49,75]

Estrogens and progestogens have been tried with limited success. The specificity is not great enough for reliable response. Corticoids have also been experimented with and offer promise.[38]

SUPEROVULATION

Programs of multiple births and embryo transfer are dependent upon the production of multiple ova. The cow, ewe, and mare produce single or double ovulations and therefore must be stimulated to superovulate.

Relying upon material already discussed, we know that some product or products must be introduced into the female to cause the desired response. These include a compound to grow follicles (FSH or a source such as PMSG) and a compound to rupture the follicle (LH or a source such as HCG) and release the ovum. A third product would be desirable to make the time of ovulation more exact or closely grouped. Prostaglandins perhaps are our answer here.

Early studies were devoted more to the study of mechanisms involved in ovulation than in the applied areas. Today superovulation is very practical as a tool to use in multiple births and embryo transfer.

Cow

Gonadotropins, steroids, and prostaglandins have been used for superovulating cattle.

Gonadotropins Follicle stimulating hormone (FSH) in conjunction with luteinizing hormone (LH) was shown to superovulate cattle in 1940.[13] Since that time much work has been done to improve and discover new approaches to superovulation. It was also discovered in early research that although FSH would cause follicular growth at any time of the estrous cycle, ova that were produced during the luteal phase were not fertile. This, then, has limited the use of FSH.

FSH is usually given in a series of injections intramuscularly for 5 days starting on day 16 of the cycle. At the end of the series of FSH injections, LH is injected intravenously for rapid response and rupture of the follicles. Dose levels of 10 mg FSH per day for 5 days plus 100 mg LH have given good response of 3 to 11 ovulations.[3,57,69]

Difficulties with the FSH-LH scheme lie in the necessity of knowing the period of the cycle, need for multiple doses, and the cost of the purified product.

Combinations of progestogens to synchronize the cycle plus FSH have given acceptable results of 91, 75, and 111 percent calf crop.[8]

Pregnant mare serum gonadotropin (PMSG) is high in FSH activity and has a limited amount of LH activity. This combination of hormones in a single product is advantageous, since the two are necessary and are synergistic in their actions.

Many approaches as far as time and dosage have been tried using PMSG. At first it was thought that PMSG would be limited as in FSH according to the time of the cycle. The best response in these trials came by injecting PMSG an estimated 5 days before ovulation. At this time progesterone is beginning to fall and follicles are growing. PMSG has a very distinct advantage over FSH in that the activity is prolonged in the body and a single injection is then sufficient instead of the multiple injections needed with FSH. Figure 11-6 shows the response to PMSG injected at this time.

It is now known that PMSG may be utilized at any time of the cycle, which is another distinct advantage over FSH. The more accepted schedule now is an injection of PMSG followed by $PGF_2\alpha$ or an analogue. Treatment with 1500 to 2000 IU PMSG in midcycle followed 48 hours later by two daily injections of 1 mg $PGF_2\alpha$ in the lumen of the ipsilateral horn (same side as ovulation) gave very good response.[25] This yielded 13.2 average ovulations in 24 cows of which 18 ovulated, and 14.1 average ovulations in a second group of 10 cows. PMSG alone gave 8.0 ovulations average in 17 of 35 cows treated. The most important factor in all of the trials is the number of fertilized ova, but data are very limited in this important aspect. In the 10 cows that had 141 ovulations, 97 ova were recovered and 85 of these were fertile. That gives an average of 8.5 fertilized ova per cow, which is very good. Other studies have indicated the advantage of the PMSG-$PGF_2\alpha$ combination even when the $PGF_2\alpha$ is given intramuscularly.[19,37,40,57,97] It just takes a much greater amount—about 10 to 20 times the dose.

The dose level of PMSG is very difficult to standardize for several reasons, and as a result the response to a given level varies considerably under different condi-

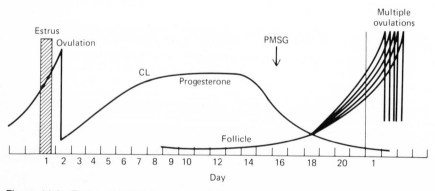

Figure 11-6　Timing of PMSG for superovulation.

tions.[5] A level of 1000 IU PMSG gives fair response under most circumstances. An additional 1000 gives better response, and even another 1000 IU will increase ovulations. However, as the dosage increases, the response becomes more erratic.[35]

Another factor to consider is the source and potency. There needs to be a standardization of the hormone to allow a repeatable pattern of ovulation.[57]

PMSG is a foreign protein to the cow and she will build an immunity to it.[69,82] The response to the first treatment is better than the succeeding treatments. One experiment[82] showed a recovery in response when heifers were repeatedly treated over a period of 14 months at 7- to 9-week intervals. Response started with an average of 5 ovulations, dropped to zero on treatments 3 and 4, but recovered on treatment 6 with some variation following. There is a possibility of overcoming some of the lack of response with higher dose levels, but the refractoriness of the ovary may be increased as well. Giving the female a rest may allow time for clearing the immune reaction.

Breed differences are also apparent[35] where it appears that beef cattle respond better than dairy, and there are even differences between breeds.[54]

All of the ovulations do not occur at the same time. Some cows may ovulate over a period of 5 to 7 days. $PGF_2\alpha$ has helped this situation considerably by closing the time to 2 or 3 days. Inseminations will give best response if continued from midestrus at intervals of 12 to 24 hours until the cow is out of estrus.[40]

Some cows will not show estrus, and observations reveal that the number of ovulations is lower in these cows than in those that do show signs of estrus. Many of these animals are discarded in commercial transfer operations.

The prepuberal calf has been investigated as an early source of genetic material. It is possible to superovulate these young animals[69] with good ovulatory response. Inseminating these small animals is a problem and fertility of the ova needs improving, but the possibility of shortening generation interval by several months certainly exists.

Three very good review articles are suggested to the reader. Check the reference at the end of the chapter for Gordon[35,36] and Graham.[37] This area of ovulation control offers an exciting future in research and practical use. It will be interesting to follow these changes.

Ewe

The main purpose for superovulating sheep is to increase multiple births. There may be a time in the future when embryo transfer places more demand on the process to establish herds from outstanding parents in a brief period of time.

As in the cow, the use of hormones will induce multiple follicles and ovulations in the ewe. Synchronization with pessaries followed by 500 IU PMSG on the day of removal yielded 1.5 to 1.7 lambs per conception.[34]

Horse anterior pituitary (HAP) has been used for superovulating ewes using 100 mg in mature ewes and 75 in ewe lambs over a period of 6 injections 12 hours apart. These commenced on day 12 of the cycle.[66] Over two years, 86 ewes were treated, of which 74 ovulated with 841 CL. Flushing harvested 667 ova, of which 482 were fertilized. This is an average of 5 fertilized ova from those that were treated or 6.5 ova per ewe that ovulated. Other studies with HAP are similar.[11]

PMSG during the normal breeding season may be injected on day 12 or 13 of the cycle with good response.[68] Injections of 1250, 1500, and 2000 IU PMSG resulted in 2.61, 2.81, and 2.44 lambs per ewe. Many other studies have been conducted in a similar manner with similar results.[46,65,67,71]

There would be several advantages to breeding ewes during their anestrous period. Shelton[87] outlined these advantages as follows:

1   A year-round supply of fresh lamb would be possible.
2   Highest lamb prices are in the spring and could be obtained by planning out-of-season lambing.
3   Lambing in the cool season is advantageous to growth in the southern states.
4   Noxious plants and plants such as needle grass and spear grass dictate seasons to some extent and could be circumvented.
5   Better utilization of labor and equipment could result.

Numerous combinations of synchronizing drugs and gonadotropins have been investigated for bringing the anestrous ewe to a fertile estrus.[42,46,102] The suggested program by Shelton[87] is a progestogen such as the vaginal pessary for 12 days followed by 500 IU PMSG at the time of pessary removal. Ewes showing signs of estrus should be bred, and a second injection of 500 IU PMSG should follow 16 days later with subsequent breeding at estrus.

The use of prepuberal ewe lambs as a supply of ova is possible through hormonal treatment similar to that for the anestrous ewe.[30]

Sow

The sow may already be considered superovulated under normal circumstances; however, in most instances it would be a definite advantage to add one or two more offspring.

Most of the superovulation research has used PMSG for stimulation. Cycling females are injected with 1200 to 2000 IU PMSG intramuscularly on day 5 or 16 of the estrous cycle.[7,59,99] Fertility of the ova produced has varied from approximately 50 percent being fertilized to 93 percent.[15,32,111]

Combinations of FSH and HCG have not given favorable response; HCG in combination with PMSG does not seem to merit its use.

Some of the best response has been the result of a synchronization regime using methallibure followed by 1250 to 1500 IU PMSG 24 hours after the last feeding of the methallibure and insemination of 100 ml diluted boar semen 24 to 96 hours after first signs of estrus. Ovaries had 12.9 more CL per gilt than did controls and 2.5 (11.1 vs. 8.6) more live fetuses at 70 days of pregnancy.[22] Another trial showed 3.8 (15.5 vs. 11.7), 10.8 (22.5 vs. 11.7), and 8.6 (20.3 vs. 11.7) more ovulations in response to 1000, 1250, and 1500 IU PMSG than controls.[105]

Attempts have been made to superovulate during the luteal phase of the cycle with poor success.[99] Ovulation seems to respond very well, but fertilization is very low. Many ova are immature, and even though sperm penetrate the ovum and form male pronuclei, the ovum does not respond.

Prostaglandin analogues have been tried and have given some increase with PMSG but no better than the PMSG alone.[74] Surely we will see more research on prostaglandins.

Mare

Superovulation in the mare is still in its infancy. Multiple births in mares are very undesirable because if there is not fetal death and abortion, at least one of the foals is weak and does not develop properly. There has been little incentive, then, to superovulate mares for breeding; however, with the advent of embryo transfer, interest is increasing.

Attempts similar to those used with other classes of livestock have not given ovulatory response as anticipated. Early studies indicated that the mare ovary would not respond to the gonadotropins during the anovulatory period and would respond only poorly to hormones during the estrous cycle.[21] More recent studies with pony mares have yielded more positive results.[23,56] An equine pituitary extract given over a 6-day period to cycling mares gave a response in diestrus of 4 of 7 mares ovulating more than two ova, and 3 of 7 mares stimulated in estrus had double or more ovulations. There was an average of 1.7 ova per mare in each treated group. Anovulatory mares responded to higher dose levels and HCG with 8 of the 11 that ovulated having multiple ovulations. A more recent trial resulted in 58 percent of 12 mares treated with $PGF_2\alpha$ having double ovulations and 36 percent of 24 mares treated with $PGF_2\alpha$ plus GNRH or $PGF_2\alpha$ plus GNRH plus estradiol 17β having double ovulations.[9]

Another method of superovulation has been through the use of methallibure (ICI 33828) fed over a period of 20 days followed by 2000 IU HCG 10 days after withdrawal. Three mares out of 9 responded with double ovulations 4 days after the beginning of estrus.[28] Lower dose levels gave the same response as control mares; 1 out of 7 in each case had double ovulations.

It is apparent that we can control ovulation in the mare. Now, perfection of techniques and dose levels remain to be determined.

Woman

Superovulation in the woman is undesirable, particularly when more than twins are involved. In most instances multiple births result from overstimulation in attempting to cause an anovulatory woman to ovulate and conceive.

The treatments for ovulation control mentioned earlier in this chapter frequently result in multiple pregnancies. Most occur due to dose level and the response of the individual. Clomiphene has yielded as high as 16 percent multiple pregnancies,[47] and gonadotropins have yielded 20 percent.[49] Many abortions result from multiple pregnancies, and attempts are being investigated to standardize treatments to guarantee the desired response of single ovulations.

WHAT DID YOU LEARN?

1   Why would one wish to breed calves before they normally reach puberty?
2   What is an intravaginal coil? What is a pessary?
3   What is the difference between prostaglandin and prostaglandin analogue? Why not use the natural product?
4   Why is intrauterine $PGF_2\alpha$ injected at a lower rate than intramuscular?
5   How would you cause an anestrous ewe to start cycling and conceive?
6   What detrimental side effects are present in swine synchronization with progestogens?
7   Why is it necessary to have a functional CL before using prostaglandins?
8   What hormone sequence is commonly used to superovulate the cow?
9   What is the source of FSH, LH, PMSG, HPG, and HMG?
10   What is the purpose of using HCG when PMSG is used for stimulation?

REFERENCES

1   Arthur, G. H. 1970. The induction of oestrus in mares by uterine infusion of saline. *Vet. Rec.* 86:584–586.
2   Averkin, G. and R. Schiltz. 1976. Summary of the effect of prostalene, a new synthetic prostaglandin, on the breeding efficiency of mares. *Vet. Med./Small Anim. Clinician* 71:1616–1623.
3   Avery, T. L., M. L. Fahning, and E. F. Graham. 1962. Investigations associated with the transplantation of bovine ova. II. Superovulation. *J. Reprod. Fert.* 3:212–217.
4   Bailey, V. E. and R. H. Douglas. 1977. Induction of ovulation in seasonally-anovulatory mares with GNRH. *Amer. Soc. Anim. Sci. 1977 Mtg. Abstr. 336.* P. 133.
5   Baker, A. A. 1973. Ovum transfer in the cow. *Australian Vet. J.* 49:424–426.
6   Baker, L. N., L. C. Ulberg, R. H. Grummer, and L. E. Casida. 1954. Inhibition of heat by progesterone and its effect on subsequent fertility in gilts. *J. Anim. Sci.* 13:648–657.
7   Bazer, F. W., O. W. Robison, and L. C. Ulberg. 1969. Effect of dichlorvos and PMS on reproduction in swine. *J. Anim. Sci.* 28:145. (Abstr.)
8   Bellows, R. A., D. C. Anderson, and R. E. Short. 1969. Dose-response relationships in synchronized beef heifers treated with follicle stimulating hormone. *J. Anim. Sci.* 28:638–644.
9   Booth, L. C., W. D. Oxender, R. H. Douglas, and S. L. Woodley. 1977. Effects of $PGF_2\alpha$ and GNRH on ovulation in mares. *Am. Soc. Anim. Sci. 1977 Mtg. Abstr. 350A.* P. 138.
10   Breuer, D. J., B. N. Day, J. W. Massey, and G. B. Thompson. 1977. Fertility of beef cows following controlled ovulation by progesterone releasing intravaginal coil. *Amer. Soc. Anim. Sci. 1977 Mtg. Abstr. 353.* p. 139.
11   Burfening, P. J. and J. L. Van Horn. 1970. Induction of fertile oestrus in prepubertal ewes during the anoestrous season. *J. Reprod. Fert.* 23:147–150.
12   Carrick, M. J. and J. N. Shelton. 1967. The synchronization of oestrus in cattle with progestagen-impregnated intravaginal sponges. *J. Reprod. Fert.* 14:21–32.

13   Casida, L. E., A. Nalbandov, W. H. McShan, R. K. Meyer, and W. Wisnicky. 1940.
      Potential fertility of artificially matured and ovulated ova in cattle. *Proc. Amer. Soc.
      Anim. Prod.* 33:302–304.

14   Chipepa, J. A. S., J. E. Kinder, and J. J. Reeves. 1977. Synchronized breeding in cattle
      using PGF$_2$α and LHRH/FSHRH stimulatory analogs. *Therio.* 8:25–32.

15   Christenson, R. K., C. E. Pope, V. A. Zimmerman, and B. N. Day. 1970. Synchroniza-
      tion of ovulation in superovulated gilts. *J. Anim. Sci.* 31:219. (Abstr.)

16   Christenson, R. K. and H. S. Teague. 1975. Synchronization of ovulation and artificial
      insemination of sows after lactation. *J. Anim. Sci.* 41:560–563.

17   Chupin, D., J. Pelot, and P. Mauleon. 1977. Control of estrus and ovulation in dairy
      cows. *Therio.* 7:339–350.

18   Cunningham, J. M. M., D. W. Deas, and J. Fitzsimons. 1967. Synchronisation of
      oestrus in ewes. *Vet. Rec.* 80:590–591.

19   Cupps, P. T., G. B. Anderson, M. Drost, B. Darien, and M. B. Horton. 1977. Synchron-
      ization of estrus in cattle for embryo transfer. *Therio.* 8:111–115.

20   Day, B. N., J. D. Neill, S. L. Oxenreider, A. B. Waite, and J. F. Lasley. 1965. Use of
      gonadotropins to synchronize estrous cycles in swine. *J. Anim. Sci.* 24:1075–1079.

21   Day, F. T. 1940. Clinical and experimental observations on reproduction in the mare.
      J. Agr. Sci. 30:244–261.

22   Deneke, W. A. and B. N. Day. 1973. Effect of superovulation on litter size of swine
      at 70 days of gestation. *J. Anim. Sci.* 36:1137–1138.

23   Douglas, R. H., L. Nuti, and O. J. Ginther. 1974. Induction of ovulation and multiple
      ovulation in seasonally-anovulatory mares with equine pituitary fractions. *Therio.*
      2:133–142.

24   Ellicott, A. R., J. W. Kelley, J. E. Gotti, and C. E. Thompson. 1977. Optimum time
      of insemination of heifers following removal of a progesterone-releasing intravaginal
      device. *Amer. Soc. Anim. Sci. 1977 Mtg. Abstr. 390.* P. 155.

25   Elsden, R. P., S. Lewis, I. A. Cumming, and R. A. S. Lawson. 1974. Superovulation
      in the cow following treatment with PMSG and prostaglandin F$_2$α. *J. Reprod. Fert.*
      36:455–456.

26   Evans, J. M. 1976. The veterinary uses of progestagens. *New Zealand Vet. J.* 24:25–34.

27   Fairnie, I. J., R. G. Wales, and P. B. Gherardi. 1977. Time of ovulation, fertilization
      rate, and blastocyst formation in ewes following treatment with a prostaglandin ana-
      logue ICI 80996. *Therio.* 8:183. (Abstr.)

28   First, N. L. 1973. Synchronization of estrus and ovulation in the mare with methalli-
      bure. *J. Anim. Sci.* 36:1143–1148.

29   First, N. L., F. W. Stratman, E. M. Rigor, and L. E. Casida. 1963. Factors affecting
      ovulation and follicular cyst formation in sows and gilts fed 6-methyl-17-acetoxypro-
      gesterone. *J. Anim. Sci.* 22:66–71.

30   Foote, R. H. 1972. Induced ovulation and fertility in prepuberal cattle, sheep and swine.
      J. Anim. Sci. Suppl. 1:49–55.

31   Gerrits, R. J. and L. A. Johnson. 1965. Synchronization of estrus in gilts fed two levels
      of ICI 33,828 and the effect on fertility, embryo survival and litter size. *J. Anim. Sci.*
      24:917. (Abstr.)

32   Gibson, E. W., S. C. Jaffe, J. F. Lasley, and B. N. Day. 1963. Reproductive performance
      in swine following superovulation. *J. Anim. Sci.* 22:858. (Abstr.)

33   Godke, R. A. 1974. Recent advances in research with potential applications in swine
      reproduction. *LSU 14th Livestock Producers' Day Proc.* P. 41–49.

34   Gordon, I. 1974. Controlled breeding in sheep. *Ir. Vet. J.* 28:118–126.

35   ———. 1975. Problems and prospects in cattle egg transfer. Part 2. *Ir. Vet. J.* 29:39–62.

36   ———. 1976. Controlled breeding in cattle. Part 1. Hormones in the regulation of reproduction, oestrus control, and set-time artificial insemination. *Anim. Breed. Abstr.* 44:265–275.

37   Graham, E. F. 1974. Do you know these transplant facts? *Simmental Shield.* June 1974. P. 63.

38   Greenblatt, R. B., A. T. Zarate, and V. B. Mahesh. 1975. Other ovulation-inducing agents: Clomiphene and other regimens. In J. J. Gold, ed. *Gynecologic Endocrinology.* 2nd ed. Harper & Row, New York. Pp. 384–398.

39   Hackett, A. J., H. A. Robertson, and H. F. Peters. 1977. Synchronization of estrus in ewes using PGF$_2\alpha$ in conjunction with GFA and PMSG. *Amer. Soc. Anim. Sci. 1977 Mtg. Abstr. 415.* p. 165.

40   Hafez, E. S. E., T. Sugie, and W. L. Hunt. 1963. Superovulation and related phenomena in the beef cow. II. Effect of oestrogen administration on production of ova. *J. Reprod. Fert.* 5:381–388.

41   Hallford, D. M., R. P. Wettemann, E. J. Turman, and I. Y. Omtvedt. 1975. Luteal function in gilts after prostaglandin F$_2\alpha$. *J. Anim. Sci.* 41:1706–1710.

42   Hansel, W. 1964. A summary of estrous cycle experiments. *Proc. Conf. on Estrous Cycle Control in Domestic Animals,* Nebr. Agr. Exp. Sta. MP 1005. Pp. 1–16.

43   Hays, R. L. and C. H. Carlevaro. 1959. Induction of estrus by electrical stimulation. *Amer. J. Physiol.* 196:899–900.

44   Hignett, P. G. and H. Boyd. 1968. Synchronisation of oestrus in Ayrshire heifers by the use of progestinated intravaginal sponges. *Proc. 6th Int. Congr. on Anim. Reprod. and A.I.* 2:1453–1455.

45   Hulet, C. V. and W. C. Foote. 1967. Physiological factors affecting frequency and rate of lambing. *J. Anim. Sci.* 26:553–562.

46   ———. 1967. Induction of fertile estrus in lactating and dry anestrous ewes using oral progestogens and repeated PMS treatment. *J. Anim. Sci.* 26:545–548.

47   Jewelewicz, R. 1975. Management of infertility resulting from anovulation. *Amer. J. Obstet. and Gynecol.* 122:909–920.

48   Kaltenbach, C. C. and W. G. Graves. 1975. Ovulation control in lactating beef cows. *Proc. 9th Conf. on A.I. of Beef Cattle.* Pp. 15–18.

49   Kase, N. 1975. Gonadotropins in the treatment of anovulation. In J. J. Gold, ed. *Gynecologic Endocrinology.* 2nd ed. Harper & Row, New York. Pp. 377–383.

50   Kraeling, R. R. and G. B. Rampacek. 1977. Synchronization of estrus and ovulation in gilts with estradiol and prostaglandin F$_2\alpha$. *Therio.* 8:103–110.

51   Kraemer, D.C. 1977. Prostaglandins for synchronization of estrus in cattle. In *Management Methods for Improving Beef Cattle Reproductive Performance, Proceedings: Food Animal Medicine Conference.* Texas A&M Univ., College Station. Pp. 165–167.

52   King, G. J. 1969. Deformities in piglets following administration of methallibure during specific stages of gestation. *J. Reprod. Fert.* 20:551–553.

53   Lagar, John J. 1977. Synchronization of the estrous cycle with Prostaglandin F$_2\alpha$ for use of artificial insemination in cattle (a review). *Vet. Med./Small Anim. Clinician* 72:87–92.

54   Lamond, D. R. 1972. Hormonal induction of multiple ovulation in the bovine. *J. Anim. Sci.* 34:901–902. (Abstr.)

55   Lamond, D. R., J. R. Buell, and W. S. Stevenson. 1975. Efficacy of a progstaglandin analogue in reproduction in the anestrous mare. *Therio.* 3:77–86.

56   Lapin, D. R. and O. J. Ginter. 1977. Induction of ovulation and multiple ovulations in seasonally anovulatory and ovulatory mares with an equine pituitary extract. *J. Anim. Sci.* 44:834–842.

57 Laster, D. B. 1973. Ovulation, fertility and prenatal mortality in heifers treated with PMSG or porcine FSH. *J. Reprod. Fert.* 33:275-282.

58 Lauderdale, J. W., B. E. Seguin, J. N. Stellflug, J. R. Chenault, W. W. Thatcher, C. K. Vincent, and A. F. Loyancano. 1974. Fertility of cattle following $PGF_2\alpha$ injection. *J. Anim. Sci.* 38:964-967.

59 Longnecker, D. E. and B. N. Day. 1968. Fertility level of sows superovulated at post-weaning estrus. 1968. *J. Anim. Sci.* 27:709-711.

60 Manns, J. G. and H. D. Hafs. 1976. Controlled breeding in cattle: A review. *Can. J. Anim. Sci.* 56:121-130.

61 Mares, S. E., L. A. Peterson, E. A. Henderson, and M. E. Davenport. 1977. Fertility of beef herds inseminated by estrus or by time following Syncro-Mate-B[R](SMB) treatment. *Amer. Soc. Anim. Sci. 1977 Mtg. Abstr. 464.* pp. 185-186.

62 Menge, A. C. and J. J. Christian, Jr. 1968. Estrus synchronization in cattle following feeding six progestogens. *J. Dairy Sci.* 51:1284-1287.

63 Miller, P. A., J. W. Lauderdale, and S. Geng. 1976. Effects of various doses of Prostin F_2 Alpha ® on estrous cycles, rectal temperature, sweating, heart rate and respiration rate in mares. *J. Anim. Sci.* 42:901-911.

64 Moody, E. L. and J. W. Lauderdale. 1977. Fertility of cattle following $PGF_2\alpha$ controlled ovulation. *Amer. Soc. Anim. Sci. 1977 Mtg. Abstr. 473.* P. 189.

65 Moore, N. W. and J. N. Shelton. 1962. The application of the technique of egg transfer to sheep breeding. *Australian J. Agr. Res.* 13: 718-724.

66 ———. 1964. Response of the ewe to a horse anterior pituitary extract. *J. Reprod. Fert.* 7:79-87.

67 Neville, W. E., Jr. 1966. Reproduction of ewes affected by level and time of PMS injection. *J. Anim. Sci.* 25:927-928. (Abstr.)

68 Newton, J. E. and J. E. Betts. 1968. Factors affecting litter size in the Scotch half-bred ewe. II. Superovulation and the synchronization of oestrus. *J. Reprod. Fert.* 17:485-493.

69 Onuma, H., J. Hahn, R. R. Maurer, and R. H. Foote. 1969. Repeated superovulation in calves. *J. Anim. Sci.* 28:634-637.

70 Oxender, Wayne D. 1974. Prostaglandin $F_2\alpha$ control of ovulation in cows and mares. *Proc. 6th Tech. Conf. on A.I. and Reprod.* Pp. 36-40.

71 Palsson, H. 1962. Augmentation of fertility of Iceland ewes with pregnant-mare serum in successive years. *J. Reprod. Fert.* 3:55-63.

72 Pexton, J. E. and P. J. Chenoweth. 1977. Using bulls to breed beef heifers at a synchronized estrus. *Amer. Soc. Anim. Sci. 1977 Mtg. Abstr. 488.* P. 195.

73 Pope, C. E., R. K. Christenson, V. A. Zimmerman-Pope, and B. N. Day. 1972. Effect of number of embryos on embryonic survival in recipient gilts. *J. Anim. Sci.* 35:805-808.

74 Pope, C. E., C. K. Vincent and D. M. Thrasher. 1968. Effect of ICI 33,828 and PMS on reproduction in gilts. *J. Anim. Sci.* 27:303. (Abstr.)

75 Rabau, E., D. M. Serr, S. Mashiach, V. Insler, M. Salomy, and B. Lunenfeld. 1967. Current concepts in the treatment of anovulation. *Brit. Med. J.* 4:446-449.

76 Reeves, J. J., J. E. Kinder, G. K. Tarnavsky, P. I. Chakraborty, D. Coy, and A. V. Schally. 1975. Synchronized breeding in cows with PGF_2 and LH-RH/FSH-RH analog. *J. Anim. Sci.* 41:376. (Abstr.)

77 Robinson, T. J. 1968. The synchronization of the oestrous cycle and fertility. *Proc. 6th Int. Congr. on Anim. Reprod. and A.I.* 2:1347-1383.

78 ———. 1971. The seasonal nature of reproductive phenomena in the sheep. II. Variation in fertility following synchronization of oestrus. *J. Reprod. Fert.* 24:19-27.

79   Roche, J. F. 1976. Retention rate in cows and heifers of intravaginal silastic coils impregnated with progesterone. *J. Reprod. Fert.* 46:253–255.

80   ———. 1976. Calving rate of cows following insemination after a 12-day treatment with silastic coils impregnated with progesterone. *J. Anim. Sci.* 43:164–169.

81   Rowson, L. E. A., H. R. Tervit, and A. Brand. 1972. The use of prostaglandins for synchronization of oestrus in cattle. *J. Reprod. Fert.* 29:145–154.

82   Saumande, J. and D. Chupin. 1977. Superovulation: A limit to egg transfer in cattle. *Therio.* 7:141–149.

83   Scanlon, P. F., J. N. Sreenan, and I. Gordon. 1972. Observations on the retention of intravaginal sponge-pessaries by cattle. *Vet. Rec.* 90:437–439.

84   ———. 1972. Synchronization of oestrus in heifers by intravaginal application of progesterone. *Vet. Rec.* 90:440–441.

85   Schultz, R. H., D. R. Beerwinkle, C. J. Bierschwal, M. J. Fields, R. A. Godke, D. C. Kraemer, J. G. Manns, B. E. Seguin, and R. J. Vatthaver. 1977. Synchronizing beef cows with cloprostenol (mult.-location trial). *Amer. Soc. Anim. Sci. 1977 Mtg. Abstr. 513.* P. 206.

86   Seguin, B. E., B. K. Gustafsson, J. P. Hurtgen, K. R. Refsal, R. A. Wescott, and H. L. Whitmore. 1977. Use of synthetic prostaglandin (Cloprostenol, ICI 80,996) in dairy cattle with unobserved estrus. *J. Dairy Sci. Suppl.* 1:82. (Abstr.)

87   Shelton, M. 1968. Lambing out of season and accelerated lambing. *Proc. Symp. on Physiology of Reproduction in Sheep,* Okla. St. Univ. Pp. 136–149.

88   Shelton, M. and J. M. Klindt. 1974. Hormonal control of reproduction in sheep. *Texas Agr. Exp. Sta. P.R.* 3285.

89   Shimizu, H., Y. Toyoda, S. Takeuchi, T. Kawai, and S. Adachi. 1967. Synchronization of oestrus and subsequent fertility of beef cattle following the intravaginal administration of gestagen. *J. Reprod. Fert.* 13:555–558.

90   Singleton, W. L. 1975. Synchronization of estrus and ovulation in sows following lactation. Mimeo., Purdue Univ., Lafayette, Ind.

91   Smith, J. F. 1976. Techniques and hazards of oestrus synchronization. *New Zealand Vet. J.* 24:65–69.

92   ———. 1976. Use of a synthetic prostaglandin analogue for synchronization of oestrus in heifers. *New Zealand Vet. J.* 24:71–73.

93   ———. 1977. Estrus, ovulation and conception following timed insemination in Romney ewes treated with progestagen and gonadotropins. *Therio.* 7:63–72.

94   Sorensen, A. M., Jr. 1972. Heat synchronization and multiple births. *Proc. 21st and 22nd Beef Cattle Short Course,* Texas A&M Univ., College Station. Pp. 219–225.

95   Sorensen, A. M., Jr. and L. H. Carroll. 1969. Conception following expression of corpora lutea in synchronized heifers. *J. Anim. Sci.* 29:199. (Abstr.)

96   Sorensen, A. M. and J. H. Foster. 1963. Natural and artificial breeding of synchronized cattle. *J. Anim. Sci.* 22:865. (Abstr.)

97   Sreenan, J. N. and J. P. Gosling. 1977. The effect of cycle stage and plasma progesterone level on the induction of multiple ovulations in heifers. *J. Reprod. Fert.* 50:367–369.

98   Stratman, F. W. and N. L. First. 1965. Estrus inhibition gilts fed a dithio-carbamoylhydrazine (ICI 33828). *J. Anim. Sci.* 24:930. (Abstr.)

99   Tanabe, T. Y., A. C. Warnick, L. E. Casida, and R. H. Grummer. 1949. The effect of gonadotrophins administered to sows and gilts during different stages of the estrual cycle. *J. Anim. Sci.* 8:550–557.

100   Testart, J. 1972. Synchronization of induced ovulation in the female calf. *Proc. 7th Int. Congr. on Anim. Reprod. and A.I.* 1:493–498.

101 Turman, E. J., R. P. Wettemann, T. D. Rich, D. Lyons, W. E. Sharp, and R. R. Frahm.
     1975. Synchronization of estrus in beef cattle with prostaglandin. *Animal Sciences and
     Industry Research Rept. MP-94,* Agr. Exp. Sta., Okla. St. Univ. and USDA. pp.
     176–185.

102 Wagner, J. F. 1964. Hormonal control of reproductive activity in the ewe. *Proc. Conf.
     on Estrous Cycle Control in Domestic Animals,* Nebr. Agr. Exp. Sta. MP 1005. Pp.
     28–38.

103 Wagner, J. F. and R. W. Seerley. 1961. Synchronization of estrus in gilts with an orally
     active progestin. *J. Anim. Sci.* 20:980–981. (Abstr.)

104 Weaver, L. D. and R. H. Schultz. 1977. Synchronization of estrus and ovulation in
     lactating dairy cows using cloprostenol. *J. Dairy Sci. Suppl.* 1:81–82.

105 Webel, S. K., J. B. Peters, and L. L. Anderson. 1970. Control of estrus and ovulation
     in the pig by ICI 33828 and gonadotropins. *J. Anim. Sci.* 30:791–794.

106 Wiggan, L. S. and J. B. K. Clark. 1968. The effect of synchronization of oestrus on the
     fertility of ewes inseminated artificially. *Brit. Vet. J.* 124:460–468.

107 Wiltbank, J. N. and S. E. Mares. 1977. Breeding at a predetermined time following
     syncro-mate-B treatment. *Proc. 11th Conf. on A.I. of Beef Cattle.* Pp. 57–65.

108 ———. 1977. Breeding at a predicted time following synchromate B and shang. In
     *Management Methods for Improving Beef Cattle Reproductive Performance, Proceed-
     ings: Food Animal Medicine Conference.* Texas A&M Univ., College Station. Pp.
     169–186.

109 Witherspoon, D. M., D. R. Lamond, F. N. Thompson, and W. Stevenson. 1975.
     Efficacy of a prostaglandin analogue on reproduction in the cycling mare. *Therio.*
     3:21–30.

110 Zimbelman, R. G., J. W. Lauderdale, and E. L. Moody. 1977. Beef A.I. and Prostaglan-
     din F_2 Alpha. *Proc. 11th Conf. on A.I. of Beef Cattle.* Pp. 66–75.

111 Zimmerman, D. R. 1972. Consequence of additional ova to variation in litter size in
     swine. *J. Anim. Sci. Suppl.* 1:57–66.

Artificial Insemination

When you complete this chapter you should be able to:

- Discuss advantages and disadvantages of artificial insemination for the various classes of livestock,
- Know differences between the various techniques of artificial insemination such as rectocervical, vaginal, intracervical, vaginocervical, etc.,
- Discuss the many helps that are available for checking estrus in cattle,
- Briefly outline an AI program for any class of livestock,
- Relate time of insemination to optimum conception, and
- Understand some of the problems that arise with registration of offspring from AI.

INTRODUCTION

The first accounts of artificial insemination date to 1780 when Spallanzani, an Italian physiologist, experimented with the dog and successfully inseminated a bitch by injecting fresh semen directly into the uterus. Pups were born a normal gestation period later. There are tales of an Arab chieftain stealing semen from the sheath of a stallion belonging to his enemy and using this to inseminate his mare, but no documentation is available. It does make a good story, however, and indicates the extremes to which man will go to acquire semen from superior breeding stock.

In 1890, Repiquet in France advised the use of artificial insemination to overcome sterility.[49] Ivanov, in Russia, undertook insemination in horses at the turn of the century and cattle and sheep about 1928, and furthered interest in it so that a physiology section was established in the veterinary laboratory of the Ministry of Agriculture.[46]

The rectovaginal or rectocervical approach was developed in Denmark in 1937 and resulted in an increase of approximately 10 percent conception.[49]

The first artificial insemination organization in the United States was Cooperative Artificial Breeding Association No. 1, established in New Jersey in 1938. There were 102 members and 1,050 cows to begin with. Today there are over 10 million dairy cows and over 1 million beef cows being bred artificially.

The reader is referred to Dr. Nishikawa's presentation to the 5th International Congress on Animal Reproduction and Artificial Insemination, 1964, entitled "History and Development of Artificial Insemination in the World,"[46] for a comprehensive review to that date. A book entirely devoted to artificial insemination is *The Artificial Insemination of Farm Animals* by E. J. Perry.[49]

CATTLE

Actual figures are not available, but it is estimated that 55 to 60 percent of the dairy cows were inseminated in 1976 and 3 to 5 percent of the beef cows. The number of beef cattle inseminated is very difficult to ascertain because of the large number of ranchers who inseminate their own stock. There are also many custom-freezing operations that process thousands of units of semen without record except for the owner of the bull. The low percentage inseminated for both classes of livestock leaves considerable room for improvement.

Several factors favor artificial insemination in our changing livestock situation. Dairies are becoming fewer and larger, which lends itself to greater organization and regimentation. Experts in breeding can then become an integral part of the overall program. Beef cattle production is becoming more concentrated so that the stock are managed in smaller areas with more attention being paid to feeding, health, and breeding. Although a rapid increase in AI is not apparent, its growth has been gradual and rather constant, with enthusiasm and interest increasing.

There are advantages and disadvantages to all artificial insemination programs, so let us take a look at some of them.

Advantages

1 Widespread use of outstanding sires offers a great opportunity for genetic improvement of livestock. As previously noted, semen may be collected from a bull to potentially breed 500,000 cows in his lifetime through use of frozen semen. And even after a bull's death his semen may be used for improvement.

2   Rapid proof of a sire is available. The bull may be sampled on a random group of cows to measure his potential. This may be done in a single generation where it would usually take a lifetime to accumulate the same information. Milk production of his daughters, growth of offspring, feed conversion, birth weight, calving difficulty, and carcass data are only some of the measures available in a short period of time. These criteria may be used in indexes of value for the sire and comparison with other possible sires. The breed associations make use of these, and the breeding organizations use them heavily in advertising. The cattleman should pay close attention to them in his sire selection.

3   Availability of sires gives the producer an opportunity for selecting from a large battery of bulls. The breeding organizations publish catalogs listing the bulls and their records of performance. Other bulls are available through custom freezing as well. Today a rancher or dairyman can breed to a bull anywhere in the world. The newly introduced breeds of the late 1960s are a good example of availability. Cattle could not be imported, but quarantined semen could. The breeds became established then through upgrading using artificial insemination.

4   Incompatability is overcome. Some bulls are not capable of breeding cows because of injury, physical size, age, or even for psychological reasons. Bulls are often crippled in transit, fights with other bulls, or some accident and cannot then mount and serve cows. Collection of semen and insemination extends the use of outstanding sires under these circumstances. Young sires or sires of a different breed may not be large enough to successfully complete the act of copulation. On the other hand, large bulls may be too heavy for young heifers and this is overcome by insemination. Aged bulls may lose their libido or become arthritic, which prevents their serving the cow. And then there are some bulls that are not interested in particular females. This has been observed in some Zebu breeds when mixed with European breeds. Artificial insemination can overcome all these difficulties.

5   Danger of a bull is eliminated. Bulls are more excited than cows and must be handled with greater caution. Dairy bulls as a rule are more excitable than the docile beef bulls. Don't ever depend on any of them to be docile all the time. Certain breeds are more excitable than others. It is pretty difficult to be injured by a catheter at the time of insemination.

6   Disease is reduced through artificial insemination in two ways. More attention is paid to the health of the sire from which semen is collected. The breeding organizations have veterinarians available at all times and follow a strict disease control program. Semen is not processed from diseased animals. The second control is through the addition of antibiotics to the semen during processing.

7   New crosses can be tried experimentally without purchasing a sire of a different breed. Many dairymen prefer to buy replacement heifers rather than raise them. They will breed their milk cows to beef bulls in order to attract a little better price for the calf. Sampling a number of breeds is possible on a smaller herd.

8   Management is improved. In order to operate an artificial insemination program successfully, certain factors are a must and some come as bonuses. The cattle must be selected for the program to insure success. They must be identified, and in turn the producer gets to know them better. Pastures may need dividing into

smaller areas for control. New fences and waterers result. Nutrition is much better controlled and it may become evident that nutrition is essential under range conditions as well as concentrated operations.

9   Economics is a major factor in livestock production, and the cost of using an outstanding sire through AI is certainly less than through natural service. Use of mediocre bulls may not be economically feasible. The following example is given to compare costs for the two methods of breeding (Table 12–1).

10   Pride in a successful program or using a relatively new approach is an advantage for some producers. There is a great deal of satisfaction in pointing to livestock that result from specific programs and efforts of the individual. This cannot be discounted.

Disadvantages

Most of the disadvantages result from poor techniques, controls, and management of factors that usually are categorized as advantages.

Table 12-1   Comparison of Natural and AI Service

Cost per cow, natural service			
Bull purchased	$400	$600	$1,000
Plus maintenance (3 years*)	450	450	450
Plus risk (10%)	55	75	115
Minus salvage	300	300	300
Net cost/bull	605	825	1,265
Cost/cow bred (25 cows/year/bull for 3 years)	8.07	11.00	16.87

*Based upon $150 annual beef production in place of bull.

	Cost per cow, AI Twenty-five day breeding period	
	250 cows	1,000 cows
Semen purchase—$3.00 per ampule		
(80% heat detection)	$600.00	$2,400.00
Supplies—16¢ per cow bred	20.00	80.00
Freight—refrigerator	20.00	20.00
Service—refrigerator and nitrogen	45.00	45.00
Riders/labor—$12.00/day (25 days)	300.00	500.00
Total	$ 985.00	$3,145.00
Cows left for "follow-up" bulls (from 80% detection with 70% conception)	110	440
Cost of breeding with $400.00 follow-up bulls (@$8.07 per cow—see natural service cost)	887.70	3,550.80
Total cost for herd	$1,872.70	$6,695.80
Cost per cow	$ 7.49	$ 6.60

American Breeders Service.[4]

1 Widespread use of poor bulls is just as possible as use of good bulls, so selection must be accurate and properly enforced.

2 The number of sires available to the producer depends on what the technician has in his tank. Proper selection ahead of time can eliminate this.

3 Reduced bull sales by purebred producers results from the use of fewer sires. Actually the increased price of the fewer top bulls tends to offset this. The consistently good producer has the advantage over the producer of mediocre and poor bulls.

4 Inbreeding results from the use of fewer sires. Records of production and relationship to a common sire have been studied, and the animal breeders assure us that there is no cause for alarm.

5 Disease may be spread rapidly through indiscriminate use of untested sires. This certainly can present a problem in custom-frozen semen because of the lack of disease control. The semen user must insist on high-quality, healthy semen. Just antibiotics in the extender cannot control all diseases that may be present.

6 The cost of initiating a program must be considered. For many producers, it may mean a complete change in management. Construction of new facilities may be costly, and training of personnel must be considered as well as equipment necessary for the insemination itself and the cost of semen. An individual going into the program must look at long-term advantages to see if they outweigh the immediate costs.

7 Trained personnel are a must. The inseminator should be trained at a reliable school and practice diligently before the breeding season. The major breeding organizations conduct short courses in artificial insemination all over the United States, and contact with them will allow scheduling a school for this training. The cost is nominal when considered as part of the whole program. Some state extension programs are available, and field representatives of the major breeding organizations are available also to help set up a program and assist in procuring semen and supplies.

Personnel must also be trained to check cows for signs of estrus. This is one, if not the biggest, problem in an AI program. A man with cow sense is invaluable.

8 Weather is a very important factor to livestock as well as personnel. Cattle cycle best in the spring and fall, yet much breeding is conducted in the summer and winter. Many stock are bred in the mid to late winter months when rain, sleet, and snow make it extremely uncomfortable to ride looking for cattle in estrus and also uncomfortable for breeding. If you have never ridden in this kind of weather or tried to breed a cold cow with ice water running off the brim of your hat down your neck this disadvantage may mean little to you.

Management

A positive attitude on the part of the owner and/or manager is most essential in an artificial insemination program. It must be established as a goal that the program will work, and then everything that is done must be aimed in that direction. To make a success of the program all the personnel must be of the same attitude.

Cattle Selection The cows that go into the program should be selected with care. The same thing could be said for breeding stock in any type of program. It would be foolish to select cattle that were not cycling to put into a breeding program such as AI where concentrated manpower and effort are over a short period of time. The cows should be in a growing condition, putting on daily gain to yield optimum results. Herd health should be optimum. Select cows to match the potential of the sire to be used. The mating should yield an offspring superior to one from your cows and a bull you would purchase for pasture breeding.

A nutrition program should be initiated several weeks before the breeding program begins to insure the growing condition. This usually means bringing the cattle into smaller pastures for closer control. A set of scales and periodic check is a good investment.

Synchronization A choice needs to be made early before the breeding season if synchronization is to be used, when compounds become available.

Semen Source Seek a reliable source of semen. Use sources of known quality. Discuss the advantages and disadvantages of available bulls. In dairy cattle, if you want to increase pounds of milk, select a bull with greater potential than your cows. If you have poor udders on your cows, select bulls whose daughters have udders that are better supported or better shaped. To lengthen the loin of offspring from beef cows, select bulls with a great deal of stretch. Plan the matings between your cows and that special bull.

Inseminator Hire or train the inseminator. Dairymen mostly hire a technician, while most ranchers send one or more of their hands to a school for training.

Facilities Facilities must be adequate for holding, moving, and securing the stock. Most dairy cows are docile enough that they can be bred in a stanchion. Beef cows are usually worked through a chute into some restraining area. Figure 12–1 gives a simple plan for moving cattle and restraining them. Choose systems that do not excite the livestock.

A holding pen should be designed with water and feeding facilities available to keep cows found in estrus until they are to be bred.

Alleyways or chutes leading to the restraining area should be free of any sharp objects that would damage the stock. They should be narrow enough to prevent the stock from turning around. Cattle will resist walking into a vacant chute; therefore, it should be long enough to accommodate four or five cows so that one animal is always kept in the chute to attract others to enter. A bar may be used to eliminate backing out of the chute. Spring-loaded stops may be built into the walls of the chute to eliminate some labor when filling it with stock.

The breeding chute should be large enough for one cow and should restrict lateral, forward, and backward movement during the insemination. A wooden chute with dirt floor is more natural for the animals, but sometimes a squeeze chute is needed for highly excitable stock. A bar behind the cow prevents backing and

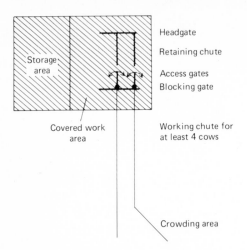

Headgate

Retaining chute

Access gates
Blocking gate

Storage area

Covered work area

Working chute for at least 4 cows

Crowding area

Figure 12-1 Simple AI breeding area.

kicking the inseminator. A chain device slipped through one wall and secured on the other gives some variance in length to accommodate cows of different lengths (Fig. 12–2). An opening or gate behind the cow is a must. One of the best arrangements consists of a gate the same width as the chute that can be swung into the chute and latched during insemination to prevent other cows from coming up behind the inseminator. The release gate may be straight ahead, to the side, or, in some arrangements, the cow may be backed out. All of these factors can usually be worked into existing chutes with little difficulty.

The breeding chute should have some protection over it and a storage area for the semen storage and inseminating equipment. This is usually found to be a convenient area for working cattle for other purposes than insemination.

Estrous Detection Those individuals checking the females for estrus, or heat, should be trained in their job. The signs of estrus have already been discussed and will not

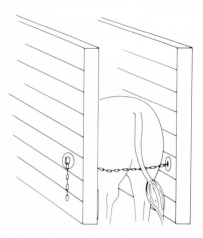

Figure 12-2 Restraining chain in the chute.

be repeated. The checker must have some cow sense and try to think like a bull. One rancher once said that the checker needs to practice bull psychology, and that is very close to the truth. Dedication as well as knowledge are essential to select those cows that are ready for breeding.

The livestockman took on a tremendous job when he decided to replace the bull in detecting cows in estrus. He has accumulated a number of methods of assistance in an attempt to make him as successful as the bull. Following are discussions of the various methods and the feasibility of their use.[6]

Personal observation Dedication and knowledge of the job are essential. A minimum of 30 minutes early in the morning and 30 minutes late in the evening is essential. This means constant and accurate observation. Driving through the pasture is not good enough. More than twice a day will increase the number observed in estrus. Personal observation is a very good method, but labor expense is a real problem. Some helps for this observation will be discussed.

Marker animals These are usually males that have been adjusted in some way that they cannot breed. Cows may also be used after hormone treatment. They leave their mark in some way on the cow in estrus.

Grease Grease smeared on the brisket of the marker animal will leave a mark on the rump of the mounted cow. Colors may be used to identify animals by days. Some animals will be mounted and marked without actually standing; therefore, the method has some disadvantage.

Collar A cushion of some sort may be fastened as a collar under the neck. They may be bought commercially or homemade. A piece of foam plastic may be covered with porous nylon cloth to form a pillow and neck strap. Crankcase oil or various dyes may be used to saturate the pad. A mark will be left higher on the back than by the previous method, and this is therefore more accurate. It is necessary to detect the difference between a mark made on a standing cow and a moving one.

Chin-ball marker A ball-type device similar to a ball-point pen has been developed to fit on a halter with the reservoir and ball under the chin. Paint inside the unit is smeared on the back and sides of the cow (Fig. 12–3) when the bull mounts. The paint is rather expensive, and an active bull may result in considerable cost as he continues to re-mark the same cow. The mark is poorly made in wet weather. Interpretation of the marks is important.

Heat-mount detector A device loaded with dye has been developed for placement on the rump of cows being observed for estrus (Fig. 12–4). The placement is very important, and directions should be followed explicitly.[12] Pressure on the device causes an escape of the dye from a small container into a larger area so that the color changes in response to the teaser animal or other cow mounting. Response has been mixed among breeders, with some praising it and others feeling it to be a loss of time and effort.[17,69]

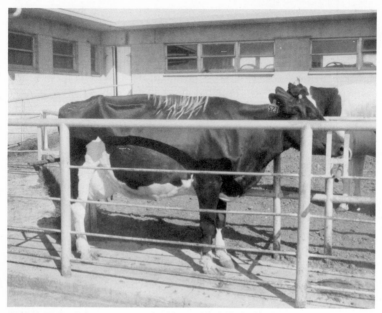

Figure 12-3   Estrous cow marked by a chin-ball device.

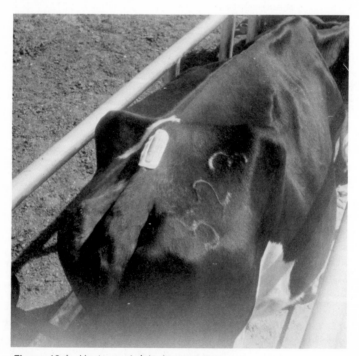

Figure 12-4   Heat mount detector on a cow.

The loss of detectors is a problem under certain circumstances. They should not be used in very crowded conditions as some are scraped off and many are ruptured by mistake when cows cannot move away from being mounted. Brushy pastures are a detriment, as low branches will scrape the patches off. Back rubbers in the pasture should be removed during the period of use. Detectors should not be placed on cattle with excessive long or dry hair or in wet weather.

Teaser animals Some intact animals may be used in estrous detection. Males may be surgically prepared to be used as teasers without resulting conception. Females may be treated with hormones and act as nymphomaniacs. Numerous teaser types will be discussed.

Young bulls Young bulls approaching puberty will be sexually active and follow and attempt to mount cows in estrus. It is important that these young bull calves not be able to mount and mate. Many undesired matings are traced to matings of young bulls that have reached puberty unknown to the owner.

Pseudohermaphrodites and nymphomaniacs Male pseudohermaphrodites have testes but appear as females exteriorly. The testes produce testosterone, and libido is therefore present. They are good teasers because of the lack of male external genitalia but are rare animals to find.

The nymphomaniac or sex-crazy female results from a high level of estrogen, which usually is derived from a cystic follicle. These highly excitable animals are also mounted by other animals because they too are in constant or intermittent estrus. They may be damaged by the constant activity and are of detriment to management other than during the breeding season. Nymphomaniacs may be developed by continued high levels of estrogens being injected.

Treated steers Steers may be treated with testosterone to bring about libido. An injection of 100 to 500 mg testosterone in oil should result in increased libido for several weeks duration. Additional injections may be required. The main disadvantage of this method is the extension of the penis and intromission. The teaser may then be a carrier of any disease within the herd. Age of castration apparently affects the extent of penile extension; those castrated at a very young age show little extension, while those castrated at a later age extend their penis farther.

Treated females Ovariectomized (spayed) females may be injected with an estrogen to increase libido. They in turn will mount cows in estrus. Repeated injections may be necessary. Other animals will attempt to mount these teasers because they are also in estrus. Continued mounting of the hormone-treated cow may damage or cripple her permanently. She would not be a desirable animal after the breeding season is finished.

Vasectomy (tube removal) Vasectomy or vasoligation is probably the most common method of sterilizing the male.[32] The vasa deferentia are exposed and a section removed to interrupt passage of sperm (Fig. 12–5). The operation is simple and of short duration, without undue stress on the animal. The section of vas deferens should be examined for the presence of sperm for positive identification, and the animal should be allowed approximately 2 weeks for recovery. Ejaculates should be examined after this time to make sure no sperm are present at the time of introduction of the teaser to the cow herd. The major difficulty with vasectomized males is the ability to insert the penis into the cow in estrus and spread disease if it is present. There is also the rare possibility of the vas recanalizing to allow sperm passage.

Epididymal resection The tail of the epididymis may be removed[47] with similar simplicity and response as in vasectomy. The bull should not be placed with cows for about 4 weeks or until the sperm in the vas deferens have been expelled. Problems are the same as with vasectomy.

Epididymal transection The tail of the epididymis may be cut in several areas to interrupt sperm passage.[67] Remember that the epididymis is a single tube, and by sectioning across the tail several loops will be cut. The scar tissue formed in healing seals the tube. These animals are similar to the vasectomized bulls.

Epididymal occlusion Injection of sclerotherapeutic (hard-healing) agents into the tail of the epididymis occludes passage as in transection.

Preputial closure and fistulation The prepuce may be sutured closed and a small fistula (opening) formed about 5 cm (2 in) posterior to the normal orifice on the ventral surface[28] for urination. Vasectomy or epididymal removal usually accompanies the closure, and 2 weeks are needed for recovery. Some complications have arisen through reopening of the prepuce, copulation through the fistula, and development of calculi in the blind prepuce.

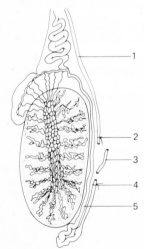

1 — Deferent duct
2 — Ligature
3 — Excised section
4 — Ligature
5 — Epididymis

Figure 12-5 Vasectomy in the bull.

Preputial restriction A restriction can be formed in the preputial canal to restrict extension of the penis by passing a suture of umbilical tape in the skin of the prepuce about 2 cm (.75 in) posterior to the opening in a purse-string manner.[9] This may be removed later for natural use of the bull. The animal may be used immediately without impairment of libido. Tearing loose of the suture is the main problem.

Penile retraction and fixation There are several ways this may be done, but the most common is exposing and anchoring the penis with wire sutures anterior to the scrotum[7] or by anchoring the penis in the escutcheon, halfway between the scrotum and anus.[24] The penis is restricted from extension upon erection. Complications arise from occlusion of the urethra by sutures and tearing of adhesions to release the restriction.

Penile deviation A very popular method currently is a displacement of the penis to one side so that intromission is absent due to misalignment.[31,57,80] The penis is isolated by a midventral incision and an incision around the prepuce. The penis and prepuce are then realigned about 45° to one side and the incisions closed (Fig. 12–6). Careful consideration must be given to vascularity of the newly relocated penis. The surgery is relatively simple and young bulls are easiest to displace. It is possible that the bull may realign his sights and complete copulation, but experience shows this to be very rare.

Figure 12-6 Penile deviation in the bull.

Phallectomy of penectomy Removal of a portion of the penis has been used in developing teaser bulls. The shortening prevents intromission. The penis may be removed either anterior or posterior to the scrotum.[22,38,70] A new urethral orifice is formed at the point of removal, and a period of at least 7 to 10 days is needed for recovery. The increased blood pressure associated with libido may cause hemorrhage, and granulation tissue may develop. There appears to be an associated decrease in libido with time in these animals more than in those prepared by other means. Close observation of the penile area is required.

Pen-o-block This is a device made of a plastic tube about 2.5 cm (1 in) in diameter and 15 cm (6 in) long and a stainless steel pen and washers.[36] The tube is placed in the prepuce until the distal end is 5 to 10 cm (2 to 4 in) from the orifice and anchored there by piercing the sheath with a trocar and cannula and anchoring the stainless steel pin through the sheath and tube. The prepuce is held open for urination but the pin prevents extension of the penis. The bull may be used in natural service upon removal. Difficulties lie in rubbing of the sheath causing inflammation and infection with subsequent adhesions and loss of use of the bull. Selection of a bull with a desirable sheath that is not too tight or too loose is essential. Frequent checks of the preputial area can detect difficulties so that corrective measures may be taken.

Ring restriction An ordinary bull nose ring may be passed through the sheath and prepuce to block extension of the penis. Bypassing the ring is possible, so this is not a desirable method.

Aprons Aprons covering the sheath and area of penile extension may be used on animals under close observation. With activity the apron may shift, allowing mating. Sanitation is a problem and the penis becomes chaffed and sore.

Gomer bulls The term "Gomer" is a readily accepted term for an altered bull that cannot make sexual contact with the cow. The origin of the term was described by Wayne Clews,[14] a rancher in Canada, as a name given a detector bull by the children of one of his customers. It just seemed to catch on, and today it is commonly used.

Precaution Teaser males are not super-animals. They are capable of detecting only as many cows in estrus as a normal bull. It is therefore necessary to supply teaser bulls at the same ratio to cows as breeding bulls, about 1:20 to 1:40.

Trained dogs Dogs that have been trained in olfactory discrimination have successfully identified samples of estrous mucus from cows in 73 to 90 percent of the cases. Dogs trained in such a manner would certainly enhance detection.[33]

Comparisons Numerous comparisons have been made between times for checking estrus and methods. Only a sample will be given here.

When a group of 270 dairy cows was observed for estrus at 0600, 1200, 1800, and 2400 hours, the percent found in estrus varied little at any single time; 28.6, 21.7, 23.6, and 26.1, respectively.[26] Others have found similar results.[13] The percent found in a regular morning and evening check could be increased by 10 percent if a noonday check were added and 19 percent if a midnight check were added. Over half the cows came in estrus at night.

Another large dairy operation[76,77] used KaMar heat-mount detectors with good success. Heat-mount detectors (75 percent) were better than observation by herdsmen, who detected only 56 percent of those determined to be in estrus by follicular palpation for ovulation.

A vasectomized bull in combination with heat-mount detectors yielded 100 percent detection over 108 estrous periods.[17] Observations were made at 0700, 1200, and 1600 hours in which 91 percent of the cows were detected, and only 1 percent accuracy would have been sacrificed if the 1200-hour observation had been omitted. The importance of early checks is pointed out by the fact that if the 0700 observation had been changed to 0800, efficiency would have been reduced to 84 percent.

One of the best controlled experiments was conducted at the Meat Animal Research Center in Nebraska.[6] The cattle were maintained in drylot or in small pastures. Visual observation was made twice daily for a period of 3 hours. Standing heat was the criterion used for breeding. One heat checker observed 250 to 300 cows.

The teaser animals were penectomized bulls with chin-ball markers. Libido was checked on each teaser and was excellent in each bull. Some restricted-penis bulls were used but libido was not as persistent as in penectomized bulls.

The teaser bulls were placed with cows at ratios of 1:30, 1:60, and 1:100. Table 12–2 gives the results. It should be noted that 95 percent of the cows were marked in the 30:1 ratio compared to 66 and 51 in the 60:1 and 100:1 groups.

Based on a 60 percent reduction in labor by using teaser bulls and utilizing the 1:30 ratio, the teaser system was more economical.

KaMar patches were used on cattle at the same station, and in 152 cows 30 percent of the patches were lost. This was due primarily to wet hair when they were put on. Thirty-three percent changed color on the day of estrus, 31 percent one day or more proestrus, and 6 percent did not change.

Table 12-2 Heat Detection Utilizing Penectomized Bulls with Chin-Ball Markers

Item	Cow:bull ratio		
	30:1	60:1	100:1
Cows, no.	210	295	300
Bulls, no.	7	5	3
Detected, no.	156	210	239
Detected, percent	74	71	79
Marked, no.	148	138	123
Marked, percent	95	66	51
Total marked/bull	21	28	41
Marked/bull/day	1.1	1.5	2.1
Marked, not observed standing	9	3	3

Adapted from Beerwinkle.[6]

Records should be kept on all the cows. These should include her history of breeding, ease of calving, time to rebreeding following parturition, and cyclic activity. A calendar is a great help for tracking estrous periods, whereby a mark can be made 18 days after estrus to start observing that particular cow for her next cyclic estrus. She should show signs within a few days of that predicted date if she is not bred.

Records necessary for registration by the Purebred Associations will not be covered because of the variances between breed associations. If the owner wishes to register the offspring he should contact his registry association for details. Dairy cattle associations have had a policy of registration through artificial insemination without vigorous restrictions for many years. Records of service must be submitted for registration certificates on the offspring.

Time of Insemination

The optimum time for inseminating the cow has been studied in detail.[13,23,43,54] The universally accepted time is a rule of thumb called the A.M.-P.M. rule. Those cows detected first in estrus in the morning are bred that same afternoon and those found in the afternoon and night are bred the following morning. More exacting measures have been attempted, but the rule of thumb is apparently as simple and successful as we have at the present time.

Optimum time for insemination appears to be 12 to 18 hours after beginning of estrus (Fig. 12–7).

One of the major breeding organizations has established a pattern of breeding only once during the day. In this way, their technician only stops by a dairy once a day and breeds any animals that have come into estrus since that time the day before. Their conception rates have held very closely to two-times-a-day breeding.

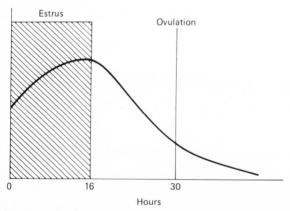

Figure 12-7 Optimum time for breeding cattle.

Factors Determining Insemination Response

An equation of reproduction has been compiled by American Breeders Service that is worth examining. Figure 12–8 shows the effect of the variables involved upon the percent calves produced.

Factor A—Percent of Herd Detected and Inseminated is governed by the percentage of cows that are cycling, the nutritive condition of the herd, and the estrous-checking ability of the crew.

Factor B—Herd Fertility in Percent must be determined from the breeding history of the cow herd.

Factor C—Semen Fertility from the Semen Package in Percent depends largely

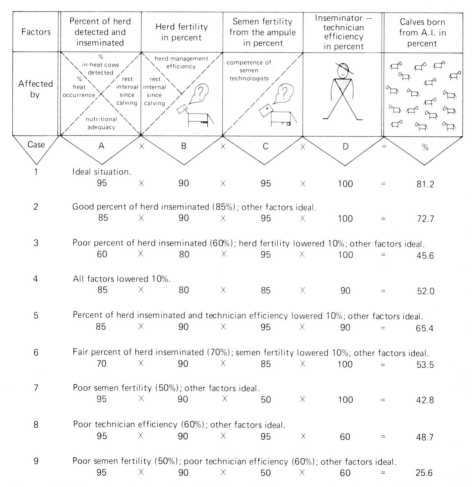

Factors	Percent of herd detected and inseminated		Herd fertility in percent		Semen fertility from the ampule in percent		Inseminator – technician efficiency in percent		Calves born from A.I. in percent
Affected by	% in-heat cows detected / % heat occurrence / rest interval / nutritional adequacy		herd management efficiency / rest internal since calving / rest since calving		competence of semen technologists				
Case	A	X	B	X	C	X	D	=	%
1	Ideal situation.								
	95	X	90	X	95	X	100	=	81.2
2	Good percent of herd inseminated (85%); other factors ideal.								
	85	X	90	X	95	X	100	=	72.7
3	Poor percent of herd inseminated (60%); herd fertility lowered 10%; other factors ideal.								
	60	X	80	X	95	X	100	=	45.6
4	All factors lowered 10%.								
	85	X	80	X	85	X	90	=	52.0
5	Percent of herd inseminated and technician efficiency lowered 10%; other factors ideal.								
	85	X	90	X	95	X	90	=	65.4
6	Fair percent of herd inseminated (70%); semen fertility lowered 10%; other factors ideal.								
	70	X	90	X	85	X	100	=	53.5
7	Poor semen fertility (50%); other factors ideal.								
	95	X	90	X	50	X	100	=	42.8
8	Poor technician efficiency (60%); other factors ideal.								
	95	X	90	X	95	X	60	=	48.7
9	Poor semen fertility (50%); poor technician efficiency (60%); other factors ideal.								
	95	X	90	X	50	X	60	=	25.6

Figure 12-8 Percent calves born from AI during a single estrous cycle. *(Adapted from American Breeders Service.)*

upon the source of the semen and the producer's ability to maintain high quality.

Factor D—Inseminator-Technician Efficiency in Percent is based upon previous experience and results.

Each of these factors is critical, as can be seen in Figure 12–8. It is not a matter of trying to maintain a single high factor; all factors must be high.

Technique

There are several techniques available for inseminating the cow. A description of the most popular and most successful technique, called "rectocervical," will be presented first, followed by brief comments about other methods.

Rectocervical with Straws This method consists of inserting one arm in the rectum and directing the inseminating tube through the vagina and cervix for deposition of the semen in the anterior cervix (Fig. 12–9).

Equipment Certain equipment should be assembled and maintained for breeding purposes. A list is given here with brief explanation.

Semen tank (Fig. 12–10)—liquid nitrogen refrigerator capable of storing the amount of semen needed between scheduled contact with the supplier of semen and liquid nitrogen.

Inseminating kit (Fig. 12–11)—carrying case for keeping equipment together and clean. A tool box works very satisfactorily.

Forceps—for lifting the straw from the goblet in the semen tank.

Breeding gun—stainless steel instrument for holding straws. Size must coincide with the particular size straw that is used. An alternative exists in other forms of inseminating tubes and should be investigated for the one most suitable to the

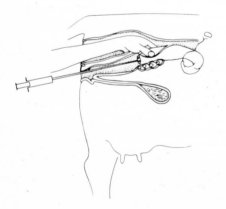

Figure 12-9 Rectocervical insemination in the cow.

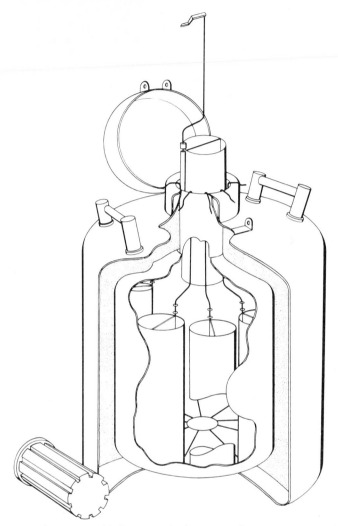

Figure 12-10 Liquid nitrogen tanks for semen storage.

inseminator. A metal tube and plunger with a different cover is available, and a tube similar to a plastic catheter with a plunger also works very satisfactorily. A universal unit is now being introduced to accommodate all size straws as well as liquid semen.

Sheaths—a thin plastic cover to go over the straw and inseminating gun. This is used only once and then discarded.

Thaw box—preferably a widemouthed thermos with a thermometer. The accepted method of thawing until recently has been in ice water, but a much higher temperature is now recommended. A compilation of data from numerous experi-

Figure 12-11 Inseminating kit and supplies.

ments indicates that thawing at 35 to 37°C (96 to 98°F) for 10 to 30 seconds is optimum under most conditions.[2,4,15,16,48,55,56,58,59,64] Commercial thaw units are now on the market to keep the equipment warm and for thawing straws.

Straw cutter—a commercial snipper is available. Scissors or small animal toenail clippers work satisfactorily. The straw should be cut straight across regardless of the instrument.

Plastic sleeve—a thin disposable plastic covering for the arm to be inserted into the rectum. It is for protection of the inseminator and cow as well as for cleanliness. Many varieties are on the market. These are very useful in cases of pulling calves, retained afterbirth, and prolapsed vaginas as well.

Bucket—to contain water for lubricating the sleeve before insertion and cleaning up afterward.

Towels—for cleaning the vulva and drying later.

Record book—necessary forms for the particular insemination being conducted. This may vary from a simple notebook to forms required for registration purposes.

Procedure A stepwise procedure is presented for inseminating the cow.

Secure the cow—restrain her as little as possible.

Prepare thaw box—this may be done some time earlier, but the temperature should be checked and adjustments made if necessary. Carry a spare thermos of hot water.

Procure the semen—straws should be stored in goblets on canes in canisters in the semen tank. Raise the canister only high enough in the neck of the tank to identify the correct cane. Use forceps to lift a single straw from the goblet. Check identity and place the straw in the thaw box. The straw thaws very quickly; therefore it is very important that straws not be replaced once they have been lifted and exposed. Discard exposed straws or expect poor conception.

It is important to maintain the stored semen at the semen tank temperature; –194°C (–320°F) The neck of the tank is the area for removal as the temperature changes drastically in and above it (Fig. 12–12). Straws warm at a rate of 14 to 15°C per second, and exposure to room temperature for only 7 to 9 seconds damages the sperm.[51]

Thawing at 35 to 37°C (95 to 98°F) for 10 to 30 seconds is recommended when the semen is to be used immediately. Conditions dictate the method of thawing, and careful consideration should be given ambient temperature and time lapse from thawing until insemination. If over a few minutes elapse between thawing and insemination an ice water thaw (4°C, 39°F) is in order (Fig. 12–13).[4] The semen should then be used within 30 minutes. Under extremely cold conditions the semen may refreeze upon removal from the thaw container. This must be eliminated. Equipment must be warmed before inserting the straw and kept warm until insemination. Refrozen semen is no good.

Towels—place one or two in your pocket to be used shortly.

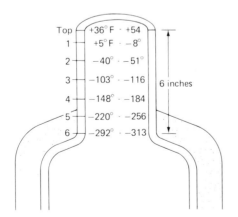

Figure 12-12 Temperature range in the neck of a semen tank. *(Adapted from Saacke.[59])*

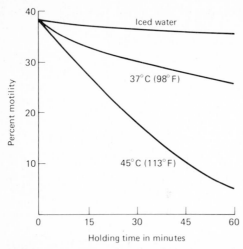

Figure 12-13 Effect of holding thawed semen in thaw water.

Dry the straw.

Insert straw into gun—the sealed part will extend beyond the sleeve of the gun.

Snip end of straw—this must be perpendicular to the length to insure proper seating in the sheath to prevent backflow and leakage.

Slip the sheath over gun—secure with retainer rings and make sure the straw is seated firmly in the tip (Fig. 12–14).

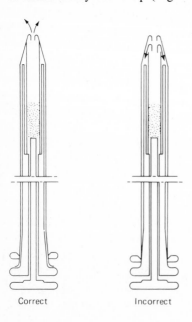

Correct   Incorrect

Figure 12-14 Seating the straw in the sheath to prevent leakage.

Place assembled gun between teeth—this acts as a third hand during the following steps.

Put on the plastic sleeve—either arm may be used for entering the rectum. Most people prefer to use the right arm because of better sensitivity in feeling the cervix and inseminating tube.

Insert protected arm into rectum—this is performed easily by moistening the sleeve with water and forming a wedge of the fingers pointed into the anus. The other hand grasps the tail and by pulling on the tail with one hand and pushing through the anus with the other the arm may be inserted about elbow deep. With downward pressure of the fingers, the cervix should be located. Its feel is firm and lumpy like a turkey neck.

Clean vulva with towel—discard the soiled towel and press a second towel into the ventral vulvar lips to afford easy entrance of the inseminating gun.

Insert inseminating gun—this is most easily accomplished by riding the tip along the roof of the vagina for about 15 cm (6 in) to bypass the suburethral diverticulum and urethral orifice on the floor. The tube may then be aimed for the os cervix (Fig. 12–15). During the insertion into the vagina, the hand in the rectum should grasp the cervix and stretch the vagina forward for easy passage of the tube. When the tube reaches the cervix, the cervix should be directed to align with the tube, and as a gentle forward pressure is exerted on the tube, the cervix should be gradually manipulated onto the tube. The annular folds will be discerned as the cervix moves onto the tube, and sometimes the tube will become lodged in a fold. This necessitates backing up slightly and seeking the central passageway to move forward. When the tube is felt to move free, it has penetrated the cervix and is moving into the body of the uterus. A finger over the cranial cervical opening may also feel this position of the tube. The tip of the tube should be in the cranial cervix at the time of insemination.

The site of insemination has been investigated, with comparisons made between the cervical os, mid-cervical, deep cervical, uterine body, and uterine horns. There is apparent improved conception when the semen is deposited in the anterior cervix and allowed to spill into the body of the uterus.[40,45] As much as 10 percent difference was noted in one trial favoring deep cervical deposition compared to the caudal cervix and 5 percent better than uterine insemination.

Insemination—this is accomplished by pushing the plunger to deposit the semen slowly. This is accomplished by counting slowly to 10 during expulsion. The tube is then slowly removed followed by the arm from the rectum.

Clitoral massage immediately following insemination has been advocated as a stimulus to improve conception. A 10-second massage in beef cattle gave an increase of 6 percent over no massage (58 vs. 52 percent)[53] in cows but no effect in heifers. Another trial using 3 seconds of massage gave a decrease of 1 percent (71 vs. 72

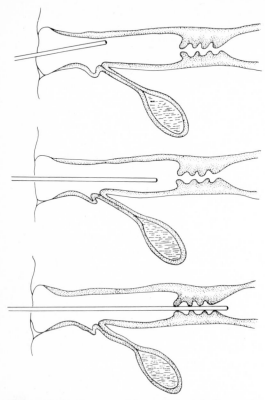

Figure 12-15   Passage of the catheter into the cervix.

percent) in a group of dairy cows.[44] It remains to be seen if there is truly a response to massage.

Discard disposable equipment—the sheath is bent to prevent further use and discarded in the sleeve along with the spent straw.

Record—a record of the cow, information from the straw, date, and any other remarks are recorded.

Cleanup—set everything back in order in preparation for the next insemination.

Release cow—if everything has gone properly you may expect a calf in about 283 days.

Rectocervical (Liquid) A plastic tube called a catheter 4 mm in diameter and 40 cm (16 in) long with an adapter and syringe is used to draw 1 ml of extended semen from the storage tube. The procedure then follows the rectocervical approach.

Rectocervical (Ampule) The ampule is slipped off the cane and placed in the thaw box. The recommended procedure is to thaw at 35 to 37°C (95 to 98°F) for 30 seconds. The semen is then treated as liquid semen. Thaw temperatures are subject to the same conditions as with straws.

Rectocervical (Pellet) The extender is prepared first. Usually this is an ampule of frozen extender that must be thawed and opened. Following extender preparation, the pellet is identified and retrieved from the storage tube. Again, be careful to lift the tube only high enough to gain access to the desired pellet. Place the pellet quickly in the extender for thawing and mixing. Thereafter, treat it as liquid semen.

Speculum (Mirror) Everything is prepared as with the rectocervical approach. A speculum of metal, plastic, or glass approximately 5 cm (2 in) in diameter and 32 cm (14 in) long is inserted into the vagina until it seats around the projecting cervix in the cranial vagina (Fig. 12–16). A headlamp or built-in light illuminates the os cervix, and the inseminating tube is directed into the cervix. It is usually stopped after about 2.5 cm (1 in) by the annular folds and the semen is deposited at this point in the same manner as described for the rectocervical approach. Conception is lower with this method than with rectocervical.

Vaginal This is used only as a last resort. The semen is deposited as near to the os cervix as possible by simply passing the inseminating tube into the cranial vagina without further direction and depositing the semen.

Uterine In rare instances semen is placed directly into the uterus. This may be accomplished by surgically exposing the uterus and injecting semen by means of a hypodermic syringe. An alternate nonsurgical method consists of passing a long hypodermic needle through the cranial dorsal wall of the vagina through the body

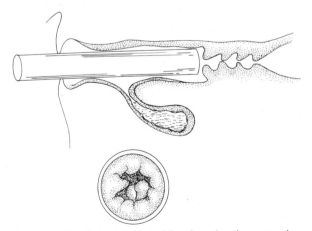

Figure 12-16   Speculum seated for observing the os cervix.

cavity and into the uterus that has been manipulated by a hand in the rectum. These methods are rarely used and are mostly related to research endeavors.

Comparisons have been made of rectocervical, vaginal, and speculum approaches, with the rectocervical approach being best in all trials. There is approximately a 10 percent improvement over the speculum and vaginal approaches. The speculum and vaginal approaches should be used only as a last resort.[72]

Insemination training schools are conducted by most of the major artificial breeding organizations. For names and addresses to contact, write to National Association of Animal Breeders, Inc., P. O. Box 1033, Columbia, MO 65201. These schools give basic anatomy as well as semen handling and insemination techniques with training to produce inseminator technicians.

An interesting retraining program is sometimes necessary when conception rates are not as high as expected. The fault many times lies in the point of semen deposition. The use of reproductive tracts and dyes placed in the catheter locate exactly the point of deposition, and accuracy improves very quickly. Improvement has increased from 2 to 8 percent.[19,25,34] Most inseminators place the semen farther into the tract than they think. As many as 50 percent of the inseminations may be in the horns of the uterus.

SHEEP

Artificial insemination in sheep is not widespread in the United States. The larger sheep herds are on rangeland that requires many acres for nutritional needs and therefore discourages concentration of stock. There is interest in the Midwest and East where smaller flocks are maintained, and certain advantages are apparent under these circumstances.

It has been suggested that sheep offer a means of increasing available animal products to man, and artificial insemination offers opportunities all over the world to supply this need.[39]

Semen volume that is used ranges from .05 ml to 1 ml, but the lower volumes are difficult to manipulate. Volumes of .5 to 1 ml are more desirable, containing 100 $\times$ 10^6 sperm per insemination. Conception rates have been reported from 55 to 79 with combinations such as this.[42,62]

Advantages

    1 Intensive use of outstanding sires is the main advantage.
    2 Genetic improvement is more rapid through proofs and selection of breeding stock.
    3 Crossbreeding is possible for improving less productive breeds.
    4 Reduced investment is made in rams and lowered maintenance.

Disadvantages

    1 Costs involved, particularly with labor, may be prohibitive.
    2 Inbreeding is undesirable.
    3 It requires skilled technicians and helpers.

Management

The ewe herd must be concentrated and checked for estrus twice daily or more. Teaser animals most frequently include aproned or vasectomized rams. A crayon secured in a chest harness is used to mark ewes in estrus.[52]

A synchronizing agent is available (Synchromate, G. D. Searle & Co.), if desired by the management. This is a pessary to be placed in the cranial vagina, and progestogen is released to maintain an anestrous condition until removal after 14 days. Conception rates are approximately 50 percent.

Facilities include an alley for crowding the ewes and a crate to hold the individual ewe for insemination. Various arrangements are described by Inskeep[29] and Emmens and Robinson.[20] Some designs include a rotating set of three crates that afford one for loading a ewe, one for breeding, and one for releasing (Fig. 12–17). It is estimated that 300 ewes may be inseminated per day with this arrangement.

Time of Insemination

The estrous period of the ewe lasts approximately 30 hours and ovulation occurs in the latter hours. Optimum time for insemination is mid-estrus or about 15 hours after the onset of estrus (Fig. 12–18).

Technique

The speculum method using liquid semen is most widespread for inseminating sheep. Some vaginal breeding has been conducted but the success has been poor.

Speculum. This method entails placing a speculum in the vagina and passing a catheter through it into the cervix as far as possible before depositing the semen.

Equipment

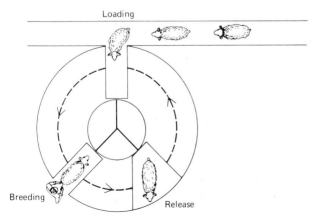

Figure 12-17 Breeding arrangement for ewes.

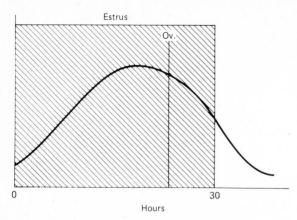

Figure 12-18 Optimum time for inseminating ewes.

Refrigeration—for storing the extended liquid semen at 5°C (39°F).

Speculum—a tube approximately 4 X 15 cm (1.5 X 6 in) for viewing the os cervix. It may be metal, plastic, or glass with or without a built-in light source. A duck-bill stainless steel speculum is preferred by some.

Light—headlamp or special light for illuminating the cervix.

Catheter—plastic inseminating tube 5 mm X 30 cm (.2 X 12 in) with adapter for syringe. Multiple dose units are used in some instances.

Syringe—2 ml plastic syringe or polybulb.

Lubricant—KY jelly or other sterile nontoxic substance.

Record book—to record breeding and other pertinent remarks.

Procedure

Secure ewe—either by someone holding the ewe or using a stanchion or crate for restraint.

Prepare semen—assemble catheter and syringe and draw .5 ml of extended semen into the catheter. Hold prepared tube in the teeth.

Lubricate speculum—only a small amount.

Insert speculum—a slight twisting assists in insertion all the way to cervix.

Locate os cervix—direct the light into the speculum and seat the speculum so the os cervix is in the center.

Inseminate—pass the tube through the speculum into the cervix as far as possible. This is usually to the first annular fold. Slowly depress the plunger on the syringe to deposit the semen. Remove the speculum and catheter.

Cleanup—discard disposable catheter, keep syringe and speculum for cleaning and later use.

Record—write down information on time, inseminator, identification of dam and sire, and other information for future use.

Release ewe—if all has gone well a lamb should be born in approximately 150 days.

Ampules and Pellets

Ampules The ampule is removed from the liquid nitrogen storage and placed in a thaw box at 5°C (41°F) for thawing. Once it is thawed, the procedure is the same as for liquid semen.

Pellets The extender is prepared either fresh or thawed. The pellets are removed from the semen tank and added to the extender for thawing. The procedure then is the same as for liquid semen.

Conception with frozen semen is not as good as that obtained with liquid semen. Research is continuing on improving conception through improved processing methods.

SOW

Artificial insemination of swine has been practiced on an experimental basis for many years in the United States. In 1971, only about 5000 sows and gilts were artificially inseminated.[21] The future of the program depends more on freezing and storage of semen than any other factor.

Conception rates have been acceptable, with some trials showing equal conception from AI and natural service and even better numbers of pigs per litter. Conception rates of 50 to 90 percent have been reported.[21,71] Commercial studies have shown litter sizes of 9.4 for sows and 8.45 for gilts following AI.[30]

Advantages[65,66]

1 Extension of superior sires. Everyone wants to breed to the outstanding boars. Between 4 and 10 times as many sows can be bred to a single boar.
2 Economical. Greater use of the boar makes the price more reasonable.
3 Disease control.
4 Use of heavier boars on small females. Injury is eliminated.
5 Outside boars may be utilized. Semen can be shipped great distances.
6 Process is relatively simple and easy to learn.

Disadvantages

1 Heat detection. Manager must be trained to detect females in estrus. Constant observation is important.
2 Trained inseminator. Experience is important.
3 Equipment. Special items are required.
4 Labor is increased.
5 Semen storage. Most is now used as liquid semen with storage life of about 48 hours.
6 Number of inseminations per ejaculate are small (4 to 10).

Management

The sow herd must be observed frequently for signs of estrus. Twice a day the sows should be observed for the various symptoms, and most herdsmen will use the swollen vulva as the best indicator, followed by pressure on the rump and loin for positive identification. It is usually easiest to separate the sow from the herd for insemination.

Chutes are usually unnecessary, as the sow will stand for insemination. Recordings have been made of boars grunting that assist in maintaining a quiet condition during insemination. If the sow is nervous, she may be quieted by massaging the clitoris and mammary.[27]

Concentrations of semen ranging from 2 to 50×10^9 sperm per insemination have given good results when inseminated properly.[1,18,37,41] Volume is also important, with ranges from 20 to 100 ml being satisfactory.

Time of Insemination

The sow is in estrus for approximately 2 days. Ovulation occurs in the latter portion of this time, and the best time for inseminating is the beginning of the second day or about 30 hours after beginning of estrus[27,65] (Fig. 12–19).

The season of the year is important in breeding swine. During the hot summer

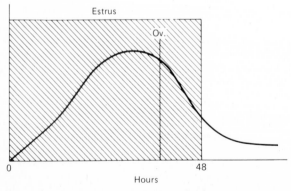

Figure 12-19 Optimum time for inseminating sows.

months the sow will stay in estrus a shorter period of time, and the effect on time of ovulation is unknown. If the herdsman waits until the second day during this time he may find it necessary to restrain the sow and have difficulty inseminating her.

Technique

Liquid semen is commonly used to inseminate swine, and the vaginocervical method is by far the most popular one.

Vaginocervical. This procedure is accomplished by inserting the inseminating tube through the vagina into the cervix where the semen is deposited.

Equipment

Refrigerator—for storage of semen if held over one day for use.

Inseminating tube—this may be a regular plastic catheter as used in cattle with a terminal 1 cm (.4 in) bent at a 45° angle. This angle may be made by heating the catheter and gently bending the warm plastic. This bend assists in penetrating the cervix among the raised areas and depressions. A commercial inseminating tube resembling the penis of the boar with a corkscrew tip, called the hog-breeding spirette, is available and works very well. It must be sterilized between use, while the plastic catheter is disposable.

Syringe—a normal 50 ml plastic syringe works fine. A short length of plastic tubing, 10 cm (4 in) long, affords flexibility during insemination. A plastic bottle of at least 50 ml capacity may be used, with an adapter to the catheter, instead of the syringe.

Record book—for information concerning the insemination.

Procedure

Isolate sow or gilt—this is needed only if the other females become a nuisance. The sow in estrus will usually stand wherever she is for breeding. If she will not stand, place her in a crate or some other restricted area.

Obtain semen—identify the container and if in question about quality, make a quick microscopic check.

Assemble inseminating tube—put the syringe, adapter, and tube together and draw up 50 ml of semen into the syringe.

Inseminate—detach inseminating tube and insert the bent end into the vagina. Push it forward with the tip up until it strikes a point of resistance. This will be the cervix. The vagina tapers into the restricted cervix. A slight turning of the catheter counterclockwise should allow passage of the catheter until it passes free into the body of the uterus. The catheter should be retracted to the cervical portion and the syringe attached (Fig. 12–20). The semen should be slowly expelled into the body of the uterus and the tube gently removed. Proper seating of the tube and deposition of the semen should result in an absence of backflow from the vagina.

Discard disposables—break the catheter to eliminate reuse and retain the syringe and tubing for cleaning and reuse.

Record—make an entry regarding the date, identification of the sow and boar, and any other information needed.

Release sow—if she has been restrained. With success she should have 8 to 10 piglets in about 113 days.

Pellets The extender is prepared fresh or thawed and the pellets retrieved from the semen tank. The required number of pellets to make up 2 to 5 $\times$ 10^9 live sperm is thawed and extended to 20 to 50 ml for insemination. From this point on, the procedure is the same as for liquid semen.

Surgical insemination of frozen semen directly into the uterus has resulted in 50 percent conception when 8 $\times$ 10^6 motile sperm in .10 ml volume was used.[61] Although this is not practical, it does indicate the possibilities of lower concentrations and volumes under refined techniques.

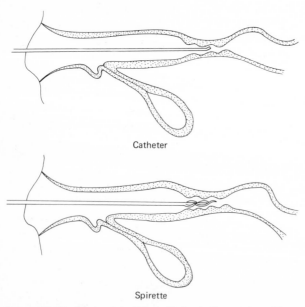

Catheter

Spirette

Figure 12-20 Placement of the catheter in the sow's cervix.

MARE

Because of the extended estrous period in the mare and the practice of breeding multiple times during estrus, artificial insemination is used primarily to conserve the stallion. The major difficulty in horse breeding is long-term storage of semen. When this has been perfected, numbers of mares bred artificially should increase rapidly.

Horses are relatively easy to breed artificially because of size and anatomical structures, and the practice dates back almost to the beginning of AI.

Conception in the mare is as good or better than natural service when AI is used. One reason it is so good is that the selection of stock is more critical. The condition of the mare's reproductive system is very important to conception. Under good management, conception rates should be 75 to 90 percent.[11,63]

Number of sperm per insemination is still undecided, but 100 to 500 $\times$ 10[6] appears to give good results.[3,50] and there seems to be little need for the 1 $\times$ 10[9] suggested by Berliner in 1968.[8]

Advantages

1 Outstanding performing sires are in great demand and their number of breedings is limited. AI partially removes that restriction.
2 Distance is overcome by shipping semen.
3 Danger of the stallion is eliminated.
4 Disease is more easily controlled.

Disadvantages

1 Fear of reduced breeding fees for ordinary stallion owners.
2 Registration restrictions by purebred associations.
3 Personnel must be trained for inseminating.

Management

The mares to be inseminated should be selected on the basis of their past performance and the desired mating to a particular stallion. They should be in a growing, healthy condition when the season of breeding begins.

Estrus should be checked twice a day and palpation of ovaries practiced where a heavy demand is placed on a particular stallion.

Facilities should be so arranged that the mares may be separated easily without undue excitement. Passing the mares through chutes, alleyways, and the breeding stall before estrus will accustom them to the area and alleviate difficulties when they come in for breeding.

Breeding restrictions related to registration in the various breed associations should be studied carefully and adhered to strictly. A "second cover" by AI as indicated in some associations means that there is a natural cover by the stallion followed immediately by artificial insemination with semen from the same stallion.

Restraining the mare for breeding may be accomplished in several ways. A breeding chute constructed of heavy lumber should be restrictive to side movement as well as forward and backward movement (Fig. 12–21). A solid tailgate to within 15 cm (6 in) of the vulva will restrict kicking. One side and the front should also be constructed as gates to release the mare.

Hobbles work very well on most mares. The best ones are soft cotton ropes about 2 cm (.75 in) in diameter. A meter (3 ft) loop is tied in the middle of a 12 m (40 ft) length of rope to slip over the mare's neck (Fig. 12–22). The two ends are passed through the front legs and one end passed around each of the rear pasterns, over the rope and back around the pastern to lock a double loop around it to prevent slipping. The end is then twisted around the rope and secured at the shoulder to the neck loop. The hobbles should be tight enough to prevent kicking but loose enough to allow the mare to stand without being uneasy.

Leather hobbles with chains and ropes are available, but some skill is necessary to manipulate them, which is not necessary with the method described here.

The tail should be wrapped with gauze, elastic bandage, or some fabric to prevent the long hairs from getting in the way of the inseminator. The tail is pulled to one side and secured.

Nervous mares may require twitching. A twitch is an instrument such as an axe handle with a loop of rope or chain passed through a hole in one end. The loop is passed over the upper lip of the mare and twisted to squeeze and control movement of the mare (Fig. 12–23). The ear may also be twitched with similar control response.

Do not attempt to breed a mare that is not properly restrained!

Figure 12-21 Breeding chute for the mare.

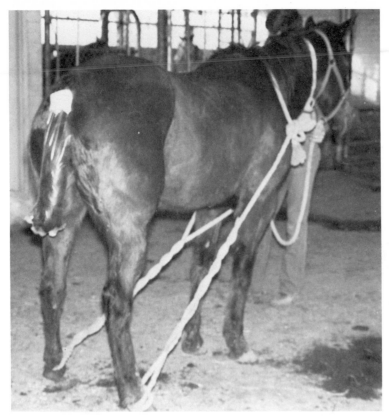

Figure 12-22 A hobbled mare prepared for breeding.

Time of Insemination

The estrous period of the mare is much longer than the other domestic animals, and it may seem somewhat confusing when trying to ascertain the optimum time for breeding to obtain maximum conception. Most horse breeders use a program consisting of breeding the mare every other day beginning 2 days after the first observed signs until she goes out of estrus. This usually means breeding on days 3, 5, and sometimes 7. Since ovulation occurs in the latter stages of estrus, this method is very successful. The difficulty lies in the number of matings per conception required of a stallion in high demand. He may exhaust his semen supply, and conception rates consequently decrease.

Some breeders have resorted to palpation of the ovaries per rectum and determining the maturation of the follicle and estimated time of ovulation. The mare is bred when the follicle softens, and ovulation usually occurs within 24 hours. Palpation of the ovaries to determine ovulation on an every-other-day frequency allows rebreeding if the follicle is still present. Mid to late estrus is the recommended time for inseminating (Fig. 12–24).

Figure 12-23 A twitch placed on a mare's upper lip for control.

Prostaglandins have been cleared for use in horses and are advantageous particularly where it is difficult to check estrus. Injections of $PGF_2\alpha$ or an analogue result in estrus in 3 to 6 days with conception rates comparable to normal insemination.[5,10,74]

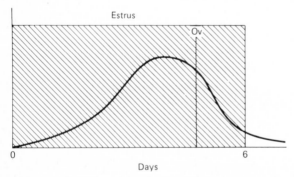

Figure 12-24 Optimum time for inseminating mares.

Technique

The most popular and successful inseminating techniques in horses is the vaginocer-

Figure 12-25 Vaginocervical approach for inseminating the mare.

vical approach. The speculum, rectocervical, and capsule methods are also used to a limited extent.

Vaginocervical-catheter. This method consists of inserting an arm into the vagina and locating the os cervix followed by passing a catheter alongside the arm into the cervix and depositing the semen at that point (Fig. 12–25).

Equipment

Refrigerator—a standard home refrigerator to maintain the extended semen at 5°C (41°F).

Catheter—horse-inseminating plastic tube 5 mm (.2 in) × 45 cm (18 in) with adapter for syringe.

Syringe—50 ml plastic syringe that may be sterilized.

Plastic sleeves—thin disposable covering for the arm and hand.

KY jelly—sterile nontoxic lubricant for inserting the arm without friction.

Bucket and water—for washing vulva.

Towels—to dry vulva.

Record book—information and registration forms that are required.

Procedure

Secure mare—either by hobbles or in a restrictive stall.

Wash vulvar area—cleanse the area thoroughly to eliminate carrying foreign material into the vagina.

Put on plastic sleeve

Prepare semen—identify the semen and draw 20 to 30 ml into the syringe. Have assistant hold the tube or hold it in your teeth.

Lubricate sleeve—put a small amount of KY jelly on the sleeve.

Insert arm into vagina—move to the cranial vagina and locate the protruding os cervix. Place the index finger in the cervical opening.

Insert inseminating tube—alongside the arm and guide the tip of the tube into the cervix as the index finger is removed. Insert the tube approximately 5 cm (2 in) and deposit the semen slowly by exerting pressure on the syringe. Following deposition of semen, remove the arm and tube.

Discard disposable equipment—break the catheter and discard tube and sleeve. Keep syringe for cleaning and later use.

Cleanup—use towels to wipe vulva dry and pick up debri so that things are in order for the next insemination.

Record—write down identification of mare, stallion, inseminator, and other pertinent information.

Release mare—with everything going properly a foal should be expected in about 330 days.

Vaginocervical-Capsule Gelatin capsules may be used as containers of the extended semen. These capsules usually contain 10 to 20 ml of semen and are placed in a gloved hand and carried through the vagina to the mouth of the cervix. They are then manipulated by the fingers and pushed into the cervix by the index finger. This is an acceptable method resulting in good conception. The main difficulty lies in filling the capsules and completing the insemination before the capsules melt in the warm environment of the vagina and cervix releasing the semen prematurely from the container.

Speculum A tube of metal, plastic, or glass may be inserted into the vagina to expose the os cervix. The catheter is then guided into the cervix and semen deposited in the mid or cranial cervix. The speculum method has been criticized by some because of the exposure of the vagina and cervix to debri in the air of the breeding area that may contaminate the organs and be a detriment to sperm livability and subsequent fertilization. This indicates the need for clean conditions during insemination regardless of the method.

Frozen Semen Ampuled frozen semen is thawed similar to bull semen and drawn into the catheter for use as liquid semen thereafter. Capsules may be used.

WOMAN

Artificial insemination in the human is complicated by social and psychological factors not confronted in domestic animals. Therefore, certain criteria must be considered in determining the feasibility of AI.[35]

Artificial insemination of a woman with her husband's semen should result due to restrictions such as:

  1 Husband has very low sperm concentration or lacks motility or good morphology, or
  2 Anatomical anomalies are present that prevent union of the sperm and egg. This may be in either of the couple.

Insemination with a donor's semen would be proposed if:

1 The husband is sterile,
2 The husband has genetic characteristics that will produce abnormalities, or
3 Rh factors are not compatible.

Insemination techniques are several and rather simple.

  1 Cervicovaginal entails deposition of semen by means of a speculum and catheter into the cervix and on the surface of the cranial vagina and cervix.
  2 Intravaginal deposition is simply introducing the semen into the vaginal vault.
  3 Intracervical is used to bypass anatomical difficulties.
  4 Intrauterine is used when the vaginal and cervical environment are detrimental to sperm viability.

There is no exacting method of determine the time of ovulation; therefore, the best estimate possible is made and several inseminations conducted around that period. In one study, an average of 2.3 inseminations per month resulted in conception. One hundred fifty-six pregnancies were reported from 158 women with 142 healthy children born.[35]

WHAT DID YOU LEARN?

1   Why do you think Spallanzani chose the dog to inseminate artificially?
2   Discuss four advantages of artificial insemination in the bovine.
3   Diagram a corral and working chutes for inseminating cattle.
4   How does a chin-ball marker work?
5   What precautions must be taken when using bull calves for estrous detection?
6   What is nymphomania? What causes it?
7   What is a "Gomer" bull?
8   What system would you use for checking estrus in a herd of beef cows?
9   What is the A.M.-P.M. inseminating rule?
10 Briefly describe the rectocervical approach for inseminating cows.
11 What is the best temperature to thaw frozen semen to be used immediately?
12 Why is sheep artificial insemination so poorly accepted in the U.S.?
13 What conception rates can be expected from AI in sheep?
14 Describe the insemination of a sow.
15 Describe one method of restraint for mares during insemination.
16 Where is semen deposited when inseminating the mare?
17 What is a speculum? Describe one.

REFERENCES

1   Aamdal, J. 1964. Artificial insemination in the pig. *Proc. 5th Int. Congr. on Anim. Reprod. and A.I.* 3:147–177.
2   Aamdal, J. and K. Andersen. 1968. Fast thawing of bull semen frozen in straws. *Proc. 6th Int. Congr. on Anim. Reprod. and A.I.* Pp. 973–976.
3   Allen, W. R., J. M. Bowen, C. J. Frank, L. B. Jeffcott, and P. D. Rossdale. 1976. The current position of A.I. in horse breeding. *Equine Vet. J.* 8:72–74.
4   American Breeders Service. 1977. Recommended thawing procedures. Mimeo, American Breeders Service, DeForest, Wisc.
5   Averkin, M. A. and R. Schiltz. 1976. Breeding efficiency in mares. *Vet. Med./Small Anim. Clinician* 71:1616–1623.
6   Beerwinkle, L. G. 1974. Heat detection programs and techniques. *Proc. 8th Conf. on A.I. of Beef Cattle,* Denver, Colo. Pp. 24–29.
7   Belling, T. H., Jr. 1961. Preparation of a teaser bull for use in a beef cattle artificial insemination program. *J.A.V.M.A.* 138:670–672.
8   Berliner, V. 1968. Horses and jackstock. In E. J. Perry, ed. *The Artificial Insemination of Farm Animals.* Rutgers Univ. Press, Rutgers, N.J. Pp. 196–214.
9   Bieberly, B. F., Jr. and S. Bieberly. 1973. A simple method for preparing teaser bulls. *Vet. Med./Small Anim. Clinician* 68:1086.
10 Booth, L. C., W. D. Oxender, R. H. Douglas, and S. L. Woodley. 1977. Effects of PGF$_2\alpha$ and GnRH on ovulation in mares. *Proc. Amer. Soc. Anim. Sci. 1977 Mtg. Abstr. 350A.* p. 138.
11 Bowen, J. M. 1969. Artificial insemination in the horse. *Equine Vet. J.* 1:98–108.
12 Boyd, H. and P. G. Hignett. 1968. A device for the detection of oestrus in cattle. *Vet. Rec.* 83:2–3.

13 Broadway, J. L. 1973. Optimum time for artificial insemination of the bovine species at various times of the year. M.S. thesis, Texas A&M Univ., College Station.

14 Clews, W. 1975. Gomer bull management and experiences. *Proc. 9th Conf. on A.I. of Beef Cattle.* Pp. 40–42.

15 Curtiss Breeding Service. 1977. The storage and handling of frozen semen. Mimeo, Curtiss Breeding Service, G. D. Searle Agric. Inc., Cary, Ill.

16 D'Abreu, T. T. Olar, W. E. Berndtson, and B. W. Pickett. 1977. Effect of rate of warming, after thawing, on bovine spermatozoa thawed at different rates in French straws. *Proc. Amer. Soc. Anim. Sci. 1977 Mtg. Abstr. 370.* P. 147.

17 Donaldson, L. E. 1968. The efficiency of several methods for detecting oestrus in cattle. *Australian Vet. J.* 44:496–498.

18 Dziuk, P. J. and G. Henshaw. 1958. Fertility of boar semen artificially inseminated following in vitro storage. *J. Anim. Sci.* 17:554–558.

19 Elgersma, A. et al. 1972. Some new aspects of dye inseminations. *Proc. 7th Int. Congr. on Anim. Reprod. and A.I.* 2:1455–1462.

20 Emmens, C. W. and T. J. Robinson. 1962. Artificial insemination in sheep. In J. P. Maule, ed. *The Semen of Animals and Artificial Insemination.* Commonwealth Agri. Bureau, Edinburgh, pp. 205–251.

21 Erickson, W. E. 1974. Update on swine A.I. *Proc. 5th Tech. Conf. on A.I. and Reprod.* Pp. 82–84.

22 Frazer, J. W. 1973. Phallectomy: Procedure for preparing marker bulls for artificial insemination of beef cows. *Vet. Med./Small Anim. Clinician* 68:863–870,

23 Garrett, W. R. 1977. Effect of seasonal variations and time of insemination on reproduction in Brahman heifers. M.S. thesis, Texas A&M Univ., College Station.

24 Gloyd, J. S., H. D. Schroeder, and K. W. Ritthaler. 1972. Preparation of detector bulls by penile retraction and fixation. In *Proc. 5th Ann. Convention, American Association of Bovine Practitioners,* Milwaukee, Wisc.

25 Graham, E. F. 1966. The use of a dye indicator for testing, training and evaluating technicians in artificial insemination. *Proc. 1st Tech. Conf. on Reprod. and A.I., NAAB.* Pp. 57–60.

26 Hall, J. J., C. Branton, and E. J. Stone. 1959. Estrus, estrous cycles, ovulation time, time of service, and fertility of dairy cattle in Louisiana. *J. Dairy Sci.* 42:1086–1093.

27 Hess, E. A., T. M. Ludwick, and H. S. Teague. 1960. Artificial insemination of swine. *Ohio Agr. Exp. Sta. Res. Circ. 90.* Pp. 8–14.

28 Hudson, R. S. 1972. Surgical preparation of heat detector bulls. Symposium on Reproduction in Cattle and Horses. American Vet. Soc. for Study of Breeding Soundness (AUSSBS). American College of Theriogenology. Mimeo.

29 Inskeep, E. K. 1974. Artificial insemination and preservation of ram semen. In *Artificial Insemination in Sheep, West Va. Univ. Agr. Exp. Sta. Bull. 629.* Pp. 5–28.

30 Jackson, W. P., V. B. Mayrose, H. W. Jones, and C. W. Foley. 1967. Artificial insemination and estrous synchronization in swine. Cooperative Extension Service, Purdue Univ., Lafayette, Ind. AS-373.

31 Jochle, W., T. Jimenez, H. Esparza, and M. A. Hidalgo. 1973. Preparation of teaser bulls, rams, and boars by penis and prepuce deviation. *Vet. Med./Small Anim. Clinician* 68:395–400.

32 Johari, M. P. and P. C. Gangwar. 1961. The technique of vasectomy (vasoligation) in cattle and buffaloes. *Brit. Vet. J.* 117:366–367.

33 Kiddy, C. A., D. S. Mitchell, D. J. Bolt, and H. W. Hawk. 1977. Use of trained dogs

to detect estrous-related odors from cows. *Amer. Soc. Anim. Sci. 1977 Mtg. Abstr. 443.* Pp. 176–177.

34   King, G. J. and J. W. Macpherson. 1965. Observations on retraining of artificial insemination technicians and its importance in maintaining efficiency. *Can. Vet. J.* 6:83–85.

35   Langer, G., E. Lemberg, and M. Sharf. 1969. Artificial insemination: A study of 156 successful cases. *Int. J. Fert.* 14:232–240.

36   Larson, L. L. 1973. Memo on Pen-O-Block. American Breeders Service, DeForest, Wisc.

37   Licon, M. A. 1971. Effect of age and concentration of semen on conception rate and litter size in swine. M.S. thesis, Texas A&M Univ., College Station.

38   Lindner, E. R. and J. D. Samuelson. 1972. Preparation of teaser bulls by penectomy using the method described by Straub and Kendrick. In *Proc. 5th Ann. Convention, American Association of Bovine Practitioners,* Milwaukee, Wisc.

39   Lunca, N. 1964. Artificial insemination in sheep and goats on the international plane. *Proc. 5th Int. Congr. on Anim. Reprod. and A.I.* 3:118–119.

40   MacPherson, J. W. 1968. Semen placement effects on fertility in bovines. *J. Dairy Sci.* 51:807–808.

41   ———. 1970. A system for artificial insemination of swine. *Proc. 3rd Tech. Conf. on A.I. and Reprod.* Pp. 75–78.

42   Martin, I. C. A. and P. F. Watson. 1976. Artificial insemination of sheep: Effects on fertility of number of spermatozoa inseminated and of storage of diluted semen for up to 18 hours at 5°C. *Therio.* 5:29–35.

43   Massey, Joe. 1974. Determination of ovulation from the onset of estrus in beef cows. M.S. thesis, Texas A&M Univ., College Station.

44   McDonnell, W. E., L. A. Edgerton, D. Olds, and F. D. Harned. 1977. Clitoral stimulation and non-return rate in the bovine. *J. Dairy Sci. Suppl.* 1:85. (Abstr.)

45   Moller, K., K. L. Macmillan, and P. Shannon. 1972. Site of insemination and subsequent non-return rates in cows. *Proc. 7th Int. Congr. on Anim. Reprod. and A.I.* 2:1437–1439.

46   Nishikawa, Y. 1964. History and development of artificial insemination in the world. *Proc. 5th Int. Congr. on Anim. Reprod. and A.I.* 7:162–259.

47   Oehme, F. W. 1968. Resection of bovine epididymis—a procedure for preparing teaser bulls and securing increased weight gain in male feeder cattle. *Vet. Med./Small Anim. Clinician* 63:603–606.

48   Olar, T. T., W. C. Becker, and P. L. Senger. 1977. Effect of thawing rate and cold post-thaw temperatures on bovine semen packaged in glass ampules. *J. Anim. Sci.* 44:95–101.

49   Perry, E. J. 1968. *The Artificial Insemination of Farm Animals.* 4th ed. Rutgers Univ. Press, Rutgers, N.J.

50   Pickett, B. W., D. G. Back, L. D. Burwash, and J. L. Voss. 1974. The effect of extenders, spermatozoal numbers and rectal palpation on equine fertility. *Proc. 5th Tech. Conf. on A.I. and Reprod.* Pp. 47–58.

51   Piper, A. 1974. Development and experience with the U.S. straw. *Proc. 5th Tech. Conf. on A.I. and Reprod.* Pp. 88–90.

52   Radford, H. M., R. H. Watson, and G. F. Wood. 1960. A crayon and associated harness for the detection of mating under field conditions. *Australian Vet. J.* 36:57–66.

53   Randel, R. D., R. E. Short, D. S. Christensen, and R. A. Bellows. 1975. Effect of clitoral massage after artificial insemination on conception in the bovine. *J. Anim. Sci.* 40:1119–1123.

54   Roche, J. F. 1974. Attempts to determine the optimal time of artificial insemination to heifers. *J. Reprod. Fert.* 41:223–225.

55 Robbins, R. K., R. G. Saacke, and P. T. Chandler. 1976. Influence of freeze rate, thaw rate and glycerol level on acrosomal retention and survival of bovine spermatozoa frozen in French straws. *J. Anim. Sci.* 42:145–154.

56 Rodriquez, O. L., W. E. Berndtson, B. D. Ennen, and B. W. Pickett. 1975. Effect of rates of freezing, thawing and level of glycerol on the survival of bovine spermatozoa in straws. *J. Anim. Sci.* 41:129–136.

57 Royes, B. A. P. and W. S. Bivin. 1973. Surgical displacement of the penis in the bull. *J.A.V.M.A.* 163:56–57.

58 Rugg, C. D., W. E. Berndtson, R. G. Mortimer, and B. W. Pickett. 1977. Effect of thawing procedures on fertility of bovine spermatozoa frozen in .25-ml straws. *J. Anim. Sci.* 44:266–270.

59 Saacke, R. G. 1974. Concepts in semen packaging and use. *Proc. 8th Conf. on A.I. in Beef Cattle.* Pp. 11–17.

60 Saacke, R. G., R. K. Robbins, and P. T. Chandler. 1974. Effect of freeze rate, thaw rate and glycerol level on bovine sperm frozen in straws. *Proc. 5th Tech. Conf. on A.I. and Reprod.* Pp. 41–46.

61 Salamon, S. and D. Visser. 1974. Fertility after surgical insemination with frozen boar semen. *Australian J. Biol. Sci.* 27:499–504.

62 Schindler, H. and D. Amir. 1973. The conception rate of ewes in relation to sperm dose and time of insemination. *J. Reprod. Fert.* 34:191–196.

63 Self, Leon C. February 1970. A comparison of different breeding methods. *The Quarter Horse J.* Pp. 34–56.

64 Senger, P. L., W. C. Becker, and J. K. Hillers. 1976. Effect of thawing rate and post-thaw temperature on motility and acrosomal maintenance in bovine semen frozen in plastic straws. *J. Anim. Sci.* 42:932–936.

65 Shelby, D. R. 1977. On-the-farm artificial insemination of swine. Mimeo, South Dakota State Univ., Brookings.

66 Singleton, W. L. 1976. Artificial insemination of swine. Mimeo, Purdue Univ., Lafayette, Ind.

67 Smith, A. P. 1967. Epididymal transection for sterilizing bulls. *J.A.V.M.A.* 150:633.

68 Sorensen, A. M., Jr. 1975. Estrous detection in cattle. *Southwestern Vet.* 28:127–134.

69 Stevenson, J. S. and J. H. Britt. 1977. Detection of estrus by three methods in Holstein cows. *J. Dairy Sci. Suppl.* 1:85–86. (Abstr.)

70 Straub, O. C. and J. W. Kendrick. 1965. Preparation of teaser bulls by penectomy. *J.A.V.M.A.* 147:373–376.

71 Stratman, F. W. and H. L. Self. 1962. Fertility studies with naturally mated or artificially inseminated sows. *J. Anim. Sci.* 21:647–650.

72 Sullivan, J. J., D. E. Bartlett, F. I. Elliott, J. R. Brouwer, and F. B. Kloch. 1972. A comparison of recto-vaginal, vaginal, and speculum approaches for insemination of cows and heifers. *A.I. Digest* 20:6–8, 20.

73 Trimberger, G. W. 1944. Conception rate in dairy cattle by artificial insemination at various intervals before and after ovulation. *J. Dairy Sci.* 27:659.

74 Wallace, R. A., E. L. Squires, J. L. Voss, B. W. Pickett, and R. K. Shideler. Appointment breeding in mares using prostaglandin $F_2\alpha$, human chorionic gonadotropin and gonadotropin releasing hormone. *Proc. Amer. Soc. Anim. Sci. 1977 Abstr. 534.* P. 214.

75 Weissenberg, Y. and R. Cohen. 1971. The preparation of teaser bulls by surgical deflection of the penis. *Refuah Veterinarith* 28:38–41.

76 Williamson, N. B., R. S. Morris, D. C. Blood, and C. M. Cannon. 1972. A study of

oestrus behaviour and oestrus detection methods in a large commercial dairy herd. I. The relative efficiency of methods of oestrus detection. *Vet. Rec.* 91:50–57.

77   Williamson, N. B., R. S. Morris, D. C. Blood, C. M. Cannon, and P. J. Wright. 1972. A study of oestrous behaviour and oestrus detection methods in a large commercial dairy herd. II. Oestrus signs and behaviour patterns. *Vet. Rec.* 91:58–62.

Fertilization and Embryo Transfer

When you complete this chapter you should be able to:

- Describe the mechanisms involved in sperm and ovum transport,
- Enumerate in order the barriers to sperm penetration of the ovum,
- Discuss the advantages and disadvantages of embryo transfer, particularly for the bovine,
- Understand the importance of synchronization, condition, superovulation, and insemination to embryo transfer,
- Describe in outline form embryo transfer in any domestic species,
- Distinguish between "good" and "bad" eggs, and
- Appreciate some of the problems of and need for continued research on embryo transfer.

GAMETE TRANSPORT

Movement of the ovum from the point of ovulation and of the sperm from the point of deposition is a function of the various segments of the reproductive tract studied thus far. The sperm is motile and therefore travels partly of its own ability. The ovum is nonmotile and must depend upon other anatomical structures for passage.

Ovulation occurs in the upper oviduct, which means that the sperm must travel a great distance compared to the ovum (Fig. 13–1).

Remember that the sperm cell is about $60\,\mu$m long and has a fertile life of 24 to 48 hours. The ovum is about 110 μm in diameter and lives only 6 to 24 hours. Timing of breeding is therefore very important to guarantee the union of two viable gametes.

Sperm Deposition and Transport

The sperm is ejaculated as a mature cell. The bull, ram, and man spray sperm on the face of the cervix and the cranial vagina. Volume is low and concentration is high for the bull and ram (Fig. 13–2). The boar's penis is seated in the cervix, and sperm flow into and through the cervix and into the uterus in large quantities of low concentration. The uterus of the sow is filled with sperm, accessory fluids, and coagulum following copulation distending the uterus markedly.[17,47] The stallion ejaculates into the open cervix and semen flows into the uterus. A large volume with low concentration is ejaculated.

The sperm pass into the cervix by their own movement as they are oriented

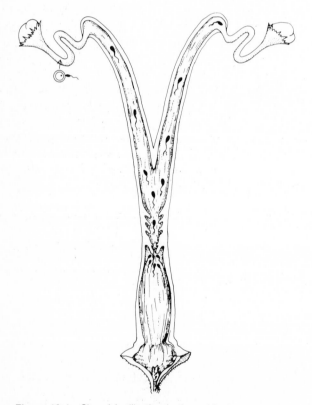

Figure 13-1 Site of fertilization in the oviduct.

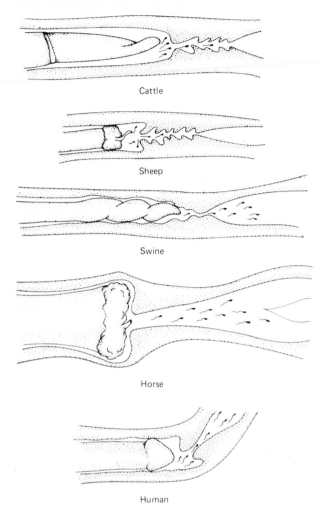

Cattle

Sheep

Swine

Horse

Human

Figure 13-2 Site of ejaculation.

against the flow of mucus from the cervix. Most of the cells remain in the vagina, with only a small proportion reaching the site of fertilization. Approximately 70 percent of the sperm stay in the vagina of the cow, with 30 percent entering the cervix. Most of these remain, as only about 10 percent reach the uterus and less than 1 percent reach each oviduct. Most of the sperm are in the vagina and cervix 1 hour after insemination at the os cervix, with few in the oviduct. The greatest number are found in the oviduct 8 hours after insemination, with some decrease following.[22] Estimates of the number of sperm reaching the site of fertilization range from 4200 to 27,500[14] (Table 13-1). As the sperm enter the cervix the live sperm orient themselves into the current of thin mucus during estrus. How the sperm traverse the cervix is still unknown. Many find their way into the numerous crypts of the folds

Table 13-1 The Ejaculate and Its Transport to the Site of Fertilization

Species	Site of deposition	Time from ejaculation to presence in oviduct	No. sperm reaching site of fertilization
Cattle	Vagina	12–13 min	4,200–27,500
Sheep	Vagina	8 min	600–5,000
Swine	Cervix and uterus	30 min	Few
Horses	Cervix and uterus	—	—
Human	Vagina	30 min	Few

and remain there until released or phagocytized[44] (Fig. 13–3). The cilia of the cervical epithelium is beating toward the vagina, so no assistance is available here for movement.

Once the sperm pass the cervix and enter the uterus, the myometrium becomes the major factor in transport. The contractions are numerous during estrus as estrogen activates the myometrium. The fluids and sperm are churned and caused to flow toward the oviduct.[107] Many sperm are lost along the way as they penetrate the endometrial glands and are phagocytized by leucocytes in the lumen. The movement of sperm through the uterus far exceeds the actual spermatozoon's ability to swim. It is interesting to note that 1 day before estrus and 1 day after estrus the direction of contractions and flow is reversed.[107] It is during the sojourn in the uterus that capacitation takes place in some species.

Capacitation This term applies to changes in the sperm that make it capable of fertilization. Initial research was conducted concurrently by Chang [18] and Austin[4] in rats and rabbits where it was found that sperm must remain in the female reproductive tract for several hours before it was capable of fertilizing the ovum.

Capacitation time, and even method, differ between species. Although we know

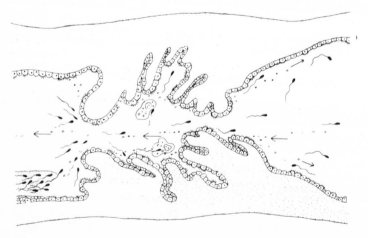

Figure 13-3 Sperm moving against the mucous current of the cervix and leucocytes phagocytizing sperm.

fertilization is highest following insemination of the cow 12 to 20 hours before ovulation, there is still no proof of capacitation being necessary. Sheep apparently require capacitation of about 1.5 hours.[49] There is some question concerning capacitation in the pig, and if it does happen, it must be very rapid.[42] Man and primates are still in question.[25] A decapacitation factor has been found in horses, but no proof of capacitation.[26]

Changes in the sperm surface have been studied as capacitation takes place, and although slight changes occur in the outer cell membrane, the greatest change occurs in the acrosome following capacitation.[8] Suffice it to say that capacitation prepares the sperm for penetration of the outer structures of the egg cell mass.

No practical significance regarding the addition of a capacitation or decapacitation factor to sperm to enhance fertilization has resulted from studies thus far. Amylase, an enzyme found in sweet potatoes, was added to sperm in an attempt to mimic capacitation, and conception results were 2 to 4 percent greater than control semen.[34] Other enzymes should also be evaluated for action of a similar nature.

The tubouterine junction acts as a valve to some extent in all animals because of the constriction. Sperm reach this point within 40 minutes in pigs and 50 minutes in mares.[48] The tubouterine junction in the sow has been shown to house up to 1 million sperm as much as 24 hours after insemination.[66] This number was comparable to those in the lower oviduct. The uterus proper had virtually no sperm present at this time.

Experiments with sperm transport in the oviduct show very active contractions under the influence of estrogen at the time of estrus. These contractions have been measured accurately in the sow[107] and show a contraction of the isthmus followed by a lower uterine contraction, then contractions of the ampulla followed by an upper uterine contraction. These contractions move the sperm very quickly to the ampullar area for fertilization. The presence of large amounts of thin fluid secreted by the glandular cells of the oviduct assist in sperm transport. Ciliated cells are not as numerous in the lower oviduct and therefore do not interfere with transport.

Ovum Transport

Movement of the ovum into the oviduct requires special consideration. The fimbria on the terminal oviduct become rigid during estrus and act as a funnel to receive the ovum. Fluid from the abdominal cavity and that escaping from the follicle at ovulation serve as a medium for the free-floating ovum.[107] The activity of the cilia lining the oviduct, inflow of fluids, and forming of the fimbria around the ovary all assist in moving the ovum in the proper direction for uniting with the sperm (Fig. 13–4). Flow of fluids in the oviduct are primarily toward the ampullar end until after ovulation when the direction changes toward the tubouterine junction and the ovum is moved on into the uterus following fertilization.[9]

Unfertilized ova in most species are either passed on through the tract or else degenerate and are phagocytized in the oviduct.[35] The mare is peculiar in that the ova evidently are retained for indefinite periods.[82] Some are estimated to be 192 days

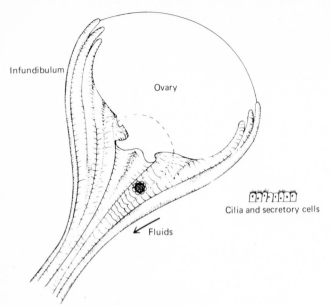

Figure 13-4   Ovum transport into the oviduct.

old based on cycle length and number of ova recovered. The ova may be in various stages of degeneration, particularly the cytoplasmic contents, except for the freshly ovulated one.[96]

FERTILIZATION

When the mature spermatozoa reach the ovum it is covered with the follicular cells in which it grew. The outer layer of the egg cell mass is the cumulus oophorus, the next layer is the corona radiata, and these cells rest on the zona pellucida which surrounds the vitelline membrane and its contents, the vitellus and nucleus (Fig. 13-5). Most ova of domestic animals will have divided to a point in which the first polar body has been extruded and rests in the perivitelline space. This space is very small at this stage of development. The nucleus of the maturing ovum is in metaphase of the secondary oocyte in the cow and ewe. The second division may not have begun in the mare.

Barriers to Penetration

Outer Cells As the sperm approaches the ovum, it has been prepared by capacitation so that the acrosome now is capable of releasing enzymes to digest the bonds between the protecting cells of the cumulus oophorus and corona radiata[5] (Fig. 13-6). The major enzyme is hyaluronidase, but numerous other lytic enzymes are present.[16]

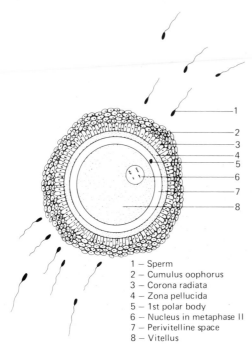

1 — Sperm
2 — Cumulus oophorus
3 — Corona radiata
4 — Zona pellucida
5 — 1st polar body
6 — Nucleus in metaphase II
7 — Perivitelline space
8 — Vitellus

Figure 13-5   Sperm approaching the egg cell mass.

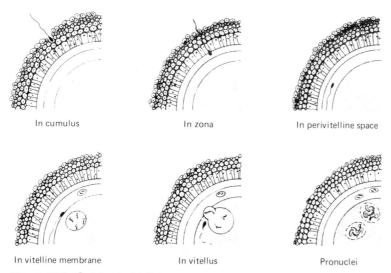

In cumulus

In zona

In perivitelline space

In vitelline membrane

In vitellus

Pronuclei

Figure 13-6   Sperm penetration.

Zona Pellucida The sperm penetrates the matrix of the outer cell mass, and as the sperm approaches the zona pellucida, enzymes of the inner acrosome membrane permit penetration. The sperm forms a channel through the zona and passes into the perivitelline space (Fig. 13-6). The sperm tail is whipping rapidly during the penetration thus far. Chemical reactions between the products of the sperm and the zona pellucida cause a sealing to prevent penetration by other sperm.[32] This may result from fusion of cortical granules from the acrosome with the zona.[5] This is called the *zona reaction.*

If there is some fault in the sealing of the zona, supplementary sperm may penetrate and swim freely in the perivitelline space. Microscopic observation of the ovum at this time may reveal several sperm lodged in the zona.

Vitelline Membrane This thin membrane is the last barrier to penetration of the ovum. The sperm head is now denuded of the acrosome and the exposed perforatorium penetrates the vitelline membrane. The sperm head lies flat against the vitelline membrane and fuses with it as the membrane and vitellus engulf the sperm. There is an immediate sealing of the vitelline membrane called the *vitelline block* to prevent other sperm from penetrating. The entire sperm is usually engulfed in the process, although the tail does remain outside in some species. If additional sperm penetrate the membrane, supernumerary sperm are then present and the condition is called *polyspermy.* The formation of two sperm into pronuclei brings about a condition called triploidy because of the presence of three sets of chromosomes, and the condition is almost always lethal in the embryonic state. Aged ova are more liable to have greater penetration than fresh ones,[42] leading to death.

Pronuclei Formation

Penetration of the vitelline membrane is the stimulus for completion of the second metaphase, anaphase, and telophase stages to expel the second polar body into the perivitelline space and form the female pronucleus with 1N complement of chromosomes (Fig. 13–6). The first polar body may or may not divide; therefore, two or three polar bodies may be present.

The sperm head begins to enlarge once it penetrates the vitellus and gradually separates from the membranes and tail to form a rounded male pronucleus. The tail and membranes disintegrate.

Syngamy

The male and female pronuclei migrate toward one another and fuse (Fig. 13–7). There is a loss of the nucleoli and nuclear membrane followed by organization of the chromosomes so that at prophase of the first organized cell division the chromosomes begin to align themselves and form along the equatorial plate by metaphase. The new nucleus and its surrounding cytoplasm are now considered a *zygote,* which is ready for mitotic cell division to form a new life.

Figure 13-7 Syngamy, fusion of the male and female pronuclei, and cleavage.

Cleavage

The new cell divides to form two blastomeres, which are smaller daughter cells. Cleavage occurs without loss in mass but with increased numbers of cells.

The zygote continues its cell division and forms a ball of cells called the morula, which transforms into a hollow sphere called a blastula while still in the zona pellucida (Fig. 13–8). It is during this time that embryo transfer is most easily performed and most successfully.

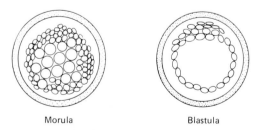

Morula   Blastula

Figure 13-8 Morula and blastula.

EMBRYO TRANSFER

Simply, embryo transfer consists of removing an embryo in its early developmental stage from its own mother's reproductive tract and transferring it to another female's reproductive tract for development and subsequent birth (Fig. 13–9).[46]

The early work was conducted more from an experimental approach than practical. In 1890 Heape[39] transferred ova in rabbits. It was almost 50 years later that Warwick, Berry, and Horlacher[100] experimented with sheep. A great amount of interest was generated in the late 1940s when livestock researchers felt this could be the female sequel of artificial insemination. Much—in fact too much—publicity was given to a program that did not materialize.

Cattle

Embryo transfer was given a great stimulus when exotic (nonestablished) breeds of cattle were introduced into the United States from other countries. Animals could not be imported because of strict quarantine against diseases, particularly foot and mouth disease. Semen could be shipped from specific bulls that were under strict

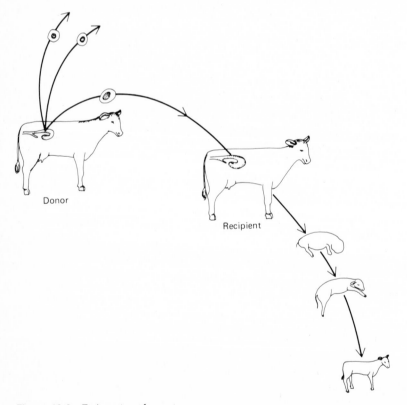

Figure 13-9 Embryo transfer.

health restrictions after a period of quarantine of the semen. In order to upgrade to as pure a breed as possible it was necessary to breed the offspring back to bulls of the same breed until the genetic makeup approached pure blood. Most established associations set a 3/4 or 7/8 blood animal as acceptable for registration. Thus a desirable cow of any breed could be bred with semen of a purebred bull and the offspring would be 1/2 blood. A 1/2 blood heifer bred to a purebred bull results in a 3/4 blood offspring and its mating to a purebred bull would result in a 7/8 blood offspring which would be as far as needed for registration and rather uniform characteristics for a breed. This means three generations to reach a "purebred" status. Gestation takes about 9 months, and a heifer should be at least 12 months old before breeding. Four generations at a minimum of 21 months is almost 4 years —and that is if everything works to perfection. Only one purebred offspring results from such an approach. With embryo transfer, a cow may be superovulated and produce multiple offspring, so that even though generation intervals may stay the same, a donor cow may produce multiple offspring through transfer to recipient cows.

One of the most common questions asked is "How many offspring can be produced by a cow?" With surgical methods of superovulation and transfer, about four transfers can be made on each cow that responds to hormone treatment. The frequency of treatment is not positively resolved, but it appears that a cow may be superovulated about every 60 days. Most cows are used two or three times and then rested or bred to conceive naturally before reuse. A survey of seven organizations and 635 successful transfers revealed only 1.6 pregnancies per donor.[31]

At the present time embryo transfer is a tool for extending the productivity of outstanding females. There are other advantages as well as some disadvantages. A good review of some of the problems is given by Gordon.[29,30]

Advantages

1 Extend the productivity of valuable dams. The potential of the dam has not been approached.

2 Continue productive life of females that are injured or for some other reason cannot develop a young but are still fertile.

3 More rapid proof of a dam through greater numbers of offspring in a short period of time.

4 Shorten generation interval by superovulating prepuberal females and transferring embryos to mature recipients.

5 Transfer embryos from proven stock to underdeveloped areas with native unproductive stock, thereby utilizing the genetic potential in an entirely different environment.

6 Importation of new bloodlines and breeds where restrictions prohibit importing the entire animal.

7 Induced twinning by transferring an additional embryo to the existing pregnancy. Present methods for inducing multiple births are not satisfactory because of varied response of females to a particular dosage of hormones. This would almost guarantee twins, and calf crop percentage of 120 to 150 would be feasible.[24] Numerous successful transfers have been conducted with as high as 72 percent twins resulting.[3,15,20,70,79,81,92]

Disadvantages

1 Propagation of low-fertility cattle is very undesirable but is possible if a particular animals's merits are based on factors other than reproduction.

2 Cost is prohibitive under most circumstances. With improved technique and commercial competition, costs are decreasing. In 1976 it was estimated that an offspring from embryo transfer was worth $4,000. This took into consideration the pregnancy fee of about $2,500 plus the many other factors such as cost of recipient, semen insurance, blood typing, feed and board, veterinary fees, registration and transfer fees, plus future pregnancy losses.[74]

3 Loss of outstanding dams through surgery or adhesions following surgery. Most transfers are now nonsurgical in nature so this is becoming less of a problem.

4 Response to hormones is erratic. Some females respond while others do not. No explanation is available.

5 Repeated treatment with protein hormones (PMSG and FSH) induces antibody formation,[43] and animals become refractory with repeated treatment.[10,27] Allowing the donor to conceive between uses may decrease refractoriness.[88]

Preparation

Estrous synchronization It has become evident that the timing of transfer must be rather exact with regard to stage of the estrous cycle. An example of experimental results yielded 91 percent conception when the donor and recipient were in estrus on the same day, compared to 54, 35, and 10 percent when there was a difference of 1, 2, or 3 days, respectively.[71,73]

Estrus must be checked on donors and recipients to match animals. This requires a rather large herd of recipients to have sufficient in estrus at a given time for transfer.[84] An alternative is synchronization with progestogens and prostaglandins.[89]

Cattle condition Only healthy cattle in good flesh should be considered for transfer.

Superovulation Superovulation may be induced as discussed in a previous chapter.

PMSG and FSH are both used, with PMSG giving a better response but costing more. PMSG may be given as a single treatment while FSH must be given in daily injections for as long as 10 days. $PGF_2\alpha$ may be used for better estrous synchronization and detection.

All donor animals will not respond to treatment. Some will not superovulate and others will not come in estrus. The best method of determining response is palpation of the ovaries per rectum. No response eliminates insemination, and the donor then is recycled after a rest of two or more cycles. Animals not showing estrus, even though superovulation occurs, are poor risks for conception and transfer and should not be inseminated and used.

A relatively recent innovation is the use of the laparoscope for observing ovarian changes (Fig. 13–10). Repeated palpations may cause rupture of follicles prematurely, and therefore palpation should be limited. Observation of ovulation could determine the length of time required for inseminating. It is also very difficult to determine by palpation the number of ovulations and stages of follicular development when multiple follicles are present.[67]

The currently used technique involves a small-diameter laparoscope with a fiber-optic light system that gives cold light transmitted through a fiber cable.[104] A small incision is made in the right paralumbar fossa and by means of a trocar and cannula the laparoscope is passed posteriorly between the parietal peritoneum and the greater omentum. Probes may also be inserted for manipulating the ovaries.[51] Multiple laparoscopies may be conducted through the same incision if aseptic procedures are followed.

Insemination Ovulation occurs over a period of several hours, perhaps days, and it is necessary to maintain fresh viable sperm present at all times. Inseminations are

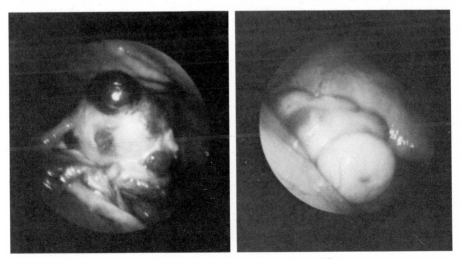

Figure 13-10   A corpus luteum observed by laparoscopy. *(Maxwell.[51])*

conducted shortly after detection of estrus and at 12-hour intervals for three inseminations. High-quality semen is a must regardless of whether it is liquid or frozen.

Embryo collection

Nonsurgical Since there is a definite trend toward the nonsurgical approach, this
will be discussed first.

Most recoveries are scheduled for 6 to 11 days postestrus because by this time
most of the embryos should be in the upper horns of the uterus.[56] The tip of the
uterine horn is therefore the target area for flushing.

Some of the first uterine flushings included the entire uterus with limited success
in recovery (12 of 37 ova).[23] Numerous nonsurgical approaches have been tried,
some with success and some without.[67,68,69,72,78,91] The generally accepted method
now includes a catheter, flushing medium, and collecting dishes (Fig. 13–11).

The catheter is an elongated three-way Foley catheter about 70 cm (28 in) long.
One of the tubular openings leads to a small balloon with a capacity of 25 to 35 ml
of air. A second tube leads to an opening near the tip through which fluid is forced
into the uterine tip. The third tube leads to another opening about 20 cm (8 in) from
the tip through which the flushing medium is returned to a collecting dish.

A steel stylet is placed in the catheter for rigidity, and it is then threaded
through the cervix as in insemination until the tip is in the upper horn of the uterus.

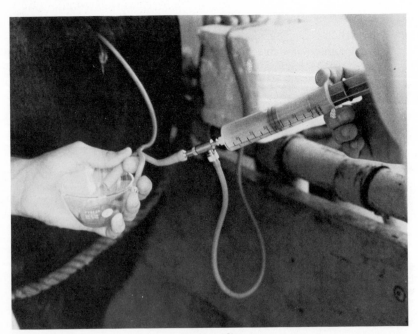

Figure 13-11 Nonsurgical flushing. *(Maxwell.[51])*

The balloon is then inflated so that it occludes the lumen of the horn just beyond the bifurcation. The stylet is then removed.

A filling apparatus, which may be a syringe with an adapter, is attached to the inlet tube, and, with the recovery tube clamped, about 15 ml of medium are infused to prime the tube. Additional medium is infused to a point of turgidity of the uterus as determined by palpation per rectum and then the delivery tube is released and the fluid is drained from the horn into a collecting dish (Fig. 13–12). Manipulation of the uterus per rectum enhances recovery of the medium. The process is usually repeated to assure successful recovery. About 500 ml of medium are used for each flushing. If corpora lutea are on both ovaries, indicating points of ovulation, then both horns are flushed.

Following flushing, the balloon is deflated and the catheter removed.

Infusing an antiseptic solution into the uterus after completion assures a healthy reproductive tract.

Surgical The surgical approach may be either midventral or via the paralumbar fossa. It depends on personal preference. There is usually less manipulation of the tract with the midventral approach.

The oviducts were flushed in earlier trials. This meant recovery was necessary within 4 days of ovulation. After exposure of the oviducts, a plastic tube is inserted in the infundibulum and secured. A hypodermic syringe needle is inserted into the oviduct just above the tubouterine junction and the medium is forced through the oviduct and tube into a collecting dish.

A later approach was to flush the uterine horn. This must be conducted after 5 days as in the nonsurgical approach. The tubouterine junction is clamped as well as the miduterine horn. A glass tube is inserted into the horn for recovery, with caution practiced to eliminate any hemorrhage. The tapered tip should be finely polished. A blunt hyperdermic needle is inserted carefully and the flushing medium forced through the horn and out the recovery tube into a collecting dish.

The recovery is satisfactory with the surgical approach, but the difficulty lies

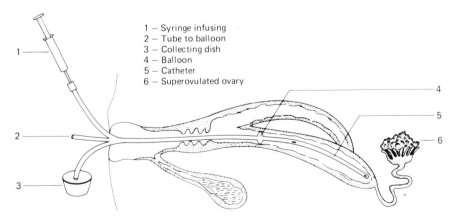

1 — Syringe infusing
2 — Tube to balloon
3 — Collecting dish
4 — Balloon
5 — Catheter
6 — Superovulated ovary

Figure 13-12 Nonsurgical flushing approach.

in adhesions and damage to the ovaries and uterus. Four recoveries from a single animal without adhesions is considered very good.

Slaughter Embryos recovered from slaughtered donors have resulted in much higher conception rates but lower embryo survival rates than surgically recovered ova.[87]

Embryo Examination Ova or embryos flushed from the oviduct may contain 2 to 64 cells depending upon the time of flushing following ovulation.[52] Those recovered from the uterus range from 64 cells to the blastula stage.

The embryos must be located under a scanning microscope and examined to determine if they appear normal and will develop following transfer (Fig. 13–13).

Single-cell ova are nonfertilized and should not be transferred.

Two-cell ova are fertilized (except in rare instances of division) and may be considered normal if they are only 2 days old. If flushings are made later than 2 days postestrus, these should be considered abnormal and not transferred. Ova with small numbers of blastomeres should be considered according to age at time of flushing for normality.

Misshapen ova are abnormal, and there are many types and shapes that fall into this category.

The embryos should be round and full with an intact zona pellucida and the normal stage of development according to time of recovery.

The ova should be maintained at an incubator temperature of 37°C (98°F) and remain sealed in the collecting dish. Embryos should be utilized as quickly as possible to insure viability.[7]

Transfer Most transfers are being surgically performed, but nonsurgical approaches are being developed and no doubt will replace surgical ones.

The recipient is prepared for surgery the same as the donor. The reproductive tract is exposed and the presence of a corpus luteum on the ovary determined. If no CL is present the animal should not be used, since it is necessary for continuation of pregnancy.

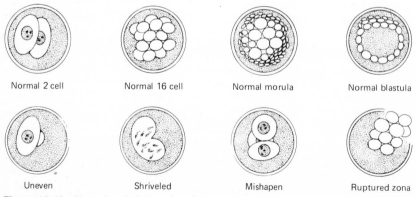

Normal 2 cell   Normal 16 cell   Normal morula   Normal blastula

Uneven   Shriveled   Mishapen   Ruptured zona

Figure 13-13 Normal and abnormal embryos.

The embryo is selected under the microscope and drawn into a Pasteur pipette or similar fine glass tube. The uterus is then punctured carefully and the pipette inserted and the ova discharged into the lumen. One should be certain that the ovum is placed in the lumen of the horn in an area similar to recovery. The embryo also should be placed on the ipsilateral (same side as) the ovary with the CL.[86] If twins are desired an embryo is also placed in the contralateral (opposite side) horn.[80]

Nonsurgical methods are similar to artificial insemination. The embryo is drawn into a fine tube or straw and passed into the upper ipsilateral horn before expulsion.[81] As high as 50 percent conception has resulted from bilateral transfers via the cervix.[65] Most difficulties have arisen from disease, since the uterus is very susceptible at this time under the influence of progesterone. No doubt refinement of technique and greater success are very near.[97]

Sheep

The majority of embryo transfers in sheep have been directed toward a method for developing a population of outstanding genetic individuals from a relatively small select base.[28] This is a distinct possibility.

Embryos have been transferred both tubally and uterine, but the uterine method appears to be best by far. Results of one research program yielded 59 percent of the recipients lambing from tubal transfers (41/69) compared to 70 percent for uterine transfers (136/193).[54] The percentage of the eggs transferred that developed into lambs also favored uterine transfers (59 vs. 42 percent).

The age of the embryos transferred is usually between a few hours and 5 days. The older embryos appear to withstand transfers better.[6]

PMSG has been used for superovulation in most instances. It may be given on day 12 to day 14 of the cycle in a single injection with good response.[36] Synchronization is important.[55]

The technique for recovery and transfer is very similar to the surgical procedures discussed for the cow. It is almost impossible to penetrate the tortuous cervix of the ewe, and therefore the nonsurgical approach is not used. A modification of the surgical approach using nonsurgical techniques has been developed.[85] A catheter with a balloon is inserted near the bifurcation and the balloon inflated to occlude one horn of the uterus. The catheter is the return flow for fluid infused through a hypodermic needle in the upper horn. Recovery was 83 percent of the ova shed (97/117).

Work has also been conducted in goats with the precaution that they are different from sheep.[57,58,59] Ovulation does not result from PMSG alone but must have HCG in addition. Many follicles can be stimulated (10 to 30).

Swine

The sow is a multiple ovulator with litters of pigs produced. Why then should we discuss embryo transfer in swine? The major reason is to increase the size of litters. Although most gilts and sows could suckle 14 pigs, the average litter is 6 to 8. And if only 3 or 4 pigs develop, the sow is as pregnant as if 12 were developing. There is no "little bit" pregnant; it is all or nothing.

Swine may also be used for studying effects of toxic substances or disease by transferring embryos from exposed dams to healthy dams and studying survival and normality.

PMSG injected on day 16 of the estrous cycle gives good response.[64] Ovulations may number 25 to 30, and most ova are recovered from the oviducts surgically.[98] Sometimes the flushing fluid and ova are recovered from the clamped uterus after infusing fluid into the infundibulum. Ova remain in the oviduct only 50 to 60 hours, and maximum recovery usually occurs on the day following breeding.[76]

Synchrony of the donor and recipient is essential in the sow as with other livestock. If the donor is 1 or 2 days earlier or 1 day later there appears to be no deleterious effect.[101]

Embryos have been transferred surgically into the oviducts by passage of a polyethylene tube into the fimbriated end and then depositing the embryos from a Pasteur pipette.[101] Those deposited in the uterus have been by a simple puncture and deposition into the lumen.[37] Success has been reported for the latter method of 12/18, 13/14, and 6/10 survival.

A nonsurgical approach using two or three polyethylene catheters has met with limited success, 3/14.[62] The outer catheter is inserted against the cervix with the second catheter then penetrating the cervix into the uterus. The ovum may be flushed through the inner catheter or a thin tube passed for ova transfer.

Horses

Embryo transfer in horses is suggested as a means of overcoming some anatomical or disease problem. Some mares conceive but are unable to carry the foal to term.

Superovulation is not feasible in the mare at the present time; therefore, multiple ova for transfer is not a consideration. Synchronization is critical and can best be accomplished by $PGF_2\alpha$ injections into both donor and recipient or either. Recoveries may be made from 5 to 20 days postbreeding.[40,99]

A nonsurgical approach is most popular and is similar to that in the cow.[60,99] The three-way system catheter is directed into the cervix by a hand in the vagina. Once the catheter is directed into the cervix, the arm is removed from the vagina and inserted into the rectum for further manipulation of the catheter into the uterus. The longitudinal folds of the cervix make passage relatively easy, although the mucus is thick and tenacious at this time.

Surgical approaches include exposing the reproductive system and flushing from the infundibulum of the oviduct into the uterine horn from whence the fluid and ova are collected.

Transfer of horse embryos may be conducted with a method similar to insemination. The catheter is longer with a straw or other small-volume container for the embryo. It is deposited into the ipsilateral horn to the active ovary.

Horse zygotes have been collected from mares and transferred to donkeys and vice versa. None of the embryos survived from nine transfers. Four mule zygotes were transferred to a donkey with one successful pregnancy, and six hinny zygotes were transferred to mares with two successes.[1] This opens the way for further study of genetic ramifications in the horse-donkey complex.

Another method that has met with success is a telescoping triple tube[83] that is passed into the anterior vagina, then the second tube into the uterus via the abdominal cavity, and the third tube into the uterine cavity with the ovum. Manipulation per rectum is necessary and gas is infused into the uterus to determine the cavity.[61] Fifteen blastocysts were transferred on days 5 to 7, of which six mares conceived and four healthy foals were born.

Embryo Culture and Storage

Numerous attempts have been made to store embryos for a prolonged period. Some of the attempts were to grow the embryos, while others were to arrest the embryo and hold it dormant for later transfer.

Culturing fertilized bovine ova in the two- to eight-cell stage has resulted in development to the blastocyst stage and hatching.[77,90,94,106] Hatching refers to rupture of the zona pellucida releasing the blastocyst. Various media and temperatures have been utilized in culture procedures.

Storage has primarily centered around cooling or freezing of the embryos. In one instance, 20 blastocysts were stored, following culture, for 48 hours at 0°C (32°F) and transferred to 10 recipients. A single blastocyst was placed in each horn. Eight normal fetuses developed in six of the recipients.[94] Other research showed that freezing embryos is possible as six pregnancies resulted from 17 transferred blastocysts that had been frozen in liquid nitrogen and flown from New Zealand to Australia.[11] The same workers froze morulae and early blastocysts and stored them for 2 to 3 months before transferring 10 well-developed and 6 poorly developed embryos to 11 recipient cows. Palpation revealed five pregnancies, and five calves were subsequently born.[13] Another pregnancy resulted from an embryo frozen for 6 days in liquid nitrogen.[103] So you see, it can be done, and now refinement will make it practical.

Sheep ova have been successfully stored at 10°C (50°F) for 10 days with two pregnancies resulting from 11 transfers.[45] A group of one- to four-cell ova were stored at 5°C (40°F) for up to 6 hours and then cultured at 37°C (98°F) for 2 days with the majority of the younger ova developing to eight cells and the older ova to blastocysts.[53] Thirty transferred ova to 20 recipients resulted in 11 lambs. Deep-freezing embryos has been successfully conducted with five lambs being produced from 11 ova that were frozen in liquid nitrogen and cultured in rabbit oviduct.[102] These lambs resulted from eight transfers following freezing only.

Goat embryos collected 5 to 7 days after mating have been cultured at 37°C (98°F) for 2 days followed by storage in liquid nitrogen for 2 to 4 weeks.[12] Ten embryos were transferred with five resulting kids born.

Swine ova have been collected at the one- to four-cell stage and cultured in vitro for 24 to 48 hours before transfer.[63] Five of six recipient gilts averaged 7.6 normal embryos. Culture of swine ova appears to elicit response in ova up to the blastocyst stage as in other species.[21,105] Gaseous atmosphere, humidity, and the medium constituents are very important in culture.

It is possible to use another animal, such as the rabbit, for an intermediate host in transporting embryos. Five morulae and one eight-celled embryo were flushed from mares in Cambridge and placed in ligated oviducts of three estrous rabbits. These were transported to Krakow in a trip lasting 33 hours. The six embryos were flushed from the excised oviducts after storage of 49 hours and held at 37°C (98°F) for 2 hours before transfer. Three of four mares conceived.[2]

Further work with culturing oocytes offers possibilities of aspirating follicles and even culture of ovaries for germ cell production.[19,75] This would necessitate in vitro fertilization, which has met with very limited success in domestic animals.

Induction of identical offspring by dividing the fertilized ovum is also in its infancy. Sheep ova 6 and 7 days old have been mechanically divided and cultured to form two blastocysts. Transfer of these blastocysts has resulted in pregnancies, but only of a single blastocyst from a divided ovum.[93] Perhaps the division was made after cell specialization had occurred.

Sexing Embryos

Sexing embryos is possible before transfer by removing a small fragment of the trophoblast and culturing it to determine chromosome makeup.[38] Day-14 and day-15 bovine embryos were cultured at 37°C (98°F). Sex determination was successful in 20 transfers, uncertain in 3, and unsuccessful in 11.

WHAT DID YOU LEARN?

1 How does sperm move so rapidly from the point of natural deposition to the point of fertilization?
2 Where does fertilization take place?
3 How long does it take sperm to reach the point of fertilization in the cow, ewe, and sow?
4 Where is sperm deposited in normal copulation of horses?
5 List and describe each barrier to fertilization.
6 What is syngamy?
7 What is so critical about synchronization of donor and recipient for embryo transfer?
8 What must be considered when inseminating the donor cow?
9 Briefly describe the nonsurgical approach to embryo transfer in the mare.
10 What is the main reason for transferring embryos in swine?

REFERENCES

1 Allen, W. R. and L. E. A. Rowson. 1972. Transfer of ova between horses and donkeys. *Proc. 7th Int. Congr. on Anim. Reprod. And A. I.* 1:484–488.
2 Allen, W. R., F. Stewart, A. O. Trounson, M. Tischner, and W. Beilanski. 1976. Viability of horse embryos after storage and long-distance transport in the rabbit. *J. Reprod. Fert.* 47:387–390.

3   Anderson, G. B., J. N. Baldwin, P. T. Cupps, M. Drost, M. B. Horton, and R. W. Wright, Jr. 1976. Induced twinning in beef heifers by embryo transfer. *J. Anim. Sci.* 43:272. (Abstr.)

4   Austin, C. R. 1951. Observations on the penetration of the sperm into the mammalian egg. *Australian J. Sci. Res. Ser. B.* 4:581–589.

5   ———. 1975. Membrane fusion events in fertilization. *J. Reprod. Fert.* 44:155–166.

6   Averill, R. L. W. and L. E. A. Rowson. 1958. Ovum transfer in sheep. *J. Endocrinol.* 16:326–336.

7   Baker, A. A. 1973. Ovum transfer in the cow. *Australian Vet. J.* 49:424–426.

8   Bedford, J. M. 1970. Sperm capacitation and fertilization in mammals. *Biol. Reprod. Suppl.* 2:128–158.

9   Belve, A. R. and M. F. McDonald. 1968. Directional flow of fallopian tube secretion in the Romney ewe. *J. Reprod. Fert.* 15:357–364.

10   Betteridge, K. J. and D. Mitchell. 1974. Embryo transfer in cattle: Experience of twenty-four completed cases. *Therio.* 1:69–82.

11   Bilton, R. J. and N. W. Moore. 1976. Storage of cattle embryos. *J. Reprod. Fert.* 46:537–538.

12   ———. 1976. In vitro culture, storage and transfer of goat embryos. *Australian J. Biol. Sci.* 29:125–129.

13   ———. 1977. Successful transport of frozen cattle embryos from New Zealand to Australia. *J. Reprod. Fert.* 50:363–364.

14   Blandau, R. J. 1973. Gamete transport in the female mammal. In R. O. Greep, ed. *Handbook of Physiology: Endocrinology II.* Williams & Wilkins, Baltimore. Pp. 153–163.

15   Boland, M. P., T. F. Crosby, and I. Gordon. 1975. Twin pregnancy in cattle established by non-surgical transfer. *British Vet. J.* 131:738–740.

16   Brown, C. R. 1975. Distribution of hyaluronidase in the ram spermatozoon. *J. Reprod. Fert.* 45:537–539.

17   Burger, J. F. 1952. Sex physiology of pigs. *Onderstepoort J. Vet. Res. Suppl.* 2:3–218.

18   Chang, M. C. 1951. Fertilizing capacity of spermatozoa deposited into the Fallopian tubes. *Nature* 168:697–698.

19   Crosby, T. F., P. O. M. Ryan, and I. Gordon. 1971. Culture and fertilization of sheep ovarian oocytes. IV. Observations on sperm penetration in oocytes transferred to the sheep oviduct. *J. Agr. Sci.* 76:379–382.

20   Cupps, P. T. and M. Drost. 1977. Twinning in beef cattle following unilateral and bilateral embryo transfer. *Amer. Soc. Anim. Sci. 1977 Mtg. Abstr. 332.* P. 131.

21   Davis, D. L. and B. N. Day. 1977. Cleavage and blastocyst formation by pig eggs in vitro. *Amer. Soc. Anim. Sci. 1977 Mtg. Abstr. 372.* Pp. 147–148.

22   Dobrowolski, W. And E. S. E. Hafez. 1970. Transport and distribution of spermatozoa in the reproductive tract of the cow. *J. Anim. Sci.* 31:940–943.

23   Dracy, A. E. and W. E. Petersen. 1950. Isolation of ova from the living bovine. *J. Dairy Sci.* 33:797–802.

24   Drost, M. November 1974. Embryo transfer in cattle. *Bovine Prac.* Pp. 18–26, 56.

25   Dukelow, W. R. and H. N. Chernoff. 1969. Primate sperm survival and ejaculation in a foreign uterine environment. *Amer. J. Physiol.* 216:682–686.

26   Dukelow, W. R., H. N. Chernoff, and W. L. Williams. 1967. Properties of decapacitation factor and presence in various species. *J. Reprod. Fert.* 14:393–399.

27   Foote, R. H. and H. Onuma. 1970. Superovulation ovum collection, culture and transfer: A review. *J. Dairy Sci.* 53:1681–1692.

28   Gordon, I. 1974. Controlled breeding in sheep. *Irish Vet. J.* 28:118–126.

29   ———. 1975. Problems and prospects in cattle egg transfer. *Irish Vet. J.* 29:21–30.

30   ———. 1975. Problems and prospects in cattle egg transfer. Part II. *Irish Vet. J.* 29:39–62.

31   Graham, E. F. 1974. Ova transfer. *Proc. 5th Tech. Conf. on A.I. and Reprod.* Pp. 21–28.

32   Guyton, Arthur C. 1966. Fertilization of the Ovum. In A. C. Guyton, ed. *Textbook of Medical Physiology.* 3rd ed. W. B. Saunders Co., Philadelphia. Pp. 1152–1153.

33   Hafez, E. S. E., A. A. El-Banna, and J. A. Lineweaver. 1968. Gamete transport in beef cattle. *Proc. 6th Int. Congr. on Anim. Reprod. and A.I.* 1:707–709.

34   Hafs, H. D. 1968. Capacitation of spermatozoa and fertility of bull sperm with added amylase. *Proc. 2nd Tech. Conf. on A.I. and Reprod.* Pp. 23–26.

35   Hancock, J. L. 1961. Fertilization in the pig. *J. Reprod. Fert.* 2:307–331.

36   Hancock, J. L. and G. J. R. Hovell. 1961. Transfer of sheep ova. *J. Reprod. Fert.* 2:295–306.

37   ———. 1962. Egg transfer in the sow. *J. Reprod. Fert.* 4:195–201.

38   Hare, W. C. D., D. Mitchell, K. J. Betteridge, M. D. Eaglesome, and G. C. B. Randall. 1976. Sexing two-week-old bovine embryos by chromosomal analysis prior to surgical transfer: Preliminary methods and results. *Therio.* 5:243–253.

39   Heape, W. 1890. Preliminary note on the transplantation and growth of mammalian ova within a uterine foster-mother. *Proc. Roy. Soc. London* 48:457–458.

40   Hershman, L., P. J. Burns, and R. H. Douglas. 1977. Effects of nonsurgical blastocyst removal on interovulatory interval in mares and progesterone production in vitro by the equine blastocyst. *Amer. Soc. Anim. Sci. 1977 Mtg. Abstr. 425.* P. 1969.

41   Howe, G. R. and D. L. Black. 1963. Spermatozoan transport and leucocytic responses in the reproductive tract of calves. *J. Reprod. Fert.* 6:305–311.

42   Hunter, R. H. F. and P. J. Dziuk. 1968. Sperm penetration of pig eggs in relation to the timing of ovulation and insemination. *J. Reprod. Fert.* 15:199–208.

43   Jainudeen, M. R., E. S. E. Hafez, P. D. Gollnick, and L. A. Moustaffa. 1966. Antigonadotrophins in the serum of cows following repeated therapeutic pregnant mare serum injections. *Amer. J. Vet. Res.* 27:669–675.

44   Jaszczak, S. and H. Kanagawa. 1972. Physiological mechanisms of spermatozoa transport through the cervix. *Proc. 7th Int. Congr. on Anim. Reprod. and A.I.* 2:2290–2293.

45   Kardymowicz, O. 1972. Successful in vitro storage of fertilized sheep ova for ten days. *Proc. 7th Int. Congr. on Anim. Reprod. and A.I.* 1:500–502.

46   Kraemer, D. C. and J. E. Dula, Jr. 1972. The role of embryo transfer in beef cattle production. *Proc. 21st and 22nd Beef Cattle Short Course.* Texas A&M Univ., College Station. Pp. 241–245.

47   Lovell, J. E. and R. Getty. 1968. Fate of semen in the uterus of the sow: Histologic study of endometrium during 27 hours after natural service. *Amer. J. Vet. Res.* 29:609–625.

48   Mann, T., C. Polge, and L. E. A. Rowson. 1956. Participation of seminal plasma during the passage of spermatozoa in the female reproductive tract of the pig and horse. *J. Endocrinol.* 13:133–140.

49   Mattner, P. E. 1963. Capacitation of ram spermatozoa and penetration of the ovine egg. *Nature* 199:772–773.

50   Mattner, P. E. and A. W. H. Braden. 1963. Spermatozoa in the genital tract of the ewe. *Australian J. Biol. Sci.* 16:473–481.

51   Maxwell, D. P. 1977. Determination of ovulation time in superovulated and synchronized bovine. M. S. thesis, Texas A&M Univ., College Station.

52   McGaugh, J. W., D. Olds and D. D. Kratzer. 1974. Ovum recovery in superovulated cows and cleavage rates in the fertilized ova. *Therio.* 1:213–217.

53 Moore, N. W. and R. J. Bilton. 1973. The storage of fertilized sheep ova at 5°C. *Australian J. Biol. Sci.* 26:1421–1427.

54 Moore, N. W. and J. N. Shelton. 1962. The application of the technique of egg transfer to sheep breeding. *Australian J. Agr. Res.* 13:718–724.

55 ———. 1964. Egg transfer in sheep: Effect of degree of synchronization between donor and recipient, age of egg, and site of transfer on the survival of transferred eggs. *J. Reprod. Fert.* 7:145–152

56 Newcomb, R. 1976. Fundamental aspects of ovum transfer in cattle. *Vet. Rec.* 99:40–44.

57 Nishikawa, Y. and H. Onuma. 1963. Studies on the transplantation of ova (artificial pregnancy) in goats. I. Experiments on excessive development of follicles. *Proc. Japan Acad.* 39:519–524.

58 Nishikawa, Y., T. Horie, and H. Onuma. 1963. Studies on the transplantation of ova (artificial pregnancy) in the goat. II. Experiments on a method of inducing ovulation of artificially developed follicles and estrus in treated animals. *Proc. Japan Acad.* 39:611–615.

59 Nishikawa, Y., T. Horie, T. Sugie, H. Onuma, and T. Niwa. 1963. Studies on the transplantation of ova (artificial pregnancy) in the goat. III. Experiments on the speed of ova descending the genital tract. Progress of cleavage of ova, and collection of ova from the donor. *Proc. Japan Acad.* 39:671–676.

60 Oguri, N. and Y. Tsutsumi. 1972. Non-surgical recovery of equine eggs, and an attempt at non-surgical egg transfer in horses. *J. Reprod. Fert.* 31:187–195.

61 ———. 1974. Non-surgical egg transfer in mares. *J. Reprod. Fert.* 41:313–320.

62 Polge, C. and B. N. Day. 1968. Pregnancy following non-surgical egg transfer in pigs. *Vet. Rec.* 82:712.

63 Pope, C. E. and B. N. Day. 1977. Transfer of preimplantation pig embryos following in vitro culture for 24 or 48 hours. *J. Anim. Sci.* 44:1036–1040.

64 Rampacek, G. R., O. W. Robison, and L. C. Ulberg. 1975. Uterine capacity and progestin levels in superinducted gilts. *J. Anim. Sci.* 41:564–567.

65 Renard, J. P., Y. Heyman, and F. du Mesnil du Buisson. 1977. Unilateral and bilateral cervical transfer of bovine embryos at the blastocyst stage. *Therio.* 7:189–194.

66 Rigby, J. P. 1964. The fate of spermatozoa in the genital tract of the sow following artificial insemination. *Proc. 5th Int. Congr. on Anim. Reprod. and A.I.* 3:421–425.

67 Rowe, R. F., M. R. Del Campo, C. L. Eilts, L. R. French, R. P. Winch, and O. J. Ginther. 1976. A single cannula technique for nonsurgical collection of ova from cattle. *Therio.* 6:471–483.

68 Rowe, R. F., M. R. Del Campo, and O. J. Ginther. 1977. Nonsurgical collection and transfer of bovine embryos. *Amer. Soc. Anim. Sci. 1977 Mtg. Abstr. 506.* P. 203.

69 Rowson, L. E. A. and D. F. Dowling. 1949. An apparatus for the extraction of fertilized eggs from the living cow. *Vet. Rec.* 61:191.

70 Rowson, L. E. A., R. A. S. Lawson, and R. M. Moor. 1971. Production of twins in cattle by egg transfer. *J. Reprod. Fert.* 25:261–268.

71 Rowson, L. E. A., R. A. S. Lawson, R. M. Moor, and A. A. Baker. 1972. Egg transfer in the cow: Synchronization requirements. *J. Reprod. Fert.* 28:427–431.

72 Rowson, L. E. A. and R. M. Moor. 1966. Non-surgical transfer of cow eggs. *J. Reprod. Fert.* 11:311–312.

73 Rowson, L. E. A., R. M. Moor and, R. A. S. Lawson. 1969. Fertility following egg transfer in the cow: Effect of method, medium and synchronization of oestrus. *J. Reprod. Fert.* 18:517–523.

74 Seidel, G. E., Jr. June 1976. Embryo transfer. *Int. Limousin J.* pp. 17–24, 64, 68.

75 Shea, B. F., J. P. A. Latour, K. N. Bedirian, and R. D. Baker. 1976. Maturation *in vitro* and subsequent penetrability of bovine follicular oocytes. *J. Anim. Sci.* 43:809–815.

76 Smidt, D., J. Steinbach, and B. Scheven. 1963. Modified method for the in vivo recovery of fertilized ova in swine. *J. Reprod. Fert.* 10:153–156.

77 Sreenan, J. 1968. In vivo and in vitro culture of cattle eggs. *Proc. 6th Int. Congr. on Anim. Reprod. and A.I.* 1:577–580.

78 Sreenan, J. M. 1975. Successful non-surgical transfer of fertilised cow eggs. *Vet. Rec.* ·96:490–491.

79 Sreenan, J. M. and D. Beehan. 1976. Effect of site of transfer on pregnancy and twinning rates following bilateral egg transfer in the cow. *J. Reprod. Fert.* 48:223–224.

80 ———. 1976. Embryonic survival and development at various stages of gestation after bilateral egg transfer in the cow. *J. Reprod. Fert.* 47:127–128.

81 Sreenan, J. M., D. Beehan, and P. Mulvehill. 1975. Egg transfer in the cow: Factors affecting pregnancy and twinning rates following bilateral transfers. *J. Reprod. Fert.* 44:77–85.

82 Steffenhagen, W. P., H. M. Pineda, and O. J. Ginther. 1972. Retention of unfertilized ova in uterine tubes of mares. *Amer. J. Vet. Res.* 33:2391–2398.

83 Sugie, T. 1965. Successful transfer of a fertilized bovine egg by non-surgical techniques. *J. Reprod. Fert.* 10:197–201.

84 Tervit, H. R. 1976. Techniques and hazards of embryo manipulation and induction of parturition. *New Zealand Vet. J.* 24:74–79.

85 Tervit, H. R. and P. G. Hawk. 1976. A modified technique for flushing ova from the sheep uterus. *New Zealand Vet. J.* 24:138–140.

86 Tervit, H. R., P. G. Havick, and J. F. Smith. 1977. Egg transfer in cattle: Pregnancy rate following transfer to the uterine horn ipsilateral or contralateral to the functional corpus luteum. *Therio.* 7:3–10.

87 Tervit, H. R. and L. E. A. Rowson. 1972. The viability of fertilized ova from slaughtered cattle. *Proc. 7th Int. Congr. on Anim. Reprod. and A.I.* 1:489–494.

88 Tervit, H. R., L. E. A. Rowson, and M. F. McDonald. 1974. Application of the egg transfer technique in cattle and sheep. *Proc. New Zealand Soc. Anim. Prod.* 34:56–60.

89 Tervit, H. R. and J. F. Smith. 1975. Egg transfer in cattle: Effect of hormonal treatment on synchronization of oestrus and ovarian response. *Proc. New Zealand Soc. Anim. Prod.* 35:78–82.

90 Tervit, H. R., D. G. Whittingham, and L. E. A. Rowson. 1972. Successful culture in vitro of sheep and cattle ova. *J. Reprod. Fert.* 30:493–497.

91 Testart, J. and C. Goard-Siour. 1975. Transvaginal recovery of uterine eggs in the cow. *Therio.* 4:157–161.

92 Testart, J., C. Godard-Siour, F. du Mesnil du Buisson, P. Chesne, and J. Thibaud. 1975. Transvaginal transplantation of an extra egg to obtain twinning in cattle. *Therio.* 4:163–168.

93 Trounson, A. O. and N. W. Moore. 1974. Attempts to produce identical offspring in the sheep by mechanical division of the ovum. *Australian J. Biol. Sci.* 27:505–510.

94 Trounson, A. O., S. M. Willadsen, and L. E. A. Rowson. 1976. The influence of in-vitro culture and cooling on the survival and development of cow embryos. *J. Reprod. Fert.* 47:367–370.

95 VanDemark, N. L. and A. N. Moeller. 1951. Speed of spermatozoan transport in reproductive tract of estrous cow. *Amer. J. Physiol.* 165:674–679.

96 van Niekerk, C. H. and W. H. Gerneke. 1966. Persistence and parthenogenetic cleavage of tubal ova in the mare. *Onderstepoort J. Vet. Res.* 33:195–232.

97   Vincent, C. K. 1970. Culture and transplantation of eggs and twinning in cattle. *Proc. 3rd Tech. Conf. on A.I. and Reprod.* Pp. 91–94.

98   Vincent, C. K., O. W. Robison, and L. C. Ulberg. 1964. A technique for reciprocal embryo transfer in swine. *J. Anim. Sci.* 23:1084–1088.

99   Vogelsang, S., A. M. Sorensen, Jr., and D. C. Kraemer. 1977. Fertility of donor mares following nonsurgical collection of embryos. *Proceedings of the Second International Symposium on Equine Reproduction. J. Reprod. Fert. Suppl.* 27 (In Press).

100   Warwick, B. L., R. O. Berry, and W. Horlacher. 1934. Results of mating rams to Angora female goats. *Proc. Amer. Soc. Anim. Prod.* Pp. 225–227.

101   Webel, S. K., J. B. Peters, and L. L. Anderson. 1970. Synchronous and asynchronous transfer of embryos in the pig. *J. Anim. Sci.* 30:565–568.

102   Willadsen, S. M., C. Polge, L. E. A. Rowson, and R. M. Moor. 1976. Deep freezing of sheep embryos. *J. Reprod. Fert.* 46:151–154.

103   Wilmut, I. and L. E. A. Rowson. 1973. Experiments on the low temperature preservation of cow embryos. *Vet. Rec.* 92:686–690.

104   Wishart, D. F. and J. B. Snowball. 1973. Endoscopy in cattle: observation of the ovary *in situ. Vet. Rec.* 92:139–143.

105   Wright, R. W., Jr. 1977. Successful culture in vitro of swine embryos to the blastocyst stage. *J. Anim. Sci.* 44:854–858.

106   Wright, R. W., Jr., G. B. Anderson, P. T. Cupps, and M. Drost. 1976. Blastocyst expansion and hatching of bovine ova cultured in vitro. *J. Anim. Sci.* 43:170–174.

107   Zerobin, K. and H. Sporri. 1972. Motility of the bovine and porcine uterus and fallopian tube. *Adv. Vet. Sci. Comp. Med.* 16:303–354.

Gestation and Pregnancy Determination

When you have completed this chapter you should be able to:

- Give gestation lengths for domestic animals and the woman,
- Relate the importance of progesterone and its source to maintenance of pregnancy,
- Develop the extraembryonic membranes of the embryo,
- Enumerate stepwise the major developments of the prenatal young,
- Relate age to developmental periods of the embryo,
- Distinguish placentae by structure, shape, and animal in which each is found,
- Give reasons for pregnancy determination and outline methods for determining pregnancy,
- Give determining characteristics for age of the fetus in the cow at different stages of development,
- Be conversant on other palpable factors in addition to pregnancy, such as postpartum tract, freemartin, mummy, and enlarged cervix, and
- Discuss methods of determining pregnancy in the ewe, sow, mare, and woman.

GESTATION (To Bear)

The gestation period is that time involved in developing the young and its membranes from conception until birth. It varies with the species and even with breeds (Table 14–1). The gestation period in livestock prepares the newborn so that at birth it is capable of standing and nursing of its own ability. The newborn of the human is not so well developed and must have assistance.

The gestation period for the cow is 283 days average with considerable variation between breeds. Sheep carry their young about 147 days. Swine have a gestation length of 113 days. Mares carry their young 336 days. The woman has a gestation period of 267 days.

Gestation begins with the fertilized ovum and a signal to the corpus luteum to maintain its structure and continue to produce progesterone. The uterus responds by continued vascularity and glandularity to supply a secretion termed uterine milk, which nourishes the new life until attachment to the uterus occurs.

Hormonal Control

The mechanism by which the female knows she is pregnant is still unknown.[25,51,73] It evidently occurs very quickly so that the corpus luteum may be maintained.

Table 14-1 Gestation Lengths of Selected Animals

Animal	Length
Bison (American)	276 days
Cat (domestic)	52 days
Chinchilla	111 days
Cow	283 days
Coyote	60–65 days
Deer	7½ months
Dog	60 days
Elephant	21 months
Ewe	127 days
Goat	150 days
Guinea pigs	68 days
Hamster (Golden)	16 days
Jennet	164 days
Mare	336 days
(mule foal)	346 days
Mink	42 days
Monkey (rhesus)	163 days
Mouse	20 days
Opossum	13 days
Rabbit	32 days
Rat	21 days
Skunk	62 days
Sow	113 days
Squirrel	45 days
Woman	267 days

Production of progesterone by the blastocyst may be one reason; antiluteolytic products of the developing ovum may be the factors.

The production of progesterone, whether it be by the corpus luteum or placenta, maintains a quiet condition in the uterus with increased ability to transfer nutrients and remove waste products.

The corpus luteum is necessary for varying periods of time in different species. A few of these are shown in Table 14–2.

This points out the importance of progesterone regardless of its source and shows that the cow and sow depend very heavily on the corpus luteum for supply. Ovariectomy at any stage will cause abortion. However, in the ewe, mare, and woman, the production of progesterone is assumed by the placenta, and removal of the ovaries does not cause abortion after a given time for each species.

All of the species produce corpora lutea associated with ovulation, and all except the mare retain this corpus. The mare poses a rather different sequence of events. The corpus luteum develops and then may or may not regress after about 40 days, and secondary or accessory corpora lutea develop from either ruptured or unruptured follicles.[1,4] The original corpus is maintained until the other corpora regress at about 160 to 180 days.[69]

The hormonal pattern of progesterone and estrogen is somewhat similar for the various species (Fig. 14–1, 2, 3, 4, 6). The cow produces a relatively high level of progesterone as the CL develops. This level increases slowly until around 250 days of gestation when it starts to decline. The decline becomes a precipitous drop just before parturition. Estrogen is maintained throughout the gestation period by follicular growth and other sources until about the same time as a change occurs in progesterone. When progesterone decreases, estrogen increases and reaches a peak just before birth. There is a precipitous drop in estrogen at birth.[14,50,58]

The ewe follows a similar pattern of progesterone and estrogen with a lag in estrogen increase until a few days before parturition. At this time, estrogen increases rapidly and then falls suddenly at parturition.

The sow maintains a high level of progesterone only briefly that coincides with the peak in a normal cycle. The level then decreases and maintains a rather low level until a sudden drop just prior to parturition. Estrogen gradually increases until a rapid rise starting about 100 days in gestation. It continues to increase rapidly until parturition and drops very quickly.

The mare produces a rather irregular progesterone activity because of the

Table 14-2   Effects of Ovariectomy on Gestation

Species	Gestation length (days)	Day before which abortion would occur
Cow	283	Term
Ewe	147	50
Sow	113	Term
Mare	336	150, 200
Woman	267	30–60

Adapted from Catchpole,[14] Allen,[4] and Thorburn.[72]

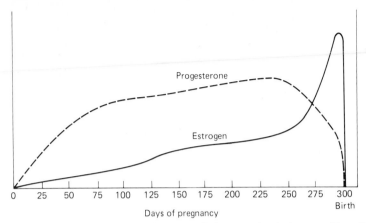

Figure 14-1 Progesterone and estrogen during gestation in the cow. *(From Catchpole[14]; Peterson et al.[50]; Robertson and Sarda[58]; and Thorburn.[72])*

ovarian changes.[3] There is a peak at about day 70, which is maintained for about 50 days. The level is then rather low until a brief rise just prior to parturition and a drop followed by parturition. Estrogen is rather erratic also and rises to a peak at day 200 before decreasing and maintaining itself until parturition when it too drops quickly.

The mare is peculiar in another way. Structures called endometrial cups develop on the surface of the endometrium at about 35 to 40 days of pregnancy. These structures resemble cups or channels with ridged walls (Fig. 14–5) and develop from cells sloughed from the chorioallantoic membrane. These attach themselves to the endometrial surface and form the ridges around the cups. The area is secretory and

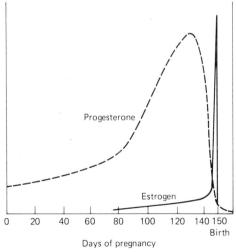

Figure 14-2 Progesterone and estrogen during gestation in the ewe. *(From Catchpole[14]; Robertson and Sarda[58]; and Thorburn.[72])*

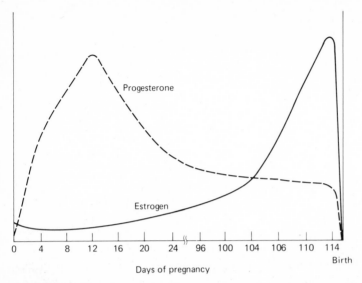

Figure 14-3 Progesterone and estrogen during gestation in the sow. *(From Catchpole[14]; and Thorburn.[72])*

is not a point of placental attachment. They are most abundant in a circle around the junction of the pregnant horn and the body of the uterus.[4] They actively produce gonadotropic hormones particularly rich in follicle stimulating activity with lesser luteinizing activity, called pregnant mare serum gonadotropin (PMSG). This production lasts for a period of approximately 100 days and then gradually disappears as the cups disintegrate.[4] This phenomenon is the basis for pregnancy determination in the mare and will be covered under that subject shortly. The gonadotropic hormone circulates in the blood of the mare and may be recovered in the blood serum for pharmaceutical uses.

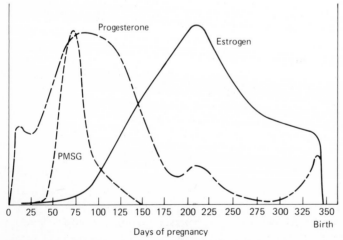

Figure 14-4 Progesterone, estrogen, and PMSG during gestation in the mare. *(From Catchpole.[14])*

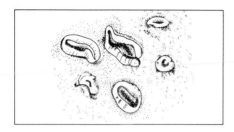

Figure 14-5 Endometrial cups of the mare.

The woman has a pattern of hormones similar to that of the mare (Fig. 14-6). Progesterone rises until about day 240 when it starts to decline. Estrogen is rising gradually until about the same point but continues to rise rapidly until parturition when it falls suddenly. The human chorionic gonadotropic hormone (HCG) rises particularly at about day 40 and peaks around day 90 to 100 after which it declines slowly to a basal level at approximately 150 days.

The woman produces hormones from the ovaries in early pregnancy but the placenta takes over quickly and produces the hormones necessary for maintenance. The precursors for these steroids are present in the vascular system and the conversion is believed to take place in the placenta.

The rise in HCG forms the basis for pregnancy determination by biological and immunoassay procedures.

Prenatal Period

The development of the new life is easily divided into three stages of development: ovum, embryo, and fetus.

Period of Ovum This period spans the time from fertilization until a change in shape and cellular makeup. The ovum goes through its various stages of cell division without changing drastically in shape or size. The newly fertilized ovum is a zygote.

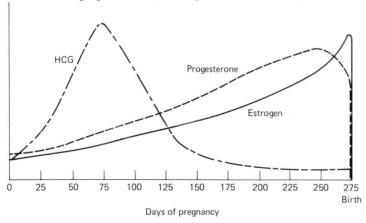

Days of pregnancy

Figure 14-6 Progesterone, estrogen, and HCG during gestation in the woman. *(From Fuchs[21]; Jaffe and Josimovich[35]; and Vaitukaitis.[74])*

Zygote The fertilized ovum divides to form two blastomeres, then four and so on in multiplication to form a solid mass of cells called the morula (Fig. 14–7).

Morula (mulberry) The mass of cells has no particular form and is encased in the zona pellucida. It floats free in the cavity of the uterus and is bathed by fluids of the endometrial glands in domestic animals.

Blastula (germ bladder) The blastula, also called blastocyst or blastocoele, is a fluid-filled cavity surrounded by a single layer of cells called the trophoblast in the early stages. It develops from the morula as the central cells begin to separate and continue to form a cavity. In the later stages of development, the cells at one pole congregate to form the embryonic disc or blastoderm. During this process the zona pellucida ruptures, releasing the "hatched" egg (Fig. 14–8). The continued multi-plication of cells causes thickening of the embryonic disc, and differentiation begins.

Embryo The period of the embryo is marked by the changing of cell structures from indifferent types to specialized cells to develop into tissues and organs to form the gastrula.

Gastrula (belly) Gastrulation is marked by a thickening of the trophoblast to form the ectoderm. There are three cell layers that develop in gastrulation: ectoderm, mesoderm, and entoderm. Gastrulation begins at about day 13 in the cow.

   Ectoderm (outer skin) This embryonic cell layer is destined to form the outer skin, epidermis, and the hair and hooves on the outside and the brain and nervous

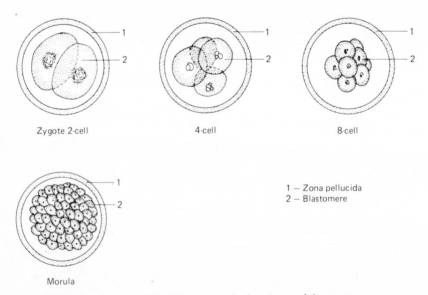

Zygote 2-cell   4-cell   8-cell

Morula

1 — Zona pellucida
2 — Blastomere

Figure 14-7 Development of the blastomeres in the stages of the ovum.

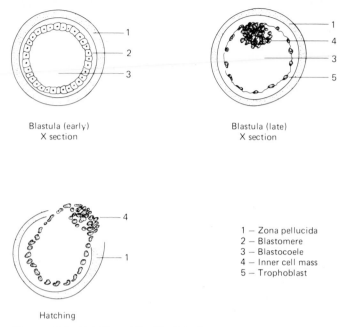

Blastula (early)
X section

Blastula (late)
X section

1 — Zona pellucida
2 — Blastomere
3 — Blastocoele
4 — Inner cell mass
5 — Trophoblast

Hatching

Figure 14-8 Hatching of the blastocyst.

system internally. It lines the mouth as an invagination. The early ectoderm forms the outer shell in gastrulation over the embryonic disc and surrounding the cavity of the gastrula (Fig. 14–9).

Mesoderm (middle skin) The middle cell layer originates from the embryonic disc and spreads under the ectoderm and over the entoderm. It eventually forms the structural tissues such as muscle, cartilage, ligaments, and bones as well as such organs of circulation as the heart, vascular system, and lymph vessels. It forms the gonads and the genital ducts.

Entoderm (inner skin) This sheet of cells forms under the embryonic disc and gradually becomes the inner lining of the cavity. Resulting structures of the entoderm include some of the glands, the liver, and the lining of the gastrointestinal tract.

It is during and following gastrulation that the organs are formed as the cell layers differentiate. During this period of the embryo the individual forms the extraembryonic membranes that surround it for protection and as a means of nourishment.

Growth and development of the young are shown in Tables 14–3, 4, 5, 6, 7 and Figures 14–10, 11, 12, 13, and 14 for the cow, ewe, sow, mare, and woman embryos. Other patterns of growth in the calf are given by Winters, Green, and Comstock.[79]

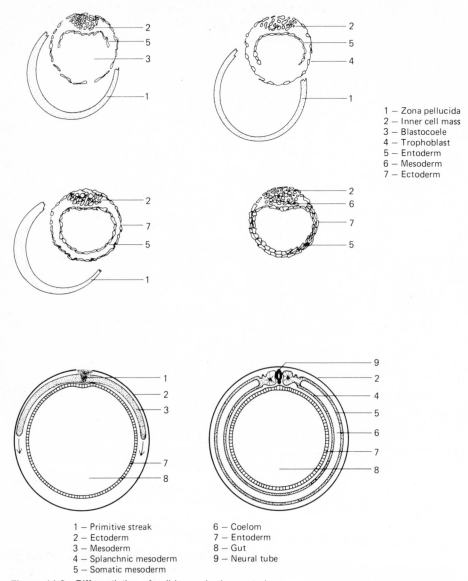

1 — Zona pellucida
2 — Inner cell mass
3 — Blastocoele
4 — Trophoblast
5 — Entoderm
6 — Mesoderm
7 — Ectoderm

1 — Primitive streak   6 — Coelom
2 — Ectoderm   7 — Entoderm
3 — Mesoderm   8 — Gut
4 — Splanchnic mesoderm   9 — Neural tube
5 — Somatic mesoderm

Figure 14-9 Differentiation of cell layers in the gastrula.

Extraembryonic membranes It has already been mentioned that the fertilized ovum is floating free in the uterus of domestic species. This is an extended period of 30 to 35 days in the cow,[37,46] 20 days in the ewe, 18 days in the sow, and 25 days in the mare.[59] The blastocyst of the woman imbeds itself in the wall of the uterus about 6 days after fertilization, and the extraembyonic membranes then grow out into the uterine cavity. The membranes consist of the chorion, amnion, and allantois.

Table 14-3 External Characteristics of Cow Embryos

Days of gestation	Characteristics
18	Primitive streak present; amnion complete
19	Neural folds and first somites forming
23	Neural tube closed; first branchial arch present; allantois crescent-shaped sac; eye and ear vesicles present
24	Three primary brain vesicles visible; second branchial arch present; fore-limb bud present
25	Embryo C-shaped; third branchial arch present
26	Fourth branchial arch and mammary ridge present; hind limb bud forming
30	Eye pits forming; eyes pigmented; hand plate present
34	Facial clefts closed; eye pits deep; acoustic groove present; grooves between forelimb digits
38	Eyelids forming; ear present as ridge; genital tubercle present; grooves between hind-limb digits
40	Ear partly covers acoustic groove
45	Tactile hair follicles on upper lip and above eyes; tongue visible; ear covers acoustic groove; digits separated distally
50	Eyelids begin to cover eyes
56	Palate fused
60	Eyelids fused; external genitals differentiated; hooves forming; horn bud appears
76	Tactile hairs appear on face; hair follicles present on body
80	Ear directed caudally exposing groove with its epithelial plug; teats present; hooves begin to cornify
83	Scrotum present
100	Acoustic groove open again; hooves becoming firm and opaque
110	Tooth eruption begins
150	Lower lip and chin covered with fine hair; eyelashes present; tactile hairs on chin; color markings appear; hooves and dew claws become hard; teats well formed; descent of testes complete
182	Horn bud covered with hair; tail-tip hairs present
196	Eyelids separated
230	Body fully covered with hair
278–290	Birth

Adapted from Evans and Sack.[17]

CHORION (Skin) This is the outer membrane and forms at the same time as the amnion.

AMNION (Lamb) This is the innermost membrane surrounding the embryo. The amnion and chorion form as a folding of the outer ectoderm and the underlying somatic mesoderm (Fig. 14–15) so that an envelope forms around the embryo, which is called the amnion, and an outer envelope is formed on the outside, called the chorion. The amnion and its fluid protect the embryo, and in later stages the amnion collects excretions from the urinary and gastrointestinal systems.[59]

YOLK SAC The yolk sac is formed by the entoderm lining the cavity of the gastrula in the midgut region. It is covered with splanchnic mesoderm. It has no

Table 14-4   External Characteristics of Sheep Embryos

Days of gestation	Characteristics
10–13	Embryonic shield; rapid elongation of blastocyst
13–14	Formation of neural plate, primitive streak, and amnion
15	Neural folds appear; somites forming; amnion complete
16	Allantois visible grossly; closure of neural tube begins
17	Allantois crescent-shaped sac; three primary brain vesicles present; torsion of caudal end of embryo
18	Two branchial arches present
19	Eye vesicle, ear plate, and third branchial arch present
20	Forelimb bud present; heart bulge prominent
21	Embryo C-shaped; neural tube closed; fourth branchial arch appears; hind-limb bud present
22	Hand plate present; eye plate present
23	Foot plate present; eye pits appear
25	Eye cup and lens well formed; eye pigmented
27	Acoustic groove present; ear present as ridge; eyelids forming; third and fourth forelimb digits prominent
29	Grooves between hind-limb digits
30	Ear triangular; facial clefts closed; tongue visible
34	Tactile hair follicles above and below eyes; ear partly covers acoustic groove; digits separated distally
38	Tactile hair follicles on upper lip; eyelids partly cover eyes; palate fused
43	Groove in upper lip present; eyelids fused; ear covers acoustic groove; external genitals differentiated; teats present
57	Fine hair appears on head
64	Hair follicles present on body
60–67	Hair begins to cover body
66	Ear directed caudally, exposing acoustic meatus
70	Scrotum, penis, labia, and clitoris well developed
70–77	Horn bud present
75–90	Tactile hairs appear on face
80	Testes have descended into scrotum
104	Color markings appear
116	Hair covering complete
119–126	Eyelids separated
120	Wooly hair begins to grow
147–155	Birth

Adapted from Evans and Sack.[17]

useful function in domestic animals and gradually disappears with age. It is best observed in the mare where it persists longer.

ALLANTOIS (Sausage) The third membrane, the allantois, forms as an outpocketing of the hind gut near the yolk sac along the umbilical cord. The umbilical cord prior to this is primarily amnion. The allantois is covered with splanchnic mesoderm as it grows sacklike into the chorionic vesicle. Until this time we have had only two vesicles or sacs, the amnion inside and the chorion outside. Now a third sac is invading and displacing the second one (Fig. 14–16). Try to picture this displacement three-dimensionally. The allantois starts as a rounded protuberance and forms

Table 14-5   External Characteristics of Pig Embryos

Days of gestation	Characteristics
12	Primitive streak complete
13	Neural tube open
14–15	First somites forming
15–16	Eye vesicle, ear plate, and first and second branchial arches present
16	Neural tube closing
15–17	Third and fourth branchial arches present; torsion of caudal end of embryo; amnion complete
16–17	Forelimb bud forming
17–18	Embryo C-shaped; allantois crescent-shaped sac; ear vesicle present; heart bulge prominent; hind-limb bud forming
19	Lens and eye cup well developed
20–21	Eyes pigmented; eye pits present; intestines herniate into umbilical cord; genital tubercle and lateral swellings present
22	Hand plate and foot plate present; mammary ridge present; end of somite formation
28	Tactile hair follicles appear; eyelids forming; mammary primordia present; external genitals differentiated; digits forming
32.5	Third and fourth digits most prominent
34.5	Palate fused; facial clefts closed
36–49	Eyelids begin to cover eyes
44	Prepuce, scrotum, labia, and clitoris present
50	Eyelids fused; intestines returned into abdomen
90	Eyelids separated
112–116	Birth

Adapted from Evans and Sack.[17]

an anchor shape in cross section, then starts to push out in all directions. Remember balloons that you saw or purchased at carnivals. A balloon in the shape of Mickey Mouse or some other creature was inside a second rounded balloon. If you could put a third balloon between the two and gradually displace the air in the outer one with the intermediate one then you get the picture of what is happening.

The allantois eventually fills the much elongated chorionic cavity so that only a small amount of chorionic fluid may remain in the very tips.

As the allantois touches the outer surface of the amnion and the inner surface of the chorion, there is fusion of the splanchnic and somatic mesoderm layers to form the *amnioallantoic membrane* and the *chorioallantoic membrane.* Thus there are now only two membranes with two sacs of fluid as we had earlier. Meantime the yolk sac has regressed.

The allantois is responsible for vascularization of the outer membrane, and following its fusion with the chorion there is organization of a vascular system in the chorioallantoic membrane connected to the embryo.

The allantois collects urine through the urachus in the umbilical cord in early development. This closes and the excretions then enter the amnion.[59]

The extraembryonic membranes become the *placenta* through which nutrients and wastes are exchanged and which finally is expelled as the afterbirth at parturition.

Table 14-6   External Characteristics of Horse Embryos

Days of gestation	Characteristics
20	Allantois forming; eye vesicle and ear present
21	Amnion complete
24	Embryo crescent-shaped
26	Pontine fissure present; forelimb bud present; three branchial arches present; eye appears 0.5 mm in diameter
30	Genital tubercle present; lens visible
36	Feet tapered with rudiments of three digits; eyes pigmented; facial clefts closing; acoustic groove forming
40	Ear forming; nostrils visible; elbow and stifle regions evident; eyelids developing
42	Ear triangular and pointing cephalad; mammary ridge present
45	External genitals differentiated
47	Palate fused
49	Teats present
55	Eyelids almost closed; ear covers acoustic groove
63	Eyelids fused; wall, sole, and frog of hoof recognizable
75	Clitoris prominent
80	Scrotum present
95	Ear curls cephalad and ventrally; hoof is yellow; coronary corium present as ridge
112	Tactile hairs on lips; teats well formed
120	Fine hair on muzzle, chin, and around eyes; orbital area prominent; ergot prominent
150	Eyelashes emerging; udder forming
180	Mane and tail hair present
210	Mane hair 2.5 mm long
240	Hair appears on poll, ears, throat, chin, and muzzle; mane hair 5 mm long; hair covers distal half of tail
270	Body covered with fine hair; mane hair 15 mm long; short switch on tail
335	Birth

Adapted from Evans and Sack.[17]

Figure 14–17 outlines changes in the human membrane development.

Fetus This period is begun by attachment of the extraembryonic membranes to the endometrium and a change from a free-floating structure to one that is attached directly. There is organ and structure development at this time, and the major changes from now until parturition are in growth and development (Fig. 14–10 through 14–14).

Placenta (pancake) The placenta forms differently in the various animals. It is usually classified according to its structural relations to the uterus and by its shape.

Structure Structure is determined primarily by the layers of cells that are present in the extraembryonic membranes and uterus separating the two vascular systems. There are six layers of cells, maximum, separating the two systems, and in some species some of the layers are sloughed during attachment.

Table 14-7 External Characteristics of Human Embryos

Days of gestation	Characteristics
18	Primitive streak prominent; allantois present
25	Neural groove deepens and closes; somites present; branchial arches 1 and 2 forming; eye and ear vesicles present
28	Heart prominent; all somites present; eye present; body C-shaped; lung buds; neural tube closed; ear pit closed
35	Nasal pits; tail prominent; heart and liver protrude; Rathke's pouch becomes stalked pouch
42	Upper jaw forming; lower jaw halves fuse; external ear; limbs recognizable
49	Face and neck forming; digits forming; tail regressing; muscles differentiating; eyelids forming
56	Nose flat; digits formed; head elevating; fetal state reached; Rathke's pouch detaches; gonads distinguishable; Mullerian ducts ready to unite; ossification indicated
70	Head erect; limbs modeled; palate fused, eyelids fused
84	Sex differentiation visible; continued growth
112	Face looks human; hair beginning on head; hypophysis differentiating; body hair beginning; eye, ear, and nose become typical in shape; muscular movement
140–280	Lanugo hair; eyelids reopen; nail reaches fingertip; nose and ear ossify; continued growth
267–285	Birth

Adapted from Arey.[6]

The six cell layers include the *endothelium* lining the blood vessels of the endometrium, the *connective tissue* forming the matrix or network holding things together, and the *epithelium* covering the surface of the uterus. Continuing to the vascular bed of the placenta, the *epithelium* of the chorion is encountered first, followed by *connective tissue* and *endothelium* as on the dam's side (Fig. 14–18). Thus six layers separate blood systems.

EPITHELIOCHORIAL (Surface Cells–Skin) This structural type of placenta is found in the cow,[37] sow, and mare. The first part of the word relates to the dam and the second part to the fetus. Therefore, the epithelium is present on the uterus, and the chorion is adjacent and intact. There are, then, six layers of cell types present because none are missing (Fig. 14–18).

Table 14-8 Placental Structures and Shapes

Structural type	Shape	Cell layers present						Animal
		Dam			Fetus			
		Endo	CT	Epi	Epi	CT	Endo	
Epitheliochorial	Diffuse	+	+	+	+	+	+	Mare, sow
	Cotyledonary	+	+	+	+	+	+	Cow
Syndesmochorial	Cotyledonary	+	+	−	+	+	+	Ewe
Hemochorial	Discoid	−	−	−	+	+	+	Woman

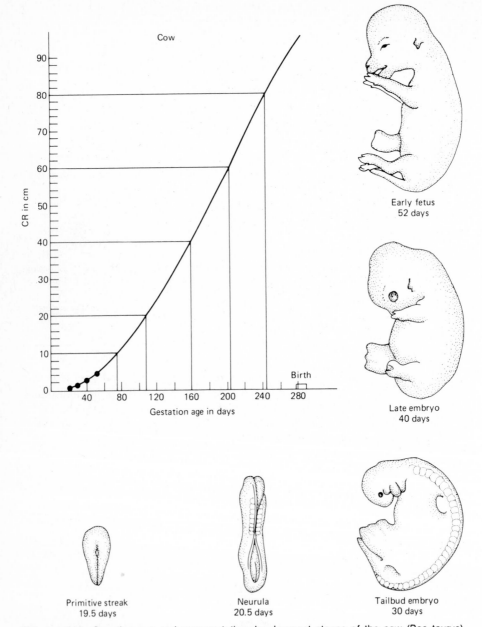

Figure 14-10 Growth curve and representative development stages of the cow (Bos taurus). *(From Evans and Sack.[17])*

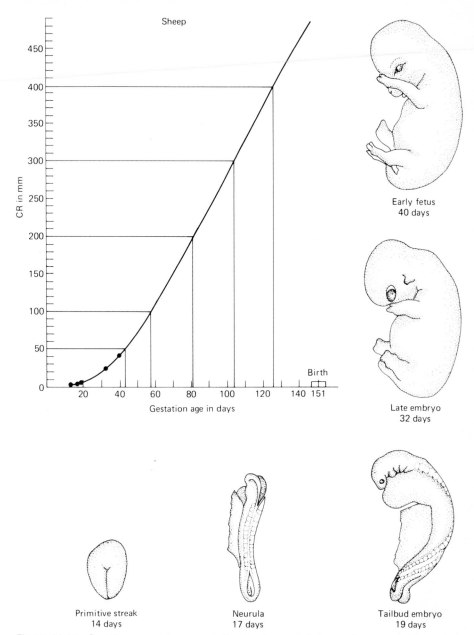

Figure 14-11 Growth curve and representative developmental stages of the sheep (Ovis aries). *(From Evans and Sack.[17])*

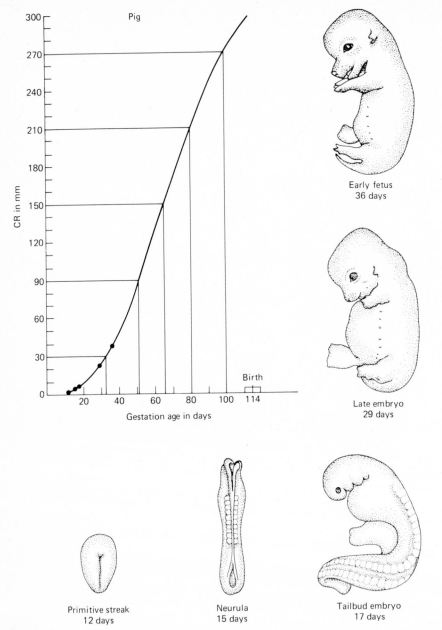

Figure 14-12 Growth curve and representative developmental stages of the pig (Sus scrofa). *(From Evans and Sack.[17])*

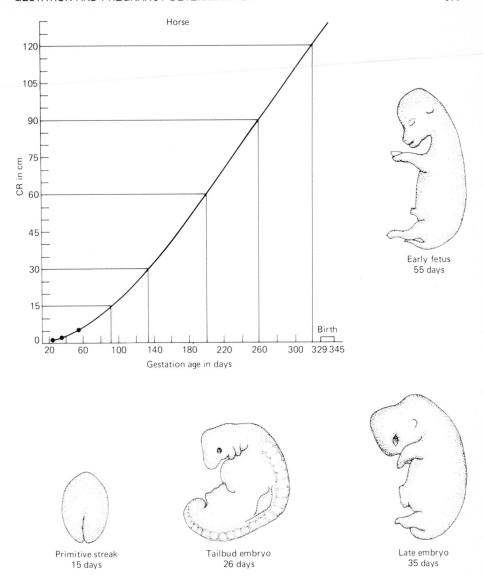

Figure 14-13 Growth curve and representative developmental stages of the horse (Equus caballus). *(From Evans and Sack.[17])*

SYNDESMOCHORIAL (Band Skin) The syndesmochorial type consists of connective tissue as the surface cell layer against the intact chorion. Thus only five layers separate the blood systems with two on the dam's side and three on the fetus's side. This type is found in the ewe.

HEMOCHORIAL (Blood Skin) The hemochorial structural type has the blood of the dam bathing the intact fetal placenta. It must be realized that in instances such

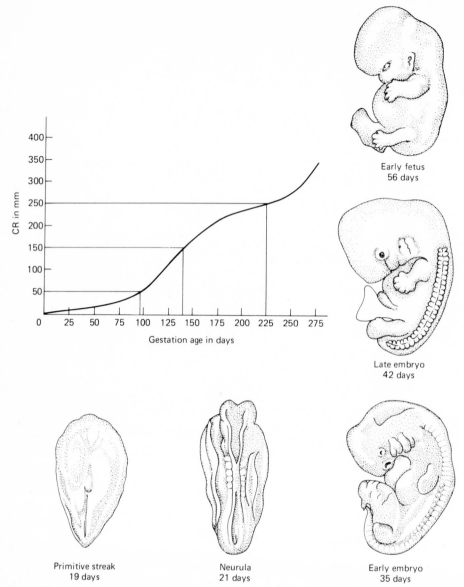

Figure 14-14 Growth curve and representative development stages of the human (Homo sapiens). *(Adapted from Arey[6] and Gruenwald.[26])*

as this there are areas of cellular attachment, but the nearest the blood systems approach one another is three cell layers in the fetal placenta. This type is present in the woman.

Table 14–8 summarizes the structural types of placentae.

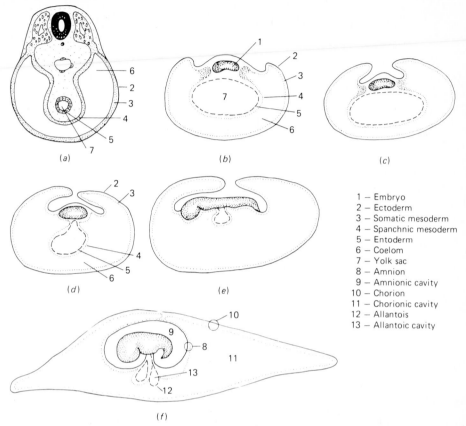

Figure 14-15 Development of extraembryonic membranes.

1 – Embryo
2 – Ectoderm
3 – Somatic mesoderm
4 – Spanchnic mesoderm
5 – Entoderm
6 – Coelom
7 – Yolk sac
8 – Amnion
9 – Amnionic cavity
10 – Chorion
11 – Chorionic cavity
12 – Allantois
13 – Allantoic cavity

Shape Placental shape offers a method of classification related to the attached areas.

DIFFUSE The diffuse-shaped placenta is found in the mare and sow and refers to attachment over most if not the entire placental surface. The attachment is by means of *villi,* or fingerlike projections, on the surface of the chorion penetrating the crypts, or depressions, on the surface of the endometrium (Fig. 14–19). These attachments are very firm during gestation, and this is the surface at which exchange takes place. There is a thinning of the cellular tissues with age to assist in diffusion across the membranes.[60]

The villi deteriorate and are released at parturition for expulsion of the placenta.

COTYLEDONARY (Cup) Cotyledon is a name that should be familiar to anyone who has studied biology. Seeds of plants such as beans form cotyledons to feed or nourish the new plant. So, these cotyledons serve as points of nutrient exchange. They are localized areas of villi in the cow and ewe placentae that develop opposite the caruncles that are present on the endometrial surface.

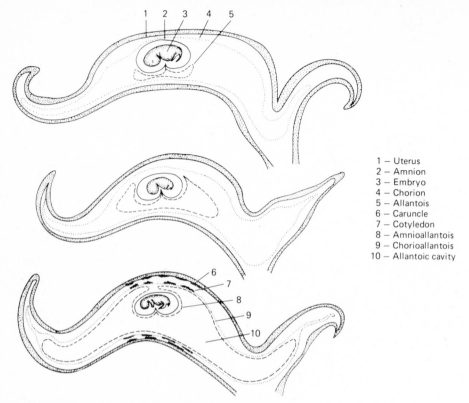

1 – Uterus
2 – Amnion
3 – Embryo
4 – Chorion
5 – Allantois
6 – Caruncle
7 – Cotyledon
8 – Amnioallantois
9 – Chorioallantois
10 – Allantoic cavity

Figure 14-16 Development of the allantois in the cow.

There are villi on the chorion surface and crypts on the uterine surface, and as the cotyledon and caruncle fuse they are called a *placentome*.

The cow placentome has the cotyledonary portion growing to cover the caruncle (Fig. 14–19), while the sheep cotyledon grows into the concave surface of the caruncle. The placentome becomes rather pendulous with age. Figure 14–20 shows a portion of the placenta of a 4-month-old calf and the many placentomes may be seen as the termination of blood vessels emanating from the umbilical cord.

DISCOID The name is descriptive. The placenta is round and flattened with some curvature like a disc. This shape is found in the woman and primates. There are villi and crypts as in other species but they are localized in a particular disc-shaped area. The remainder of the placenta is not attached (Fig. 14–21).

Other types of placentae are found in different species: zonary in dogs and cats; discoid in rats and rabbits.

Reproductive Embryology The indifferent stages of the reproductive organs for male and female are present in the embryo. The genetic makeup of the embryo determines the sexual organs that will develop and which structures will regress (Table 14–9).

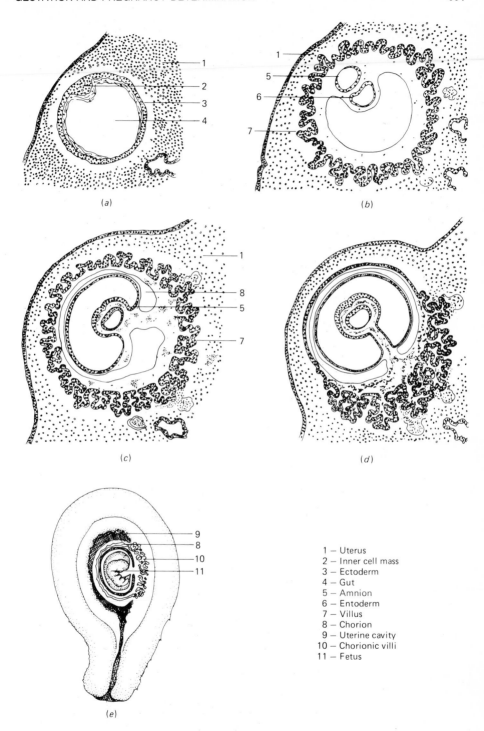

Figure 14-17 Extraembryonic membranes of the human.

1 — Uterus
2 — Inner cell mass
3 — Ectoderm
4 — Gut
5 — Amnion
6 — Entoderm
7 — Villus
8 — Chorion
9 — Uterine cavity
10 — Chorionic villi
11 — Fetus

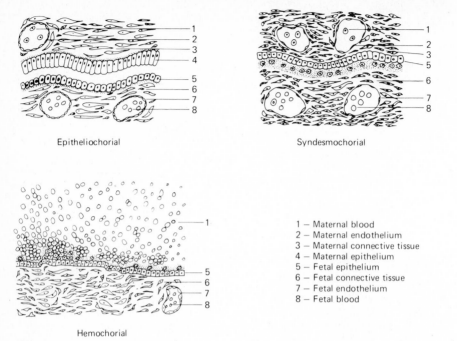

Epitheliochorial

Syndesmochorial

Hemochorial

1 — Maternal blood
2 — Maternal endothelium
3 — Maternal connective tissue
4 — Maternal epithelium
5 — Fetal epithelium
6 — Fetal connective tissue
7 — Fetal endothelium
8 — Fetal blood

Figure 14-18   The cell layers separating the vascular systems of the dam and fetal membranes.

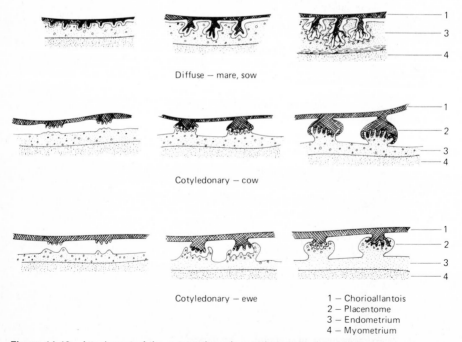

Diffuse — mare, sow

Cotyledonary — cow

Cotyledonary — ewe

1 — Chorioallantois
2 — Placentome
3 — Endometrium
4 — Myometrium

Figure 14-19   Attachment of the extraembryonic membranes to the uterus.

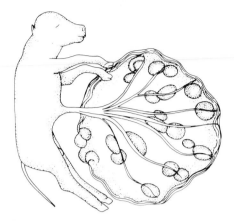

Figure 14-20 Portion of the placenta from a 4-month pregnant cow.

Figure 14–22 shows some of the embryonic structures for orientation. Each structure will be discussed briefly as it differentiates.

Gonad (from semen) The indifferent gonads develop in the genital ridges, which protrude along the dorsal wall of the peritoneal cavity on each side of the midline. The primordial germ cells migrate from the mesentery into the genital ridge, and these develop as the gonads differentiate into the *testes* of the male and *ovaries* of the female. The testes follow a route of descent into the scrotum as described earlier, and the ovaries remain in the same general area.

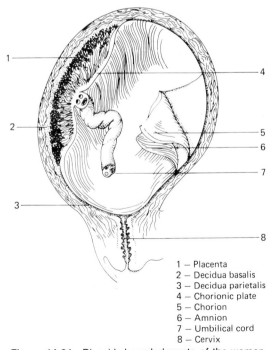

1 — Placenta
2 — Decidua basalis
3 — Decidua parietalis
4 — Chorionic plate
5 — Chorion
6 — Amnion
7 — Umbilical cord
8 — Cervix

Figure 14-21 Discoid shaped placenta of the woman.

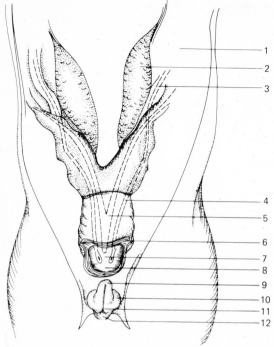

1 — Peritoneal cavity
2 — Gonads
3 — Mesonephric tubules
4 — Mesonephric ducts
5 — Mullerian ducts
6 — Wall of urogenital sinus
7 — Site of Muller's tubercle
8 — Urogenital sinus
9 — Phallus
10 — Labio-scrotal swellings
11 — Fissure
12 — Anus

Figure 14-22   Embryonic urogenital ducts and structures.

Mesonephric tubules (middle-kidney tubules) There is no male tubular system laid down per se. It borrows a portion of the mesonephros or urinary system and develops this into structures of the male system. The cranial portion of the mesonephric tubules branch to form numerous tubules that form the efferent ductules coming from the testes. The tubules regress in the female so that only vestigial structures remain. The mesonephric portion may be called Wolffian.

Mesonephric ducts The straighter portion of the mesonephric tube is called the duct and extends from union with the tubules to Muller's tubercle. The cranial portion forms the coiled epididymides followed by the deferent ducts with outpocketings forming the vesicular glands. The ducts or deferent ducts open on the surface of Muller's tubercle. There are no female structures forming from the mesonephric ducts.

Mullerian ducts The term *mullerian* is used for Dr. Johannes Muller, a German physiologist, who first found these structures. There is no structural name for them. They develop specifically as a part of the female system and are not borrowed as the mesonephric portion. The long ducts develop into the tubular structures, specifically the *oviducts, cornua* and *body of the uterus, cervix,* and *vagina.* The paired ducts flair at the cranial end to form the infundibulum and join caudally to form the body of the uterus, cervix, and vagina. The vagina ends at the urogenital sinus in the area of Muller's tubercle. Only vestigial structures remain in the male.

Table 14-9 Indifferent Embryonic Structures and Their End Products

Male	Indifferent	Female
Testes	Gonads	Ovaries
Efferent ductules	Mesonephric tubules	Vestigial
Epididymides	Mesonephric ducts	Vestigial
Deferent ducts		
Vesicular glands		
Vestigial	Mullerian ducts	Oviducts
		Uterus
		Cervix
		Vagina
Colliculus seminalis	Muller's tubercle	Site of the hymen
Urethra	Urogenital sinus	Vestibule
Prostate gland		
Bulbourethral glands		
	Genital tubercle	
Penis	Phallus	Clitoris
Glans penis	Glans	Glans clitoris
Scrotum	Labioscrotal swellings	Vulva

Partially from Arey.[6]

Muller's tubercle This bulging area in the wall of the urogenital sinus forms the *colliculus seminalis* in the male and later joins the urethra to the exterior. The tubercle forms the *site of the hymen* in the female. It is the end of the internal tubular structures.

Urogenital sinus This cavity forms from the exterior. The invagination in the male becomes a portion of the pelvic urethra, and outgrowths of the wall form the *prostate* gland cranially and the *bulbourethral* glands caudally. The *vestibule* is formed in the female with vestibular glands in some species.

Genital tubercle The swelling that develops caudally to the umbilical cord forms the phallus, urethral groove, and the labioscrotal swellings.

Phallus The phallus is destined to form the *penis* of the male or the *clitoris* of the female. The *glans* indifferent structure forms the glans of the respective organs.

Urethral groove The groove closes as the lateral folds envelop the urethra of the penis. They form a portion of vaginal labia or lips in the female. The shaft of the penis is formed by the walls of the tubercle closing over the urethra. The fissure closes to form the *raphe* along the penis to the anus.

Shaft The cavernous tissue of the tubercle forms the structural body of the penis or clitoris.

Labioscrotal swellings These swellings lie lateral to the tubercle base and close and join in the male to form the *scrotum*. The raphe of the penis continues over the union of the two folds. The *labia* of the vulva form in the female and the urethral groove remains exposed as the vestibule.

PREGNANCY DETERMINATION

The determination of pregnancy is very important, since the date of predicted parturition may be calculated and preparations made.[38] Pregnant animals must be treated differently in supplying necessary nutrients and management.

Cow

The major advantage in determining pregnancy in cattle is to eliminate nonbreeders and thereby select for the better-reproducing dams.[10] In turn, economic returns are increased through a higher percent calf crop and more salable pounds of beef. Table 14–10 was derived from cost and production figures to yield the effect of improved calf crop percent on economic return. The figures given are calculated on the basis of $120 per year operating cost for a cow. This figure certainly changes with the times, but it may be used in a relative sense. The following formula and procedures yield the cost per pound of calf produced at weaning.

Weaning weight in kg $\times$ calf crop % $=$ kg calf per cow

$$\frac{\text{operating cost per cow}}{\text{kg calf per cow}} = \text{cost per kg of calf}$$

Example:

227 kg $\times$ .80 $=$ 181 kg

$$\frac{\$120}{181 \text{ kg}} = \$.66 \text{ or } 66¢/\text{kg}$$

The higher the calf crop percent at any given weight, the lower the cost per kilogram of calf and therefore the greater profit. For example, a calf that weighs 227 kg at weaning from a herd with a 70 percent calf crop would cost 66¢ per kilogram to produce. Any selling price above that means profit, while a price below means a loss. Any combination can be read off the chart.

Better management of the stock is possible when the cattle can be separated or culled based on a knowledge of pregnancy.

In the dairy industry, milk production depends on calving and therefore is directly related to pregnancy: no calf, no milk.

Various methods of determining pregnancy have been devised: hormone changes, feeling for the pregnancy, antibody reactions, change in shape and size, and electronics. Methods of choice will be discussed with a word about alternative methods. The *first sign of pregnancy* is skipping an estrous period, and good records will assist in determining this. The major means of determining pregnancy in the cow is by palpation per rectum.

Table 14-10   Production Cost Per Kilogram (Pound) Beef Produced
When the Cow Operating Cost Is $120

Calf crop percent	Weaning weight, kilograms (pounds)					
	272 (600)	249 (550)	227 (500)	204 (450)	181 (400)	159 (350)
100	272 (600)[1]	249 (550)	227 (500)	204 (450)	181 (400)	159 (350)
	44 (20)[2]	48 (22)	53 (24)	59 (27)	66 (30)	75 (34)
90	245 (540)	225 (495)	204 (450)	184 (405)	163 (360)	143 (315)
	49 (22)	53 (24)	59 (27)	65 (30)	74 (33)	84 (38)
80	218 (480)	200 (440)	181 (400)	163 (360)	145 (320)	127 (280)
	55 (25)	60 (27)	66 (30)	74 (33)	83 (38)	94 (43)
70	191 (420)	175 (385)	159 (350)	143 (315)	127 (280)	111 (245)
	63 (29)	69 (31)	75 (34)	84 (38)	94 (43)	108 (49)
60	163 (360)	150 (330)	136 (300)	122 (270)	109 (240)	95 (210)
	74 (33)	80 (36)	88 (40)	98 (44)	110 (50)	126 (57)

[1] Top figures indicate kilograms (pounds) of calf produced per cow.
[2] Bottom figures relate the cost per kilogram (pound) of calf, cents.

Palpation Palpation means "to feel," and this method consists of feeling the reproductive tract for signs of pregnancy.[47] These signs may be enlargement, displacement, presence of the fetus, or presence of secondary factors such as fluid, placentomes, and uterine artery change. The description shall be given for palpating a cow in a stepwise manner following consideration of a few factors involved in palpation.

Facilities The facilities for palpation are very similar to those for AI. A working chute to hold the cow with a gate behind her is a must if any number of animals is to be palpated. The crowding chute for keeping cows available to the palpator should be sufficiently long to eliminate delays due to lack of stock. A cutting gate should be arranged as the cattle leave the palpation chute so divisions of cattle can be made quickly and efficiently. Figure 14–23 shows a simple arrangement for cutting cattle three ways. An example of a three-way cut would be one pen for culling nonpregnant cows, one for short pregnancies, and one for advanced pregnancies.

A division such as this also allows undesirable cows to be culled even though they may be pregnant. These may be cows with poor structural udders, mastitis, cancer eye, foot rot, or any other factors affecting reproductive efficiency.

Equipment and supplies There is little needed in the way of equipment and supplies. A protective sleeve should be worn. Palpating without protection leaves the individual susceptible to disease, particularly if there are any cuts or open wounds on the hands or arms. Plastic sleeves are very inexpensive and should be shoulder length. Thinner sleeves give better feel of the organs but do not last as long as heavier ones. Whichever is used is the choice of the palpator. Most prefer the thinner sleeves. If care is taken, as many as 20 to 50 cows may be palpated with one sleeve before a

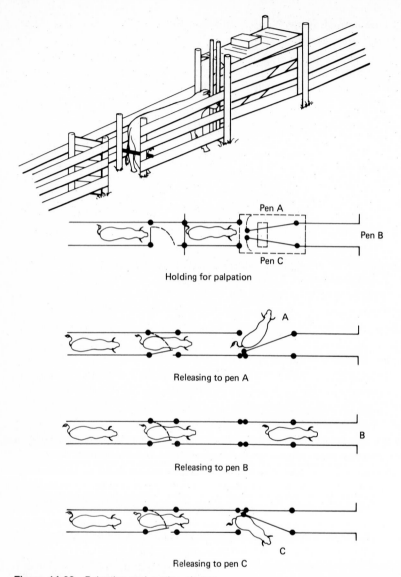

Pen A

Pen B

Pen C

Holding for palpation

Releasing to pen A

Releasing to pen B

Releasing to pen C

Figure 14-23 Palpating and cutting chutes.

leak occurs. A rubber band around the sleeve on the upper arm helps retain it when extracting the arm from the rectum. Rubber sleeves have been available until recently but are very rare and expensive. Care is a definite problem since they will rot, puncture, and split. They do give a better feel if a surgeon's glove is attached to the heavier sleeve. It is not necessary to change sleeves after each cow if they are in a common herd.

A lubricant is also needed. If the cows are on lush pasture, a little water is sufficient. If pasture is dry or the cattle are on hay, a considerable amount of lubricant may be needed. Many lubricants are available: liquid soap, mineral oil, many commercial veterinary lubricants, and KY jelly, just to mention a few. These are to lubricate the hand, arm, and anus on insertion and the rectum as penetration occurs. A little lubricant saves damaging the rectum and discomfort to the cow. The most common lubricants are liquid soap and mineral oil. Detergents are not satisfactory as lubricants.

Records Some record of the condition of the cow should be kept. This may be a record on the cow herself, such as marking her with crayon, paint, or branding, or by cutting the tip of the tail off. Crayon marks are of short duration—a few days to a few weeks. Water-base exterior paint works very well. Cutting off the tail is fairly long-lasting but also tends to disfigure the appearance of the cow and indicates something is wrong to a prospective buyer. An explanation that she is not pregnant must then follow. A cow that is not pregnant is commonly called "open."

A written record with a brand, tattoo, or ear tag number identifies the cow for the future. All cattle should be identified permanently in some way. These records are essential in instances where a cow has produced several calves and then is open at the time of palpation. She may be kept another year, but the history needs to be recorded. The age of the calf, or stage of pregnancy, can be recorded as indicated by an experienced palpator.

Time and labor The time for actual palpation should be less than a minute. Short-term pregnancies of 30 to 40 days require longer times than mid-pregnancies, and these take longer than advanced pregnancies. An experienced palpator with a good working crew should be able to palpate 600 to 800 cows in a day's time. Conditions determining the speed are mainly labor and livestock.

If livestock are gentle, handled without excitement, and the facilities are adequate, then a minimum of help is needed. Excited stock in poor facilities and with green help prolongs the exercise and is very frustrating.

The dairy situation eliminates many of these problems, and the cows may be palpated as they stand in the stanchion or are held by the herdsman in most instances. Dairy cattle kick, so be forewarned. Records of insemination are usually available that remove guesswork in determining age. The best palpating experience available is in palpating dairy cattle with accurate records and checking observations against them.

Preparation The palpator must be familiar with the reproductive system, stages of pregnancy, anatomy of the abdominal organs, and the pelvic skeleton. The previous studies on the tract and growth and development of membranes, fetus, and fluids should be reviewed if you have forgotten them. These structures are moved around in the abdominal cavity according to the various pressures of other organs, movement of the animal, and position of the animal.

The rumen is the largest compartment of the stomach (Fig. 14–24). It is located on the left side of the abdominal cavity and when full may protrude into the pelvic opening, making palpation very difficult. The pendulous uterus supported by the

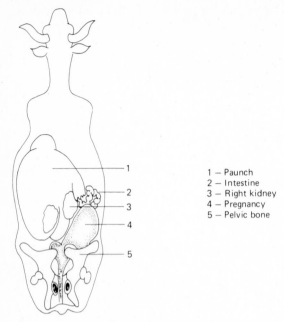

1 — Paunch
2 — Intestine
3 — Right kidney
4 — Pregnancy
5 — Pelvic bone

Figure 14-24   Abdominal structures involved in palpation for pregnancy.

broad ligament may be forced to the right side and ventrally as the uterine content increases with pregnancy.

The kidneys are lobulated structures about the size of an apple just off center and high in the abdominal cavity. They are pendulous and must be recognized so that they are not confused with pregnancy. They are about elbow-deep and higher than the pregnant uterus in most cases.

The bladder may be full and the rectum may be distended at the time of palpation. If cattle are gathered and allowed to fast overnight there is usually little difficulty experienced with palpating the bladder because the urine has been voided. Even without this preliminary step, palpation of the bladder is rare. The wall is thicker feeling and the contents are fluid without restraining membranes giving it a characteristic texture. If the rectum is full of dry feces it may be necessary to clean the rectum. Usually the hand can "submarine" under the feces to feel the underlying reproductive tract.

The pelvic bone is home base for the inexperienced palpator. It does not move, and orientation is usually given according to its landmarks. Study Figure 14–25 carefully and practice on a real pelvis. The cranial ventral rim is commonly referred to as the rim of the pelvis and is an important structure for orientation.

Procedure

Restrain and observe the cow. Look at her. A cow in poor condition, that is, with most of the bones showing and little flesh covering, is likely to be open. She

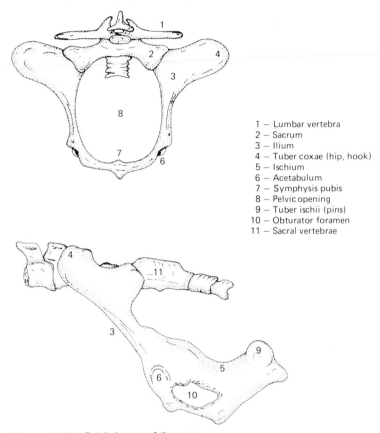

1 — Lumbar vertebra
2 — Sacrum
3 — Ilium
4 — Tuber coxae (hip, hook)
5 — Ischium
6 — Acetabulum
7 — Symphysis pubis
8 — Pelvic opening
9 — Tuber ischii (pins)
10 — Obturator foramen
11 — Sacral vertebrae

Figure 14-25 Pelvic bones of the cow.

has not had adequate feed to maintain her organs and be fertile. An overly fat cow is one that probably skipped calving last year and has retained all the energy of feed for herself rather than suckling a calf. She should be pregnant. The cow in medium condition is usually the one performing best. She should be suckling a calf and have another inside.

Look at the udder. If the teats are polished and the udder taut, she is suckling a calf. If the calf is very young, under 2 months, you will probably not find another calf inside even though it is present. If the calf is older, she could be pregnant. An empty, or dry, udder indicates she is not suckling and she should be pregnant because the time from last calving should be at least 6 months. The dry udder should be pliable and hang limp.

The hair condition may be used as an indication of the health of the animal and her nutritive state. Cows with shiny, fine coats of hair are in good health, while those with dry, brittle hair coats are usually malnourished or diseased. Animals in good condition are more liable to be pregnant.

Make sure the restraint on the rear legs is in place and that the palpator is well protected.

Put on the sleeve Either hand may be used for palpation, and the sleeves are interchangeable. It is usually best to start with the hand most commonly used, but many find either hand suitable. Place a rubber band around the upper arm.

Lubricate the glove Squeeze some of the lubricant on the back of the hand and wrist. Lubricant in the palm will not be utilized properly.

Insert the hand and arm The free hand grasps the tail for leverage while the gloved hand wipes the lubricant across the anus to lubricate the entrance. The hand is made into a point or wedge shape (Fig. 14–26) and inserted into the anus and rectum with a push as well as pulling on the tail. This should be a thrusting motion penetrating about elbow-deep in the rectum. As the wedge-shaped hand enters, it should assume the shape of a modified fist so that a rounded structure opens the rectum as the hand moves in. This prevents perforating the rectal wall if there is a sharp turn in it. By inserting the arm this far, quickly, the cow has farther to push the hand out and usually responds by better relaxation than if there is gradual penetration. The hand is opened to a mittenlike form under any feces to begin feeling for the underlying reproductive organs. Rectal contractions may make palpation uncomfortable as the cow uses peristaltic contractions to expel the hand. Patience and perseverance usually prevail. Let the contractions move over the hand and usually a relaxation follows permitting palpation. A few cows are very obstinate and contract severely. Pressure on the back midline with the fingers or some sharp object may cause relaxation. In severe instances, squeezing and rolling the clitoris and vulvar lips between the thumb and forefinger will cause a drooping of the loin and relaxation. There is no guaranteed method for causing relaxation.

Occasionally some blood may be present on the hand as it is removed. This usually comes from small hemorrhages of the rectum and are not critical. Excessive bleeding indicates abrasion of a greater surface; palpation should cease, and the animal should be allowed to heal before repalpating. A rough feeling like sandpaper indicates that the mucosal lining has been rubbed off, and the cow should be released and rechecked later. Tearing of the rectum is not common, and if the palpator just realizes that he is in a living organ and takes necessary precautions no mishap should occur. Penetration usually is followed by peritonitis and death of the animal. Minor penetrations with resulting inflammation may be controlled with antibiotics. It is usually best to slaughter the cow and salvage the meat from one that has been ruptured.

Feel down The reproductive tract is usually down, because as it fills it becomes heavy and pendulous (Fig. 14–27). It is foolish to feel high where the kidneys and space are located. The hand should be maintained in a mitten shape so that a broad surface encounters the structures. A gentle paddling motion and movement from side to side as the hand moves down assists in ascertaining the contents of the abdominal cavity. Any firm object should be a calf. If you feel your own elbow with your hand and fingers you will notice firm bone with a little flesh covering. This is a very similar feeling to a developing calf. If such an object is felt, the palpator should

Figure 14-26 Inserting the hand into the rectum.

explore by moving gently over the surface to distinguish structures. It could be a head, back, rump, feet, or other structures that are felt.

If no firm object is encountered, the search continues to the farthest point the palpator can reach. Then a cupping of the hand and continued paddling motion searches upward in the direction of the pelvic rim. The cupped hand may encounter a sac of fluid, which is an earlier pregnancy (Fig. 14–28). Further investigation should reveal the size, location, texture, presence, and size of a calf if it is large enough, and an estimation of its stage of development. This is accomplished by gently rolling the hand over and under the uterus with gentle pressure of the fingers into the fluid and a slight popping motion like bobbing for apples in a tub of water. The calf may be felt from about 75 days of age upward as it floats in the embryonic fluids.

Suppose no pregnancy is found. The cupped fingers should continue to search until the fingertips reach along the pelvic rim from side to side and far up on each side to determine if any structure is passing over the rim that was missed earlier. This may be uterus, cervix, or vagina, depending on stage of pregnancy. Follow the structure down to determine its contents.

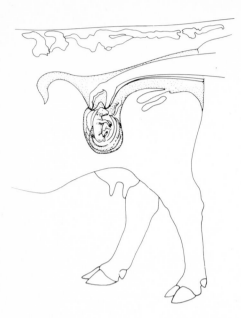

Figure 14-27 Initial palpation down into the abdominal cavity.

Assuming nothing is found thus far, continue with the cupped fingers onto the floor of the pelvis. An open uterus will roll into the hand, and the fingers may gently separate the horns at the bifurcation to determine the condition of each horn (Fig. 14–29).

The terms "usually," "gently," "carefully," and "about" have been used many times in the descriptions thus far. That is on purpose, because it is difficult to describe a "normal" situation. The uterus may sometimes be on the dorsal surface of the pelvis and may also be pregnant. It may be hiding under the rumen, or paunch. It

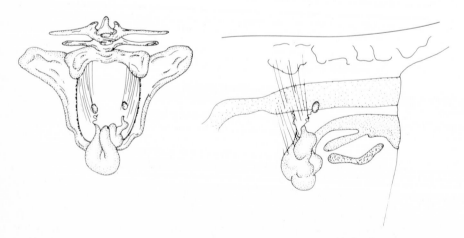

Figure 14-28 An early stage of pregnancy just over the pelvic rim (60 days).

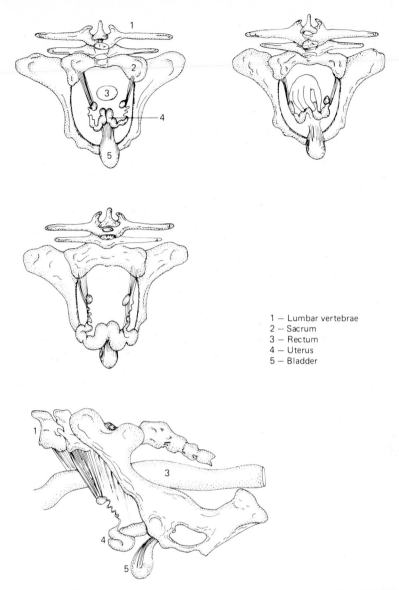

1 — Lumbar vertebrae
2 — Sacrum
3 — Rectum
4 — Uterus
5 — Bladder

Figure 14-29 The open cow reproductive tract and separation of the uterine horns at the bifurcation.

may be so pendulous and the calf so small that the arm and hand are not long enough to reach a recognizable structure. There are many "ifs," "ands," and "buts" associated with describing pregnancies. Do not make a definite statement until some distinguishing structure is identified.

The thrill of feeling a new life in its developmental stages makes all the effort worthwhile. When the calf moves, as happens so frequently at about 6 to 7 months, it feels like he wants out to play. When a calf about 5 months is being palpated around the muzzle and he takes your finger in his mouth in a sucking manner, it is a surprise, but a realization that there is a functioning young animal inside already. Enjoy these wonders of life while palpating.

Stages of pregnancy

Nonpregnant The heifer tract is usually on the floor or inside the pelvic cavity. It seldom extends past the rim (Fig. 14–29). The cow tract is larger and usually extends over the rim of the pelvis. The procedure for inserting the arm and searching applies regardless of the stage of pregnancy, because that stage is usually not known before the palpation.

The hand should be cupped over the uterus and a slight pressure by the middle finger used to separate the horns at the bifurcation. Slipping the thumb and index finger around one horn allows a milking motion to determine the presence or absence of a vesicle. Both horns are milked in the process. The absence of any bulge, fluid, or membranes indicates a nonpregnant or very early pregnant condition.

30-day Pregnancy The location may be the same as the open uterus. There may be some extension over the rim (Fig. 14–30). The same procedure is followed as with the open cow. In this instance, however, the amnionic vesicle is felt.[80,81] It may feel similar to a knuckle on your finger. The vesicle is approximately 20 mm (.8 in) in diameter and very turgid. Be very gentle since rupture means death of the embryo.[9] It will slip from between the fingers. The chorioallantoic membrane may be slipped between the fingers with gentle pressure on the uterus. A corpus luteum should be present on the same side as the pregnancy. It is not necessary to palpate ovaries for determining pregnancy because they tell you very little. A corpus luteum of a cycling cow and that of a pregnant one are indistinguishable. The calf at this stage is approximately 12 mm (.5 in) long and should not be palpated (Fig. 14–31) (Table 14–11).

45-day pregnancy The amnionic vesicle has enlarged to about the size of a hen egg (4 cm, 1.5 in) and is easier to discern. The uterus is still carried high in the cavity. Uterine tone has increased and placentomes are newly forming. Cupping the hand under the uterus assists in feeling.

60-day pregnancy The uterus begins to hang over the pelvic rim as the contents increase (Fig. 14–28). The shape resembles a fat banana on the pregnant side with a smaller shorter horn on the other. Cupping the uterus in the hand at this stage allows a weighing and sense of mass without feeling the delicate fetus. The calf is now about 6 cm (2.5 in) long and has begun to look like a calf. The uterus is beginning to thin as it stretches, and inside, the placentomes are loosely attached and growing (Fig. 14–32). The cervix is in the pelvic cavity approaching the brim.

90-day pregnancy The calf and fluids have enlarged so that the calf is now about 15 cm (6 in) long and the mass of fluid is approaching the size of a large

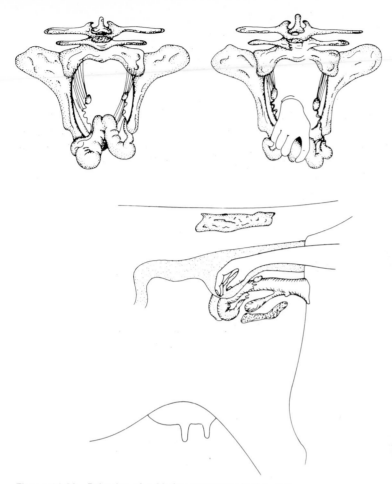

Figure 14-30 Palpation of a 30-day pregnancy in the cow.

softball. The head is about the size of a ping-pong ball and may be palpated. It is usually the first part of the fetus found. There is still a large amount of fluid, but the calf is the best determinant of age. The uterus now hangs deeper in the abdominal cavity and one horn is considerably larger than the other (Fig. 14–33). It assumes the shape of a boxing glove.

The placentomes have reached a size of about 25 mm (1 in) in diameter but are soft and difficult to palpate (Fig. 14–34).

The uterine artery supplying the uterus and branching to the ovary and cervix enlarges as pregnancy advances.[48] At this stage it has reached the size of a pencil and the pulsing blood may be felt. The uterine artery is located along the cranial border of the broad ligament and has a particular feel. The blood can be felt rushing or buzzing through the artery, and this slushing is called *fremitis*. The artery may be identified in two ways. With the hand inserted past the pelvic rim, the fingers are partially folded and drawn back to entrap the broad ligament on one side. The thumb

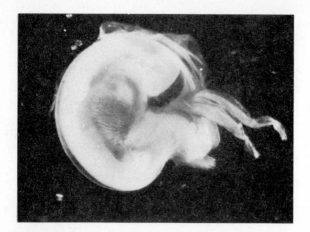

Figure 14-31   30-day-old calf embryo in its amnion.

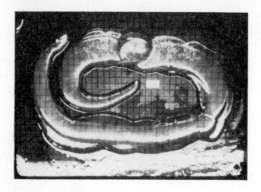

Figure 14-32   A 53-day-old calf fetus showing the membranes and cotyledons in early stages.

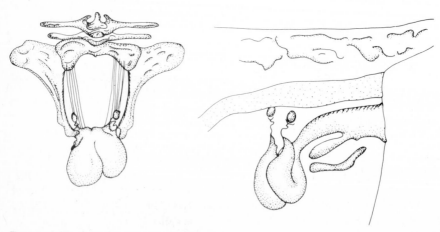

Figure 14-33   A 90-day pregnancy in the cow.

Table 14-11   Fetal Size and Characteristics Used in Determining Pregnancy

Days of gestation	Weight, gm (oz)	Length, mm (in)	Identifying characteristics
30	.28 (.01)	12 (.05)	One uterine horn slightly enlarged and thin; embryonic vesicle size of marble. Uterus in approximate position of nonpregnant uterus. Fetal membranes may be slipped between fingers from 30 to 90 days.
45	3.5–7.1 (.12–.25)	25–32 (1–1.25)	Uterine horn somewhat enlarged, thinner walled and prominent. Embryonic vesicle size of hen egg.
60	7.1–14.2 (.25–.5)	64 (2.5)	Uterine horn size of banana; fluid filled and pulled over pelvic brim into body cavity. Fetus size of mouse; head size of marble.
90	85–170 (3–6)	127–152 (5–6)	Both uterine horns swollen, 75–90 mm (3–3.5 in) in diameter and pulled deeply into body cavity (difficult to palpate). Fetus is size of rat. Head, size of ping-pong ball. Uterine artery 3–4 mm (.12–.2 in) in diameter. Cotyledons 20–25 mm (.75–1 in) across.

Days of gestation	Weight, kg (lb)	Length, cm (in)	Identifying characteristics
120	.453–.907 (1–2)	.25–.30 (10–12)	Similar to 90-day but fetus more easily palpated. Fetus is size of small cat with head the size of a lemon. Uterine artery 5 mm (.25 in). Cotyledons more noticeable and 25–40 mm (1.5 in) in length.
150	2–3 (4–6)	30–40 (12–16)	Difficult to palpate fetus. Uterine horns are deep in body cavity with fetus size of large cat. Head, size of baseball. Horns 150–200 mm (6–8 in) in diameter. Uterine artery 5–10 mm (.25–.4 in) in diameter. Cotyledons 50–65 mm (2–2.5 in) in diameter.
180	4–7 (10–16)	50–61 (20–24)	Horns with fetus filling cavity. Fetus, size of small dog. Head size of orange. Uterine artery 10–12 mm (.4–.5 in) in diameter. Cotyledons more enlarged. From 6th month until calving a movement of fetus may be elicited by grasping the feet, legs, or nose.
210	9–14 (20–30)	61–81 (24–32)	From 7 months until parturition may be felt. Age is difficult to determine by fetal size. The uterine artery continues to increase in size—210 days, 12 mm (.5 in) in diameter; 240 days, 12–15 mm (.5–.6 in) in diameter; 270 days, 12–20 mm (.5–.75 in) in diameter.
240	18–27 (40–60)	71–91 (28–36)	
270	27–45 (60–100)	71–96 (28–38)	

Adapted from Sorensen.[66]

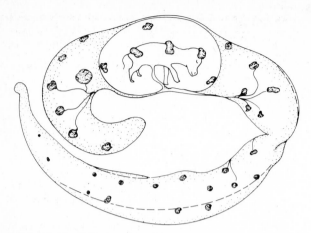

Figure 14-34 A 78-day-old calf fetus with definite cotyledonary areas pulled from the uterus.

and index finger then palpate the leading edge of the broad ligament (Fig. 14–35). As pregnancy advances, the uterus hangs over the pelvic rim and such entrapment is difficult. An alternative method is to flatten the hand in the pelvis and trap the artery against the inside wall. A precaution must be mentioned. The femoral artery is just lateral to the uterine artery and courses down the internal thigh. It is not movable and does not have fremitis.

120-day pregnancy The fetus has now enlarged and pulled down into the abdominal cavity (Fig. 14–36). The palpator must reach very deep in some large

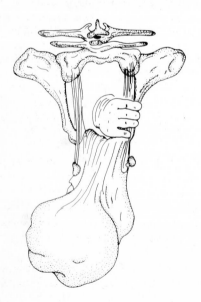

Figure 14-35 Palpating the uterine artery of a 4-month pregnancy.

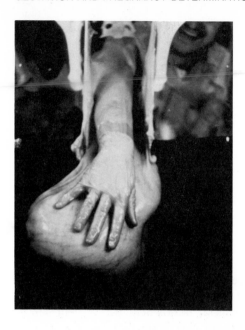

Figure 14-36 Position of the calf and hand at 4 months of pregnancy.

animals such as the Holstein, Brown Swiss, Charolais, and Santa Gertrudis. The calf is now 25 cm (10 in) long and the head is the size of a lemon. The cotyledons are much firmer and can usually be palpated. They will measure about 40 mm (1.5 in) and are oval in shape. The uterine artery is enlarged some at this stage.

If the fetus itself cannot be palpated, then pressure with the paddle-shaped hand should allow palpation of the placentomes in the body of the uterus. Other helps in determining pregnancy include location of the uterus and its contents and presence of fremitis in the uterine artery.

Figure 14-37 Palpation of a 6-month pregnancy in the cow.

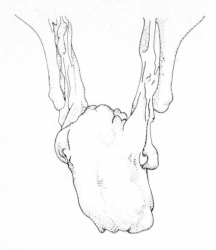

Figure 14-38 A mummified 5-month-old calf.

Over 150 days The major differences from this point until gestation are involved in growth of the fetus and a change in proportion of fluid to fetus. In the very early stages of pregnancy the uterine contents are mostly fluid, with a small calf. As pregnancy advances, the proportion changes to a small amount of fluid and nearly all calf. These changes are outlined in Table 14–10. The sizes of the heads, placentomes, and uterine artery are the best indicators of age. As the calf enlarges and fills the cavity, palpation becomes easier (Fig. 14–37) but determination of age becomes harder.

Other Factors

Mummification Some fetuses die and are completely resorbed by the uterus unknown to anyone, some are aborted, and some mummify. Mummies become dehydrated and may remain in this condition indefinitely. It is not proven to be genetically related but may be.[56] Fetal mummification should be expected if a cow approaches the time of parturition and no outward changes are noticeable.[57] The texture of the uterus and its contents under such conditions are firm and dry feeling (Fig. 14–38). No fluids, cotyledons, or uterine arteries are present. It is very difficult to expel the mummy, and many times the endometrial surface is damaged beyond further usefulness.

Freemartin A freemartin is a sterile heifer born twin to a bull. The reproductive system does not develop fully. The condition should be identified quickly through palpation because of the absence of the uterus and small size of the ovaries if they can be found. Fusion of the two placentae allow mixing of the fetal blood, and male hormone dominates the development of the reproductive system. The vulva will be hypoplastic. Freemartins are of no reproductive usefulness and should be culled.

Pyometra and endometritis Pyometra refers to accumulation of pus, or white blood cells, in response to endometritis, which is an inflammation of the uterus.

These cells accumulate and cause a swelling of the uterus. The tone of the uterus is usually plastic and the walls are thickened. Some discharge from the vulva may be seen before palpation and more due to the pressure during palpation. A veterinarian should examine the animal and initiate treatment immediately. This may result from a reproductive disease or abortion.

Postpartum uterus After birth, the uterus collapses immediately and begins a return to normal size and shape. Palpation in the early postpartum period will reveal a uterus that feels like soft heavy folds of leather. Tone will gradually return with time. This condition should not be confused with pregnancy unless some fluid is present from a very recent birth. Observation of the udder should reveal a strutted appearance with the teats and mammary very tight.

Enlarged cervix Some cows have an enlarged cervix that may be mistaken for a fetus. This is common in the Santa Gertrudis breed and cattle with some Zebu breeding. The first impression of pregnancy should be corrected upon further investigation for indicative structures. This is not in itself cause for culling a cow. The record of the cow's productivity should be evaluated rather than the anatomical difference.

Breeds Some breeds appear to be easier to palpate than others. Dairy cattle are usually easiest, which may result from the cow's being more docile and accustomed to people. The larger breeds are more difficult because of their size and the inability to reach deep into the abdominal cavity. Charolais and Brahman seem to have a thicker rectum with less freedom of movement.

Double-muscled stock The double-muscled cattle are very difficult to palpate because of the restrictions of entry and movement. The muscles grow internally as well as externally, evidently, and restrict the arm as it pushes into the rectum.

Fat stock Overfat cows that have been fed for show or are on experiments are very difficult to palpate because of the displacement internally. The cervix is enlarged, the uterus is enlarged, and the rectum is restricted. It is like trying to feel through a stovepipe. Cattle should not be this fat in the first place, and it is exhausting and exasperating to the palpator.

Other Methods

Hormone Assay Numerous attempts have been made to determine the hormone changes in the pregnant cow, but without a great deal of success. No feasible method for field use has been developed yet. Determining the progesterone content of peripheral blood at 20 to 22 days past breeding has proven 85 to 100 percent accurate in trials.[23,58] This is based upon the cyclic activity of progesterone and its relation to pregnancy. Progesterone is at base level during estrus and therefore should be at this level 20 days following breeding if the cow did not conceive. If the cow is bred and pregnancy then causes persistence of the CL, progesterone continues to be produced and is at a high level 20 days postbreeding. The assay involves rather strict laboratory procedures using radioisotopes and is not adaptable to the livestock producer.

Mucus and pressure It is known that mucous crystallization patterns change with cyclic activity. Heavy crystals form in the estrogenic phase,[22] and very few form in the progestational phase. If the animal is pregnant, few or no crystals should form. This alone is not proof of pregnancy. Injection of the hormone oxytocin causes contraction of the vagina when a cow is in estrus or when she is pregnant, but not during the progestational phase of the cycle.[71] An absence of long crystals and contraction of the vagina in response to oxytocin indicate pregnancy.[24] Accuracy at 15 days postbreeding has been 85 percent, and 90 percent at 27 days. The method is too complicated for practical use but is useful for short-term determination in research.

Ultrasonic measure Differences in tissues give varying responses to sound as an echo. The echo changes when sound is bounced off the body wall compared to fluid in the pregnant uterus. These echoes can be read on an electronic meter to tell whether fluid, and therefore pregnancy, is really present. Rectal probes are being tested. Refinements are being made presently to make the instrument more adaptable to cattle. Tests are showing about 85 percent success at 5 months of gestation.

Bumping A word should be said about bumping cows. This is done in the latter stages of pregnancy (after about 6 months) to feel the developing calf.[8] The fist is clenched and placed against the abdomen in the right flank area with the thumb up to increase feeling. A short jab is made into the area, which may result in feeling the firm fetus or, more usually, will push the fetus inward like a pendulum. The fist is held in the area to determine the swinging fetus returning to the area of pressure. The method is used by some older stockmen with a great deal of experience but is unreliable in general.

Appearance The enlargement of the lower abdomen is used by some cattlemen in the very late stages of pregnancy. The major change is in the lower right side where the calf is lying. Size and shape are important. Experiences from palpation indicate that this is not a reliable method, since the amount of feed and condition of the animal govern the condition greatly and many "piggy" cows may in reality be open. Consequently, many cows that are flat sided and not springing may also be pregnant, contrary to appearance.

Others Untried methods are also available for those that care less for accuracy. Pouring water in the cow's ear causes shaking of the whole body in those that are pregnant. Pressing the spinous process and moving caudally with pressure followed by release causes ventral curvature of the spine, raising of the tailhead, and lowering the head in nonpregnant cows. Sleek hair along the topline indicates pregnancy, whereas curly dry hair indicates a nonpregnant condition. The "look in her eye" is used by some. You may choose your own method, but just be sure it is accurate. These are not.

An allergen injected intradermally into a pregnant cow over 21 days pregnant has revealed good results: 93 percent from 21 to 60 days and 100 percent over 60 days.[12] More testing is needed to verify the encouraging results.

A pregnancy-specific protein in the pregnant cow has been used to develop an antibody for use in pregnancy determination. It is produced by the uterus containing a blastocyst before day 15 of gestation and is specifically from the pregnant uterus.[40] Further work should give an early test.

Ewe

Most pregnancy determination in sheep has occurred in Australia and New Zealand. There has not been as much interest in the United States. The lack of practicality of methods devised has prevented widespread use.

As in the cow, it would be desirable to know if the ewe is pregnant so a decision can be made as to her future.

Several methods will be briefly discussed.

Rectal-Abdominal Palpation Since the anus and rectum prevent the hand from going to the uterus, a method has been developed to bring the uterus to the hand.[31] The ewe is inverted and restrained while a plastic rod 15 mm (.5 in) in diameter and 50 cm (20 in) long is lubricated and inserted in the rectum (Fig. 14–39). The rod is used to lift the fetus or fetuses against the abdominal wall where they may be palpated through the thin tissues in that area. It may be used to distinguish twins as well as single pregnancies. The disadvantage of this procedure is the age at which the determination can be performed. The ewe should be 65 to 70 days in gestation for good accuracy. As many as 200 ewes can potentially be examined in an hour.

A comparison of various tests in the ewe is given in Table 14–12.

Laparotomy This method involves a small incision and insertion of a finger to palpate the uterus. In this procedure the ewe is sat on her rump or upended in a cradle (Fig. 14–40). An incision just large enough to insert one or two fingers is made cranially to the udder as close as possible without cutting into the mammary tissue. The index finger or index and middle fingers probe the abdominal cavity for the enlarged uterus indicating pregnancy.[39] In a group of 278 ewes, the error was only 3 percent when in weeks 4 to 8.5 of gestation. A similar technique may be used for observing ovaries.[33]

Hormones Progesterone has been assayed as in the cow to determine pregnancy. Blood samples taken at 17 days postbreeding reading above .5 ng/ml proved ewes pregnant in 87 per cent of 33 ewes.[58] The usefulness is highest if time of mating is known.[45] Progesterone assays of goat's milk have proven accurate in 26 of 27 does measured.[67]

Laparoscopy Observation of the ovaries for maintenance of the CL at 15 to 17 days postbreeding gives a good relationship to pregnancy.[64] The uterine color is also fairly definitive, with the pregnant uterus appearing pale and vascular.

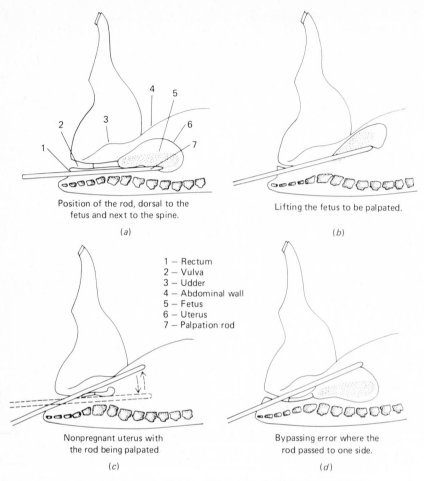

Position of the rod, dorsal to the
fetus and next to the spine.

(a)

Lifting the fetus to be palpated.

(b)

1 — Rectum
2 — Vulva
3 — Udder
4 — Abdominal wall
5 — Fetus
6 — Uterus
7 — Palpation rod

Nonpregnant uterus with
the rod being palpated

(c)

Bypassing error where the
rod passed to one side.

(d)

Figure 14-39   Rectal-abdominal palpation of the ewe. *(Adapted from Hulet.[31])*

Doppler The doppler technique of ultrasonics depends upon movement, and the heartbeat of the fetus is the distinguishing factor used for determining pregnancy. Instruments have been devised to be placed on the abdomen or in the rectum aimed toward the uterus.[19,30,42] Accuracies have been reported of about 90 percent from 60 to 100 days gestation. Multiple fetuses cannot be distinguished. Cost of the instrument currently prohibits field use.

Ultrasonic Scanning Scanning the abdominal area ultrasonically yields a reading on the contents due to differing response to sound waves. In the last half of gestation, 100 percent accuracy can result from scanning just anterior to the udder.[43] The scan can also be used in determining the presence of multiple fetuses (Fig. 14–41).

Vaginal Biopsy Biopsies taken from the cranial vagina have proven 84 per cent accurate in diagnosing pregnancy in sheep.[55] The tissue is fixed and studied. The

Table 14-12 Comparison of Methods of Determining Pregnancy in Ewes

Technique	No. ewes correctly diagnosed Pregnant	Nonpregnant	Accuracy %	Av min/ exam/ewe
(64 to 88 days postbreeding)				
Laparotomy	66	12	100	—
Sonicaid $(2.2\ MH_2)_z$	53	12	87	1.9
Doptone $(5.0\ MH_2)_z$	63	12	96	1.3
Palpation (sloping)*	64	10	95	1.0
(85 to 109 days postbreeding)				
Laparotomy	61	18	100	—
Sonicaid $(2.2\ MH_2)_z$	57	18	94	1.6
Doptone $(5.0\ MH_2)_z$	60	18	99	1.4
Palpation (horizontal)	61	18	100	.2

*Ewe held hind feet up at 45° angle.
Adapted from Hulet.[32]

presence of small cells with rounded nuclei as the predominant cell indicates pregnancy. The technique is too time-consuming to be feasible. A vaginal smear is not reliable.[27]

Sow

Determination of pregnancy in the sow is not a common practice presently but is gaining momentum with the advent of developments in electronic probes. As with other classes of livestock, the manager must know if his sows are pregnant or open so he can make a decision to continue breeding or cull.

Advantages include eliminating open sows and reducing feed costs, grouping sows for farrowing, culling for farrowing at a specific time, aiding in detecting infertile boars, and giving information for sales.[63]

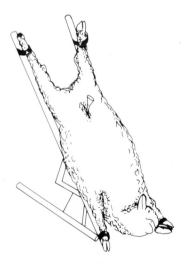

Figure 14-40 Position of the ewe for surgical palpation.

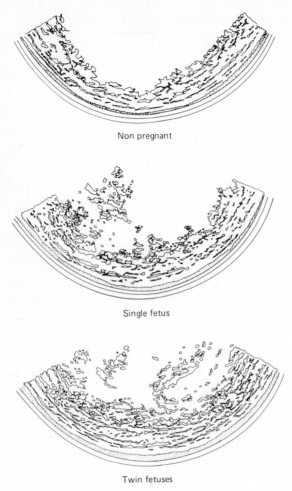

Non pregnant

Single fetus

Twin fetuses

Figure 14-41 Ultrasonic scanning of the ewe's belly with patterns for a ewe that is nonpregnant, pregnant with a single fetus, and pregnant with twin fetuses.

Only a few developing embryos are necessary to indicate to the sow that she is pregnant,[53] so it is essential that we develop methods of measuring how many piglets are developing as well as the pregnant condition.

Uterine space has an apparent influence on the size of the litter. Normally about 30 percent of the pigs die before birth.[78] There are plenty of ova shed and fertilized, but the uterus is incapable of supplying needs for large numbers. In research where one horn of the uterus and its ovary were removed to reduce space, the number of ovulations was almost equal to intact controls (14.5 vs. 13.7) and fertilization and development to 25 days was almost equal (8.7 vs. 9.3 embryos), but the number of fetuses at 105 days was much lower in the reduced space as compared to the intact sows (5.5 vs. 9.6).[18] It is necessary, then, to select for sows with larger litters to insure adequate space for embryonic development.

Intrauterine migration is common in swine and occurs in about the first 2 weeks of gestation.[52] If there is an imbalance of fertilized ova between the two horns, the migration tends to balance them. Intrauterine migration tends to reduce embryonic mortality.[75]

Ultrasound Detection Ultrasound or ultrasonic equipment is capable of detecting masses of different density. The body wall has a different reflected sound than fluid in the uterus. By placing a probe on the belly wall about 5 cm (2 in) behind the navel and just outside the nipple line the echoes are transmitted to a cathode screen for observation (Fig. 14–42).[49,63] A field trial involving 755 diagnoses yielded an accuracy of 91 percent.[49] The greatest accuracy was from 30 to 90 days of gestation (98 percent).

Hormones Estrogen in the urine of pregnant sows increases considerable over the nonpregnant condition and may be used to diagnose pregnancy.[44,76] A reliable test is too expensive and complicated for field use. It should be measured after about a month of pregnancy.

Progesterone offers another avenue of diagnosis. Levels above 5 ng/ml blood serum 22 days postbreeding have yielded 88 percent accuracy in 25 sows.[58] Progesterone levels are high in the sow compared to other species, and more study is needed.

Palpation This is rare but has been reported in instances where a small individual

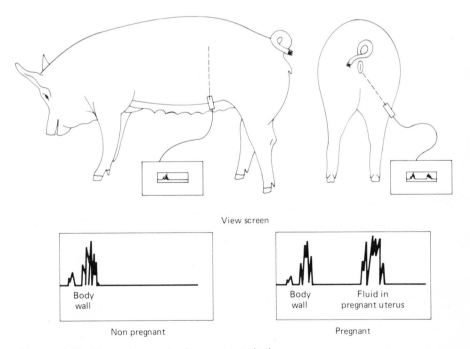

View screen

Body wall — Non pregnant

Body wall — Fluid in pregnant uterus — Pregnant

Figure 14-42 Electronic scanning for pregnancy in the sow.

and a large sow made the determination possible.[5,11] An innovation of the uterine palpation has led to palpating the uterine artery for fremitis and enlargement associated with pregnancy.[5] The external iliac artery is palpated in the pelvis and it should course along the cranial border of the ilium. The uterine artery crosses the external iliac cranioventrally and is very small in the nonpregnant sow but enlarges to the size of the external iliac in advanced pregnancy. The fremitis is present in the uterine artery of a pregnant sow.

Mare

The horseman who maintains a breeding center uses pregnancy determination to the greatest extent in the horse industry. He usually has limited facilities and wishes to send a mare home as quickly as possible "safe in foal." The earlier the decision can be made, the better, so he can bring in other mares. Trading of horses often depends upon whether they are pregnant or not. Zemjanis[83] has given good descriptions of the pregnant mare.

Palpation The size of the mare and anatomy of the tract make palpation a suitable method of determining pregnancy. A big factor in its favor is the time element. Pregnancies may be determined as early as 20 days with high accuracy. The method resembles that of the cow, but some differences need to be presented.

Refresh your memory on the suspension and anatomy of the mare reproductive tract. When the hand is inserted in the rectum there are usually dry feces that must be removed. The rectal wall will feel thinner than that of the cow, and care should be taken so that no damage or penetration occurs.

The mitten-shaped hand is pressed down in the bifurcation of the uterus and grasps the body of the uterus between the thumb and heel of the hand on top and the fingers underneath (Fig. 14–43). The early pregnancies in the mare occur in the body and lower horns;[82] therefore the hand is in the correct area naturally. Gentle manipulation of the uterus reveals the condition. The very early pregnancy will consist of an enlargement the size of an egg at about 20 days.

As pregnancy advances, the uterus enlarges and drops over the pelvis into the body cavity. The uterus then feels very similar to that of a pregnant cow because the tract becomes pendulous rather than slinglike. The fetal head is pointed toward the pelvis in most instances—90 percent.[2] Transuterine migration may be as high as 54 percent.[2]

The size of the mare and the flaccid condition of the uterus even in pregnancy join to make palpation a more difficult task in later stages than in the cow. So, early pregnancies are usually easier and midpregnancies harder.

Excessive palpation of a daily frequency for the duration of the estrous cycle or the first 50 days of gestation reduced pregnancies considerably over control animals in one experiment,[77] but it seems unlikely that anyone would palpate that often under normal conditions.

Immunologic Tests These tests depend upon a reaction of PMSG to prepared antibodies and sheep red blood cells sensitized to PMSG. When the mare's serum

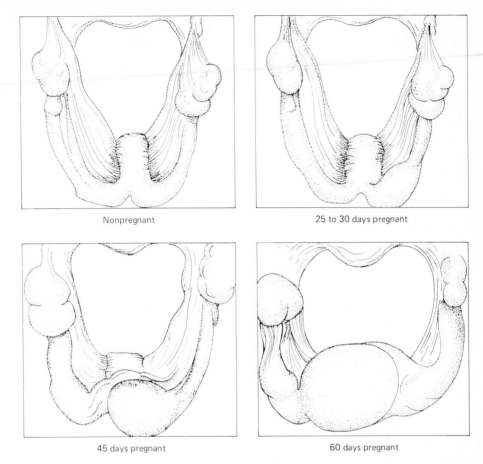

Nonpregnant

25 to 30 days pregnant

45 days pregnant

60 days pregnant

Figure 14-43 Palpating the body and lower horns of the mare's uterus.

is combined with the reagents in the prescribed order, hemagglutination inhibition (HI) results in settling the red blood cells in a ring pattern at the base of the test tube and the diagnosis then is positive (Fig. 14-44). If the cells agglutinate, the mare is open.[36,65]

Hormone Assay The presence of PMSG indicates pregnancy. This hormone, or hormones, is present from about 40 to 120 days of pregnancy in large quantities. The biological test is rather simple, accurate, and inexpensive.

The common test animal used is the male toad (Bufo woodhousi), which is found around ponds and damp areas in the spring and summer. He is identified by his dark throat and makes an excellent animal because of his abundance, economy, ease in keeping a short period, and ability to produce sperm in response to gonadotropic hormones in a short time. Toads may be kept in captivity in a cool, moist place and force-fed bits of liver twice weekly.

The test is based upon the fact that the toad emits sperm only when stimulated by amplexus with a female or when stimulated by gonadotropic hormones. If a toad

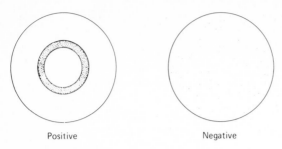

Figure 14-44 Immunoassay for pregnancy.

is to be used for a pregnancy test immediately after being captured he should be checked for the presence of sperm before use. Aspirate the cloaca with a small amount of water and check for the presence of sperm under a microscope. Sperm appear as curved motile rods. If no sperm are present, he may be used. If sperm are present, rest him and retest in 3 days. Draw 50 to 60 ml of blood from the jugular vein of a mare that has been bred between 45 and 120 days into a test tube. Place a cork stopper in the tube and put the blood in the refrigerator and allow to clot. Slant the tube slightly so that the serum rises to the top. Pipette off the strawcolored serum and inject 3 ml of serum into the dorsal lymph sac of the toad. Check the toad 3 hours after injection for the presence of sperm by aspirating the cloaca with a pipette containing a few drops of water. Mount the fluid on a slide and observe it under the microscope. The presence of sperm either motile or nonmotile indicates a positive test. Recheck all negatives with another toad.

Other toads and frogs have been used successfully, and the tests are equal to rabbit tests.[54,70] Other tests for gonadotropins have also been borrowed from those of the human and used successfully. The major ones are the Cole and Hart,[15] Hart and Cole,[28] and Ascheim-Zondek using the mouse or rat, which are approximately 95 percent accurate,[36] and the Friedman test using the rabbit.[7,20] Best response is from 55- to 80-day pregnancies.[68] Each depends on follicular stimulation of the ovaries of prepuberal animals compared to no development in similar control animals.[84] Growth and/or rupture of follicles indicates pregnancy. Growth of male accessory glands results from the presence of gonadotropins and has been used as a measure of pregnancy following injection of serum.[16] One of the major difficulties with mouse, rat, and rabbit tests is the prolonged time of injection and reaction of about 2 to 6 days.[61] Care should be exercised in handling the serum. It should be collected under sterile conditions, kept away from heat and light, stored at 4°C (39°F), and treated with antibiotics, if necessary.[62]

Other methods have been studied but are not used widely.

Woman

The woman wishes to know if she is pregnant as soon as possible for her own information. Missed menstruation about 15 days following ovulation is the first indication of pregnancy. A very good review of the various type tests may be found in *Population Reports* by Hunt.[34]

Bioassay The long-standard Ascheim-Zondek and Friedman tests for HCG are still used to some extent. These have been replaced mostly by shorter tests for HCG using the hyperemic condition of the rat and the male toad. The presence of sperm in the cloaca of toads 1 to 5 hours after injection with pregnancy urine has been used for years. Bioassays are limited to periods when HCG is high, which is between 50 and 90 days of gestation. Accuracy is high, but cost and need of laboratory facilities limit their use.

Hormone Withdrawal This test based on menstruation in nonpregnant women, following estrogen-progestogen injection and withdrawal, is not recommended because of complications.

Immunoassay These assays depend on antibodies reacting with HCG. Commercial preparations are available, and urine is mixed with the prepared antibody to cause agglutination in the case of nonpregnancy or nonagglutination and formation of a ring in the bottom of the tube for the pregnant condition (Fig. 14–44). Similar agglutination tests using slides with latex particles are available. The tests require a time of 1.5 to 2 hours. There are also anti-HCG tests which result in agglutination for pregnancy. These tests may be utilized 4 to 7 days past the missed menstrual period with increased accuracy around 2 weeks past the missed period. False-positive tests are rare. The slide tests are quicker (1 to 2 minutes) but are more difficult to read. A capillary tube test has been developed that is very simple, accurate (.07 percent false-positive and .28 percent false-negative), early diagnosis (as early as 3 to 5 weeks from the last menstrual period), rapid (1 hour), and very sensitive.[41]

Radioimmunoassay (RIA) These assays are also based on the presence of HCG but are much more sensitive and can be used at an earlier time—about the time of a missed menstrual period. An innovation of the RIA is radioreceptor assay (RRA). Accuracy is high (100 percent) at the time of a missed menstrual period, and the test requires only one hour. Expense of special facilities and the need for trained personnel are the major disadvantages.

Other Tests Tests depending on the presence of a new life in later stages include *diasonography (through-sound)* that measures the presence of the embryonic vesicle at 6 to 8 weeks by ultrasonic means,[13] sound of the fetal pulse by ultrasonic measurement,[29] and radiological by the use of X-rays after the eighteenth week.

WHAT DID YOU LEARN?

1 How long does each domestic species carry its young?
2 Is the corpus luteum necessary throughout pregnancy in the ewe? In the mare? What other source of progesterone is available?
3 Draw an embryo developing the amnion, chorion, and allantois.
4 Where are endometrial cups found? What do they look like? Of what use are they?

5   Name the three distinct periods of the prenatal period and tell what distinguishes the beginning and end of each.
6   What are the three embryonic cell layers and into what does each develop?
7   What structural-type placentae do the cow and mare have? What distinguishes this type from others?
8   What is a cotyledonary placenta? Where is it found?
9   Outline the procedure for palpating a pregnant cow of unknown gestation.
10 What four major criteria can be used to determine pregnancy in the cow at 5 months of gestation?
11 How big is the head of a 3-month-old calf fetus?
12 What is the principle on which the ultrasonic diagnosis works?
13 Why aren't hormone assays used more?
14 Describe rectal-abdominal palpation in the ewe.
15 What is intrauterine migration?
16 What is the most popular method of pregnancy determination in the mare?
17 How does early palpation of the mare differ from that of the cow?
18 What hormone may be measured for pregnancy in the mare? When is it present?
19 Explain the toad biological test for the mare.
20 What is the first indication of pregnancy in domestic species?

REFERENCES

1   Allen, W. E. 1974. Ovarian changes during gestation in pony mares. *Equine Vet. J.* 6:135–138.
2   ———. 1974. Palpable development of the conceptus and foetus in Welsh pony mares. *Equine Vet. J.* 6:69–73.
3   ———. and J. C. Hadley. 1974. Blood progesterone concentrations in pregnant and non-pregnant mares. *Equine Vet. J.* 6:87–93.
4   Allen, W. R. 1970. Endocrinology of early pregnancy in the mare. *Equine Vet. J.* 2:64–70.
5   Anonymous. 1961. Pregnancy diagnosis of swine by rectal examination. *J.A.V.M.A.* 138:672. (Abstr.)
6   Arey, L. B. 1965. *Developmental Anatomy: A Textbook and Laboratory Manual of Embryology.* 7th ed. W. B. Saunders Co., Philadelphia.
7   Arnold, J. J. 1935. Results of a rabbit ovulation test for equine pregnancy. *Mich. Agr. Exp. Sta. Quarterly Bull.* 18:46.
8   Bailey, J. W. September 1952. How to tell when a cow is with a calf. *Successful Farming.* P. 160.
9   Ball, L. and E. J. Carroll. 1963. Fetal death in cattle. *J.A.V.M.A.* 142:373–374.
10 Bay, M. 1961. You must detect the freeloaders. *Successful Farming* 59:36–37.
11 Bollwahn, W. 1972. Inspection and palpation of the genital organs of the sow. *Vet. Med. Rev.* Pp. 59–67.
12 Bratanov, K. and L. Kozhuharova. 1972. Immunological methods for diagnosing pregnancy in heifers. *Proc. 7th Int. Congr. on Anim. Reprod. and A.I.* 1:735–740.
13 Brown, D. 1976. *Obstetric, Contraception and Gynaecology.* Pitman Med., New York. Pp. 3–7.
14 Catchpole, H. R. 1977. Hormonal mechanisms in pregnancy and parturition. In H. H. Cole and P. T. Cupps, eds. *Reproduction in Domestic Animals.* 3rd ed. Academic Press, New York. Pp. 341–368.

15 Cole, H. H. and G. H. Hart. 1942. Diagnosis of pregnancy in the mare by hormonal means. *Amer. Vet. M. Ass. J.* 101:124–128.

16 Dybing, Fred. 1949. Biologic test for pregnancy in mares by use of male mice and rats. *Nord. Vet. Med.* 1:51–56.

17 Evans, H. E. and W. O. Sack. 1973. Prenatal development of domestic and laboratory mammals: Growth curves, external features and selected references. *Anat. Histol. Embryol.* 2:11–45.

18 Fenton, F. R., F. W. Bazer, O. W. Robison, and L. C. Ulberg. 1970. Effect of quantity of uterus on uterine capacity in gilts. *J. Anim. Sci.* 31:104–106.

19 Fraser, A. F. and J. G. Robertson. 1968. Pregnancy diagnosis and detection of foetal life in sheep and pigs by an ultrasonic method. *Brit. Vet. J.* 124:239–243.

20 Friedman, M. H. and M. E. Laphan. 1931. A simple rabbit procedure for the laboratory diagnosis of early pregnancy. *Amer. J. Obstet. and Gynecol.* 21:405.

21 Fuchs, F. 1977. Endocrinology of labor. In F. Fuchs and A. Klopper, eds. *Endocrinology of Pregnancy.* 2nd ed. Harper & Row, New York. Pp. 327–349.

22 Garm, O. and O. Skjerven. 1952. Studies on cervical mucus for early diagnosis of pregnancy and endocrine changes in the reproductive cycle in domestic animals. *Nord. Vet. Med.* 4:1098–1103.

23 Garrett, W. G. 1977. Effect of seasonal variations and time of insemination on reproduction in Brahman females. M. S. thesis, Texas A&M Univ., College Station. Pp. 1–109.

24 Ghannam, S. A. M. and A. M. Sorensen, Jr. 1967. Early pregnancy diagnosis in the bovine. *J. Dairy Sci.* 50:562–567.

25 Godkin, J. D., C. Cote, J. V. Ellinger, R. T. Duby, and D. L. Black. 1977. Stimulation of the ovine corpus luteum by the preimplantation embryo. *Amer. Soc. Anim. Sci. 1977 Mtg. Abstr. 408.* P. 163.

26 Gruenwald P. 1966. Growth of the human fetus. I. Normal growth and its variation. *Amer. J. Obstet. and Gynecol.* 94:1112–1119.

27 Hafez, E. S. E. 1953. Pregnancy diagnosis of the ewe by vaginal smear. *J. Agr. Sci.* 42:232–265.

28 Hart, G. H. and H. H. Cole. 1932. A practical method for the diagnosis of pregnancy in the mare. *J.A.V.M.A.* 80:604–614.

29 Haynes, D. M. 1977. Course and conduct of normal pregnancy. In D. N. Danforth, ed. *Obstetrics and Gynecology.* 3rd ed. Harper & Row, New York. Pp. 299–305.

30 Hulet, C. V. 1969. Pregnancy diagnosis in the ewe using an ultrasonic doppler instrument. *J. Anim. Sci.* 28:44–47.

31 ———. 1972. A rectal-abdominal palpation technique for diagnosing pregnancy in the ewe. *J. Anim. Sci.* 35:814–819.

32 ———. 1973. A rectal-abdominal technique for diagnosing pregnancy in the ewe. *Vet. Med./Small Anim. Clinician* 58:1383–1389.

33 Hulet, C. V. and W. C. Foote. 1968. A rapid technique for observing the reproductive tract of living ewes. *J. Anim. Sci.* 27:142–145.

34 Hunt, W. B. II. 1975. Pregnancy tests—the current status. *Population Reports Series J.* 7:109–124. Dept. of Medical and Public Affairs, The Geo. Washington Univ. Med. Ctr., Washington, D.C.

35 Jaffe, R. B. and J. B. Josimovich. 1977. Endocrine physiology of pregnancy. In D. N. Danforth, ed. *Obstetrics and Gynecology.* 3rd ed. Harper & Row, New York. Pp. 286–298.

36 Jeffcott, L. B., J. G. Atherton, and J. Mingay. 1969. Equine pregnancy diagnosis—a comparison of 2 methods for the detection of gonadotrophin in serum. *Vet. Rec.* 84:80–82.

37   King, G. J., B. A. Atkinson, J. A. Carnegie, and H. A. Robertson. 1977. Bovine implantation. *Amer. Soc. Anim. Sci. 1977. Mtg. Abstr. 445.* Pp. 177–178.

38   Koger, L. M. 1960. A practice builder, routine pregnancy diagnosis. *J.A.V.M.A.* 136:129–130.

39   Lamond, D. R. 1963. Diagnosis of early pregnancy in the ewe. *Australian Vet. J.* 39:192–195.

40   Laster, D. B. 1977. A pregnancy-specific protein in the bovine uterus. *Biol. Reprod.* 16:682–690.

41   Lau, H. L., S. E. Linkins, and T. M. King. 1977. A capillary tube pregnancy test. *Amer. J. Obstet. and Gynecol.* 127:394–399.

42   Lindahl, I. L. 1971. Pregnancy diagnosis in the ewe by intrarectal doppler. *J. Anim. Sci.* 32:922–925.

43   ———. 1976. Pregnancy diagnosis in ewes by ultrasonic scanning. *J. Anim. Sci.* 43:1135–1140.

44   Lunaas, T. 1961. A new method for the detection and estimation of urinary oestrogens in the sow and its application for the early pregnancy diagnosis. *Acta. Vet. Scand.* 2:301–310.

45   MacDonnell, H. 1976. Peripheral plasma progesterone in the ewe: Its application to the diagnosis of early pregnancy following oestrus synchronization treatment. *Irish Vet. J.* 30:11–15.

46   Melton, A. A., R. O. Berry, and O. D. Butler. 1951. The interval between the time of ovulation and attachment of the bovine embryo. *J. Anim. Sci.* 10:993–1005.

47   Millar, P. G. 1955. Diagnosis of pregnancy in farm animals. *J. Ministry of Agr.* (Great Britain) 62:319–322.

48   Moore, G. R. 1947. Pregnancy diagnosis in cows. *J.A.V.M.A.* 111:36.

49   O'Reilly, P. J. 1976. Pregnancy diagnosis in pigs by ultrasonic amplitude depth analysis —a field evaluation. *Irish Vet. J.* 30:165–167.

50   Peterson, A. J., J. T. Hunter, R. A. S. Welch, and R. J. Fairclough. 1975. Oestrogens in bovine fetal and maternal plasma near term. *J. Reprod. Fert.* 43:179–181.

51   Peterson, A. J., H. R. Tervit, R. J. Fairclough. P. G. Havik, and J. F. Smith. 1976. Jugular levels of 13,14-dihydro-15-keto-prostaglandin F and progesterone around luteolysis and early pregnancy in the ewe. *Prostaglandins* 12:551–558.

52   Polge, C. and P. J. Dziuk. 1970. Time of cessation of intrauterine migration of pig embryos. *J. Anim. Sci.* 31:565–566.

53   Polge, C., L. E. A. Rowson, and M. C. Chang. 1966. The effect of reducing the number of embryos during early stages of gestation on the maintenance of pregnancy in the pig. *J. Reprod. Fert.* 12:395–397.

54   Pujol, J. H. 1949. Gally Mainini pregnancy test applied to the mare. *Veterinarian (Spain)* 13:791–796.

55   Richardson, C. 1972. Diagnosis of pregnancy in the ewe by vaginal biopsy. *Brit. Vet. J.* 128:316–329.

56   Roberts, S. J. 1971. *Veterinary Obstetrics and Genital Diseases (Theriogenology).* 2nd ed. Published by the author, Ithaca, N.Y. Pp. 170–173.

57   ———. 1962. The enigma of fetal mummification. *J.A.V.M.A.* 140:691–693.

58   Robertson, H. A. and I. R. Sarda. 1971. A very early pregnancy test for mammals: Its application to the cow, ewe and sow. *J. Endocrinol.* 49:407–419.

59   Rossdale, P. 1970. Life before birth. *The Thoroughbred of California.* Pp. 778-796.

60   Samuel, C. A., W. R. Allen, and D. H. Steven. 1976. Studies on the equine placenta. II. Ultrastructure of the placental barrier. *J. Reprod. Fert.* 48:257–264.

61 Santamarina, E. and L. L. Joven. 1959. Evaluation of reliability of a diagnosis test for pregnancy in mares based on the presence of gonadotrophic hormones. *J.A.V.M.A.* 135:383–387.

62 ———. 1960. Factors influencing accuracy of a gonadotrophin test for pregnancy in mares. *J.A.V.M.A.* 137:522–524.

63 Singleton, W. L. 1975. Early pregnancy diagnosis in swine. Personal communication.

64 Snyder, D. A. and W. R. Dukelow. 1974. Laparoscopic studies of ovulation, pregnancy diagnosis, and follicle aspiration in sheep. *Therio.* 2:143–148.

65 Solomon, W. J. and G. Hoff. 1969. An immunologic pregnancy test for mares. *J.A.V.-M.A.* 155:42–44.

66 Sorensen, A. M., Jr. 1976. *Repro Lab: A Laboratory Manual for Animal Reproduction.* 3rd ed. Kendall/Hunt, Dubuque, Iowa. Pp. 125–139.

67 Spahr, S. L., J. R. Lodge, and D. Considine. 1977. Progesterone content of goat's milk and its application for pregnancy diagnosis. *J. Dairy Sci. Suppl.* 1:82–82. (Abstr.)

68 Spincemaille, J. 1968. Biological and immunological pregnancy diagnosis in the mare. *Proc. 6th Int. Congr. on Anim. Reprod. and A.I.* 1:475–477.

69 Squires, E. L., R. H. Douglas, W. P. Steffenhagen, and O. J. Ginther. 1974. Ovarian changes during the estrous cycle and pregnancy in mares. *J. Anim. Sci.* 38:330–338.

70 Tabarelli Neto, J. F. 1949. The reaction of the male toad to pregnant mares serum and its comparative study with the Cole-Hart test. *J. Vet. Res.* 10:74–76.

71 Tavenner, H. W. and W. W. Green. 1959. Diagnosis of bovine pregnancy by measuring vaginal response to oxytocin. *J. Anim. Sci.* 18:867–873.

72 Thorburn, G. D., J. R. C. Challis, and W. B. Currie. 1977. Control of parturition in domestic animals. *Biol. Reprod.* 16:18–27.

73 Trouson, A. O. and N. W. Moore. 1974. Effect of progesterone and oestrogen on the survival and development of fertilized ova in the ovariectomized ewe. *Australian J. Biol. Sci.* 27:511–517.

74 Vaitukaitis, J. L. 1977. Human chorionic gonadotropin. In F. Fuchs and A. Klopper, eds. *Endocrinology of Pregnancy.* 2nd ed. Harper & Row, New York. Pp. 63–75.

75 Vandeplassche, M. 1968. La mortalité embryonnaire et son diagnostic. *Proc. 6th Int. Congr. on Anim. Reprod. and A.I.* 1:347–377.

76 Velle, W. 1960. Early pregnancy diagnosis in the sow. *Vet. Rec.* 72:116–118.

77 Voss, J. L., B. W. Pickett, D. G. Back, and L. D. Burwash. 1975. Effect of rectal palpation on pregnancy rate of nonlactating, normally cycling mares. *J. Anim. Sci.* 41:829–834.

78 Webel, S. K. and P. J. Dziuk. 1971. Pig fetal loss due to uterine space and fetal age. *J. Anim. Sci.* 33:1164. (Abstr.)

79 Winters, L. M., W. W. Green, and R. E. Comstock. 1942. The prenatal development of the bovine. *Univ. of Minn. Agr. Exp. Sta. Tech. Bull. 151.* Pp. 1–50.

80 Wisnicky, W. and L. E. Casida. 1948. Manual method for the diagnosis of pregnancy in cattle. *J.A.V.M.A.* 113:451–452.

81 Woelffer, E. 1957. Determination of pregnancy in cows. *J.A.V.M.A.* 131:514.

82 Zemjanis, R. 1961. Pregnancy diagnosis of the mare. *J.A.V.M.A.* 139:543–547.

83 ———. 1970. *Diagnostic and Therapeutic Techniques in Animal Reproduction.* 2nd ed. Williams & Wilkins, Baltimore. Pp. 1–238.

84 Zondek, B. and F. Sulman. 1945. A twenty-four-hour pregnancy test for equine. *Nature* 155:302–303.

CHAPTER 15

Parturition and the Postpartum Period

When you have completed this chapter you should be able to:

- Discuss the factors influencing parturition,
- Describe the stages of parturition as they apply to the various species,
- Understand some of the problems that may arise during birth and methods of alleviating them, and
- Relate the postpartum period to ensuing estrous activity and conception.

PARTURITION (To Give Birth)

Parturition is the termination of gestation. It is the expulsion of the fetus that has reached maturity. The process by which the dam or fetus knows parturition is to begin is still unclear. There are certain factors operating at this time that are at least partially responsible, and these will be discussed.

Hormonal Control

Progesterone and estrogen are present throughout gestation and change in ratio rather drastically in domestic animals as parturition approaches. Progesterone decreases in the latter part of pregnancy while estrogen rises in the cow,[33,95] ewe, and sow (Fig. 14–1, 2, 3). Progesterone rises slightly in the latter stages in the mare, but estrogen is much higher in concentration (Fig. 14–4). The woman does not follow this pattern, as both progesterone and estrogen are high at the time of parturition (Fig. 14–6).

Progesterone Progesterone is responsible for the quiet condition of the myometrium; as its potency decreases, the myometrium can exert its actions again,[35] particularly in response to the rising estrogen levels.[12,50] The activity of the myometrium is a factor in expulsion of the uterine contents.

It is evident that these hormones are not the only factors acting, because progesterone is at its highest level at the time of birth in the woman and injections of progesterone have not delayed parturition in ewes and cows.[16,98] On the other hand, exogenous progesterone will prolong gestation in the sow but number of CL does not affect length of gestation.[62]

Estrogen Estrogen appears to be important in initiation of labor in the cow and particularly in expulsion of the placenta and lactogenesis. Its source is fetal-placental in the cow,[79] but little is derived from the fetal adrenal.[36] Estrogen peaks at the time of parturition in the pig and returns to basal level by 72 hours postpartum.[8,65,88] The peak is reached at parturition in sheep.[23,99]

Oxytocin Oxytocin is produced by the hypothalamus and stored in the neurohypophysis. Distension of the vagina and vulva at parturition apparently causes a release of oxytocin which supplements the action of myometrial contraction primed and initiated by estrogen. Oxytocin rises to a peak at the moment of delivery in the cow, sheep, and horse and then declines rapidly.[24]

Relaxin Relaxin is released by the ovary at least in part, just prior to parturition, and appears to be stimulated by prostaglandins.

Other Compounds

Fetal Adrenal The fetal hypophysis-adrenal axis appears to be responsible for parturition in the cow, ewe, and sow. Corticosteroids in the plasma of the fetus rise, and these high levels apparently act in conjunction with the hormones to initiate parturition in the pig,[8] cow,[37,95] and ewe. Cortisol, a glucocorticoid, rises during parturition but is explained to be the effect and not the cause.[49]

Prostaglandins Prostaglandin is produced by the pregnant horn and released into the uterine vein draining that side. A decrease in progesterone follows in 24 hours in the cow and pig.[98]

Human

There is no apparent pattern of the above influences operating in the woman. The fetus appears to have little effect, there are no abrupt changes in progesterone and estrogen, and prostaglandins seem to have little effect, so it is proposed that parturition is governed by genetics and placental factors.[59]

Summary

These previous statements may be summarized by stating that the fetal hypo-thalamus-hypophysis system interacts with the fetal adrenal to produce glucocor-ticoids. Concurrently, prostaglandin is being produced by the uterus and causes a decrease in progesterone production. At the same time, the prostaglandin is stimu-lating estrogen production by the placenta and release of oxytocin from the neurohy-pophysis. Myometrial activity results, and the birth canal is opened under the influence of estrogen and relaxin.[106] Although this sounds rather simple and method-ical, it must be realized that the interactions necessary are really rather complicated with one thing depending upon the other and all working together to bring about expulsion of the fetus.

Cattle

Table 15–1 gives an idea of the variation between breeds of cattle for the length of gestation and weight of the calf born. There is no definite trend based on size of the cow related to length of gestation, but there is a relationship between breed and birth weight of the calf.

As gestation approaches its end, there are certain actions and physical changes that tell the cattleman of the impending birth.

Prepartum (Before Labor) In the period before birth the right ventral abdomen is distended as the calf increases in size and lies on the floor of the abdominal cavity. The udder also starts filling with increased glandular and duct tissue in preparation for milk secretion. These two factors may be noted several weeks before parturition. The distension is not dependable for determining pregnancy, as some cows may be distended with feed and/or water. Also, some cows will not have an enlarged udder even at the time of parturition. These are general considerations.

Table 15-1   Gestation Length and Birth Weight in Cattle

Breed	Males		Females		Both sexes	
	Days	Kg (lb)	Days	Kg (lb)	Days	Kg (lb)
Angus	283	30 (67)	282	31 (69)	279	28 (61)
Ayrshire	279	36 (79)	279	33 (72)	278	34 (76)
Brahman	—	—	—	—	293	—
Brown Swiss	292	49 (107)	290	44 (98)	291	46 (102)
Guernsey	284	32 (71)	282	29 (64)	284	31 (68)
Hereford	287	36 (79)	286	34 (74)	286	34 (76)
Holstein	280	44 (97)	279	41 (90)	279	42 (93)
Jersey	280	27 (59)	279	25 (55)	280	25 (55)
Shorthorn	—	33 (73)	—	31 (69)	—	33 (72)
Charolais	—	50 (111)	—	46 (101)	—	46 (102)
Gir	286	—	284	—	285	22 (49)
Nellor	292	—	290	—	291	—
Simmental	286	—	285	—	286	—

Adapted from Anderson and Plum;[4] Plasse et al.[80]

The next thing noticed will be a relaxation of the musculature around the tailhead. This may be due to relaxin but is not proven. The sagging condition causes a loose appearance and the coccygeal vertebrae become prominent. The vulva will start to swell as edema increases. This fluid in the soft tissue causes a sagging of the vulva which is more noticeable in animals with large vulvas normally, such as Brahman, Santa Gertrudis, and cattle carrying some Zebu breeding.

The udder should continue to enlarge until it becomes strutted even to the extent of milk spurting from the teats, particularly when the cow moves.

Within a few hours of parturition, the cow becomes restless, will not eat, and attempts to isolate herself from the herd. She will usually lie down and get up repeatedly before the act of parturition begins.

Birth The period of birth can be divided into three stages for ease in comparing various species' activities. Stage 1 is a period immediately before birth, which may be considered that time leading up to and including uterine contractions and cervical dilation. Stage 2 is the actual period of birth beginning with the rupture of the membranes and passage of fluids and ending with expulsion of the fetus. Stage 3 begins with the passage of the placenta and includes the involution of the reproductive tract. For a more detailed division for research purposes the number of stages may be increased for clarity.[74]

Stage 1 The calf assumes a position that will give the least resistance to its passage to the exterior (Fig. 15–1). The front feet and legs form a wedge with the head between them. The shoulders continue the wedge followed by the rib cage and larger hip area with the hind legs and feet trailing.

The calf may be in almost any position prior to parturition, but the motility of the uterus and contractions of the diaphragm plus the activity of the calf should orient it into the normal position before the labor contractions begin. This change in position may be over several days or may happen instantaneously.

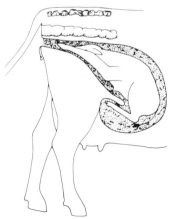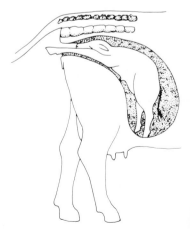

Figure 15-1 Normal presentation of the calf at birth.

During this preparation time the cervix also responds to high levels of estrogen and internal pressure due to the chorioallantoic fluids by dilating in preparation for passage of the fetus.

Stage 1, the period of preparation, may last for 2 to 6 hours.

Stage 2 This includes the time for the appearance of the fetal membranes through expulsion of the calf.

The outer chorioallantoic membrane moves into and protrudes from the cervical canal. The increased internal pressure causes a rupture of the membrane and an escape of the fluids contained in it. Almost immediately the contractions, which occur at about 15-minute intervals, push the amnioallantoic membrane into the canal and it ruptures, releasing its fluid. The ruptures may be separate or occur almost simultaneously.

The cow is usually lying on her side at this time and the contractions of labor, including uterine and abdominal forces, cause stress to the animal. The frequency of the contractions gradually increases, and the calf itself is forced through the canal so that the feet show in the vulvar opening.

Picture, if you will, the condition in the cervical canal at this point. There are two layers of fetal membranes lining the canal for protection, and fluid is present to act as a lubricant.

This period may last from 15 to 30 minutes.[74]

Uterine contractions will increase in frequency and magnitude. The contractions every 2 to 3 minutes are joined by distinct contractions of the abdominal musculature called the abdominal press, and the head is exposed.

This period may last 10 to 30 minutes.

Contined contractions increase the interval pressure so that the calf is gradually pushed from its uterine environment. The placenta remains at least partially attached during the process at the numerous placentomes. It is not known how many are needed to maintain a supply of nutrients to the calf during the process of expelling the calf. The entire birth process can last up to 8 hours without apparent difficulty. If the cotyledons do release from the caruncles the calf will open its mouth to breathe. If it is still inside it will drown in its own placental fluids.

Stage 3 As the calf is expelled, the placenta, or afterbirth, is pulled by it and may be expelled or may be severed at the umbilical cord. If the membranes are retained, they should normally be expelled in 30 minutes to 8 hours without complication. The uterus continues contractions up to 24 hours postpartum to assist in removal.[87] Expulsion is of very short duration, 3 to 10 minutes, unless complications arise.

The calf should be free of the membranes when it reaches the ground, but this is not always true. The cow will lick the calf almost immediately following birth and remove the membranes if they are still present. If the stockman is near and sees the membranes covering the nostrils, he should remove them and wipe the nose clean of mucus. The cow licks the calf and massages and dries it in the process so that it gains stability in its breathing and feels secure. The naturally severed umbilical cord should be bathed in an antiseptic such as iodine.

The calf tries to gain its feet and sometimes takes a few minutes to find that the four toothpicks supplied for legs really will support him.

This usually lasts about 20 to 40 minutes, and then he starts searching for his first meal.

This time from expulsion to nursing lasts from 40 to 60 minutes.

During this stage the calf stands and finds its mother and feels and punches until it finds the udder and teats. It may need some help, which is supplied by the dam, who moves or nudges the calf in the right direction.

The birth process itself, Stages 2 and 3, takes about 30 to 45 minutes under normal circumstances, but the cattleman should not get excited if it takes several hours.

Dystocia (Abnormal Birth) Dystocia may be of many types. It may result from a problem with size either of the calf or the dam, posture of the calf, or lack of effort on the part of the cow.

The birth weight of the calf is the main cause of dystocia in young cattle.[13,82,94] And the major loss of calves comes at the time of birth. Table 15–2 shows the calf losses in 6409 calvings over a 10-year period. This means that 4 to 6 percent of the calves died at birth while only 2 to 4 percent were lost after birth. Other studies indicate four times as many calves lost at birth due to dystocia as normal births.[57] Of the 285 deaths at birth, 205 were normal calves that had difficult births, giving 80 percent (164 calves) that were lost because of dystocia.

The influx of many of the larger beef breeds into livestock production programs has resulted in considerably more interest in calving difficulties than at any time before. Tables 15–3 and 15–4 summarize the data from the Meat Animal Research Center in Nebraska in a comprehensive study on calving difficulties.

The scores assigned the calving difficulty were:

1 No difficulty	Calves unassisted; however, it may be necessary to straighten head and/or front legs.
2 Little difficulty	Assistance given by hand, but no jack or puller used; assistance actually may not have been required.
3 Moderate difficulty	Assistance given with jack or calf puller; some difficulty encountered even with the pullers being used.

Table 15-2   Calf Losses over 10 Years in Montana

	Number	% yearly loss	% of losses
Total calving	6409		
Calf losses:			
At birth	285	4–6	75
Birth to weaning	95	2–4	25
Total	380	4–8	100

Adapted from Bellows.[13]

4 Major difficulty   Calf jack used and major difficulty encoun-
                                               tered; usually 30 minutes or more required to
                                               deliver calf.

5 Cesarean birth
6 Posterior presentation

Age is a critical factor. Two-year-old cows experience far greater incidences of
dystocia (36 percent) than 3-year-old cows and 45 percent more incidence than 4-
and 5-year-old cows.[55]

It has also been noted that male calves tend to be slightly larger than female,
are carried a little longer, and experience greater difficulty at birth.[14]

Hormonal control may be delayed in the cow, resulting in dystocia.[72] The
concentrations of progesterone and estrogen have been measured in normal and
dystocial cows and progesterone was found to be maintained at a higher level and
estrogen at a lower level in those experiencing dystocia.

Nutrition does not appear to be the answer to controlling birth weights. Precalving energy levels have been varied without significantly changing the difficulties
at calving (Table 15–5).[54] Cattle were fed a low energy ration (4.9 kg, 10.8 lb),
medium (6.2 kg, 13.6 lb), and high (7.7 kg, 16.9 lb per head per day) with subsequent
gains of .3 kg (.6 lb), .6 kg (1.4 lb), and .9 kg (2.0 lb) per day, respectively, over a
90-day prepartum period.

Apparently, the selection of breed and sire within the breed offers the best
solution to problems of dystocia.[46] This means records must be maintained on
calving criteria and sires selected accordingly. Some breed associations and breeding
organizations are beginning to accumulate such data, and these should be critically
evaluated in selecting the sire.

One of the most perplexing situations for the cattleman is "When do I step in
and help the cow during birth?" And next comes the problem of how you help her.

Many are prone to interfere too early and perhaps are of more hindrance than
help, and others wait too long and lose the calf. There is no definite answer to this
problem, but there are some signs that help in making a decision.

Trouble signs There is a good chance of difficult calving if birth has not occurred
within 2 hours of rupture and passage of the water. Internally, the cotyledons may
begin to release and this means the calf must be removed quickly.

Another sign later in delivery is the cessation of efforts by the cow. Some
animals become exhausted and quit contracting. The calf may be partially expelled
and need help to complete delivery.

If the calf's head is exposed and the tongue starts to turn blue, it is receiving
no oxygen and may be suffocating. Remove the calf as soon as possible.

Examination The cattleman must try to decide the reason for the difficulty. Palpation of the reproductive tract and the calf will answer many questions.

Is the cervix dilated? Prepare as you would for palpating for pregnancy with
a sleeve and sterile lubricant and insert the hand into the vagina. If the cervix is open

Table 15-3   Calving Difficulty Summary 1970 Calf Crop: 3-4-5-Year-Old Females

| Breed of sire | Breed of dam | No. calves | Calving difficulty score | | | | | | Dead at or shortly after birth (%) |
			1 %	2 %	3 %	4 %	5 %	6 %	
Hereford	Hereford	37	91.9	2.7	2.7			2.7	5.4
(14 bulls)	Angus	47	93.6	4.3		2.1			
	Average	84	92.7	3.5	1.4	1.0		1.4	2.7
Angus	Hereford	29	100.0						
(14 bulls)	Angus	32	93.8		3.1	3.1			6.3
	Average	61	97.0		1.5	1.5			3.2
Jersey	Hereford	29	97.0		3.0				3.0
(12 bulls)	Angus	32	100.0						
	Average	61	98.5		1.5				1.5
So. Devon	Hereford	17	70.0	6.0	12.0	12.0			6.0
(14 bulls)	Angus	12	100.0						
	Average	29	85.0	3.0	6.0	6.0			3.0
Limousin	Hereford	44	87.0	2.0	2.0	7.0		2.0	5.0
(6 bulls)	Angus	42	78.0	5.0	5.0	10.0		2.0	7.0
	Average	86	82.5	3.5	3.5	8.5		2.0	6.0
Simmental	Hereford	64	71.0	9.0	6.0	14.0			16.0
(8 bulls)	Angus	72	82.0	3.0	4.0	10.0		1.0	6.0
	Average	136	76.5	6.0	5.0	12.0		0.5	11.0
Charolais	Hereford	64	72.0	5.0	9.0	11.0		3.0	13.0
(10 bulls)	Angus	67	79.0		3.0	13.0		5.0	7.0
	Average	131	75.5	2.5	6.0	12.0			10.0
Avg. all	Hereford	284	81.7	4.2	5.3	7.4		1.4	8.5
sire breeds	Angus	304	86.5	2.0	2.6	7.2		1.7	4.6
	Average	588	84.1	3.1	4.0	7.3		1.5	6.6

Adapted from Glimp.[43]

so you can pass your hand through, then the difficulty is probably elsewhere. If it is closed then hormones and pressures are not functioning properly and a veterinarian should be summoned for a possible cesarean section to remove the calf surgically.

Is the calf alive? If the cervix is dilated, then the calf should be palpated. Pinching between the hooves, in the nostril, or in the eye should bring a responsive movement if the animal is alive.[18] If the rear of the animal is in the pelvic opening, pinch the anus.

Is the pelvic opening large enough? This is a little late to worry about this since it should have been done earlier, but palpation of the pelvic canal will give the cattleman some idea as to whether the calf can pass through or not. Many cases of dystocia result from a small pelvis and a large calf. If it can be determined that the calf cannot pass through, a cesarean operation is the only route left in order to save the calf. Unnecessary pulling may destroy both calf and cow.

Prior planning can prepare the stockman for this problem many times.

Table 15-4   Calving Difficulty Summary 1970 Calf Crop: 2-Year-Old Females

Breed of sire	Breed of dam	No. calves	Calving difficulty score						Dead at or shortly after birth (%)
			1 %	2 %	3 %	4 %	5 %	6 %	
Hereford	Hereford	25	32.0	8.0	4.0	52.0	4.0		
(14 bulls)	Angus	50	68.0	2.0	2.0	28.0			6.0
	Average	75	50.0	5.0	3.0	40.0	2.0		3.0
Angus	Hereford	37	43.2	8.1	2.7	46.0			13.5
(14 bulls)	Angus	44	65.9	2.3		31.8			9.1
	Average	81	54.6	5.2	1.4	38.9			11.3
Jersey	Hereford	27	70.4	11.1	3.7	14.8			
(12 bulls)	Angus	44	93.1	4.6		2.3			2.3
	Average	71	81.8	7.9	1.8	8.6			1.2
So. Devon	Hereford	15	33.3	13.3	13.3	33.3	6.7		6.7
(14 bulls)	Angus	33	36.4	3.0	6.1	51.5	3.0		12.0
	Average	48	34.9	8.2	9.7	42.4	4.9		9.4
Limousin	Hereford	37	10.8	2.7	5.4	70.3	8.1	2.7	8.1
(6 bulls)	Angus	27	29.6	7.4	7.4	55.6			3.7
	Average	64	20.2	5.1	6.4	63.0	4.1	1.4	5.9
Simmental	Hereford	16	12.5			50.0	37.5		6.3
(8 bulls)	Angus	17	47.0	5.9	5.9	29.5	11.7		11.7
	Average	33	29.8	3.0	3.0	39.8	24.6		9.0
Charolais	Hereford	21	19.0	9.5		52.4	14.3	4.8	14.3
(10 bulls)	Angus	22	27.3		4.6	68.1			13.6
	Average	43	23.2	4.8	2.3	60.3	7.2	2.4	14.0
Avg. all sire breeds	Hereford	178	32.6	7.3	3.9	47.2	7.9	1.1	7.3
	Angus	237	58.2	3.4	3.0	34.2	1.3		7.6
	Average	415	45.4	5.4	3.5	40.7	4.6	.6	7.5

Adapted from Glimp.[43]

Anatomy of the pelvis should be studied to realize what difficulties may arise (Fig. 15–2). The relationship of pelvic opening to ease of birth depends of course on the size of the calf. The size of the pelvic opening may be measured and predictions made concerning degree of difficulty at calving. This is accomplished by measuring the *vertical* distance from the ridge at the front of the symphysis pubis to the midline of the sacrum (Fig. 15–2). The *transverse* distance is measured between the shafts

Table 15-5   Precalving Energy Level Effects on Birth Weight and Calving Difficulty

	Low		Medium		High	
Breed	Birth weight kg (lb)	% difficulty	Birth weight kg (lb)	% difficulty	Birth weight kg (lb)	% difficulty
Hereford	26 (57)	29	28 (62)	20	30 (66)	25
Angus	26 (58)	23	28 (61)	13	28 (62)	12
Average	26 (58)	26	28 (61)	17	29 (64)	18

Adapted from Laster.[54]

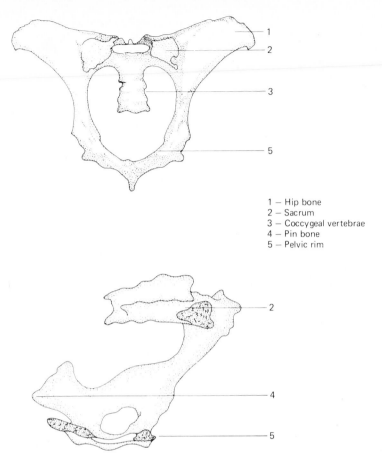

1 — Hip bone
2 — Sacrum
3 — Coccygeal vertebrae
4 — Pin bone
5 — Pelvic rim

Figure 15-2   The pelvis of the cow.

of the ileum at the widest point. These two distances are multiplied to determine an approximate pelvic area. It is realized that the opening is an ellipse and not a rectangle, but comparisons of relationship of area to dystocia are very little different and the VXT is much simpler to calculate.[85]

Several instruments have been devised to measure these distances. A screw-type plunger was used by carrying it into the rectum and adjusting it to the appropriate points and then extracting it to take a measurement. Scissor-type calipers were developed with a direct measurement read on the handle and are probably the most popular models now in use (Fig. 15–3). A hydraulic mechanism has also been developed. All must be carried into the rectum and the measurements made through the rectal wall.

Much research has been conducted to determine just what the best size area is. Of course there is none that will fit all conditions. One group of heifers was measured 3 months before parturition and it was found if pelvic areas were under 200 sq cm (31 sq in) there was a 69 percent instance of dystocia compared to 28 percent in those

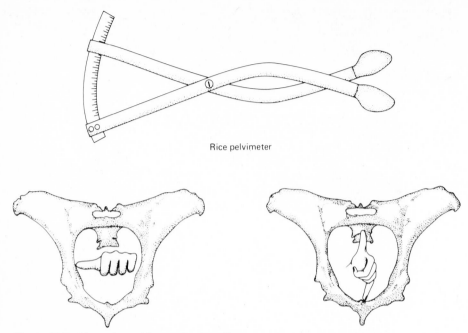

Rice pelvimeter

Figure 15-3 Measuring pelvic opening in cattle.

with pelvic areas over 200 sq cm (31 sq in).[85] Mature cows have a pelvic area over 300 sq cm (47 sq in).[109] To give an idea of the change with age of heifers, a group of 2-year-old *primigravida* (first-pregnant) heifers was measured at the time of breeding, at 6 to 7 months of gestation, 1 week before parturition and at parturition. The measurements were 147 (23), 184 (29), 228 (35), and 232 (36) sq cm (sq in), respectively.

The usefulness depends upon the relative size in a given herd of cattle. Measurements can be made and attention paid to those with small pelvic openings regardless of the exact measurements. Measurements may also be made simply by using the hand and measuring with extended thumb and little finger (Fig. 15–3).

If it is thought that the calf can pass through the pelvic opening with some help then that help should be provided. Certain instruments are needed for assistance.

EQUIPMENT There is no purpose in the cattleman's trying to duplicate the instruments of the veterinarian, but he does need some basic equipment. There will be times that the cattleman must do something or lose the calf and perhaps the cow.

Obstetrical chains and handles (Fig. 15–4) are needed for attaching to the calf and assisting in extraction. These should be sterilized between uses by boiling in mineral oil and storing in a clean cloth. Water will cause the chains to rust. Clean cotton rope is satisfactory but should not be reused because of difficulties in sterilization.

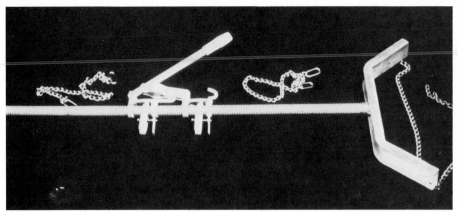

Figure 15-4   Equipment to assist in delivery of the calf.

A mechanical calf puller is an instrument designed to increase traction and is used in conjunction with the chains in difficult cases. Several models have ratchets for increasing the force for pulling the calf (Fig. 15–4).

A lubricant is needed also. This may be an obstetrical soap or a mild hand or flake soap. Mineral oil may be used.

PROCEDURE   If the feet are showing or can be manipulated in the canal, a loop is made in the end of each chain and slipped over each hoof to a point several inches above the ankle joint. The chain should be positioned to pull from the backs of the legs in order to keep the hooves and legs straight.

Both legs should be pulled at the same time. If movement is not noted then alternate pulling should maneuver the shoulders through the pelvis. Try to work with the cow by pulling when she strains and relaxing slightly when the contractions cease.

Hiplock is a common difficulty experienced when the largest portion approaches the pelvis and locks against the face of it. Continued pulling would damage both calf and dam. If the calf is pulled down over the caudal pelvis the hips are elevated to come through the widest part of the pelvis. If this does not succeed, it may be possible to twist the calf on its side and align the hips with the vertical axis of the pelvis, which is still greater in dimension. The calf-puller chain may need to be repositioned around the barrel of the calf and care should be exercised to pull gently.

There is no turning back when the calf's feet and head are exposed. It cannot be replaced and a cesarean performed.

CESAREAN (To Cut)   A cesarean section is commonly referred to as C-section. It involves surgically opening the abdominal cavity and removing the young. The approach may be midventral or in the side or flank. The uterus is exposed and opened to release the calf. The umbilical or navel cord is severed and the placenta replaced unless the dam has released it. The uterus and abdominal wall are sutured and everything should progress satisfactorily for the calf and mother.

SYMPHYSIOTOMY (Junction Cutting) The splitting of the pelvis in young heifers allows spreading and extraction of the calf through the pelvis rather than by cesarean section. It should be used only in primigravida heifers because of the difficulty in healing with older animals. The symphysis pubis ossifies at about 22 to 23 months of age. The procedure involves a chisel that is forced through the symphysis pubis. It is preferred that the heifer be standing during the procedure with an epidural anesthesia. One method involves an incision 1 to 2 inches below the vulva into the fascia, to the caudal border of the symphysis pubis. The chisel is placed at this point and guided and followed by one hand on the floor of the vagina.[60] Striking the end of the chisel drives it through the symphysis and allows the pelvis to spread. Another type of knife hooks over the cranial symphysis pubis and is forced to the rear (Fig. 15–5). The calf is extracted by chains and a mechanical extractor and the

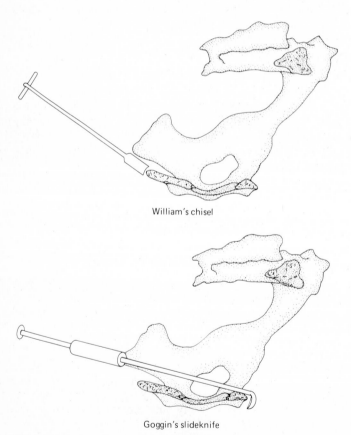

William's chisel

Goggin's slideknife

Figure 15-5 Symphysiotomy in the heifer.

pelvis may separate as much as 10 cm (4 in) to allow delivery. The heifer usually lies down upon completion, which helps retain the pelvis in a normal position. The heifer should be confined several days and recovery should be without difficulty.

The procedure sounds drastic at first, but it was used with a high degree of success in over 1200 cases by one veterinary clinic.[44]

What is the posture of the animal? Normally the front legs and head should be coming out first. This is not true in many cases of dystocia. It should be stated that a backward presentation may be considered normal. In this instance, the rear feet, legs, and hindquarters would form the wedge and the calf be expelled (Fig. 15–6). The major difficulty lies in rupture of the umbilical cord and suffocation.

Three words should be briefly explained. *Presentation* describes direction of delivery, frontward, backward, or crosswise of the pelvic opening. *Position* describes the orientation of the whole calf, right side up, upside down, or on its side. *Posture*

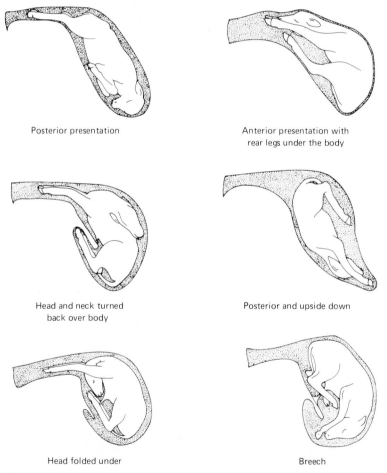

Posterior presentation

Anterior presentation with rear legs under the body

Head and neck turned back over body

Posterior and upside down

Head folded under

Breech

Figure 15-6 Positions of the calf at birth. *(Adapted from Beverly.[18])*

is used to describe the location of the legs, head, and neck in particular. Normal presentation, position, and posture are shown in Figure 15–1.

Several abnormal positions are shown in Figure 15–6. Each must be dealt with individually by replacing, repositioning, or surgical removal.

Retained Placenta The placenta should be expelled by 8 hours postpartum. The detachment of the cotyledons from the caruncles occurs as a result of mechanical pressure, hormonal balance,[25] and necrosis of the fetal villi and epithelium of the maternal crypts.

Retained placentas are more frequent in premature births, twin births, cows on a vitamin A deficient diet, and cows with uterine disease. Induced parturition results in a very high level of retained placentas.

Cows on selenium deficient diets commonly have retained placentas. In one experiment, increasing the selenium content of the ration from .02 ppm to .06 ppm decreased the incidence of retained placentas from 50 percent in control animals to 20 percent in treated.[52]

There are numerous responses to retained afterbirth. The first thought is to try to remove it because it is now a foreign object. After 2 or 3 days it becomes putrified and very odoriferous. The present accepted treatment is to leave it alone and treat the cow with high levels of antibiotics to combat infection. Data show better rebreeding response following this procedure than removal manually with treatment, or placing boluses containing various healing compounds in the uterus. Manual removal oftimes results in tearing of the membranes and retention of pieces that require considerable time for resorption.

Induced Parturition The purpose of inducing parturition is a control mechanism for the stockman. Late-calving cows can be advanced so that they can remain on schedule with earlier-calving cows and hopefully rebreed and be on schedule the following year.[97] Assistance involved with calving can be concentrated by having a group calve at a given time. One factor that was a great stimulus to research in this area was the introduction of the larger exotic breeds into a crossbreeding program. Early parturition means a smaller calf with reduced dystocia and mortality. Another reason for inducing parturition is to shorten the generation interval by shortening gestation. Corticosteroids and prostaglandins are used.

There are short-acting and long-acting corticosteroids.[63] The more common short-acting drugs are dexamethasone, flumethasone, and betamethasone. These usually act within 2 to 3 days. The major disadvantage is in retained placentas with instances ranging almost to 100 percent.[17,66,81] They are also unpredictable in response with ranges of 10 to 90 percent induction.

The long-acting drug dexamethasone trimethyl-acetate requires multiple injections and takes about 2 weeks for response. Incidence of retained placentas is lower and the cow is in good health and rebreeds satisfactorily. The response is unpredictable and the major disadvantage is in calf mortality. Reports range from 17 to 45 percent stillbirths.[73,107] Stillbirths are lower in those induced late, but the advantage of shortening the gestation period is lost.

Most of the research and the procedures now in use utilize short-acting drugs. The response is between 40 and 96 hours postinjection.[66,70,105] The earliest response occurs around 260 days of gestation with very erratic response before that time.[1] Dose levels range from 20 to 50 mg per cow in a single intramuscular injection.[58,105]

Combinations of glucocorticoids and estrogens have been attempted to try to alleviate the retained placenta difficulty. Response has varied. Some trials have shown improvement (40 percent),[29] while others have not.[19]

Synthetics are also being tested with about equal response as the natural products.

Prostaglandin $F_2\alpha$ may be used to induce parturition. The response is similar to the glucocorticoids: up to 72 hours until parturition and a high percentage retained placentas.[47] Udder development may be considerably less, which is expected if gestation is shortened by several weeks. The action of $PGF_2\alpha$ is on the corpus luteum, and the mechanism by which it works is therefore different than for glucocorticoids.

There is concern about fertility of the induced animals, particularly related to the retained placenta problem and rebreeding. Several reports indicate conception occurring within normal time limits and with similar numbers of inseminations.[73,105] One trial of 294 cows resulted in 159 retained placentas. The services per conception and days from calving to conception were 1.23 vs. 1.35 and 81 vs. 82 for those retaining the placentas and those not retaining them. Other reports indicate difficulties in rebreeding.[66] Induced cows (560) had a lower conception rate at the next breeding (74 percent) than did control (433) cows (82 percent). The retained placenta cows had a pregnancy rate 10 percent below those without retained placentas (70 vs. 80 percent).

Postpartum (After Birth Process) This period is also called *puerperium*. The postpartum interval to conception is one of the most important times in the cow's life. This is particularly true of young cows that have just given birth to their first calf and are now 2 or 3 years of age. They are still growing, they are nursing a calf for the first time, and the producer expects them to bounce right back and rebreed immediately.

The searched-for goal of the cattleman is a calf a year from each cow. This means that if 283 days gestation is subtracted from 365 days in a year, the cow has 82 days to rebreed. Let us look at some factors taking place in these few weeks.

Estrous activity The interval from parturition to first estrus varies tremendously, but some figure needs to be given as a generality and explanations made for deviations from that. The cow returns to estrus in about 30 to 40 days in dairy breeds and 40 to 60 days in beef breeds.[45] Some dairy and beef cattle will be in estrus as early as 10 to 15 days postpartum, but this is unusual. Some cattle under stress such as high temperature, high humidity, and poor nutrition may not show estrus until the calf is weaned from the cow. She will then show signs of estrus in about one week. The short intervals are a blessing, while the long intervals upset planned breeding programs.

The hormonal secretions following parturition must regain their cyclic pattern. Regardless of the time until estrus, there is a growth of follicles almost immediately after parturition and then regression.[69] There is also a rise in luteinizing hormone that occurs approximately 21 days before estrus followed by a rise in progesterone as in a normal cycle (Fig. 15–7).[34,100] This activity may be associated with an anestrous ovulation or with luteinization of a follicle. This activity apparently triggers the mechanism for a normal developing follicle, estrus, and ovulation. The anestrous ovulation is sometimes called "silent ovulation" or "silent heat," but these are poor descriptive terms. No one can hear ovulation or heat. *Anestrus* denotes "without sexual excitement." Once estrus and ovulation occur, the cyclic pattern begins. The first cycle or two may be slightly shorter but are not outside the normal range.

Induced estrus When a cow has not shown signs of estrus at 60 days postpartum the owner should be concerned. Methods of inducing estrus have been proposed and tried with varying degrees of success.

The natural way of inducing estrus and ovulation is to separate the cow and calf so there is a period of rest for the cow. This time need only be one day to cause many cows to start cycling. The calf that is suckling continually stimulates oxytocin for milk letdown. Oxytocin is related to ovarian activity and thought by many to be the depressor of activity. Numerous attempts have been made to incriminate oxytocin per se without success. One group of cows in which the sensory nerves to the mammary system were destroyed responded no differently than normal cows with suckling calves.[93] Other cows from which calves were removed at 3 to 7 days postpartum were in estrus at 28 days postpartum compared to 76 for suckled cows and 81 for suckled denervated cows.

Many comparisons have been made between cows from which calves were removed at birth; cows milked twice daily, three times daily, and four times daily;

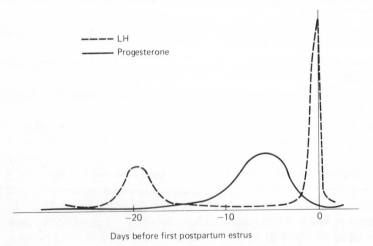

Figure 15-7 Hormone changes in the primiparous young cow in the postpartum period.

cows suckling one calf; cows suckling twins; cows from which the udder has been removed; cows from which calves are removed for varying periods of time and returned; and any sort of combination you can conceive.[11,15,56,75,76,83,104] A summary of these would reveal that the more stress removed, the sooner the cow will cycle postpartum and the quicker she will breed.

Progestogens and prostaglandins have been used in the same manner as described earlier in ovulation control. The response has been variable with a great dependency on cow condition at the time of treatment. Prostaglandin will only function if a CL is present, which means the cow has already cycled and has not been observed. A combination of calf removal and progestogens offers some promise for cattle in at least fair condition. Under circumstances such as this the progestogen has been implanted for 9 days plus an injection at the time of implantation. When the implant is removed, the calf is separated for 48 hours.[110] Conception rates have been double those in cattle from which calves were removed only (58 vs. 27 percent) in one trial and even better in another trial compared to controls (58 vs. 17 percent). Because of the close synchronization of ovulation following this treatment it may be possible to breed without estrus being observed. Limited numbers indicate about 20 percent increase in conception following a timed breeding compared to breeding according to estrus check. Unavailability of drugs makes this method impractical at the present time.

Uterine involution The uterus of the pregnant cow has expanded from a size comparable to two fingers to a container of calf and fluids that weighs nearly 45 kg (100 pounds). All of a sudden the contents are expelled and the uterus is an empty sack weighing about 9 kg (19.8 lb).[40] The many muscles, caruncles, the vascular system, connective tissue, and other constituents must return everything to its normal shape and size in preparation for another pregnancy. This return is called involution. Contraction of the uterine muscles continues for 2 or 3 days following parturition. These together with vasoconstriction stimulate most of the decrease in size.[64]

The horns of the uterus diminish quickly for the first 22 days from a diameter of 24 cm (9 in) to 4.5 cm (2 in) and then the return is slower.[68] The internal surface shrinks and the surface of the caruncles undergoes necrosis as the stalk is constricted due to vasoconstriction.[40] The sloughed cellular debri mixes with retained fluids and secreted fluids to form *lochia*, which is the fluid in the reproductive tract at this time. The caruncles repair quickly and should be normal in 3 to 4 weeks. Involution is usually complete by 30 to 40 days.[61]

The cervix has also been stretched far beyond its normal size as the calf is born. This organ responds very quickly and shrinks mostly during the first day and then more gradually for about 30 days until it returns to normal. There is a gradual enlargement of the cervix with continuous use, and older cows that have produced more calves *(multiparous)* usually have a larger cervix.

It is recommended that the cow be bred at her second estrous period. This will usually be a normal cycle and normal estrus with acceptable conception. Some have recommended waiting 60 to 90 days before rebreeding, which will coincide with second estrus in many instances. The condition of the uterus at the first estrus when the interval is short, under 30 days, may still not be conducive to fertilization and embryonic growth. Abortions may occur and longer intervals to conception result than if it had been skipped.

The dilemma of the cattleman is time. He has 82 days to get the cow safe in calf and still must contend with nature's time requirement for preparing for the next pregnancy.

Sheep

There is a little variation in length of gestation in breeds of sheep (Table 15–6). In a study of a Rambouillets, Columbias, Corriedales, and Targhees at the United States Sheep Experimental Station and Western Sheep Breeding Laboratory in Idaho, it was found that Rambouillets had the longest gestation period (151.4 days) and Columbias had the shortest (148.4). Normal ranges were 141 to 159 days.[96] Length of gestation was not significantly affected by weight at breeding time, milk production, single or twin births, or sex of the lamb.

Prepartum The ewe is very similar to the cow as parturition approaches. She is restless, enlarged, relaxed around the tailhead, has a swollen vulva, and a few hours before birth will isolate herself. One difference lies in mammary development, which is not as prominent.

Birth The lamb is usually maintained in the correct position for delivery and changes position very little. The vertebrae are dorsal and the front feet and legs caudal with the head between.[28,84] Sometimes one leg will be folded back alongside the body, but this rarely causes any difficulty. If both legs are folded back dystocia may result.[87]

The ewe usually lies down during birth on her stomach or side. Abdominal contractions resemble those of the cow, and expulsion should follow the same pattern. The time from the rupture of the first membranes until expulsion of the lamb

Table 15-6 Gestation Length Related to Breeds of Sheep

Breed	Gestation Length (day)	Range (day)	Region
Southdown	144	141–148	Missouri
Dorset Horn	146	138–149	Australia
Hampshire	145	140–147	Missouri
Shropshire	145	141–147	Missouri
Romney	148	144–153	Russia, New Zealand
Lincoln	148	—	Russia
Navajo	149	—	New Mexico
Rambouillet	150	143–157	Oklahoma, Montana
Merino	150	142–156	Germany, South Africa, Australia
Karakul	152	140–155	Russia

Adapted from Terrill and Hazel.[96]

should be .5 to 2 hours for singles and slightly longer for twins and triplets (Fig. 15–8).

The placenta is expelled similar to the cow. The umbilical cord breaks during delivery, and the afterbirth should follow within 8 hours.

If the preparation process takes over 12 hours or the birth process over 2 or 3 hours, outside help is needed. Attempts should be made to grasp the feet and legs, and with a steady pull accented by greater pressure in synchrony with the contractions of the ewe, extract the lamb. Dystocia has been reported as occurring in 34 percent of a large group of ewes in Australia.[42] Most lambs giving difficulty were single male lambs.

Cesarean sections are performed on the ewe but are rare. They would be conducted when the cervix does not dilate or a very large lamb cannot pass through the pelvis. Ewe lambs that were bred when they were too small may give difficulty. The procedure is the same as for cattle.

The placenta should shed within hours of birth but may be retained. Treatment of the ewe with antibiotics is recommended and the placenta should slough in 2 to 10 days.

Induced Parturition Glucocorticoids may be used for inducing parturition in sheep with almost 100 percent response. The dosage levels range from 8 to 20 mg dexamethasone per ewe, and response to treatment is affected by stage of gestation, with the best response nearest expected parturition.[1,20] Parturition occurs 24 to 72 hours following injection. Estradiol benzoate (20 mg) has been used to induce parturition in 48 to 96 hours in ewes 142 to 148 days of gestation with 65 to 84 percent response, respectively.[21]

Retained afterbirth is no problem in induced ewes. The uterus cleans quickly, and subsequent fertility does not appear to be affected.[20]

Lambs weigh less following induced parturition, but mortality is low and weight gains are not affected.[22]

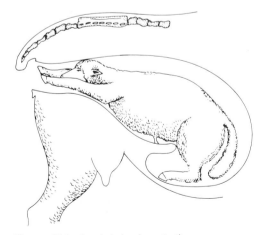

Figure 15-8 Lamb being born to the ewe.

Use of induced parturition in sheep offers a tool to be used with synchronization to concentrate lambing into a very short period of time.[9]

Postpartum Involution of the uterus occurs between 17 and 28 days.[39,101,102] By this time it has cleared internally and returned to its normal nonpregnant size and shape. Lactation slows involution slightly and uterine debri may deter fertility until about 24 days postpartum.

Sheep are seasonal breeders and their postpartum interval to first estrus is markedly affected by season of lambing. If lambs are born during the normal period of seasonal anestrus the postpartum period to estrus may be several months. If they are born during the breeding season, the ewe may return to estrus and rebreed. If lambs are not allowed to suckle, the ewe will be in estrus in about 20 days, but the uterus will not be ready so pregnancy is usually not continued even though conception may occur. The second estrus is usually a fertile estrus. Dorset Horn sheep and some fine-wool breeds will cycle year-round and will return to estrus at about 21 days, with the first fertile estrus at about 37 days.[41]

Swine

Most sows farrow close to the normal 114-day average.

Because of the concentrated program under which most sows are farrowed, the herdsman is usually cognizant of expected birthdates and is prepared for difficulties.

Facilities A farrowing facility constructed for separation and comfort should be provided. It need not be elaborate but should afford bedding, guardrails, and a heat lamp (Fig. 15–9).

Prepartum As parturition approaches, the sow exhibits external symptoms to signal the coming event. She usually becomes quieter, the vulva swells and becomes flaccid, the mammary glands become distended, and there is usually a mucous type discharge from the vulva. These symptoms become more exaggerated as parturition approaches.

The sow makes a nest in some quiet place by pushing straw or any type bedding together. She then lies down to begin farrowing.

Birth The birth process is determined by the number of pigs born, or farrowed. Each pig may take 3 or 4 minutes followed by an interval of 5 to 15 minutes. The farrowing usually begins within a few minutes of the sow's lying down. The membranes are pushed into the birth canal where they rupture, releasing the fluid. The pig is expelled very quickly and the membranes usually follow immediately.

The pigs are located in both horns of the uterus from the cervix to the oviducal origin. The sequence of birth is not fixed regarding the horn in which the pigs are located but is governed more by the proximity to the cervix at the time of the next contraction. The piglet nearest the opening is the next to be expelled. Piglets may come alternately from the horns but may follow with 2 or 3 from one side.[84]

Figure 15-9   Farrowing pen for the sow with bedding, guard rail, heat lamp, and fresh water.

The piglets are not particularly oriented in one direction in the uterus or canal, so that some will appear anteriorly and some posteriorly. There seems to be little if any difference in ease of birth.

The piglets move very quickly on the journey to the outside. The first pigs have a short way to go after they start and the release of the diffuse-type placenta is very rapid. The last pigs have been moved a considerable distance from the upper horn after release and therefore must be born before they become devoid of oxygen and open their mouths to breathe. The diffuse placenta releases all at once and all sources of nutrients cease.

Some placentas may not be expelled immediately following a single piglet. There are sometimes two piglets in one membrane due to fusion in embryonic development. The remaining placentas should be expelled about 4 hours after completion of the farrowing process. Retained placentas are not a problem.

The entire farrowing should last 1 to 5 hours, but some sows may require as long as 8 to 10 hours.

Dystocia is not very common, but large piglets sometimes must be assisted.

Cesarean sections may be required when a young gilt has a small litter of large pigs that cannot be manually extracted. A flank or midventral incision exposes the uterus, and the piglets are removed from inside the horn or milked from the outside to the incision. Recovery is good (85 to 90 percent) if the sow is not exhausted and the pigs dead.

Induced Parturition Dexamethasone has been used to induce parturition through a series of injections from day 101 to 104 of gestation with parturition occurring on day 111.[26,71] Single injections have not proven responsive.[86,99]

Prostaglandin $F_2\alpha$ injected on day 108 to day 110 of gestation has resulted in parturition 29 to 48 hours later.[31,53,108] A prostaglandin analogue has initiated parturition 26 hours after treatment.[5]

Postpartum. The uterus takes about 28 days to return to its normal size following parturition.[77] The decrease in length and weight is very rapid during this time, and it changes little during lactation and then increases slightly following weaning of the pigs.

The corpora lutea of pregnancy regress quickly and by the end of lactation are small dark structures.

The sow frequently shows signs of estrus shortly after farrowing. This may be between 3 and 10 days postpartum. It is an infertile estrus as no follicles develop at this time. The symptoms evidently are in response to the high levels of estrogen at parturition. She will not show signs of estrus again until the pigs are weaned. If pigs are removed immediately or after only 2 days of suckling, the sows will exhibit a fertile estrus in 1 to 3 weeks.[7] If pigs are weaned early, the time until estrus varies according to stage of lactation,[67] with the estrus following weaning at 10 days occurring between 5 and 30 days later, compared to 3 to 15 days after weaning at 21 days, and 2 to 10 days following weaning at 56 days.[92] The latter time (56 days) is the normal time to wean for most swine producers. Conception rates in these particular instances were 93, 91, and 98 percent, respectively. The very early weaning regime may result in high pig mortality, but the 21-day weaning is practical, based on availability and cost of feed.

A combination of hormones and pig removal offers means of continued lactation with conception thereby shortening generation interval.[27] Pigs are separated from the sow 12 hours on days 21, 22, and 23 and the sow is injected with 1500 IU PMSG at the end of the last day. No upset in growth, conception, or litter size is experienced, and the succeeding litters are about 30 days earlier.

Horse

The length of gestation is affected mostly by season of the year. Nutrition has little effect.[48] The stallion used apparently affects length also.[89] Season of breeding accounted for 43 percent of the total variance in length of gestation, nutrition 5 percent, and additive genotype 18 percent in a group of Arabian mares. Mares bred in the wet season, December through May, had longer gestation periods than those bred in the dry season, June through November (340 vs. 330). Breed differences may overcome seasons. Some studies report longer gestation for mares with male foals while others show no difference.

Prepartum The symptoms of the mare approaching parturition resemble those of other animals. There is a gradual increase in size of the abdominal area as the foal grows and a rather distinct sagging of the underline in advanced pregnancy. There is little sagging of the muscles around the tailhead as they are much more dense and supportive than in the cow.

The udder becomes engorged with glandular tissue and colostrum so that the teats become turgid and protrude vertically instead of ventromedially[51] about 3 to 4 weeks before parturition. In the last 2 or 3 days, waxy droplets will appear on the teats, indicating parturition is very near (Fig. 15–10). These are from the colostrum in the udder and may sometimes be washed away by milk leaking from the teats.

The vulva changes little compared to the cow, although there is some edema in the latter stages. Very little if any mucus is discharged.

The mare becomes nervous and turns her head to the side and rear as if looking for something to happen.

Most foalings occur at night between 1900 and 2400 hours.[6,51,91] One study showed 86 percent of the foalings taking place between 1900 and 0700 hours (Fig. 15–11).[91]

Birth

Stage 1 The cervix relaxes and dilates during this stage as the mare increasingly becomes nervous, sweats in the flank, and moves about. The uterus contracts, and it is during this time that the foal assumes the position similar to that of the calf. Prior to this time the foal may be belly upwards, and now it will gradually turn on its side and then into an upright position.[28] This stage lasts about an hour, with considerable variation.

Stage 2 The chorioallantoic membrane moves into the cervical canal and ruptures,

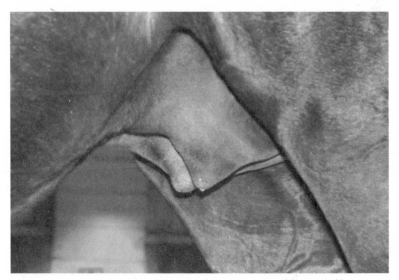

Figure 15-10   Wax beads on the teats of a mare approaching parturition.

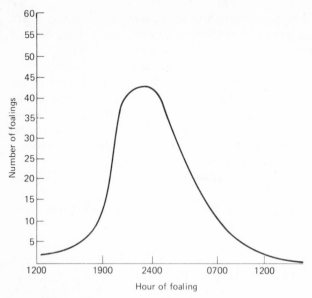

Figure 15-11   Time of parturition for the mare. *(Adapted from Rossdale and Short.[91])*

followed quickly by the amnioallantoic membrane. During this activity the mare will lie on her side and powerful contractions begin. These contractions place a great deal of stress on the mare as evidenced by sweating and grunting noises. She may rise and lie down several times.

One foot of the fetus usually appears before the other. The passage of one foot ahead of the other may present less resistance as the shoulders pass through the pelvis. The head usually affords a little difficulty, but this is shortlived, and the continued contractions quickly force the foal on to the outside.

Sometimes the foal's head is covered by the amnionic membrane and the foal throws its head and ruptures it so it can breathe. Respiratory efforts may commence when the head passes to the exterior. The remainder of the body usually moves out without difficulty.

The umbilical cord probably will not break immediately but will remain intact from 5 to 30 minutes and then break close to the foal's belly as it or the mare moves. The umbilical cord should not be severed, as a considerable amount of blood may be lost.

The mare remains on her side after expelling the fetus, apparently exhausted from the ordeal. She may lie down for a considerable time but usually is up in about 10 minutes.

Delivery, or Stage 2, is of short duration, about 10 to 20 minutes.

Stage 3   Expulsion of the placenta occurs quickly, about 1 hour. The diffuse type of attachment releases all at once and is expelled. Retained afterbirth is rare in the mare. It is usually passed by uterine contractions and the pulling of the portion that has already passed to the exterior as the mare stands.

A small padlike structure about 8 cm (3 in) by 12 cm (5 in) is usually found following foaling. This is an accumulation of cells and salts of the allantois forming the rubberlike object called a *hippomane*.[90] The word means "horse madness" and has no known significance.

The fetal membranes should be examined carefully to detect if parts are missing. Retained particles in the uterus frequently result in infection, which interferes with conception, particularly at foal heat. Many horsemen fill the afterbirth with water to check for missing pieces.

The foal usually attempts to stand almost immediately after the cord is severed. This is an enjoyable time for the observer as the long-legged youngster tries to manipulate its underpinnings and after numerous unsuccessful attempts gains its equilibrium and searches for its first meal. The foal usually suckles within an hour after birth, and the colostrum it ingests at this time helps afford protection against disease in its early days of life.

The foal usually walks around and passes the *meconium,* which is a dark mucilaginous accumulation in the rectum. There may be some pain associated with the passage, but it is essential that it be passed and a lubricated finger or enema may be required. It is usually passed within an hour of birth.

Dystocia Difficult births are rather uncommon in mares, with reports of 1 percent under good management. However, some difficulties may arise by flexion of the long, slender legs. This may cause the fetus to turn crosswise as well. The fetus also may not have completed its rotation during Stage 1 and lie on its side. All of these conditions must be corrected for the fetus to be oriented for expulsion.

Cesarean Surgical removal may be necessary in cases of fetal death, monsters, or pelvic fractures. Incisions may be made in the high or low flank or midline.

Induced Parturition Dexamethasone may be used to induce parturition in mares by repeated doses of 100 mg per day on days 321, 322, and 323, with resulting shortening of gestation by about 12 days.[2,3,9,38] Some reports of negative response to corticoids[98] may be due to low dose levels administered.

Prostaglandin $F_2\alpha$ has caused abortion at any time during gestation, with mares aborting from 34 to 55 hours after the last of several injections at 12-hour intervals.[32] Mares return to estrus in 2 to 25 days.

Postpartum

Uterine involution Little study has been made of the involution of the uterus. It must be assumed that it is rather rapid because of the ability to rebreed in 10 to 15 days after parturition. The uterus has not completely returned to its normal size by this time, but the surface has repaired itself and is ready for a new embryo. This is possible because of the diffuse type of placenta of epitheliochorial structure. No destruction of the uterine surface occurs; therefore repair is rapid.

Foal heat The mare usually exhibits signs of estrus from 5 to 15 days following parturition. This is a fertile estrus and many horsemen breed at this time in an effort to reduce foaling interval. Conception will be as high as later in the season if precautions are taken to maintain optimum conditions. The mare must be healthy, have delivered the entire placenta, have no infection or discharge, and the reproductive tract must be in the latter stages of involution.

First estrus other than foal heat will occur approximately 45 days after parturition, and the mare should be ready to breed at this time.

Human

The infant assumes a position prior to birth with its head in the base of the body of the uterus forcing into the cervical canal (Fig. 15–12). The arms and legs are folded close to the body, and the head is the main object that must be considered during birth.

Prepartum Uterine contractions occur to some extent throughout pregnancy in the woman. These are caused as the myometrium responds to stretching of the muscle fibers. Most are painless until parturition. There is a gradual enlarging of the uterus and its contents during gestation, and the weight causes an adjustment in posture to maintain the woman's upright position. The mammary system grows under the

Figure 15-12 Normal presentation of the human infant.

increased levels of estrogen and progesterone. The onset of parturition, or *labor* as it is commonly called in the woman, is still not understood but is thought to be a combination of hormonal changes, prostaglandin release, fetal influences, genetic factors, and overdistension of the uterus.

Birth or Labor The term labor entails that period of time from the beginning of uterine contractions until expulsion of the young and the placenta.[103]

Pressure of the head of the fetus against the cervix may elicit nerve stimuli to the uterus resulting in contraction. There may also be the release of oxytocin in response to this stimulus.

Labor may be dividied into stages depending upon the progression of the events of parturition.

Stage 1 This stage begins with rhythmic uterine contractions reaching a frequency of more than three every half hour and lasts until the cervix has dilated and moved to a point flush with the vagina. During this time the cervical mucous plug is extruded as a jellylike mass. Uterine contractions during this time increase in frequency and duration. The period usually lasts 10 to 12 hours in women giving birth for the first time (primigravida) and 6 to 8 hours in women who have previously given birth (multipara). The membranes may rupture in the latter phases of Stage 1 or early in Stage 2.

Stage 2 The cervix is completely dilated at this time and the fetus is forced through the birth canal by continued contractions of the uterus and abdominal pressure. Time for primigravida should not exceed 2 hours and multipara 1 hour. The stage is concluded by expulsion of the fetus.

Stage 3 The delivery of the fetus begins this stage, and expulsion of the placenta terminates it. The placenta is discoid in shape and very vascular. This is a hemochorial type of placenta and the uterus therefore has an unprotected surface during and immediately following expulsion. Contraction of the uterus reduces the surface inside the uterus, which in turn forces release of the placental disc. Hemorrhage is common even before expulsion of the placenta.[10]

Holding the infant below the vaginal opening for a period of 1 to 3 minutes before clamping the umbilical cord theoretically at least causes more blood to enter the infant, which is thought to be beneficial.

Stage 3 lasts 15 to 30 minutes.

Dystocia occurs in the woman as in other females, and the infant must be realigned, forceps may be used, and if necessary a cesarean section may be required.

Puerperium This is the period of recovery and lasts 6 to 8 weeks. The uterus involutes during this period and the bruised and stretched cervix returns to normal.

The uterus changes from a flattened pear shape measuring 15 cm (6 in) by 12 cm (5 in) to normal size and weight. Internally, the endometrium is making its recovery. The surface is irregular immediately after separation from the placenta.

Leucocytes invade the area to rid it of debri. Cellular regeneration quickly begins on the surface. The greatest damage to the endometrium has been in the area of placental attachment. The new endometrial lining is repaired in about 3 weeks except for the placental area, which takes 6 to 8 weeks.[30]

The cervix quickly regains its shape the first day and gradually regains its structure. Some tears in the wall of the vagina should heal quickly.

The return of menstruation is influenced to some extent by lactation, but nursing the infant is not reason to believe the mother is infertile during this period. One study indicated ovulation occurring an average of 112 days following delivery in mothers breast-feeding their young, compared to 49 days in those who did not.[78]

WHAT DID YOU LEARN?

1 What changes occur in progesterone and estrogen at parturition in the cow, ewe, sow, mare, and woman?
2 Describe the symptoms of a cow approaching parturition.
3 What does puerperium mean?
4 Give the beginning and ending activities of the three stages of parturition in the cow.
5 What is dystocia?
6 What should you do if the cow retains her placenta?
7 What are some of the problems involved with induced parturition in cattle?
8 When would it be profitable to induce birth in cattle?
9 Why is it so difficult to place times and events on the postpartum period until estrus in the ewe?
10 Describe the farrowing process.
11 Describe the birth process of a foal.
12 What is "foal heat"? How does it differ from postpartum estrus in the sow?
13 What do primigravida and multipara mean?
14 Why is there excessive bleeding in childbirth?
15 Does nursing the young prevent pregnancy in the woman?

REFERENCES

1 Adams, W. M. and W. C. Wagner. 1970. The role of corticoids in parturition. *Biol. Reprod.* 3:223–228.
2 Alm, C. C., J. J. Sullivan, and N. L. First. 1974. Induction of premature parturition by parenteral administration of dexamethasone in the mare. *J.A.V.M.A.* 165:721–722.
3 ———. 1975. The effect of a corticosteroid (dexamethasone), progesterone, oestrogen and prostaglandin $F_2\alpha$ on gestation length in normal and ovariectomized mares. *J. Reprod. Fert. Suppl.* 23:637–640.
4 Andersen, H. and M. Plum. 1965. Gestation length and birth weight in cattle and buffaloes: A review. *J. Dairy Sci.* 48:1224–1235.
5 Ash, R. W. and R. B. Heap. 1973. The induction and synchronization of parturition in sows treated with ICI 79,939, an analogue of prostaglandin $F_2\alpha$. *J. Agr. Sci.* 81:365–368.

6 Bain, A. M. and W. P. Howey. 1975. Observations on the time of foaling in Thorough-bred mares in Australia. *J. Reprod. Fert. Suppl.* 23:545–546.

7 Baker, L. N., H. L. Woehling, L. E. Casida, and R. H. Grummer. 1953. Occurrence of estrus in sows following parturition. *J. Anim. Sci.* 12:32–38.

8 Baldwin, D. M. and G. H. Stabenfeldt. 1975. Endocrine changes in the pig during late pregnancy, parturition and lactation. *Biol. Reprod.* 12:508–515.

9 Barragry, T. B. 1975. The pharmacological induction of parturition. *Irish Vet. J.* 29:71–75.

10 Beazley, J. M. 1976. Natural labor and its active management. In C. J. Dewhurst, ed. *Integrated Obstetrics and Gynaecology for Postgraduates.* 2nd ed. Blackwell Scientific Publ., Oxford. Pp. 194–212.

11 Beck, T. W., R. P. Wetterman, E. J. Turman, T. A. Hoagland, L. W. Brock, M. T. Fournier, and R. Totusek. 1977. The influence of 48-hour calf separation on calf growth rate and milk production in postpartum range cows. *Okla Anim. Sci. Res. Rept. MP-101.* Pp. 39–41.

12 Bedford, A., J. R. G. Challis, F. A. Harrison, and R. B. Heap. 1972. The role of oestrogens and progesterone in the onset of parturition in various species. *J. Reprod. Fert. Suppl.* 16:1–23.

13 Bellows, R. A. 1971. Calf losses in beef cattle. *Proc. 5th Conf. on AI of Beef Cattle.* pp. 9–14.

14 Bellows, R. A., R. E. Short, D. C. Anderson, B. W. Knapp, and O. F. Pahnish. 1971. Cause and effect relationships associated with calving difficulty and calf birth weight. *J. Anim. Sci.* 33:407–415.

15 Bellows, R. A., R. E. Short, J. J. Urick, and O. F. Pahnish. 1974. Effects of early weaning on postpartum reproduction of the dam and growth of calves born as multiples or singles. *J. Anim. Sci.* 39:589–600.

16 Bengtsson, L. P. and B. M. Schofield. 1963. Progesterone and the accomplishment of parturition in sheep. *J. Reprod. Fert.* 5:423–431.

17 Berndtson, W. E. 1977. Physiology on the range. *Proc. 11th Conf. on AI of Beef Cattle.* Pp. 40–56.

18 Beverly, J. R. 1975. Recognizing and handling calving problems. *Tex. Agr. Ext. Serv. M.P. 1203* Pp. 1–8.

19 Bolte, K. A., H. A. Garverick, D. J. Kesler, B. N. Day, and E. C. Mather. 1977. Dexamethasone and estradiol benzoate induced parturition in dairy cattle. *Therio.* 8:45–58.

20 Bosc, M. J. 1972. The induction and synchronization of lambing with the aid of dexamethasone. *J. Reprod. Fert.* 28:347–357.

21 Cahill, L. P., B. W. Knee, and R. A. S. Lawson. 1976. Induction of parturition in ewes with a single injection of oestradiol benzoate. *Therio.* 5:289–294.

22 Carroll, E. J. 1974. Induction of parturition in farm animals. *J. Anim. Sci.* 38, Suppl. 1:1–19.

23 Challis, J. R. G., F. A. Harrison, and R. B. Heap. 1971. Uterine production of oestrogens and progesterone at parturition in the sheep. *J. Reprod. Fert.* 25:306–307.

24 Chard, T. 1972. The posterior pituitary in human and animal parturition. *J. Reprod. Fert. Suppl.* 16:121–138.

25 Chew, B. P., H. F. Keller, R. E. Erb, and P. V. Malven. 1977. Periparturient concentrations of prolactin, progesterone and the estrogens in blood plasma of cows retaining and not retaining fetal membranes. *J. Anim. Sci.* 44:1055–1060.

26 Coggins, E. G. and N. L. First. 1977. Effect of dexamethasone, methallibure and fetal decapitation on porcine gestation. *J. Anim. Sci.* 44:1041–1049.

27 Crighton, D. B. 1968. The induction of oestrus and ovulation during the lactational anoestrus of the sow. *Proc. 6th Int. Congr. on Reprod. and A.I.* 2:1415–1417.

28 Curson, H. H. and J. B. Quinlan. 1934. Studies in sex physiology, No. 10: The situation of the developing fetus in the Merino sheep. *Onderstepoort J. Vet. Sci. Anim. Ind.* 2:657–663.

29 Davis, D. L., D. J. Kesler, A. L. Jenkins, H. A. Garverick, J. W. Massey, C. J. Bierschwal, and B. N. Day. 1977. Induction of parturition in beef and dairy cattle with long and short acting corticoids and estradiol benzoate. *Amer. Soc. Anim. Sci. 1977 Mtg. Abstr. 373.* P. 148.

30 Dewhurst, C. J. 1976. The normal puerperium. In C. J. Dewhurst, ed. *Integrated Obstetrics and Gynaecology for Postgraduates.* 2nd ed. Blackwell Scientific Publ., Oxford. Pp. 213–217.

31 Diehl, J. R., R. A. Godke, D. B. Killian, and B. N. Day. 1974. Induction of parturition in swine with prostaglandin $F_2\alpha$. *J. Anim. Sci.* 38:1229–1234.

32 Douglas, R. E., E. L. Squires, and O. J. Ginther. 1974. Induction of abortion in mares with prostaglandin $F_2\alpha$. *J. Anim. Sci.* 39:404–407.

33 Drinan, J. P., M. S. F. Wong, and R. I. Cox. 1976. Hormonal changes in cow and calf about normal and induced calving. *J. Reprod. Fert.* 46:530. (Abstr.)

34 Echternkamp, S. E. and W. Hansel. 1973. Concurrent changes in bovine plasma hormone levels prior to and during the first postpartum estrous cycle. *J. Anim. Sci.* 37:1362–1370.

35 Fairclough, R. J., J. T. Hunter, and R. A. S. Welch. 1975. Peripheral plasma progesterone and utero-ovarian prostaglandin F concentrations in the cow around parturition. *Prostaglandins* 9:901–914.

36 Fairclough, R. J., J. T. Hunter, R. A. S. Welch, H. Barr, and R. F. Seamark. 1976. Preparturient changes in plasma concentrations of estrone, estradiol-17β and estradiol-17α in the fetal calf: Effects of dexamethasone infusion. *Steroids* 28:881–886.

37 Fairclough, R. J., J. T. Hunter, R. A. S. Welch, and E. Payne. 1975. Plasma corticosteroid concentrations in the bovine fetus near term. *J. Endocrinol.* 65:138–140.

38 First, N. L. and C. C. Alm. 1977. Dexamethasone-induced parturition in pony mares. *J. Anim. Sci.* 44:1072–1075.

39 Foote, W. C. 1971. Some influences of lactation and hormone treatment on uterine changes in postpartum sheep. *J. Anim. Sci.* 32, Suppl. 1:48–54.

40 Gier, H. T. and G. B. Marion. 1968. Uterus of the cow after parturition: Involutional changes. *Amer. J. Vet. Res.* 29:83–96.

41 George, J. M. 1973. Post parturient oestrus in Merino and Dorset Horn sheep. *Australian Vet. J.* 49:242–245.

42 ———. 1976. The incidence of dystocia in Dorset Horn ewes. *Australian Vet. J.* 52:519–523.

43 Glimp, H. A. 1972. Studies on calving difficulties and calf performance in exotic and straightbred cattle. *Proc. 21st and 22nd Beef Cattle Short Course,* Texas A&M Univ., College Station. Pp. 138–153.

44 Harsch, J. A. and D. R. Hanks. 1971. Pubic symphysiotomy for relief of dystocia in heifers. *J.A.V.M.A.* 159:1034–1036.

45 Hartigan, P. J., O. H. Langley, W. R. Nunn, and J. F. T. Griffin. 1974. Some data on ovarian activity in post-parturient dairy cows in Ireland. *Irish Vet. J.* 28:236–241.

46 Heiman, M. R. 1968. Trends in some biological characters in an A.I. cattle population. *Proc. 6th Int. Congr. on Reprod. and A.I.* 2:1333–1335.

47 Henricks, D. M., N. C. Rawlings, A. R. Ellicott, J. F. Dickey, and J. R. Hill. 1977.

Use of prostaglandin $F_2\alpha$ to induce parturition in beef heifers. *J. Anim. Sci.* 44:438–441.

48 Howell, C. E. and W. C. Rollins. 1951. Environmental sources of variation in the gestation length of the horse. *J. Anim. Sci.* 10:789–796.

49 Hudson, S., M. Mullford, W. G. Whittlestone, and E. Payne. 1976. Bovine plasma corticoids during parturition. *J. Dairy Sci.* 59:744–746.

50 Hunter, D. L., R. E. Erb, R. D. Randel, H. A. Garverick, C. J. Callahan, and R. B. Harrington. 1970. Reproductive steroids in the bovine. I. Relationships during late gestation. *J. Anim. Sci.* 30:47–59.

51 Jeffcott, L. B. 1972. Observations on parturition in crossbred pony mares. *Equine Vet. J.* 4:209–213.

52 Julien, W. E. and H. R. Conrad. 1976. Selenium and Vitamin E and incidence of retained placenta in parturient dairy cows. *J. Dairy Sci.* 59:1954–1959.

53 Kraeling, R. R. and G. B. Rampacek. 1977. Susceptibility of the pig corpus luteum to $PGF_2\alpha$ at various stages of pregnancy. *Amer. Soc. Anim. Sci. 1977 Mtg. Abstr. 452.* Pp. 180–181.

54 Laster, D. B. 1976. Management to minimize calving difficulty. *Proc. 10th Conf. on AI of Beef Cattle.* Pp. 10–18.

55 Laster, D. B., H. A. Glimp, L. V. Cundiff, and K. E. Gregory. 1973. Factors affecting dystocia and the effects of dystocia on subsequent reproduction in beef cattle. *J. Anim. Sci.* 36:695–705.

56 Laster, D. B., H. A. Glimp, and K. E. Gregory. 1973. Effects of early weaning on postpartum reproduction of cows. *J. Anim. Sci.* 36:734–740.

57 Laster, D. B. and K. E. Gregory. 1973. Factors influencing peri- and early postnatal calf mortality. *J. Anim. Sci.* 37:1092–1097.

58 LaVoie, V. A., J. L. Winter, and E. L. Moody. 1977. Effect of route of dexamethasone administration on parturition, fertility and calf performance in beef cattle. *Therio.* 7:225–237.

59 Liggins, G. C., C. S. Forster, S. A. Grieves, and A. L. Schwartz. 1977. Control of parturition in man. *Biol. Reprod.* 16:39–56.

60 Lingard, D. R. 1971. A surgical treatment of dystocia in immature heifers. *Illinois Vet.* 14:10–11.

61 Marion, G. B., J. S. Norwood, and H. T. Gier. 1968. Uterus of the cow after parturition: Factors affecting regression. *Amer. J. Vet. Res.* 29:71–75.

62 Martin, P., G. W. Bevier, and P. J. Dziuk. 1977. The effect of number of corpora lutea on the length of gestation in pigs. *Biol. Reprod.* 16:633–637.

63 McGowan, L. T., R. A. S. Welch, and J. T. Hunter. 1975. Studies on induced calving in cattle. *Proc. New Zealand Soc. Anim. Prod.* 35:92–96.

64 Moller, K. 1970. A review of uterine involution and ovarian activity during the postparturient period in the cow. *New Zealand Vet. J.* 18:83–90.

65 Molokwu, E. C. I. and W. C. Wagner. 1973. Endocrine physiology of the puerperal sow. *J. Anim. Sci.* 36:1158–1163.

66 Moody, E. L. and D. K. Han. 1976. Effects of induced calving on beef production. *J. Anim. Sci.* 43:298. (Abstr.)

67 Moody, N. W. and V. C. Speer. 1971. Factors affecting sow farrowing interval. *J. Anim. Sci.* 32:510–514.

68 Morrow, D. A. 1969. Postpartum ovarian activity and involution of the uterus and cervix in dairy cattle. *Vet Scope* 14:2–13.

69 Morrow, D. A., S. J. Roberts, K. McEntee, and H. G. Gray. 1966. Postpartum ovarian activity and uterine involution in dairy cattle. *J.A.V.M.A.* 149:12, 1596–1609.

70   Muller, L. D., G. L. Beardsley, R. P. Ellis, D. E. Reed, and M. J. Owens. 1975. Calf
     response to the initiation of parturition in dairy cows with dexamethasone or dexame-
     thasone with estradiol benzoate. *J. Anim. Sci.* 41:1711–1716.

71   North, S. A., E. R. Hauser, and N. L. First. 1973. Induction of parturition in swine
     and rabbits with the corticosteroid dexamethasone. *J. Anim. Sci.* 36:1170–1174.

72   O'Brien, T. and G. H. Stott. 1977. Prepartum serum hormone concentrations related
     to dystocia in Holstein heifers. *J. Dairy Sci.* 60:249–253.

73   O'Farrell, K. J. and J. P. Crowley. 1974. Some observations on the use of two corticoste-
     roid preparations for the induction of premature calving. *Vet. Rec.* 94:364–366.

74   O'Mary, C. C. and J. K. Hillers. 1976. Factors affecting time intervals in parturition
     in beef cattle. *J. Anim. Sci.* 42:1118–1123.

75   Oxenreider, S. L. 1968. Effects of suckling and ovarian function on postpartum repro-
     ductive activity in beef cows. *Amer. J. Vet. Res.* 29:2099–2102.

76   Oxenreider, S. L. and W. C. Wagner. 1971. Effect of lactation and energy intake on
     postpartum ovarian activity in the cow. *J. Anim. Sci.* 33:1026–1031.

77   Palmer, W. M., H. S. Teague, and W. G. Venzke. 1965. Macroscopic observations on
     the reproductive tract of the sow during lactation and early postweaning. *J. Anim. Sci.*
     24:541–545.

78   Perez, A., P. Vela, G. S. Masnick, and R. G. Potter. 1972. First ovulation after
     childbirth: The effect of breast-feeding. *Amer. J. Obstet. and Gynecol.* 114:1041–1047.

79   Peterson, A. J., J. T. Hunter, R. A. S. Welch, and R. J. Fairclough. 1975. Oestrogens
     in bovine fetal and maternal plasma near term. *J. Reprod. Fert.* 43:179–181.

80   Plasse, D., A. C. Warnick, R. E. Reese, and M. Koger. 1968. Reproductive behavior
     of *Bos indicus* females in a subtropical environment. II. Gestation length in Brahman
     cattle. *J. Anim. Sci.* 27:101–104.

81   Poncelet, G. R. and E. L. Moody. 1976. Induction of parturition in conjunction with
     antibiotic treatments. *Therio.* 6:437–445.

82   Price, T. 1977. Calving difficulty. *Proc. Food Anim. Med. Conf.,* Texas A&M Univ.,
     College Station. Pp. 27–31.

83   Randel, R. D. and G. A. Welker. 1977. Effect of energy intake and once daily suckling
     on postpartum interval in Brahman X Hereford heifers. Proc. *Amer. Soc. Anim. Sci.*
     1977 Mtg. Abstr. 495. P. 198.

84   Reimers, T. J., P. J. Dziuk, J. Bahr, D. J. Sprecher, S. K. Webel, and B. G. Harmon.
     1973. Transuterine embryonal migration in sheep, anteroposterior orientation of pig
     and sheep fetuses and presentation of piglets at birth. *J. Anim. Sci.* 37:1212–1217.

85   Rice, L. E. and J. N. Wiltbank. 1972. Factors affecting dystocia in beef heifers. *J.A.V.-*
     M.A. 161:1348–1358.

86   Rich, T. D., G. W. Libal, L. R. Dunn, and R. C. Wahlstrom. 1972. Induction of
     parturition in sows with dexamethasone. *J. Anim. Sci.* 35:1124. (Abstr.)

87   Roberts, S. J. 1971. *Veterinary Obstetrics and Genital Diseases (Theriogenology).* 2nd
     ed. Published by the author, Ithaca, N. Y. Pp. 201–212.

88   Robertson, H. A. and G. J. King. 1974. Plasma concentrations of progesterone, oes-
     trone, oestradiol-17β and oestrone sulphate in the pig at implantation, during preg-
     nancy and at parturition. *J. Reprod. Fert.* 40:133–141.

89   Rollins, W. C. and C. E. Howell. 1951. Genetic sources of variation in the gestation
     length of the horse. *J. Anim. Sci.* 10:797–806.

90   Rossdale, P. D. 1970. Life before birth. *The Thoroughbred of California.* Pp. 778–796.

91   Rossdale, P. D. and R. V. Short. 1967. The time of foaling of Thoroughbred mares.
     J. Reprod. Fert. 13:341–343.

92 Self, H. L. and R. H. Grummer. 1958. The rate and economy of pig gains and the reproductive behavior in sows when litters are weaned at 10 days, 21 days or 56 days of age. *J. Anim. Sci.* 17:863–868.

93 Short, R. E., B. B. Staigmiller, J. K. Baber, J. B. Carr, and R. A. Bellows. 1976. Effects of mammary denervation in postpartum cows. *J. Anim. Sci.* 43:304. (Abstr.)

94 Smith, G. M., D. B. Laster, and K. E. Gregory. 1976. Characterization of biological types of cattle. I. Dystocia and preweaning growth. *J. Anim. Sci.* 43:27–36.

95 Smith, V. G., L. A. Edgerton, H. D. Hafs, and E. M. Convey. 1973. Bovine serum estrogens, progestins and glucocorticoids during late pregnancy, parturition and early lactation. *J. Anim. Sci.* 36:391–396.

96 Terrill, C. E. and L. N. Hazel. 1947. Length of gestation in range sheep. *Amer. J. Vet. Res.* 8:66–72.

97 Tervit, H. R. 1976. Techniques and hazards of embryo manipulation and induction of parturition. *New Zealand Vet. J.* 24:74–79.

98 Thorburn, G. D., J. R. C. Challis, and W. B. Currie. 1977. Control of parturition in domestic animals. *Biol. Reprod.* 16:18–27.

99 Thorburn, G. D., D. H. Nicol, J. M. Bassett, D. A. Shutt, and R. I. Cox. 1972. Parturition in the goat and sheep: Changes in corticosteroids, progesterone, oestrogens and prostaglandin F. *J. Reprod. Fert. Suppl.* 16:61–84.

100 Tribble, R. L., A. M. Sorensen, Jr., T. L. Woodward, J. S. Connor, J. R. Beverly, and J. L. Fleeger. 1973. Serum progestins and luteinizing hormone levels in nonsuckled primiparous heifers. *Nature* 246:494–495.

101 van Wyk, L. C., C. van Niekerk, and P. C. Belonje. 1972. Involution of the post partum uterus of the ewe. *J. S. Afr. Vet. Assoc.* 43:19–26.

102 ———. 1972. Further observations on the involution of the post partum uterus of the ewe. *J. S. Afr. Vet. Assoc.* 43:29–33.

103 Vorherr, H. 1968. The pregnant uterus: Process of labor, puerperium, and lactation. In N. S. Assali, ed. *Biology of Gestation.* Vol. 1. Academic Press, New York. Pp. 427–448.

104 Wagner, W. C. and S. L. Oxenreider. 1971. Endocrine physiology following parturition. *J. Anim. Sci.* 32, Suppl. 1:1–16.

105 Wagner, W. C., R. L. Wilham, and L. E. Evans. 1974. Controlled parturition in cattle. *J. Anim. Sci.* 38:485–489.

106 Wagner, W. C., F. N. Thompson, L. E. Evans, and E. C. I. Molokwu. 1974. Hormonal mechanisms controlling parturition. *J. Anim. Sci.* 38, Suppl. 1:39–57.

107 Welch, R. A. S., P. Newling, and D. Anderson. 1973. Induction of parturition in cattle with corticosteroids: An analysis of field trials. *New Zealand Vet. J.* 21:103–108.

108 Wettemann, R. P., D. M. Hallford, D. L. Kreider, and E. J. Turman. 1977. Influence of prostaglandin $F_2\alpha$ on endocrine changes at parturition in gilts. *J. Anim. Sci.* 44:106–111.

109 Wiltbank, J. N. 1971. Relationship of energy, cow size and sire to calving difficulty. *Proc. 5th Conf. on AI of Beef Cattle.* Pp. 18–24.

110 ———. 1977. Managing beef cows to get them pregnant. *Proc. Food Anim. Med. Conf.,* Texas A&M Univ., College Station. Pp. 101–120.

CHAPTER 16

Visual Appraisal for Breeding Efficiency

When you have completed this chapter you should be able to:

- Associate hormones with visual appearance,
- Relate specific traits to masculinity and reproduction, and
- Relate specific traits to femininity and reproduction.

Visual appraisal is utilized in telling what an animal has done, what it is doing, and predicting what it will do. In actuality, it is a study of history to predict the future.

Visual appraisal is subjective in nature. This means that the things seen are subject to the training of the individual and his knowledge in related areas. This appraisal is in contrast to objective appraisal, which depends upon facts and figures without the distortion of personal feelings. Objective appraisal is based on records.

Records cannot be replaced by visual appraisal because of variability in biological entities. All animals just do not respond to a stimulus in the same manner. And people do not always see things alike. The older the animal, the more records, or history, and the greater the predictability of the future.

In the absence of records, visual appraisal is the next best thing. So let us discuss some of its merits and pitfalls.

When an animal is born it has certain inherited characteristics and is then exposed to environmental factors for its entire life. Genetics determines the sex of the animal, and the glands and organs of the body influence and are influenced by this predetermined sex. Endocrine glands are specifically involved in causing certain things to happen, some seen and some unseen. The manifestation of these glandular secretions determines factors used in visual appraisal.

Visual appraisal is directly related to endocrine function as we see the results externally of what is going on internally. The various hormones and their actions have been discussed earlier and will not be repeated in detail here. Association will be discussed.

The person most responsible for selecting good breeding stock is the manager. His eye must be trained to select those animals that will best produce. We will discuss mostly the reproductive aspect, but visual appraisal is really broader in its scope. The good manager will study his cattle to determine nutritive state, health, and reproductive efficiency.

Most studies have been conducted with cattle, and little scientific literature has been written with factual support even for this species. Husbandry has played a strong part in developing observed traits associated with reproductive response.

One of the best approaches to study visual appraisal is to start at one end of an animal and work to the other, discussing the various characteristics pro and con regarding reproduction.

FERTILE MALE

The key word for the fertile male is *masculinity*. He must have male attributes. But what are they, exactly? A certain picture should come into the mind of the reader when the word bull, ram, boar, stallion, or man is seen or heard (Fig. 16–1). Two

Figure 16-1 A masculine bull.

words somewhat synonymous with masculinity are *muscular* and *coarse* because these traits are always present. Let us study the meaning of masculinity as seen in the male by beginning at the head.[3] The desirable male will be discussed first.

Head

The head is coarse in appearance as characterized by heavier hair, broad forehead between the eyes, calm and medium-size eyes, and a heavy jaw.

The thickness is the result of testosterone and its effect on muscle development. Nitrogen retention, amino acid formation, proteins, and resulting muscle formation are in response to testosterone. The jaw is most prominent in the stallion, and burly, coarse hair is most prominent in the bull (Fig. 16–2).

Neck

The neck is prominent due to the *crest* over the top of it (Fig. 16–1). This is a thickening of muscle due to testosterone and is most noticed in the bull. It is visible in the boar and stallion but masked somewhat by the wool of the ram most of the time.

The crest should not be confused with the natural hump of Zebu cattle. Often the two blend together and appear to be one.

Figure 16-2 A masculine head of the stallion with prominent jaws.

Shoulders

The muscles of the male are predominant in the shoulders or forequarters and the thigh or hindquarters. The shoulders should be heavily muscled with the individual structures appearing as bulges. A fat animal will mask the muscles, while muscles will be accentuated in a thinner animal. Again, testosterone is the cause.

Ribs

The spring of the rib cage should be large. This indicates strength and good ability to forage. The lungs should be well developed inside.

Rump

The rump or hindquarters and tail area should be long on top and level. The muscles of the thigh, high and low, should be distinct and bulging (Fig. 16–3). This is seen readily in the bull, stallion, and boar and if not seen, may be felt in the ram.

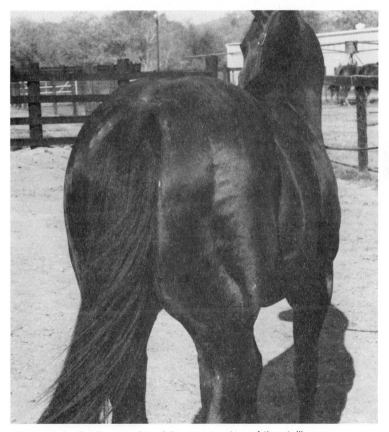

Figure 16-3 Bulging muscles of the rear quarters of the stallion.

Legs and Feet

The legs should be of medium-size bone and muscle, and the front legs should be straight and set wide apart. A narrow chest floor will deter mounting by the male.

The rear legs should also be wide because of muscular, as much as skeletal, development. From the side, they should have some curve to them, which gives spring and support without stiffness.

The pasterns should be strong to support the body on the feet.

The feet should be balanced and strong. Cleft hooves of the bull, ram, and boar should be free of defects such as corns between the toes.

Testes

This is the site of sperm production, and the testes must be in proportion to the size of the animal. They should be balanced and suspended away from the body but not in an extremely pendulous condition (Fig. 16–4). They must be far enough away to keep cool but not be damaged by bumping against the legs.

The tail of the epididymis should be clearly visible in the bull and ram unless the animal is in very heavy use. Figure 16–5 shows a group of well-developed young

Figure 16-4 Well proportioned and supported testes of the bull showing a bulging epididymis.

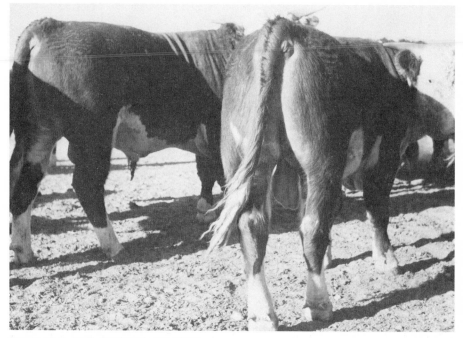

Figure 16-5   Well developed young bulls.

bulls. Most of the testes are very acceptable, but the nearest bull on the right has questionable testes. If the testes are held up like this, the animal could be a cryptorchid, or he could be responding to stress by contracting the dartos muscle and raising them. Make him walk about to observe whether it is permanent or temporary.

Sheath

The sheath should be clean and carried fairly close to the body (Fig. 16–6). The sheath is mainly a problem of the bull but not the other species. Problems arise mainly with Zebu cattle, but they are not alone.

Skeletal Size

The male that reaches puberty early does so because of testosterone. This same testosterone affects the growth of the long bones by depressing growth at the epiphyseal plates as discussed earlier (Fig. 16–7). This results in a smaller intact male than a castrate at maturity. A bull at 5 years of age will be smaller than a steer of like breeding and treatment. Eunuchs are male humans who were castrated at an early age and subsequently grew to great heights. Their selection for protecting harems was based not only on their being sterile and without sexual desire but because of their size.

Figure 16-6 A desirable sheath on the bull.

INFERTILE MALE

The infertile male can be characterized as being effeminate in many instances. There are also other factors that need to be considered in selection, based on environmental conditions, injury, and defects.

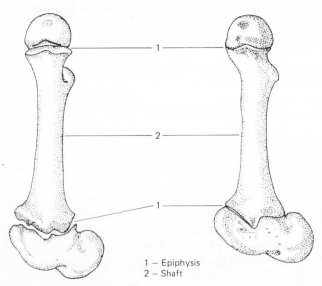

1 – Epiphysis
2 – Shaft

Figure 16-7 The epiphyseal plate in the femur of a bovine. *(Adapted from Bonsma.¹)*

Head

The head of an infertile male will be somewhat refined or effeminate and the eyes may be prominent with the appearance of excitement. The feminine appearance indicates lack of testosterone and many of these males could be characterized as "sissies." These animals are poor risks for reproduction.

Neck

The neck will be flat and thin without a crest.

Shoulders

Narrow shoulders reaching a point over the withers are undesirable and effeminate. Bulls with very heavy "buffalo" type shoulders are very undesirable because of related difficulties at calving.

Ribs

Flat, slab-sided conditions in animals indicate lack of vigor and fortitude.

Rump

A short rump and lack of muscling should be discriminated against.

Legs and Feet

Too much curvature of the hind legs is called *sickle-hocked* because of the similar shape. These are weak, as exhibited by the inability of the animal to stand for long periods of time. All of the weight is on the muscular support.

Opposite this is the *post-legged* condition in which the leg is very straight. The leg then is prone toward damage to the joints and arthritis, with resulting inability to maneuver. It is pathetic to see a bull with many desirable characteristics approach a cow but be unable to mount because of pain in the legs.

The feet are very important also, and overgrown or broken hooves reduce maneuverability. Corns between the toes are very painful and prevent mounting.

Testes

Testes may be undergrown *(hypoplastic)* or overgrown *(hyperplastic),* as well as of normal size. The hypoplastic testes are not able to produce enough sperm to maintain good reproduction (Fig. 16–8). One or both may be small, but either condition should be criticized. The hyperplastic testes may be damaged in walking or running and spermatogenesis reduced by fever or destruction of tissue.

The testes may be damaged beyond repair mechanically or physiologically. Bulls and rams in very cold climates may have the scrotum frozen, and, as healing

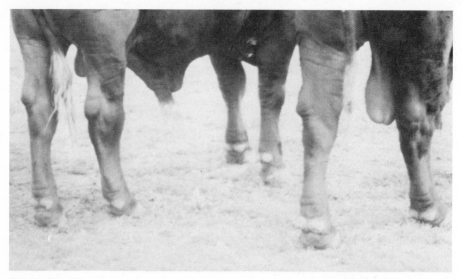

Figure 16-8 Two bulls of comparable breeding, age, and size with small undesirable testes and normal testes.

occurs, the testes are pushed and held near the body with resulting increased temperature and sterility. Bulls and rams may also incur scrapes, gouges, and tears of the scrotum in brush country, with a shortening of the scrotum due to scar tissue developing with healing.

Disease of the scrotum and its contents—such as epididymitis, which is fairly common in rams and bulls—increases temperature and may cause temporary infertility (Fig. 16–9). These animals should be removed from breeding until recovery and reevaluated before returning to the breeding herd.

Sheath

The main difficulty with the sheath occurs in cattle with Zebu breeding. The Brahman and Santa Gertrudis breeders have done a fine job of shortening the sheath through selection, but the breeder must constantly be aware of the problem. The condition is not restricted to Zebu cattle. These cattle were selected for loose skin and pendulous sheaths to have a larger surface area to dissipate heat. It was found that there was little transfer of heat by the pendulous dewlap and sheath, so it is subsequently being shortened.

The pendulous sheath is a detriment to breeding because the erection of the penis must raise it in the breeding process, but it is more liable to damage because of its proximity to the ground and undergrowth. Figure 16–10 compares an acceptable and a pendulous sheath in two Brahman bulls. Figure 16–11 shows a condition that may result from poor selection for the reproductive structures. The testes are unbalanced with an apparent defective cremaster muscle on one side. The testes are pressured by their weight in the sac, which may interfere with spermatogenesis. The

Figure 16-9 Epididymitis in a Santa Gertrudis bull.

sheath is much too long and the prepuce is prolapsed. Circumcision may be performed on such bulls, but the prognosis is not too good; this kind of male should not be used for breeding purposes, thereby propagating an undesirable trait.

Skeletal Size

Tall bulls are sometimes that way because of the lack of testosterone. Just being big is not enough. Functional testes are most important. Small bulls may result from premature functioning of the testosterone production, which may be of a genetic nature. Neither type male should be used in a breeding program.

Semen Evaluation

With all this discussion about visual appraisal of the male, it is hoped that the reader understands that most of the things seen result from testosterone. It is also necessary for libido. But none of this is of value if no sperm are present. Therefore, semen evaluation must be an integral part of selection of the herd sire.

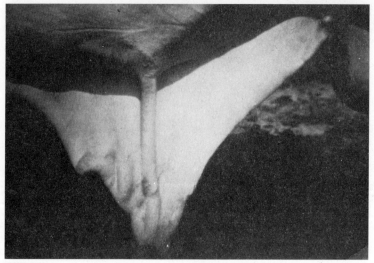

Figure 16-10 An acceptable and a pendulous sheath in two Brahman bulls.

FERTILE FEMALE

The key word is *femininity*. She must have female attributes. A certain picture of a cow, ewe, sow, mare, or woman should come into the mind of the reader when the word femininity appears. Let us study the meaning of the word in descriptive terms starting at the head.

Head

The female's head should be refined and angular with fine glossy hair and a bright eye that is calm and of medium size.

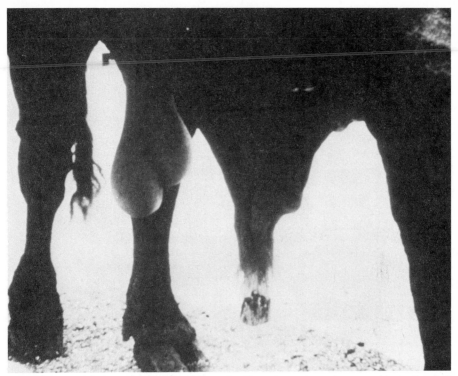

Figure 16-11 Unbalanced testes, pendulous sheath, and a prolapsed prepuce in a mature bull.

The jaw should be free of excess muscling so the appearance is that of a clean face (Fig. 16–12).

Neck

The refinement of the head carries throughout the fertile female's body. The neck is angular and sleek without thickness over the top or heavy folds.

Brisket

This area, between the front legs and protruding forward slightly, is the chest floor. It should be free of excess fat and be soft and pliable.

Dewlap

The dewlap is the fold of tissue along the lower neck that continues over the brisket. It should be soft and pliable with rather distinct folds. There should be no firmness or fullness underneath. The brisket and dewlap are important areas to observe, although no studies have shown why they are this way. The relationship to fertility, in husbandry, is high. It is noticeable in the cow and ewe particularly.

Figure 16-12   The refined head of a fertile cow.

Shoulder

The location of the *scapula,* or shoulder blade, should be high. The vertebral processes above the shoulder are called the *chine* bone. The scapula should be level with the chine. Some of the better-producing cows will appear rather loose in the shoulders because the scapulae are high.

Ribs

The rib cage should be well sprung, as in the male.

Rump

The hindquarters should be much more angular and refined than in the male. The condition of the *hooks* (hips, tuber coxae) and the *pins* (tuber ischii) is an important evaluation. They should be free of excess or patchy fat deposits. This area is also more discernible in cattle than in the other species.

The tail should hang perpendicular rather than curve over enlarged buttocks. This also means that the attachment is posterior and not forward.

Legs and Feet

Size and curvature are observed the same as in the male. Feet should be free of defects.

Udder

The mammary system grows continually under the influence of the cycling estrogen and progesterone. Pregnancy exaggerates this growth and the udder should be in proportion to the size of the female with good support and equally distributed sections.

The four quarters of the cow should be of approximately equal size and without distinct clefts. The teats should be of a size that the young calf can suckle without difficulty.

The sow's teats should be evenly spaced and without any recessed or inverted nipples.

Vulva

The vulva is the only reproductive portion visible. The vulvar shape and size varies with livestock but should be relative in size and shape.

Skeletal Size

The estrogen circulating in the female's body affects skeletal growth the same as testosterone in the male. Therefore the mature normal female will be smaller than one with difficulties in endocrine balance (Fig. 16–13).

INFERTILE FEMALE

The infertile female usually appears much coarser in appearance and many times has laid on considerable fat. The fat covers some things we would like to see but is a symptom of what is going on inside.

Head

There is coarseness of hair, thickness of the jaw, and an overall masculine appearance. In the absence of ovarian hormones, the adrenal may be producing testosterone and therefore masculinity.

Neck

The top of the neck is thicker, approaching a crest, and many times coarse darker hairs are on the topline. Folds are heavy and deep (Fig. 16–14).

Figure 16-13 Two cows 5 years of age. The larger cow was ovariectomized as a heifer and the smaller cow had produced 3 calves.

Brisket

The brisket is full and very firm. Palpating the brisket will reveal a very hard lumpy type of fat deposit. This is not a mobile-type fat, but will remain even if the female is placed on a restricted ration to try to remove it. Cammack[2] studied the relationship of triglycerides in the brisket, loin, and hip fat with reproductive history but found no reliable significance. This condition is found more often in cattle but has not been studied in other animals.

Figure 16-14 An infertile cow.

Dewlap

The fullness of the brisket and the neck causes the dewlap to appear full and tight without the pliable folds that are desirable (Fig. 16–14).

Shoulder

The scapulae blend into the shoulder so that they are often indistinguishable. The scapulae lie below the chine, so that the vertebral processes will appear more prominent.

Ribs

Many poor reproducers and infertile stock will be flat sided without the desirable spring of ribs.

Rump

Undesirable rumps, which are present on many infertile females, include those with patchy hooks and pins and abnormal vulvae.

The hooks and pins of infertile females have patches of adipose tissue on them that appear to be encapsulated. These patches may be palpated and moved about much as the patella on the knee. This is immobile fat, as in the brisket, and will appear even on poorly finished females.

Legs and Feet

Comments on the male apply to the female as well.

Udder

The udder of the hormonally deficient female will be *hypoplastic* (underdeveloped). These small udders are easily observed in the cow and ewe (Fig. 16–15).

There are other types of udders that need to be observed for reasons other than infertility and a decision made for culling the female. Most of these conditions have been noted in the cow.

Mastitis is a disease of the mammary system that causes a hardness and enlargement of the udder that may destroy the tissue. Dairy cows are usually noticed and treated, while range cows usually lose the usefulness of the infected area. They should be culled.

Large teats develop on some cows and make it impossible for the calf to suckle. These should be culled.

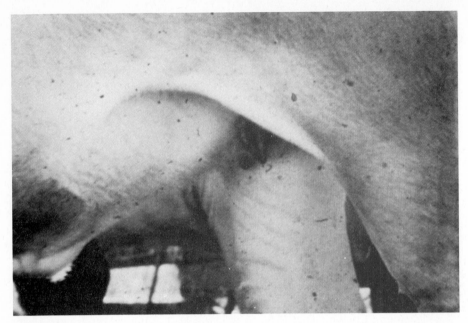

Figure 16-15   The hypoplastic udder of a 2-year-old heifer that had not reached puberty.

Vulva

The hypoplastic vulva of the female indicates an upset in hormones. Figure 16–16 shows a vulva that is considered normal for a 2-year-old crossbred heifer with Zebu

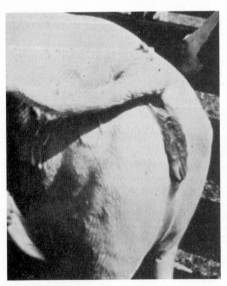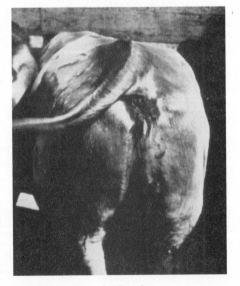

Figure 16-16   One heifer with a normal vulva and one with a hypoplastic vulva.

breeding, and a hypoplastic vulva of a heifer of comparable size and breeding. The normal heifer has cycled several times, while the hypoplastic heifer has not cycled. Heifers with small vulvas should not be retained for breeding.

The location of the vulva is important. Figure 16–17 shows a cow with the vulva almost horizontal. The tail is attached forward and feces must move over the vulva in defecation. Irritation and poor conception result. It is also difficult for the bull to serve her. A similar situation occurs in mares.

Skeletal Size

The animal lacking estrogen will grow to a larger size than the normal cycling animal (Fig. 16–13). When selecting breeding stock, many producers look for the big growthy type of heifer. In doing so, they may be selecting animals that mature sexually at a later date than the others. These can usually be spotted as they stand taller in a group of similarly bred females. The smaller, refined females are the really feminine type and will yield the best reproductive response.

GENERAL

Rarely will all the characteristics described here be found in a single fertile or infertile animal. Combinations of factors must be evaluated and a suitable answer

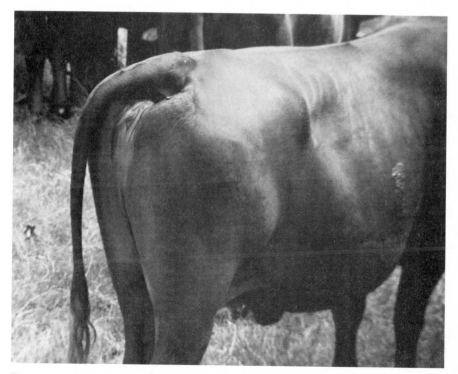

Figure 16-17   An abnormal placement of the vulva interfering with reproduction.

Figure 16-18   A highly fertile cow 9 years old that has had 7 calves.

derived. There is no doubt that some animals will be retained that should not, and some will be culled that should not.

Remember that the older the animal, the greater the reliability of what is observed. It is diffiucult to select breeding stock prepuberally with any accuracy.

Compare a few pictures of animals with the characteristics in mind that we have discussed. Figure 16–18 depicts a very fertile cow. She is 9 years old and has had seven calves. Study her and then study Figure 16–19 of an infertile cow.

With some experience an individual can make a fairly accurate estimation of the reproductive history of a cow. The age of the cow should be known.

Some cows are skippers. That is, they have a calf one year and then skip a year or two. They usually have a mixture of good and bad characteristics. Observe the cow in Figure 16–20 for this mixture. She has a feminine head and neck but the dewlap and brisket are lumpy. The scapula is satisfactory and no pones of fat are on the hooks and pins. The udder is very good. She probably has an outstanding calf every other year. This is hardly economical under present conditions, and she should be culled.

After this discussion on visual appraisal it should be repeated that *nothing can replace records.*

Figure 16-19   An infertile 4-year-old cow that has not calved.

Figure 16-20   A skipper cow that has a calf in alternate years.

WHAT DID YOU LEARN?

1 When is visual appraisal most useful?
2 On what is visual appraisal primarily based in the male?
3 What influences muscle development?
4 What results from epididymitis?
5 What breeds are particularly noted for pendulous sheaths?
6 Which is larger, a 5-year-old bull or a 5-year-old steer?
7 Describe the brisket and dewlap of a fertile cow and an infertile cow.
8 What is a hypoplastic vulva?
9 Define sickle-hocked and post-legged.
10 Start at the head and describe a highly fertile female of your choice throughout the entire body.

REFERENCES

1 Bonsma, J. C. 1965. Judging cattle for functional efficiency. In *Wortham Lectures in Animal Science,* Texas A&M Univ. Press, College Station. Pp. 53–82.
2 Cammack, J. C. 1967. Relation of bovine hip, loin and brisket depot triglycerides to reproductive performance. M.S. thesis, Texas A&M Univ., College Station.
3 Sorensen, A. M., Jr. 1976. *Repro Lab: A Laboratory Manual for Animal Reproduction.* Kendall/Hunt, Dubuque, Iowa. Pp. 147–151.

CHAPTER 17

Reproductive Diseases

When you have completed this chapter, you should be able to:

- Recognize symptoms of major reproductive diseases,
- Know the necessary specimens for diagnosing by the veterinarian or diagnostic laboratory,
- Identify those diseases transmitted by coitus only (venereal diseases), and
- Appreciate the importance of preventive measures and the need for the veterinarian and diagnostic laboratory.

The animal husbandman is expected to be cognizant of unusual events occurring in his livestock program. Disease results in the unusual, and the stockman should be able to recognize certain characteristics or symptoms to assist in diagnosing the cause of deviations from normal.

The veterinarian and the diagnostic laboratory are available for an exacting diagnosis of disease and should be relied upon.

Most reproductive diseases are abortive in nature. These abortions, or expulsion of the fetus before term, may occur in the very early stages following fertilization until the time of parturition. The abortion in the very early stages is very difficult to identify because of the very small size of the embryo and membranes. A symptom of early abortion in the absence of the embryo and membranes is elongated estrous cycles. The cycle may be 30 or 40 days compared to a normal 20 days. The embryo in these instances began development and the corpus luteum persisted for a longer period of time than in a normal cycle. When something happened to the embryo there was no longer a source of progesterone, and abortion or resorption occurred followed by reinitiation of cyclic activity. Females should be examined in instances of elongated estrous cycles. It should be recognized that some elongated estrous cycles result from a missed observation of estrus.

The later abortions are usually identified by the observation of the fetus and/or membranes or exudate from the vulva. Some mummification or resorption may occur in the later stages that will not be observed except by palpation or eventual time of parturition without birth of a young. Late abortions may be missed if they occur on the range or where predators and scavengers may abound.

Infection following abortion is relatively common. Certainly, a veterinarian should be consulted following any abortion to determine the cause. The fetus and placenta in a fresh or refrigerated condition are essential for a diagnosis in most instances.

A single abortion may be unrelated to disease, but even then, further tests should be conducted in the herd after consultation with the veterinarian.

Abortions may be expected to account for 2 to 5 percent of the pregnancies in cattle being terminated. The percent pregnancies terminating in abortions in sheep is low, 1 to 5 percent.

Abortions normally terminate pregnancy in 5 to 15 percent of mares. These are usually after about 4 months of gestation,[5] and twinning in mares usually results in abortion.

Swine abortion is normally about 5 percent, but because of the multiparous (many-born) nature of the sow a problem of stillbirths arises. These are dead fetuses at the time of birth and range in age from 4 months to mature fetuses. Stillbirths may account for 5 to 10 percent of the piglets born.

It is the purpose of this chapter to give aid to the stockman by presenting the more important diseases in alphabetical order for each species. He may be able to view the symptoms column and have some idea of the disease he is dealing with. His observations then can assist the veterinarian in making a diagnosis and plans for treatment, control, and prevention.

The tables have been compiled from a number of references on reproductive diseases.[1,2,5,6] The specific causes of abortion or reproductive failure are listed under the headings of Bacterial, Viral, Mycotic, Protozoal, Chemical, Toxic Plants, Nutritional, Hormonal, Genetic, and Physical, where applicable. The list is not exhaustive but hopefully serves as a guide to the stockman.

Abortion in women is defined as expulsion of the fetus weighing under 500 grams. From 500 to 1000 grams, the infant is considered *immature,* and infants expelled from 1000 to 2500 grams are called *premature.* The term miscarriage is often used, since the word abortion is associated in the public's mind with illegal procedures.

Loss of embryos is very high in the early stages of pregnancy, and estimates indicate about 15 percent terminate spontaneously between 4 and 22 weeks.[4] It is difficult to accumulate accurate records of early abortions, but it is estimated that about 30 percent of fertilized ova reach maturity.

About one-half of the spontaneous abortions are due to embryonic defects. Others are due to diseases of the mother, and very few are caused by falls, automobile accidents, or injury.

Sexually transmitted diseases are very important due to the increased sexual activity in the human in recent years. Table 17–5 lists some of the transmissible diseases of the human. No attempt is made to discuss these.

WHAT DID YOU LEARN?

1   What percent abortions are expected normally in a horse operation?
2   Which diseases would be considered venereal diseases in cattle?
3   What is the causative organism for brucellosis in sheep?
4   What is the symptom of early abortion?
5   What specimens are most commonly needed to diagnose the cause of an abortion?
6   What is a mycotic disease? What is its cause?
7   What hormone may be deficient during gestation?
8   Why would torsion of the umbilical cord cause abortion?
9   What is a stillbirth and why do you suppose it prevails in swine?
10   In what specie is twinning a detriment to continuation of gestation?

REFERENCES

1   Blood, D. C. and J. A. Henderson. 1974. *Veterinary Medicine.* 4th ed. Williams & Wilkins, Baltimore. Pp. 378–385.
2   Hungerford, T. G. 1970. *Diseases of Livestock.* 7th ed. Angus & Robertson, Sydney, Australia. Pp. 37–590.
3   Josey, W. E. 1974. The sexually transmitted infections. *Obstet. and Gynecol.* 43:465–470.
4   Page, E. W., C. A. Villee, and D. B. Villee. 1976. *Human Reproduction: The Core Content of Obstetrics, Gynecology and Perinatal Medicine.* 2nd ed. W. B. Saunders, Philadelphia. Pp. 206–208, 428–433.
5   Roberts, S. J. 1971. *Veterinary Obstetrics and Genital Diseases.* 2nd ed. Publ. by the author, Ithaca, N.Y. Pp. 107–178.
6   Schipper, I. A. 1975. *Preventive Veterinary Medicine for Animal Science Students.* 5th ed. Burgess, Minneapolis. Pp. 71–90.

Table 17-1 Causes of Abortion and Reproductive Failure in Cattle

Disease and causative agent	Symptoms	Samples for diagnosis	Transmission	Treatment	Incubation period	Prevention	Clinical diagnosis
Bacterial							
Brucellosis [Brucella abortus] (Bang's disease) (Contagious abortion) (Infectious abortion) (Undulant fever)	Abortion after 4 months Retained placenta Inflammation of testes and epididymis	Fetus Placenta Blood from cow Milk from cow	Ingestion Contact-mucus Skin abrasions Coitus	None practical	30 to 60 days	Calfhood vaccination Test and slaughter Segregate new stock Sanitation	Agglutination and other tests
Leptospirosis [Leptospira hardjo] [Leptospira pomona] (Redwater) (Asymptomatic abortion)	Abortion after 6 months	Fetus Placenta 2 blood samples from aborting cow 3 weeks apart	Ingestion Mucous membranes Respiratory Skin abrasions	Antibiotics in acute stages	3 to 7 days	Vaccinate Eliminate carrier Keep separated from swine	Agglutination tests
Listeriosis [Listeria monocytogenes]	Abortion after 6 months Not common	Fetus Placenta Genital exudate	Introduction of infected stock Silage Severe stress	Antibiotics ?	—	Stop feeding silage Sanitation Segregate new stock	Agglutination Culture
Vibriosis (Vibrionic abortion) [Campylobacter fetus fetus] (Vibrio fetus venerealis) [Campylobacter fecalis or C. sputorum bubulus] (Vibrio fecalis or V. bulbulus) [Campylobacter fetus jejuni] (Vibrio jejuni) [Campylobacter fetus intestinalis] (Vibrio fetus intestinalis)	Repeated long estrous cycles Abortion before 6 months	Fetus Vaginal mucus Semen Serum	Coitus	Sexual rest of at least 3 months Antibiotics in prepuce of bulls	14 to 30 days	Artificial insemination Clean bulls on clean cows Vaccination Sanitation	Agglutination Culture

Table 17-1 (Continued)

Disease and causative agent	Symptoms	Samples for diagnosis	Transmission	Treatment	Incubation period	Prevention	Clinical diagnosis
Bacterial							
Miscellaneous [Corynebacterium pyogenes] [Escherichia coli] [Mycobacterium bovis] (Tuberculosis) [Streptococcal infections]	Abortion	Veterinarian should be consulted for diagnosis and action					
Viral							
BVD (Bovine Virus Diarrhea) (BVD-MD, Bovine Virus Diarrhea-Mucosal Disease) (Virus abortion)	Abortion Fever Erosion of mouth and gums Diarrhea	Blood serum at 2-week intervals Fetus Feces	Direct contact Food and water	Antibiotics and sulfonamides for secondary infection	7 to 9 days	Vigorous sanitation Vaccinate on advice of veterinarian	Virus isolation
EBA (Epizootic Bovine Abortion)	Abortion 7 to 9 months	Blood serum Fetus	Unknown	Antibiotics ?	1 to 7 weeks	Little	None accurate
IBR (Infectious Bovine Rhinotracheitis) IPV (Infectious Pustular Vulvovaginitis) IPB (Infectious Pustular Balanoposthitis) (Red-nose)	Abortion about 6th month Fever Runny nose Eye irritation Pustules in vagina Pustules in prepuce and on glans penis	Aborted fetus 2 serum samples at 3-week interval	Contact Coitus Urine and fluids	None	3 to 7 days	Nasal spray vaccine or other—consult veterinarian	Virus isolation

Table 17-1 (Continued)

Disease and causative agent	Symptoms	Samples for diagnosis	Transmission	Treatment	Incubation period	Prevention	Clinical diagnosis
Mycotic							
Mycotic or Fungal [Aspergillus fumigatus] [Absidia] [Mucor] [Rhizopus]	Abortion 5 to 7 months	Fetus Placenta	Ingesting molded feed	?	?	Supply clean feed free of molds	Microscopic for molds
Protozoal							
Trichomoniasis [Trichomonas fetus] (Tric)	Elongated cycles Abortion 1 to 4 months	Fetus Placenta Fluids of uterus or vagina Preputial fluid	Coitus	Sexual rest 90 days	12 to 20 days	AI Clean bull on clean cows Dispose of or treat infected bull	Microscopic for flagellated organism
Chemical							
Arsenic Lead Nitrates Many other toxic substances							
Toxic plants							
Broomweed	Abortion, retained placenta	History	Ingestion	—	None	Eliminate cause	
Locoweed	Abortion, retained placenta	History	Ingestion	—	None	Eliminate cause	
Lupines	Malformed calves	History	Ingestion	—	None	Eliminate source	
Pine needles	Abortion, retained placenta	History	Ingestion	—	None	Eliminate source	
Sweet clover hay	Abortion, fetus with blood clots	History	Ingestion	—	None	Eliminate molded hay	

Table 17–1 (Continued)

Nutritional						
Malnutrition	Abortion	Blood	Ingestion	—	None	Increase nutrients
Iodine deficiency	Abortion	Blood	Ingestion	—	None	Supplement
Vitamine A deficiency	Retained placenta	Blood	Ingestion	—	None	Supplement
Hormonal						
Estrogen	Abortion	Blood serum	—	—		Use only upon re-commendation of a veterinarian during pregnancy
Progesterone deficiency	Abortion	Blood serum	—	Supplement		
Glucocorticoids	Abortion	Blood serum	—	—		
Genetic						
Lethal hereditary factors	Abortion					Select sire carefully on records
Physical						
Douching	Abortion		Mechanical			Extreme caution and only if necessary
Enucleation of corpus luteum	Abortion		Removes supporting source of progesterone			Determine pregnancy before attempting
Infusion of uterus	Abortion		Fluids of different osmotic pressure			Determine pregnancy before treatment
Insemination	Abortion		Interferes with membranes			Pass catheter only into cervix on repeat breedings
Intentional	Abortion		Mechanical or flushing			
Torsion of umbilical cord	Abortion	Check newborn membranes and cord	Mechanical			Prevent cows falling and turning over
Torsion of uterus	Abortion		Mechanical			Rotate to correct position if diagnosed in time
Unnecessary rough handling	Abortion		Hitting, gouging, punching in abdomen			Careful handling of pregnant cows

Table 17-2 Causes of Abortion and Reproductive Failure in Sheep

Disease and causative agent	Symptoms	Samples for diagnosis	Transmission	Treatment	Incubation period	Prevention	Clinical diagnosis
Bacterial							
Brucellosis [Brucella ovis] [Brucella abortus]	Abortion Lesions in testes and tail of epididymis	Fetus Placenta Uterine discharges Blood serum from rams	Coitus	Isolate Quarantine Slaughter		Mostly controlled through testing ram and maintaining clean flock	Culture
Listeriosis [Listeria monocytogenes]	Abortion after 3 months	Fetus	Ingestion Coitus ?	?	7 to 12 days	Divide and isolate	Culture
Vibriosis [Campylofactor fetus intestinalis] (Vibrio fetus intestinalis)	Abortion	Fetus	Ingestion	Antibiotics Disinfect area	7 to 25 days	Prevent contaminated feed and water	Culture
Miscellaneous Salmonellosis Pasturella tularensis Corynebacterium pyogenes Leptospirosis Streptococcal infection							
Viral							
EAE (Enzootic Abortion of Ewes)	Abortion after 100 days Retained placenta	Fetus Placenta	Ingestion	Antibiotics	7 weeks	—	Culture
Protozoal							
Toxoplasma gondii	Resorption 1 to 3 months Abortion over 4 months Retained placenta	Fetus Placenta	?	None	1 to 3 weeks	Sanitation	Microscopic

Table 17-2 (Continued)

Disease and causative agent	Symptoms	Samples for diagnosis	Transmission	Treatment	Incubation period	Prevention	Clinical diagnosis
			Chemical				
Carbon tetrachloride	Abortion					Do not use on pregnant ewes	
Chronic lead poisoning	Abortion						
Nitrates	Abortion						
Phenothiazine	Abortion						
			Toxic plants				
Locoweed	Abortion	Same as for cattle					
Lupines	Abortion						
Sweet clover	Abortion						
			Nutritional				
Malnutrition	Abortion					Supplement	
Cobalt deficiency	Abortion					Supplement	
Copper deficiency	Abortion					Supplement	
Iodine deficiency	Abortion					Supplement	
Selenium deficiency	Abortion					Supplement	
Vitamin A deficiency	Abortion					Supplement	
			Hormonal				
Estrogen	Abortion		Feeds or injection			Limit clover pasture	
Progesterone deficiency	Abortion			Supplement		Supplement?	
Glucorticoids	Abortion					Do not use on pregnant ewes	
			Genetic				
Lethal factors	Abortion					Careful selection based on records	

Table 17-3 Causes of Abortion and Reproductive Failure in Swine

Disease and causative agent	Symptoms	Samples for diagnosis	Transmission	Treatment	Incubation period	Prevention	Clinical diagnosis
Bacterial							
Brucellosis [Brucella suis]	Abortion 3 weeks on	Fetus Serum	Ingestion of contaminated feed and water Coitus	Slaughter Disinfect Restock with clean animals	10 to 21 days	Select only clean boars Sanitation	Culture Agglutination
Leptospirosis [Leptospira pomona]	Abortion last 1 to 4 weeks Stillbirth Mummification	Fetus Serum	Ingestion Coitus	Antibiotics	3 to 4 weeks	Vaccination Sanitation Separate from other livestock	Agglutination Culture Fluorescent antibody
Viral							
Parvovirus	Abortion Stillbirth Mummification Infertility	Mummy	Contact Feces	–	–	Sanitation Comingle before breeding season	Fluorescent antibody
Pseudorabies	Same as above	Fetus Serum	Contact Air borne	–	–	Test before introducing new animals Prevent wildlife mingling	Virus isolation Serum Neutralization Flourescent antibody
SMEDI (Stillbirth, mummification, embryonic death, and infertility)	Same as above	Fetus	Contact Feces	Sows recover	5 days	Sanitation Commingling prior to breeding	Virus isolation
Others							
Chemicals, plants, drugs, hormones, and nutritional causes are negligible							

Table 17-4 Causes of Abortion and Reproductive Failure in Horses

Disease and causative agent	Symptoms	Samples for diagnosis	Transmission	Treatment	Incubation period	Prevention	Clinical diagnosis
Bacterial							
Equine Infectious Abortion [Salmonella abortus equi]	Abortion 6 to 9 months Retained placenta	Fetus Placenta Genital discharge	Ingestion of contaminated feed and water	Sexual rest	10 to 28 days	Vaccination	Agglutination test
Leptospirosis [Leptospira pomona] [Leptospira grippotyphosa]	Abortion 7 to 11 months	Fetus Placenta	Ingestion	Antibiotics	3 to 7 days	Yearly vaccination May vaccinate in first trimester of gestation	Agglutination test
Streptococcal Abortion [Streptococcus genitalium] [Streptococcus zooepidemicus]	Abortion 2 to 6 months Retained placenta	Fetus Placenta Genital discharge	Present on the external genitalia all time Lowered resistance results in infection	Antibiotics	?	Breed only healthy mares Culture barren mares	Culture
Other [Shingella equirulis] [Pseudomonas]							
Viral							
Equine viral arteritis (Epizootic cellulitis—pinkeye)	Abortion 5 to 10 months Respiratory disorder Fever	Fetus Serum	Contact and inhalation	?	3 to 9 days	Separation Quarantine new stock	Culture
Equine virus abortion [Herpes virus 1]	Abortion 8 to 11 months	Fetus Serum	Contact and inhalation	?	20 to 30 days	Isolation Vaccination	Virus isolation Microscopic observation

Table 17-4 (Continued)

Disease and causative agent	Symptoms	Samples for diagnosis	Transmission	Treatment	Incubation period	Prevention	Clinical diagnosis
			Mycotic				
Fungal infection [Aspergillus fumigatus]	Abortion 4 to 8 months	Placenta Fetus	Ingestion or inhalation of mold spores	—	—	Sanitation	Microscopic observation
			Protozoal				
Babesiasis or Piroplasmosis [Babesia equi] [Babesia caballi]	Abortion	Fetus Blood smear	Blood sucking ticks	—	—	Sanitation	Fluorescent antibody Serology
			Other				
Chemicals							
Drugs							
Malnutrition							
Toxic plants							
Hormonal							
Cervical dilatation	Abortion 3 to 10 days post treatment	Intentional to cause abortion Infusion of fluids					
Mechanical injury		Trucking, kicking, mismanagement					
Torsion of umbilical cord	Abortion	Mechanical					
Twinning	Abortion	Inability of uterus to maintain multiple offspring					

Table 17-5   Venereal Diseases of the Human

Type	Disease	Causative agent
Bacterial	Syphilis	Treponema pallidum
	Gonorrhea	Neisseria gonorrhoeae
	Chancroid	Haemophilus ducreyi
	H. Vaginalis infection	Corynebacterium (Haemophilus) vaginalis
	Granuloma inguinale	Donovania granulomatis
Chlamydial	Lymphogranuloma venereum	LGV agent
	Chlamydial cervicitis	Group A (TRIC) agent
Mycoplasmas	Genital M-hominis infection	Mycoplasma hominis
	Genital T-mycoplasma infection	T-strain mycoplasma
Viral	Herpes genitalis	Herpesvirus hominis type 2
	Condyloma acuminatum	Genital paillomavirus
	Genital cytomega lovirus infection	Genital cytomegalovirus
	Genital molluscum contagiosum	Molluscum contagium virus
Protozoal	Trichomoniasis	Trichomonas vaginalis

Adapted from Josey.[3]

Index